EUROPE
and the
MEDITERRANEAN

McGRAW-HILL SERIES IN GEOGRAPHY

JOHN C. WEAVER, *Consulting Editor*

VERNOR C. FINCH was Consulting Editor of this series from its inception in 1934 to 1951.

EUROPE
and the
MEDITERRANEAN

Norman J. G. Pounds

Professor of Geography, Indiana University
Formerly Tutor, Fitzwilliam House
Cambridge University

New York   Toronto   London
McGRAW-HILL BOOK COMPANY, INC.
1953

EUROPE AND THE MEDITERRANEAN

Library of Congress Catalog Card Number: 52-5338

IV

THE MAPLE PRESS COMPANY, YORK, PA.

Preface

This book has been written as a college textbook. In writing it, the author had in mind primarily the need to bring to the student the richness and variety of the European continent, the great age of its culture, and the roots of its present civilization, deeply buried in the past. The conventional regional framework has been adopted throughout. No one is more fully aware than the author that these divisions are arbitrary and in many instances unreal. They are only a convenient framework to enable him to relate more easily and the student to comprehend more fully the differences between one place and another.

The content of the book, secondly, is organized on a basis of political units. This is almost inevitable in Europe, where man has been grouped for many centuries into national units and his imprint on the land reflects in some ways his national grouping. The first four chapters offer a last attempt to see the continent as a whole.

The author was faced with a serious problem in deciding what areas to include. The conventional boundaries of Europe—the Ural Mountains, the Bosporus and Dardanelles, and the sea—have no longer any practical validity. France, Spain, and, until recently, Italy controlled parts of both the northern and southern shores of the Mediterranean Sea. Settlers from the north were settled on the southern shore, where they tried to reproduce a society similar to that which they had left. Turkey embraces both shores of the "Straits," and Russia has never recognized the Ural Mountains as a frontier or boundary.

It thus seemed desirable to include the shores of the whole of the Mediterranean Sea. The problem of the Ural Mountains frontier was less easily settled. The only alternative courses which seemed satisfactory were to include *all* the U.S.S.R. or to omit it completely. A compromise has been reached with a short chapter on Russia, which "fades out" in Soviet Asia. The treatment of Russia is appreciably "thinner" than that of other areas. It may be sufficient for the student who is studying Europe and wishes to include western Russia, but the student who desires more than this is urged to use the textbooks listed at the end of the chapter on the U.S.S.R.

Most chapters are followed by a bibliography. There are many omissions from these lists, and works in other languages than English have, as a general rule, been omitted. There is a large proportion of books published in Europe.

References are particularly numerous to the reports and papers published by the British government. These are obtainable in America through the British Information Service, New York. For the convenience of advanced students the author has included in the bibliography of each country the title of one or more books, in English or some other language, which contain important bibliographies of the literature that is less easily obtained.

It is becoming more and more the practice in American textbooks to use place names in the forms commonly used in the countries in question. This raises difficulties when the local name differs greatly from that in conventional use. Certain familiar names, such as Rhine, Danube, Vienna, Venice, and Naples, have been retained, but in each case the local form is also given. Where, however, the place name has more than one form in common use, the alternative forms are given in parentheses after the first use of the name.

The author wishes to thank Prof. Arch C. Gerlach, head of the Maps Division of the Library of Congress, for help and encouragement; E. C. Gates, a former pupil at Cambridge University, for his help with the maps; and also his wife for her untiring help. He is deeply grateful to several friends who read through parts of the manuscript and gave him the benefit of their knowledge: Dr. Jonas Balys, Profs. Vaclav Benes, Michael Ginsburg, Chauncy D. Harris, Brian Mason, Malcolm Proudfoot, Dr. Willert Rhynsburger, Profs. Otis P. Starkey and Stephen S. Visher. The author is grateful to the several services and agencies that provided photographs. Their names appear below the photographs. Where no source is acknowledged, the photograph was taken by the author. Lastly, the author acknowledges the courtesy of authors and publishers who have permitted extracts from their writings to be quoted: Hamish Hamilton, Eric Linklater, and Brigadier R. A. Bagnold; also George Allen and Unwin, Ltd., and Hodder and Stoughton, Ltd.

Norman J. G. Pounds

BLOOMINGTON, IND.
JANUARY, 1953

Contents

CHAPTER 1: *Europe: The Land*

Europe is the most irregularly shaped of the greater land masses of the globe. It is a peninsula, with many subsidiary peninsulas, projecting westward from the continent of Asia. Across its base in European Russia it measures about 1,500 miles from north to south. It narrows westward and is only 750 miles between the Black Sea and the Baltic. Beyond this "waist" it widens again, only to contract to 250 miles between the Mediterranean Sea and the Bay of Biscay. The lesser peninsulas around its margin make up Scandinavia, Denmark, Greece, and Italy. Close to the continent is an immense number of islands—large and populous such as Great Britain, small and rocky like those of the Norwegian coast and the Isles of Greece. Europe is enclosed on all sides except the east by the sea, and stretches of water penetrate between the peninsulas deep into the land. Nowhere in western or central Europe is it possible to escape the influence of the sea; nowhere is the sea distant more than about 400 miles.

Most of Europe lies in temperate latitudes. Its most southerly point, the southern tip of Spain, is 36° north of the Equator, about the latitude of Nashville, Tennessee. Its most northerly point, the North Cape of Norway, lies at 71°, as far north as the most northerly point on the mainland of Canada. Only a very small area of Europe, however, lies within the Arctic Circle.

Europe is, with the exception of Australia, the smallest of the continental divisions into which the land surface of the globe is conventionally divided. Its area, about 3,800,000 square miles, is a little more than that of the United States and less than half that of Soviet Russia. But within this area it has a rich variety of landscape and relief, of climate, soil, and resources. The aspect of the land is generally varied, and only in Russia are there large areas that are physically uniform. Along with the variety of rock and structure there goes a diversity of mineral deposits and of agricultural land. It is in this richness and variety that we may look for at least a partial explanation of the precocity of European cultural, economic, and political developments.

We must learn to see "for ourselves that variegated mosaic of the world's surface which a bird sees in its migration, that difference between the district of the gentian and of the olive which the stork and the swallow see far off, as they lean upon the sirocco wind. Let us, for a moment, try to raise ourselves even above the level of their flight, and imagine the Mediterranean lying beneath us like an irregular lake, and all its ancient promontories sleeping in the sun: here and there an angry spot of thunder, a grey stain of storm, moving upon the burning field; and here and there a fixed wreath of white volcano smoke, surrounded by its circle of ashes; but for the most part a great peacefulness of light, Syria and Greece, Italy and Spain, laid like pieces of golden pavement into the sea-blue, chased, as we stoop nearer to them, with bossy beaten work of mountain chains, and glowing softly with terraced gardens, and flowers heavy with frankincense, mixed among masses of laurel, and orange, and plumy palm, that abate with their grey-green shadows the burning of the marble rocks. . . . Then let us pass farther towards the north, until we see the orient colors change gradually into a vast belt of rainy green, where the pastures of Switzerland, and poplar

1

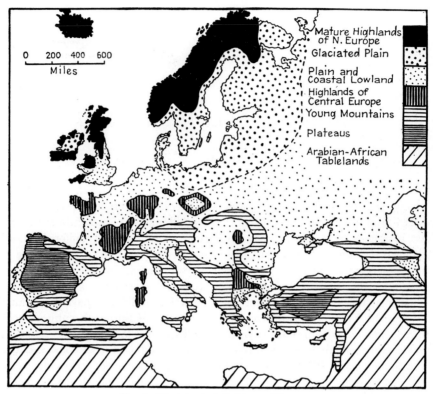

FIG. 1. The physical divisions of Europe.

valleys of France, and dark forests of the Danube and Carpathians stretch from the mouths of the Loire to those of the Volga, seen through the grey swirls of rain-cloud . . . ; and then, farther north still, to see the earth heave into mighty masses of leaden rock and heathy moor, bordering with a broad waste of gloomy purple that belt of field and wood, and splintering into irregular and grisly islands amidst the northern seas, beaten by storm and chilled by ice-drift, and tormented by furious pulses of contending tide, until the roots of the last forests fail from among the hill ravines, and the hunger of the north wind bites their peaks into barrenness. . . . And, having once traversed in thought its gradation of the zoned iris of the earth in all its material vastness, let us go down nearer to it. . . . "[1] Let us examine more closely the

detail of its terrain and of its people and their work.

There is a pattern in the immense variety of Europe. If we can learn to see this pattern as a whole, we shall the more easily fit the detail of the countries of Europe into it. Europe is built of five major physical divisions, each the product of a long epoch in the geological history of Europe. In the north is the oldest, the hilly or mountainous mass of Scandinavia, which passes eastward into Finland. South of this is the youngest, the great plain of northern Europe. To the south, stretching across Europe from west to east, from France to Poland, is a belt of hills older than the plain to their north but not so old as the Scandinavian mountains. This hilly region of central Europe passes southward into the Alps, which form one of the most distinctive of the major physical regions. The Alpine mountain system is very much more extensive than the mountains commonly called the Alps. It reaches from Spain to Russia and

The rolling hill country of Scandinavia. This photograph shows a clearing in the coniferous forest. The country is hilly rather than mountainous and has been smoothed by the ice sheets. Note the smallness of the tilled area. The farm economy is mainly pastoral. The fence has certain affinities with the American split-rail fence, also erected in well-wooded areas. (*Swedish Tourist Traffic Association.*)

encloses the western half of the Mediterranean Sea. Lastly, to the south of the Alpine mountain system and of the Mediterranean Sea is the low plateau which makes up the northeastern part of Africa. We must look more closely at each of these divisions.

Mountains of Scandinavia and the Northwest of Europe. This region includes Norway, most of Sweden and Finland, the north and west of the British Isles, and the islands such as Iceland and Spitzbergen which lie far out in the North Atlantic Ocean. It is built of ancient rocks, whose hardness has led in some areas to the development of a rugged topography. Mountains form the backbone of the Scandinavian peninsula. On the northwest they drop steeply to the indented coast of Norway but more gently toward the east to the Swedish coast of the Baltic Sea. Toward the east they extend into Finland. During the last Ice Age, glaciers covered this region. The rock surfaces were rounded and polished by the ice and the soil largely removed and spread over the lower lands to the south. The region is one of thin,

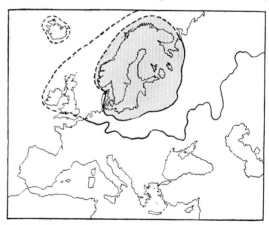

FIG. 2. The maximum extent of the ice sheet during the Quaternary Ice Age. The stippled area shows the maximum extent during the last phase of the Ice Age.

infertile soil and sparse population. Nevertheless, minerals occur in these old rocks, and the mining of iron and of lead, zinc, and nickel is important.

Heaths of the north European Plain, formed of glacial sands and gravels. The photograph was taken in the Campine of Belgium. This environment yields a dry, porous, and infertile soil. (*Belgian Railways and Marine.*)

The hills of the northern and western parts of the British Isles are similar. The mountains are not so high as in Scandinavia, but the relief is strong, soils poor, and population small.

North European Plain. This area of low-lying and undulating plain extends from the Pyrenean Mountains bordering southern France through Germany to Russia. It includes most of England as well as Denmark and southern Sweden. In few places does it exceed 1,000 feet above sea level. Its hills are gentle. Movement over them is usually not difficult in any direction, and there are few areas that are too steep for cultivation. This plain covers about half of France. It narrows in Belgium, the Netherlands, and northwestern Germany but then broadens eastward. Most of Poland lies within the plain, which then widens yet more to include almost all of European Russia as well as of Finland and Romania.

The plain may be divided into that part covered by the great glacier which spread southward from Scandinavia during the Ice Age and that part which remained free from glaciation.

Over much of glaciated Europe the ice sheets left, when they melted away, a deposit of moraine or boulder clay made up of gravel, sand, and clay which the ice had brought from the north. Large areas, particularly in North Germany, are today covered by infertile sands and gravels which originated in this way. Other areas, especially in Sweden, Germany, and Poland, were covered in a similar way with heavy clay and contain many shallow lakes and swamps. The glaciated plain is seldom fertile. The clays are often too heavy and the sand and gravel too light for profitable cultivation. Large areas remain under grass or are forested, and the average of agricultural population is less than in the unglaciated region of the plain.

The southern limit of the ice sheets was across southern England and the Low Countries. South of this line the plain is built up mainly of limestone, sandstone, and clay. The limestone and sandstone, being somewhat harder than the clay, tend to form the low hills which characterize southern England and much of France, whereas the clay is more readily

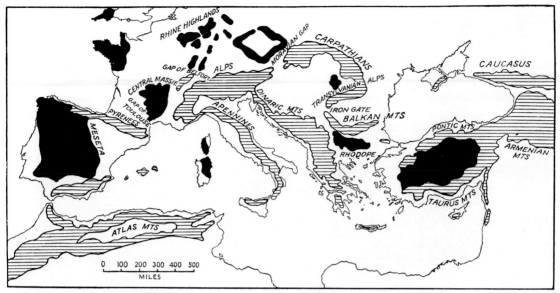

FIG. 3. The Alpine Mountain system of Europe and the Middle East.

worn away by rivers and forms lower land. The unglaciated part of the north European Plain is largely made up of low, rounded or flat-topped hills and broad, shallow valleys. Most of the land is fit for cultivation. Productivity is high, and the agricultural population is greater than in glaciated regions.

In the east also the north European Plain extends farther southward than did the ice sheets. Southern Poland, the plains of eastern Romania, and the whole of southern Russia lie outside the glaciated area. They lack the heavy boulder clay and the infertile gravels and, partly for this reason, are less forested. The contrasts between northern and southern Poland and between northern and southern Russia, which will be emphasized in later chapters, are in part due to the presence of boulder clay over the surface in the north but not in the south.

The Mountains of Central Europe. These, like the mountains of Scandinavia, are built of hard, ancient rocks, in which minerals, including iron, lead, zinc, and copper, occur. There are no sharp peaks or ice-fretted precipices. These mountains were not glaciated during the Ice Age. Instead, they consist largely of high plateaus, in which the rivers have carved deep and steep-sided valleys. The soil is often shallow on

the steep slopes, and the climate is sometimes severe on the higher surfaces. These are not fertile or productive areas, and they are now among the least well populated in Europe. These mountains are broken up by river valleys and plains into a number of separate masses, such as the Central Massif of France, the Vosges Mountains, the Ardennes, the Black Forest, the Harz, and the mountains of Bohemia.

These hills do not constitute a serious barrier to movement. The deep valleys that penetrate them and the plains that separate one hill mass from another provide routeways of no great difficulty into and across the region. The most conspicuous and the most important of these routeways is the valley of the river Rhine, but others are formed by the valleys of the Moselle, Weser, Elbe, and the upper Oder.

Mountains of the Alpine System. South of the hilly region of central Europe is the Alpine chain of high mountains. These extend from Spain through France, Switzerland, and the Balkan countries to Turkey and thence eastward across Asia. The Atlas Mountains of North Africa and the mountain ranges of Syria and Israel also belong to this complex system. The mountains are mostly young in geological age. The forces of erosion have not yet worked for a

Dissected hill country of central Europe. The photograph is of Bouillon in the Ardennes. Note the nearly level skyline and the incised river, with cultivated land along the valley floor. (*Belgian Railways and Marine.*)

long enough period to rob them of their massive grandeur. During the Ice Age most parts of the Alpine system were heavily glaciated, and even today the higher mountain ranges are clothed with perpetual snow and glaciers extend down the valleys.

The mountains are not, however, continuous. Between those of Spain and of Italy and France are large areas of land and sea. The Balearic Islands are all that is left of a former extension of the Betic Mountains of southern Spain. The Alps of France, Switzerland, and northern Italy are, however, high and continuous. There are no easy crossings, and the few passes that are in use are difficult and are closed by snow for a large part of the year. Several railway tunnels, all of them long, have been cut through the Alps to link the northern countries of Europe with Italy. The Mont Cenis Tunnel between France and Italy and the Simplon and Saint Gotthard Tunnels between Switzerland and Italy are each over 9 miles long.

Toward the east the Alps become lower and the passes easier to negotiate. In Austria the Alpine system divides. A branch extends to the southeast into Yugoslavia, where it forms the Dinaric Mountains, which continue into Greece. The other branch reaches eastward and becomes lower and narrower as it approaches the Danube. But east of that river it rises into the great curving range of the Carpathians. These stretch in a semicircle through eastern Czechoslovakia into Romania. Here they curve back toward the west, forming the Transylvanian Alps. The river Danube breaks across the eastern extremity of the Transylvanian Alps in the gorges known as the "Iron Gate." South of the river the mountains again curve to the east and, under the name of the Balkan Mountains, stretch out to the coast of the Black Sea. To the south of the Balkan Mountains is another range, the Rhodope.

The few gaps through these mountains in the Danube Valley and Balkan peninsula are of great importance. Where the Dinaric Alps branch away from the Alps of Austria, they become low and are easily crossed. The port of Trieste has grown up on the shore of the Adriatic

Young folded mountains, showing the results of recent glaciation. The photograph is of the Wildstrubel, near Adelboden, Switzerland. (*Swiss National Tourist Office*.)

to serve the traffic using this route. The Danube Valley itself provides a routeway across the Austrian Alps and the Carpathians and also across the Transylvanian Alps and the Balkan Mountains. A narrow corridor along which flow the rivers Vardar and Morava separates the Dinaric system and the mountains of Greece from the Rhodope and Balkan Mountains. The port of Thessalonike lies at the southern end of this route. Another gap, in which lies the town of Sofia, separates the Balkan Mountains from the Rhodope.

The line of the mountainous backbone of the Greek peninsula is continued through the islands of Crete and Rhodes into the Taurus Mountains, which form the southern margin of Asia Minor. The Pontic Mountains, which make up the northern edge, continue the direction of the Balkan Mountains. Both Pontic and Taurus Mountains unite in the mountainous mass of Armenia, from which the ranges of Central Asia extend eastward.

The Apennines of Italy extend from the Alps of France and are themselves continued through Sicily and, beyond the sea, through the Atlas Mountains of North Africa. In the Crimean peninsula of southern Russia are mountains which appear to have been once continued westward as the Balkan Mountains and eastward as the Caucasus.

The Alpine system of mountains encloses within its sweep a number of plateaus and several low plains. The whole of central Spain, known as the Meseta, lies between the Cantabrian and Betic Mountains. The Tell Plateau of North Africa lies between the ranges of the Atlas Mountains, and the Anatolian Plateau of Turkey lies between the Pontic and Taurus Ranges. A smaller plateau lies in Switzerland between the Alps and the Juras.

The plain of Hungary is a large, low, and almost flat land, also enclosed by the mountains of the Alpine system. Similar in their relationship to the mountains are the Lombardy Plain of northern Italy, the plain of the lower Danube Valley, and other smaller coastal plains around

A Mediterranean coastal settlement walled for defense. Along much of its coast the Mediterranean Sea is bordered by mountains or hills. The coast is often cliffed, and low-lying land is small in area. (*Spanish Tourist Office.*)

the shores of the Balkan, Italian, and Spanish peninsulas.

The Alpine system of mountains, with its enclosed plateaus and plains and its passes and gaps, is shown in Fig. 3. The reader will notice that in certain places the Alpine mountains approach close to the mountain masses of central Europe. The gaps which separate the two systems are no less important than those which provide routeways through the Alps. Of the greatest significance are the Gap of Toulouse between the Pyrenees and the Central Massif, the Rhône Valley between the Central Massif and the Alps, the Gap of Belfort between the Vosges and the Jura, the Rhine Valley at Basel, the Danube Valley above Vienna, and the Moravian Gap, which separates Bohemia from the Carpathian Mountains.

African Tableland. Along the southeastern shores of the Mediterranean Sea the plateau of Africa and Arabia forms a nearly straight and almost harborless coast. The hinterland is sometimes low and generally flat. For climatic reasons, the land is unproductive, except where the river Nile brings its life-giving waters. This region belongs politically to the former Italian colony of Libya and to the kingdom of Egypt, while southern Israel and southern Tunis also extend into it. The Red Sea divides the African from the Arabian Plateau and approaches to within 100 miles of the Mediterranean Sea. Trade had long been carried on across this isthmus before a canal was cut to link the two seas.

These are the major divisions of Europe: the northern or Scandinavian mountains, the great plain of northern Europe, the west-to-east belt of hills and mountains which we have called the mountains of central Europe, and the Alpine system. Lastly the African tableland lies outside Europe but forms the southeastern coast of the Mediterranean Sea.

The Rivers of Europe. There is no part of western and central Europe which is not drained to the ocean. Only in European Russia do some rivers, particularly the Volga, drain toward an inland sea, the Caspian. The continent has not developed a large central drainage system like the Amazon or the Mississippi. Instead there are many small river systems, each of which makes its way to the Atlantic Ocean or to one of its many deep, branching inlets (Fig. 4).

The Spanish peninsula is very largely drained westward by the Guadalquivir, Guadiana, Tagus (Tajo), and Douro (Duero). The Ebro is the only river of large size which flows toward the Mediterranean, and its basin has acquired, partly on account of this, a political and economic orientation different from that of the rest of the peninsula.

France is drained by rivers which flow in almost every direction. The Rhône and its tributaries drain southeastern France to the Mediterranean; the Garonne system the southwest toward the Atlantic; the Seine and other rivers of the Paris Basin flow northward to the English Channel, while the Moselle, Meuse, and Scheldt drain eastern France and Belgium eastward or northeastward toward the Rhine mouth.

The Rhine is the principal river of western Germany and Switzerland. It rises on the Saint

Gotthard Pass in Switzerland and flows through a variety of landscape and topography to its mouth in Holland. To the east, the north German Plain is drained by the Ems, Weser,

Fig. 4. The drainage basins of the chief European rivers. In the stippled areas there is no appreciable surface drainage.

Elbe, Oder, and Vistula (Wisla), shorter rivers rising in the central upland areas of Europe and flowing by courses which trend from southeast to northwest into either the North Sea or the Baltic Sea.

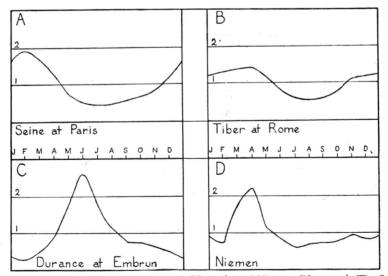

Fig. 5. The regimes of the rivers Seine, Durance, Tiber (Tevere), and Niemen (Nemunas). The Seine illustrates the all-the-year discharge and winter maximum of the rivers of western Europe; the Durance, the summer maximum of the Alpine rivers; the Tiber, the winter flow of the Mediterranean rivers, and the Niemen, the spring and summer flow of the rivers of continental eastern Europe.

In length and volume of discharge, as well as in the size of its drainage basin, the Danube is the most important of the rivers of Europe. With its tributaries, it drains not only part of south Germany but also Austria, the Hungarian Plain, Romania, and northern Bulgaria.

FIG. 6. A bridge at Mostar, Yugoslavia. This is designed to allow the sudden winter floods of Mediterranean rivers to pass.

With the exception of the Po, which takes the drainage of the Italian Alps and of the northern Apennines, the rivers of Italy are short and swift, torrents rather than rivers. The same is true of the Scandinavian rivers, which tumble down from their mountain sources direct to the Baltic Sea or the Atlantic.

The rivers of the Middle Eastern countries and of North Africa drain an area of low, seasonal rainfall. In general they are small, and the flow of some of them is intermittent. Only the Nile, which rises in the lakes of Central Africa and crosses the desert to the Mediterranean, is a really large and important river. The Jordan flows into the Dead Sea, where its waters evaporate.

The *regime* of rivers depends upon the seasonal distribution of rainfall and on the variety of environment through which they flow. Broadly speaking, they are of four kinds, according to the seasonal distribution of their flow.[1]

The Mediterranean rivers are fed by the winter rains of the Mediterranean region. This

[1] This division follows M. Pardé, "Fleuves et rivières," Paris, 1933.

may be heavy, and the rivers quickly grow into torrents. Bridges are highly arched to allow the water to pass under them at such times (Fig. 6). In summer, however, the climate is dry and the rivers are reduced to slender proportions or may even dry up entirely. Such rivers, varying with the seasons from mountain torrent to almost complete dessication, are of almost no value for navigation. Nor are they of much help to agriculture. They are often deeply incised in their beds, and water is abundant only in winter and spring, when the land is in least need of it. The depth and narrowness of their valleys, however, allow these rivers to be dammed and some of the water stored either for irrigation or for generating electric power.

Alpine rivers are fed primarily by the melting snows and ice fields of the high mountains. As melting is most vigorous in late spring and summer, these rivers show the greatest discharge at these seasons. Like Mediterranean rivers, they are often torrential and of no value for navigation, but they commonly occupy deep valleys in which the water can be impounded for the purposes of power generation.

FIG. 7. A bridge in Central Wales similar to that of Mostar. Designed to permit a rapid discharge in time of flood.

In northwestern Europe, rivers depend upon a rainfall which is better distributed throughout the year than that of the Mediterranean lands. Conditions vary from a winter maximum of rainfall to a summer maximum (see page 17), but evaporation is great enough in summer to ensure that the surface runoff and the discharge of the rivers are heaviest in winter. Thus in the rivers of the northwestern Europe, there is a tendency toward a winter high level. On the larger rivers navigation is usually possible throughout the year.

FIG. 8. A bridge in Midland England suited to the slow and relatively steady flow of Lowland England.

The rivers of eastern Europe drain an area where the winter freeze is pronounced and where the greater part of the precipitation comes as summer rains. A high water level of late spring due to the melting of snow on the steppes and in the forests is continued into a summer maximum, owing to the rains. The autumn and winter discharge is small.

Figure 5 illustrates the regimes of these four simple types of river. Large rivers, however, are more complex, as they drain more than one environment and have the characteristics of more than one regime. The Rhine in its upper course is an Alpine river with a maximum discharge in spring and summer (Fig. 9). In its middle and lower course it is joined by tributaries from France and Germany, where the rainfall is well distributed and the discharge greater in winter than in summer. These obliterate the summer maximum and produce a marked winter maximum.

The Rhône and Danube are even more complex. The former drains, in turn, areas having alpine, northwest European, and Mediterranean characteristics. The Danube also has its source in an Alpine region but flows through eastern Europe and receives tributaries from both northwestern and Mediterranean Europe.

There is not space to describe the regimes of all the larger rivers of Europe. From a study of the climate, however, it is possible to estimate how the rivers behave. The student might, for example, work out the probable regimes of the Po, the Vistula, and the Ebro in the light of the climatic conditions in which they lie.

Oceans and Seas. Europe, including the British Isles, has some 25,000 miles of coast. No point west of European Russia is more than 450 miles from the nearest sea. Only five European countries, Luxembourg, Switzerland, Austria, Czechoslovakia, and Hungary,[1] have no direct access to the sea, and in the years between the two wars these nations developed arrangements by which they regularly used the ports of their neighbors.

Europe is fringed by a belt of shallow sea of varying width known as the *Continental Shelf*. In general this does not exceed 100 fathoms in depth, and the slope from the coast outward is very gentle. Beyond the edge of this Continental Shelf the sea floor steepens into the *Continental Slope*, which descends to the great depths of the deep sea floor. The Shelf is quite narrow off the coast of Northwest Africa, only 20 miles. It remains narrow along the Spanish coast, widening in the Bay of Biscay and ex-

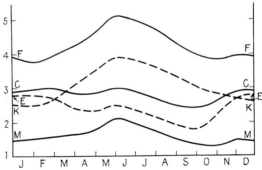

FIG. 9. The regime of the Rhine. The height of the river is shown in meters. At Frankenthal (F) and Kehl (K) the Alpine summer maximum is shown. At Mainz (M) a winter maximum is also apparent. At Coblenz (C) and Emmerich (E) the winter maximum has become dominant.

panding to enclose the British Isles and to join them to the mainland of Europe. The margin of the Shelf lies more than 200 miles west of Land's

[1] In addition to the small and economically unimportant states of Andorra, Liechtenstein, and San Marino.

An icebreaker in the Gulf of Finland. Such conditions exist along the coasts of southern Finland and also in much of Sweden and Estonia for an average of 4 to 5 months in the year. (*Finnish National Travel Office.*)

End, about 50 miles west of the Irish coast. It sends a long finger of shallow sea, known as the Wyville Thomson ridge, northwest of Scotland in the direction of Iceland. The whole of the North Sea belongs to the Continental Shelf, which along the coast of Norway is some 50 miles wide, and broadens in the Arctic Ocean into a shallow submarine extension of Russia.

The edge of the Shelf is the true margin of the continent. A number of winding deep channels cross its surface, as if it had once been above sea level and was drained by rivers. The Dogger Bank, the conspicuous shallowing of the North Sea at about 55°N, is probably an accumulation of glacial material which had been rafted southward by ice and dropped as the icebergs began to melt. This area of shallow sea has great value as a fish breeding ground, and its shallowness assists the fisheries.

Baltic Sea. A great thickness of ice covered this area during the Ice Age, and the land was depressed under the weight. The ice has melted away, and the land has risen but has not yet wholly recovered. The Baltic Sea in part oc-cupies the depression formed in this way. Its floor is still rising, though very slowly, and the sea is becoming smaller and shallower.[1]

Evaporation from the surface of the Baltic is relatively small, and the inflow of fresh water brought by the Baltic rivers is considerable. The result is an outflow between the Danish islands into the North Sea. The Baltic is comparatively fresh, and only near its outlet is it nearly as salt as the ocean. This fact causes the Baltic to freeze more readily than other seas. The Gulfs of Bothnia and of Finland are often frozen for 5 months in each year. The Gulf of Riga and other partially enclosed stretches of water farther south also freeze, though the thickness of ice is not usually too great for icebreakers to clear.

The *Mediterranean Sea*, like the Baltic, is almost completely landlocked, communicating with the ocean only by way of the narrow Strait of Gibraltar. Its present form is in large measure

[1] See R. A. Daly, "The Changing World of the Ice Age," pp. 51–80, New Haven, 1934, for a detailed consideration of the evolution of the Baltic Sea.

determined by the ranges which constitute about three-quarters of its coastline. Between Syria and Tunis, however, the ancient tableland of Africa reaches the sea. The contrast between the types of shore line produced, respectively, by the mountains and the African tableland is strongly marked. The former is irregular, has deep bays and inlets, and is fringed in many parts with islands. The African coast, by contrast, is low and straight, lacking in bays and natural harbors, and as unpropitious to the early seaman as the opposite coast was inviting.

Over much of its extent, the Mediterranean Sea has a depth much greater than that of the Continental Shelf. Depths of more than 1,000 fathoms occur over at least half the area of the sea The basin is divided into two major divisions by the constriction between Sicily and Tunis, where the sea floor rises to depths of little over 100 fathoms.

The more easterly basin is fully 5° farther south than the western. It approaches the desert more closely, and the rainfall of the eastern Mediterranean is appreciably lower than that of the western. Two seas branch from the eastern basin, the Adriatic and the Aegean. The latter communicates by the "Narrows" of the Dardanelles and the Bosporus with the Black Sea.

The *Black Sea*, like the Baltic, has a large inflow of fresh water from the rivers which enter it. Some is lost by evaporation, and the remainder escapes in a vigorous current through the Narrows into the Aegean. The salinity of the Mediterranean varies. In its southeastern portion, where evaporation is fast and few rivers bring fresh water, the salinity is very high. Elsewhere the salinity varies with the discharge of nearby rivers, being high along the southern coast and lower nearer the northern. For the Mediterranean as a whole the evaporation exceeds the inflow from rivers, and hence a current moves into the Mediterranean from the Atlantic through the Strait of Gibraltar. Saline water is heavy. It sinks and accumulates in the deep basins of the Mediterranean and Black Seas. It takes little part in the circulation of the sea and is, in consequence, not aerated.

It partly explains the relatively poor fisheries of the Mediterranean and adjoining seas.

The shores of western Europe from Gibraltar to the North Cape are washed by the Atlantic Ocean. Twenty-eight per cent of the total coastline of Europe fronts the Atlantic. In that area the surface waters of the Atlantic are relatively warm. They are drawn eastward from the West Indies and Gulf of Mexico by the prevailing westerly winds. In addition to circulating around the British Isles, they bathe the coasts of France and Spain and extend even to the coast of northern Norway. As far northeast as Murmansk, about 70°N, this warm drift of water keeps the sea ice-free. It has a profound influence on the climate of western Europe and is consequently important in transportation, agriculture, and other forms of economic development.

The Arctic Ocean extends along the northern shores of Norway, Finland, and Russia. It is relatively shallow, and the warm North Atlantic Drift reaches its more westerly parts. East of Murmansk, the coastal water freezes over in winter, and the duration and intensity of the freeze increase eastward. The White Sea, which extends some 300 miles into the forest belt of northern Russia, is frozen sufficiently to impede navigation for about half the year.

The Atlantic Ocean, unlike the other seas which fringe Europe, is subject to tides of considerable range. Twice in approximately 25 hours the sea level rises and falls as a wave passes in from the ocean. At London the tidal range is 21 feet at spring tides. The Bristol Channel has an exceptional range of 41½ feet at spring tides. Tides are generally lower on the French coast. They are small just within the Baltic and Mediterranean Seas but diminish eastward. There is, for example, a small but perceptible rise and fall of the sea in the lagoons of Venice.

The existence of the tide has two important consequences. First it helps to keep the estuaries of rivers open and navigable, whereas rivers discharging into tideless seas form deltas which impede navigation. The Rhône, Po, and Nile all have large and complex deltas. Rivers discharging into the Atlantic, while by no means free from sediment (the Thames, for example, has what amounts to a submerged delta) are very much clearer.

Second, the tides run long distances up some rivers and keep open many small inland ports. Bordeaux, Rouen, and Bristol are among the many examples of tidal ports.

Summary. Europe is a small continent of irregular shape and varied relief. If we include the Mediterranean Basin, there are five major physical divisions: the mountainous region of the extreme northwest, the plain of north Europe, a central east-west belt of hills and mountains, the Alpine mountain system, and the African tableland. The last lies entirely to the

south and southeast of the Mediterranean Sea. The rivers are numerous and, by American standards, small and short. In western Europe their flow is fairly regular through the year; in eastern and southern Europe it is more seasonal. The Mediterranean rivers discharge most in winter; the east European rivers, in summer. Europe is almost surrounded by the sea, which exercises a strong moderating influence on its climate. Most of its coastline is free of ice in winter. The tide is experienced on all coasts facing the Atlantic Ocean. This helps to keep the river mouths free from silting and enables seagoing ships to sail considerable distances up the rivers.

BIBLIOGRAPHY[1]

GENERAL

"British Admiralty Pilot," London.
Cole, Grenville A. J., "The Geological Growth of Europe," London, 1928.
Daly, R. A., "The Changing World of the Ice Age," New Haven, 1934.

ABBREVIATIONS USED IN BIBLIOGRAPHIES

A.A.A.G. Annals of the Association of American Geographers, Washington, D.C.
E.G. Economic Geography, Worcester, Mass.
G. Geography, Manchester, England.
G.J. Geographical Journal, Royal Geographical Society, London
G.R. Geographical Review, American Geographical Society, New York
I.B.G. Institute of British Geographers, Transactions, London
J.G. Journal of Geography, Chicago
S.G.M. Scottish Geographical Magazine, Edinburgh

[1] NOTE ON BIBLIOGRAPHIES: Each chapter will be followed by a short bibliography of works specific to the country considered. General works are listed only at the ends of the first four chapters. On pages 53 to 54 is a list of postwar official publications dealing with economic and geographical developments in Europe, together with a short list of periodicals likely to contain similar matters. The more important national geographical periodicals are listed after the chapters on the countries concerned.

"Introduction to Europe: A Selective Guide to Background Reading," The Library of Congress, Reference Department, Washington, D.C., 1950.
Lobeck, Armin K., "Physiographic Diagram of Europe," Madison, Wisconsin, 1923.
Pardé, M., "Fleuves et rivières," Paris, 1933.
Shackleton, M., "Europe," New York, 1950.
Steers, J. A., "The Unstable Earth," London, 1932.
Sverdrup, H. U., M. W. Johnson, and R. H. Fleming, "The Oceans, Their Physics, Chemistry, and General Biology," New York, 1942.
Wills, L. J., "The Physiographical Evolution of Britain," London, 1929.
Wright, W. B., "The Quaternary Ice Age," London, 1937.

ATLASES

Bartholomew, J., "Advanced Atlas of Modern Geography," New York, 1950.
"The Oxford Atlas," Oxford, 1951.
"The American Oxford Atlas," New York, 1951.

GEOGRAPHICAL PUBLICATIONS

Harris, Chauncy D., and Jerome D. Fellman, Geographical Serials, *G.R.*, XL, 1950, 649–656.
———, "A Union List of Geographical Series," 2d ed., University of Chicago, Chicago, 1950.

Current geographical publications are listed in: "Bibliographie géographique internationale," Association de géographes français, Paris, published annually.

The list published quarterly in *Foreign Affairs* is also most useful.

CHAPTER 2: *Europe: Climate, Soil, and Vegetation*

Most of Europe has a climate that is particularly well suited to man. It does not suffer from extremes of heat, except locally in the south and east, or from extremes of cold, except in the east and northeast. This moderation of temperature is due primarily to the influence of the ocean and of the seas, the Baltic, Mediterranean, Adriatic, Aegean, and Black Seas, which penetrate deep into the continent. The climate is characterized by rapid changes. It is often said that much of Europe experiences weather, not climate. Fine weather and wet, warm weather and cool succeed one another in rapid succession. Some winter days are as warm as those of summer, and a summer day can be as chill as winter. In most parts of Europe rain comes at all seasons of the year; only the Mediterranean region has a distinct dry season.

Atmospheric Pressure and Winds. A large part of Europe lies for most of the year in the track of the west winds. A series of depressions moves in from the Atlantic, bringing cloud and rain normally associated with low atmospheric pressure. On a map showing the *average* conditions of atmospheric pressure, Europe lies in a belt of prevailingly low barometric pressure. In reality, however, the pressure of the atmosphere varies not only from place to place but also from day to day. It is usually either dropping as a depression approaches or rising as it passes by. A warm, humid air mass, drawn in from a southerly direction to the front of the depression, yields rain. The cold front approaches; a mass of cooler air from a northerly quarter brings lower temperature, a drier atmosphere, a more broken cloud cover, and often sunny weather. Such is the sequence of weather which shows that much of Europe has a climate mild in temperature, wet, and rather stormy, with low average barometric pressure.

The eastward path of the depressions is guided by two areas of relatively high atmospheric pressure, which lie, respectively, to the north and south of Europe. The Arctic regions have normally a high barometric pressure. Cold, heavy air masses settle downward and move outward toward more southerly latitudes. At the same time, high pressure extends over the region of the Tropic of Cancer. Here also air tends to sink downward toward the earth's surface and to blow outward. Air masses from both the Tropical high-pressure area and the Arctic high-pressure area meet in the belt which lies between, and their interaction gives rise to depressions or cyclonic disturbances which move slowly eastward. In summer, the Tropical high-pressure region becomes larger; it reaches northward from Africa over the Mediterranean and may cover much of central Europe and on rare occasions even reaches northwestern Europe. This extension of high atmospheric pressure forces the eastward-moving depressions to take a more northerly route. In summer the Arctic high-pressure area is restricted, allowing the depressions to pass eastward across northern Europe. In winter the opposite conditions tend to occur. Then the Arctic high pressure becomes more extensive while the Tropical high withdraws to the south. Cyclones then take a more southerly course. The extent of both the Arctic and the Tropical high-pressure areas varies from day to day. In winter the former may extend far to the south or west for a few days, bringing with it exceptionally cold conditions. It may then retreat as a cyclonic disturbance moves across Europe from the Atlantic, only

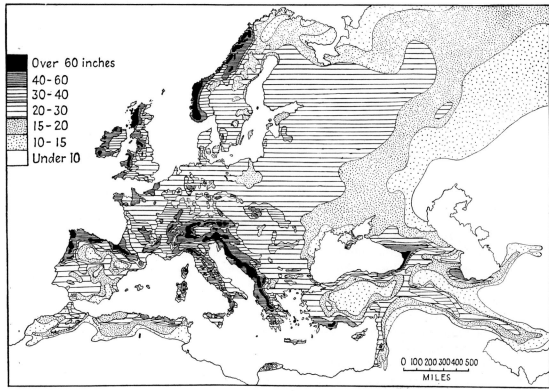

Over 60 inches
40-60
30-40
20-30
15-20
10-15
Under 10

0 100 200 300 400 500
MILES

FIG. 10. The rainfall of Europe.

to expand again a short time later. In winter, cyclone or depression tracks *tend* to lie across the Mediterranean and southern Europe, while in summer their courses are more often across the Baltic and northern Europe. Despite many exceptions, the northward and southward movement of the cyclone tracks is apparent and is responsible for some of the major seasonal climatic changes.

There are frequent variations from what has come to be regarded as the normal climatic conditions. If, for reasons which we do not yet know, the Arctic high-pressure area assumes larger proportions than usual and extends farther to the south, the cold Arctic air spans a wider area. The winter is more severe, and the duration of cold weather less broken by spells of warmer weather that result from the inflow of tropical air into a depression. The depressions are themselves fended off by the static mass of Arctic air and are forced to make a detour to the south around its edge. An exam-

ple of this occurred in the early months of 1947, when such a mass of Arctic air extended to the British Isles and for a period of many weeks prevented any cyclonic disturbance from bringing relief in the form of a stream of warm tropical air. The result was a winter of great severity. Most severe winters are due to such reasons as these rather than to any progressive change in climate.

During summer months, the reverse can happen. Much of Europe can fall for a period of several weeks under the influence of the Tropical high pressure. At such times, the cyclones are forced to take courses even more northerly than those usually followed. Then the cool Arctic air fails to break in and the summer becomes one of exceptionally intense heat and drought.

The variation with the seasons of the tracks most often followed by the cyclones suggests a threefold division of Europe. In the south is an east-to-west belt, covering approximately the

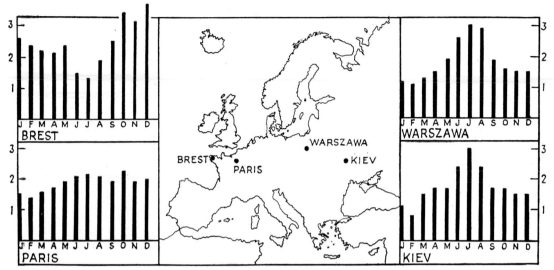

Fig. 11. The distribution of rainfall at Brest, Paris, Warsaw (Warszawa), and Kiev. The predominantly winter rain of the west turns gradually into a predominantly summer rain in the east of Europe.

Mediterranean Basin, where the depressions appear in winter. But in summer they are few and sometimes absent for considerable periods. As the rainfall depends largely on cyclonic disturbances, the Mediterranean has a dry summer. Farther to the north is a belt along which the depressions move at all seasons of the year. There is a tendency therefore for the rainfall to be well distributed, with no conspicuously dry seasons. Still farther north is a belt in which the high pressure prevails in winter, when there is, in consequence, little rainfall. The climate of Europe, however, is influenced by factors other than the tracks followed by the "lows" as they move in from the Atlantic Ocean. The local relief features are important, and the intensity of winter cold and summer heat is directly related to distance from the sea.

Cyclonic rainfall is produced by the rising of warm, moist Tropical air over the colder Arctic air. The former is cooled in its rise. Clouds form, and rain falls. A large proportion of the rainfall of Europe occurs in this way, irrespective of the surface features of the land. At the time, the moisture-laden winds, as they pass from the sea to the land, are forced to rise in order to surmount the physical obstacles that lie in their path. This brings about a cooling

of the atmosphere and the formation of cloud and rain. This orographic rainfall is superimposed upon that which is of a cyclonic origin. It is most conspicuous in hilly districts and is heavier on the windward than on the leeward side of the hills. A third form of rainfall occurs in what is called a "thermal" low. In areas which are intensely heated in summer, the air becomes unstable. A local overturning of the atmosphere takes place, and violent storms occur, often accompanied by thunder. Such rainfall happens most often in the hottest season of the year and in areas remote from the sea. In central and eastern Europe a considerable rainfall derives from summer storms.

The amount and distribution of rainfall do, however, allow us to divide Europe into regions based upon its amount and its incidence.

The Mediterranean Basin is an area of predominantly winter rainfall brought by cyclones moving in from the Atlantic. The rainfall is heaviest on the west-facing slopes of the mountains. Portugal has a markedly higher rainfall than Valencia, Rome than Ancona, Epirus than Thessaly. The southern and eastern shores of the Mediterranean receive little rainfall. The coast of Algeria and Tunis has 20 to 30 inches, almost the whole of it between October and May. In Tripolitania and Cyrenaica the rainfall

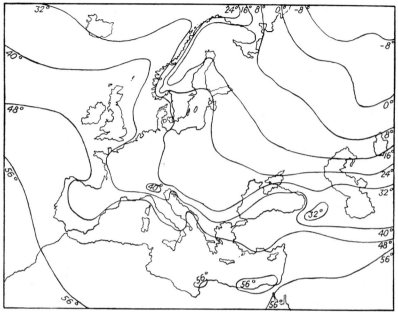

Fig. 12. The temperatures of Europe in January, reduced to sea level.

diminishes to less than 20 inches and is in large measure concentrated in the months from October to February. A similar low rainfall prevails in Egypt, Israel, and Syria, but the climate is essentially Mediterranean in as much as the rainfall occurs in the winter months.

Within the Mediterranean Basin, however, are areas which are distinguished by their summer rainfall, produced by local convectional overturning of the atmosphere. Such areas are relatively remote from the sea and are subjected to intense summer heat. The largest are the central plateau, or Meseta, of Spain and the plateau of Anatolia, or Asia Minor.

The belt of territory extending from the British Isles and France eastward to Russia is characterized by rain at all seasons of the year. The maximum amount varies, however, from the autumn and winter months in the west to the summer months in the center and east. Hilly areas have the effect everywhere within this belt of increasing the total rainfall. High totals have been recorded on the westward-facing mountain slopes of Scotland, northern England, and Wales. The average at Seathwaite in the Lake District is 129.5 inches; of Ben Nevis in Scotland, 171 inches. Bergen, on the

west coast of Norway, has 81 inches. The amount of rainfall diminishes eastward across the continent, but an area of hill country is always likely to receive an amount in excess of that received on lower land around it.

As distance from the sea increases and the intensity of summer heat becomes more pronounced, the convectional element in the total rainfall increases. Even in the English Midlands the total of summer rainfall just exceeds that of winter. Similarly in central France, July and August are the wettest months. Figure 11 illustrates the transition from the west coast, winter-maximum rainfall of the Breton coast to the continental summer maximum of southern Russia.

The total volume of rainfall diminishes northward. The summer maximum becomes less conspicuous, though it is present, in Sweden, Finland, and northern Russia. The lowering of the total precipitation is due to the reduced temperature of the air and to the fact that the cooling of the air liberates less moisture at a lower temperature.

An important factor in the temperature of Europe is the sea, which nearly surrounds the continent and also sends branches deep into the

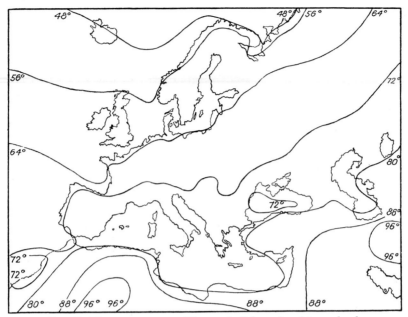

FIG. 13. The temperatures of Europe in July, reduced to sea level.

land mass. The sea gains heat slowly in summer and loses heat slowly in winter. In sharp contrast to the land, it shows only a small seasonal range of temperature. Air currents passing from the sea to the land in winter have a warming influence, whereas sea winds in summer cool the neighboring land. The effect of the sea is to moderate the extremes of temperature. The influence of the seas of western Europe is increased by the warm surface drift which comes as the Gulf Stream or North Atlantic Drift. Harbors are free of ice in winter as far north as Murmansk. Sea ice is rare, except in enclosed seas, and western Europe has a conspicuously mild winter.

Only northern Russia has temperatures which in America would be regarded as very low. The area lying north of about 56° latitude may be termed cold; here the temperature at least two-thirds of the year is below 50° Fahrenheit[1] in each month. The picture is one of winters of increasing length and intensity as one moves northward. An examination of the actual isotherms in summer and winter gives a rather fuller picture.

[1] All temperatures will be quoted according to the Fahrenheit scale.

Broadly, the predominant influence upon the winter temperatures of Europe is the sea and upon the summer temperatures, direct insolation. In January the 40° isotherm (see Fig. 12) runs almost from north to south, from the Hebrides through Ireland, west Wales, and southwest England across France from Normandy to the Mediterranean. The isotherm of 32° similarly takes a north-to-south course, lying close to the Norwegian coast, running through the Danish peninsula, and then taking a southeasterly course to the Balkans. The 20° and 10° isotherms also run from northern Scandinavia southeastward across Russia to the Caspian Sea. Winter temperatures thus do not decrease northward but rather northeastward or eastward, the Biscay coast of France being warmer by some 15° than the Crimean coast in the same latitude. The coast of southern England is more than 30° warmer than the south Russian steppe. This is closely similar to the relationship between Washington and Oregon, on the one hand, and Maine, on the other, and between California and Virginia or Maryland.

In summer, temperatures fall off more regularly toward the north (Fig. 13). In July, the average temperature of the whole Mediter-

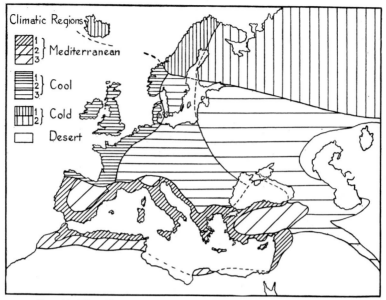

Fig. 14. The climatic divisions of Europe and the Mediterranean.

ranean coastland is 70° and over. A generalized 70° isotherm runs from the coast of Portugal somewhat north of eastward and encloses the Hungarian Plain and the steppes of the southeastern part of European Russia. The 60° isotherm is broadly parallel, from South Wales through northern Denmark and central Sweden to Finland and the White Sea. The summer isotherms are inclined, though less conspicuously, in the opposite direction to those of winter. Thus do oceanic influences modify the climate of western Europe.

The seasonal range of temperatures increases eastward. In the extreme west the summer is less than 20° warmer than the winter. It increases in central Germany to between 30° and 40°. In eastern European Russia the summers are 60° warmer than the winters. The Baltic, Black, and Mediterranean Seas reduce somewhat the range of temperature experienced in their neighborhood. The moderating effect of the Black Sea is particularly marked (Figs. 12 and 13).

Climatic Regions. In the light of this examination of the distribution of rainfall and temperature we can divide Europe into climatic regions, within each of which the climate is sufficiently homogeneous to be simply described.

A division into Mediterranean Europe, temperate Europe (stretching from the British Isles and France eastward to Russia), and cool northern Europe at once suggests itself. Each of these, however, can be divided further.

Mediterranean Climates. The Mediterranean region is characterized by a rainfall generally limited in quantity and occurring mainly in the winter half year. Temperatures are mild or warm in winter and hot in summer. Within the Mediterranean three divisions suggest themselves.

1. The northern coastlands together with the Atlas region are characterized by a rainfall that is generally above 25 inches a year. Winters in these areas are usually mild, though cold spells occur; temperatures may be below freezing for several days in succession; snow lies on higher ground; and snowfalls occur even near the sea. Summers are hot, and, except in the Atlas region of North Africa, a little rain falls in most summer months.

2. The eastern and southeastern shores of the Mediterranean lie in a lower latitude. The influence of depressions moving in from the Atlantic is less marked, and the rainfall is light. Except in Syria and northern Israel, it is less than 20 inches a year and occurs almost wholly

in the winter half year. Winters are warm, and summers are hot.

3. Within the limits of Mediterranean climate are a few areas in which the normal winter maximum of rainfall is supplemented by a considerable convectional summer rainfall. The central plateaus of Spain, Turkey, and north-eastern Italy have this characteristic. They also have severe winters owing to their separation from the sea and their relatively high altitude. Summers are very hot.

Cool Temperate Climates. This region experiences temperatures above 50° for at least 8 months in the year. The summers are occasionally and locally hot, but the extremes of the southeastern Mediterranean are not known. Over most of the area, winters are not severe. This climate belt is distinguished from the Mediterranean chiefly by the distribution of its rainfall, and from the cold climate of Europe by the number of months with a temperature above 50°. The distribution of rainfall and temperature necessitates a subdivision of cool temperate Europe into three categories.

1. In the mild, moist region of the west the rainfall is well distributed. If there is a summer maximum, it is not strongly marked. Winter temperatures are warm for the latitude; no month has an average temperature below freezing point. Summers are seldom hot, though short "heat waves" sometimes occur. The atmosphere is generally humid; fog is common in winter, especially near the industrial cities. There is a high degree of cloudiness, and the number of hours of sunshine in the year is sometimes quite small. On the other hand the climate is comparatively regular, and large departures from the average of rainfall and temperature are rare.

2. In central Europe the changes perceptible in the climate of western Europe become more clearly marked. The seasonal temperature ranges increase from about 25° to about 40°. A summer rainfall maximum appears. The winters become colder, though severe cold is experienced only for relatively short spells. The total precipitation diminishes. Central Europe is drier than western. In general there is more sunshine,

but the reliability of rainfall and temperature is less than in the climatic region lying to the west.

3. In eastern Europe the characteristics of central Europe appear in an exaggerated form. The annual range of temperature rises from 40° to 60°. The total amount of precipitation diminishes and is largely concentrated in the summer, when the rain is often torrential and accompanied by thunder.

Cold Climates. The region of cold climate has an average temperature of less than 50° during at least 8 months in the year. In Europe, however, it may be divided into a wetter western area, with a mild winter, and a drier eastern, with a winter of great severity.

1. Norway and much of Sweden have cool, cloudy, and wet summers and winters that are even wetter and more cloudy but not really cold. The winter temperatures on the Norwegian coast rarely drop to freezing point, though short distances inland, at the heads of the fiords and on rising ground, ice forms and snow lies through the winter. Similar conditions, though colder in winter and drier throughout the year, extend into Sweden.

2. The damp mild climate of the west merges gradually into one of greater severity. Winter temperatures diminish: Riga has a January average of 24°, Leningrad of 18°, Moscow of 14°, and Kazan of 7.5°. Summers are warm towards the south of this region, with July temperatures of 70° and more, but farther to the north the summers are short and cool.

Desert Climates. Desert climates are experienced to the south and southeast of Europe. There are two contrasted desert regions within the area covered by this book: the Saharan region of Africa and the desert region around the Caspian Sea. They are alike in having a small and generally unreliable rainfall. They differ appreciably in the temperature. In North Africa summers are very hot and winters generally warm; in the Caspian region summers are also hot but the winters are very cold. The Caspian region is an extreme form of the eastern European climate.

To summarize this outline of the climate of

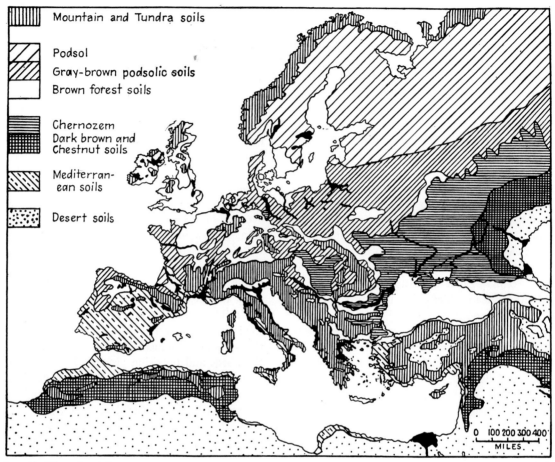

FIG. 15. The soils of Europe and the Mediterranean. Lowlands or alluvial soils are shown in black. (*Simplified from Agricultural Geography of Europe and the Near East, U.S. Department of Agriculture, 1948.*)

Europe: exposure to marine influences and the variations in the eastward movement of low-pressure areas from the Atlantic account for the general moderation of the climate of Europe. These "lows" follow tracks farther to the north in summer than those followed in winter. The result is that southern Europe receives little rainfall during the summer months and many parts have none at all. The rest of the continent receives rainfall at all seasons, but the amount diminishes eastward. In the west the winter is generally the wettest period, but in central and eastern Europe the rainfall maximum shifts to the summer. The rainfall also decreases toward the north. The temperatures in winter generally diminish with increasing distance from the sea. In summer, the greatest heat is felt in the south

and east of Europe. The climatic regions may be summarized as follows:

1. A Mediterranean region of hot and generally dry summers, with cool and mild winters.

2. A region of cool temperate climate which stretches from west to east across Europe. The rainfall diminishes and the temperatures become more extreme toward the east.

3. A region of cold climate, with cool summers and cold winters, moderated somewhat in the west by the proximity of the ocean.

Vegetation and Soils. Topography and climate, vegetation and soils are all intimately related one to another. Together they make up most of the physical environment. Though it is often necessary—as has been done in the preceding pages—to separate these phenomena from one another for purposes of description and analysis, it must be remembered that it is the totality which matters. Soils, for example, derive in part from the parent rock, but their depth and composition vary with relief and climates, and their texture will vary with the nature and distribution of the plants that contribute humus.

The vegetation of Europe, which man has profoundly modified during the last 4,000 or 5,000 years, is in the process of evolution. As the climate improved with the retreat of the glaciers, plants which had been exterminated in Europe or restricted to small areas gradually recolonized parts of their old habitat. More southerly types migrated northward. The dominant plant species in any locality yielded place to others. The natural vegetation in any place depends partly on the stage reached in this slow propagation of plant species over the continent, partly on the climate, and partly on the rock and soil. The rock and soil vary within short distances. Limestones give place to sands or clays, each with a characteristic flora; boulder clay, outwash, terrace gravels, and loess each influences the type of vegetation. There are changes with slope, altitude, and drainage.

Despite these strongly marked and often abrupt changes in flora, there is a degree of uniformity in the vegetation over large areas which allows Europe to be divided into five distinct vegetation belts or zones.

The Tundra. This occupies the extreme north: the uplands of northern Scandinavia, the plains of northern Finland and Russia, and the islands which lie north of the coast of Europe. Winters are very cold, and summers cool. Precipitation is slight and occurs chiefly as snow in winter and as light rain in summer. The plants are adapted to the extreme cold, to the conditions of drought which exist in winter and even in summer, and to the very short growing season in summer. Trees, except dwarfed varieties growing in particularly sheltered spots, are lacking. Most plants are low and stunted; in some areas, moss or lichen predominates over a land surface that is almost devoid of soil. On slopes, short woody plants appear, often with thick leaves not unlike

those of plants which grow in the Mediterranean region. Some of these bear brilliant flowers in summer. The vegetation conforms closely with the aspect of the land. A southerly slope may have stunted bushes and grass, while a northern one has chiefly lichens and bare rock.

Southward "the Arctic tundra slowly but definitely passes over into the Northern forest:

The tundra of northern Finland. The land surface is either bare rock or moss, with a few low-growing thickets. The animal is a reindeer. (*Finnish National Travel Office.*)

at first nothing but stones, and low bushes, here and there the stump of a birch tree, and dry wood, here and there the golden sparkle of cinquefoil . . . ; then the underwood continues to become thicker, it is taller and shaggier, everywhere, as far as the eye can see, the white little flames of birch stems, mingling with them slim and glistening aspens, dark bushes of alders, and silvery willows, and everywhere beneath the willows, beneath the crowberries,[1] beneath the birches surges the peat, nothing but black, wet, shining peat. And then above the low undulating growth a dried and twisted

[1] Fruit of a low-growing, heathlike shrub.

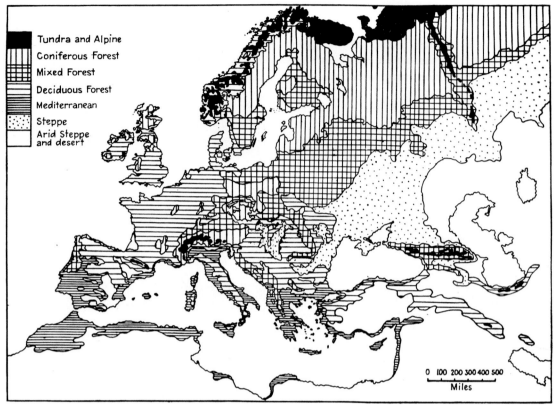

FIG. 16. The vegetation of Europe and the Mediterranean. (*Simplified from Agricultural Geography of Europe and the Near East, U.S. Department of Agriculture, 1948.*)

stem raises itself and carries a meagre crown; the shaggy brushwood of knotted pines begins to darken; strangely our mountain knee-pine is absent, here only the tall, pathetic pine struggles tenaciously for life. And now already it has won the battle; it is still gnarled, and tattered by the storms, and broken by the snow, but already its lanky stem and heavy boughs give a deep and solemn character to the whole country. The birches are becoming fewer, the pines are gaining ground. . . ."[1]

Coniferous Forest. The belt of evergreen forest consists mainly of various species of pine, spruce, and fir but includes also the larch and such hardy deciduous trees as the birch, alder, poplar, and willow. Characteristics of these northern forests are the occurrence of large uniform stands of timber and the relative

[1] Čapek, Karel, "Travels in the North," pp. 231–232, London, 1939.

absence of grass and herbs. This forest was formerly continuous over large areas of northern Europe, and south of its predominant habitat it occurs on high ground and on areas of light or acid soil on which the broad-leaved tree takes root with greater difficulty.

There is little soil in the tundra region, but southward in the region of coniferous forest a podsol develops. This gray or white soil has low fertility. It is developed in areas of moderate or heavy rainfall and cool temperatures. The coniferous trees yield little green stuff to form humus, and this is readily carried downward and dissipated by percolating waters.

Below a shallow surface layer which contains humus is a white, leached horizon, from which most of the fertility has been removed. The podsols are usually infertile and "hungry" soils, requiring heavy manuring if they are to produce well. True podsols characterize much of Norway

An agricultural settlement in the north European Plain. All areas of good soil are intensively cultivated, but there are many areas of poor glacial soils. (*Royal Danish Ministry for Foreign Affairs.*)

and Sweden, as well as Finland and northern Russia. They support only a poor agriculture. They are often acid and sour. Rye, oats, and potatoes are the commonest crops on the podsols of the northern forests.

Broad-leaved Deciduous Forest. This occupies the moist area of more temperate climate in Europe. In certain respects the broad-leaved forest resembles the coniferous: large stands of a few species are quite common, the trees form a canopy of vegetation, and on the ground there is little undergrowth except where the woodland cover is thin. The autumn leaf fall is characteristic of this forest; leaves rot on the ground and produce a forest mold which has a fertility much greater than the poor soils of the coniferous belt. The woodland trees have their particular habitats: beech and ash are characteristic of lime-bearing soils; oak with hazel thicket, of clay; poplar, willow, and osier grow on damp soils; and the elm is generally found on moist soils. Certain areas of dry and pervious soil, such as the glacial gravels of Germany, bear only a thin cover of woodland or of heath. The chalk "downland" is usually treeless unless it has a thin mantling of residual clay, when it bears patches of woodland. The loess belt, which lies along the southern margin of the formerly glaciated area, probably had a lightly wooded or parkland aspect.

The limits of the broad-leaved forest are not clearly marked. Its boundary runs across northern Spain, southern France, northern Italy and across the Balkans from the Adriatic coast to the Black Sea. In southern Russia the woodland merges into the steppe.

In this region of broad-leaved forest, there is more humus in the soil. Nevertheless, if the rainfall is heavy, as in many parts it is, there is still a great deal of solution and removal of humus. Many parts are "podsolized," the hills of the western parts of the British Isles, of Brittany, and of Germany being examples. Over much of this region, however, the soil is largely man-made. It was settled and cultivated at an early date in human history. Man has plowed and tilled, manured and drained. He has gradually altered—and in general improved—

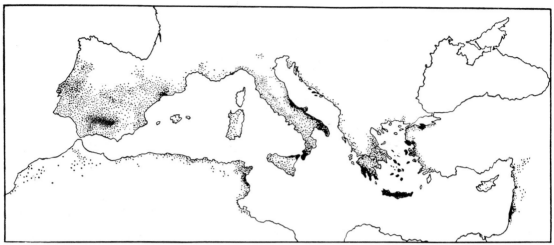

FIG. 17. Distribution of olive cultivation in Europe and the Mediterranean. This map should be compared with the area of Mediterranean climate shown in Fig. 14. (*From Agricultural Geography of Europe and the Near East, U.S. Department of Agriculture*, 1948.)

the composition of the soil. At its best, the soil of the broad-leaved forest is one of the most productive existing, but there still remain many areas of sour podsol, scarcely fit for crop husbandry.

The Steppe. The change from the forest to the steppe is gradual. "Round low hills tilled and sown to their very tops, are seen in broad undulations; ravines, overgrown with bushes, wind coiling among them; small copses are scattered like oblong islands; from village to village run narrow paths; churches stand out white; between willow-bushes glimmers a little river; in four places dammed up by dykes; far off, in a field, in a line, an old manorhouse, with its outhouses, fruit-garden, and threshing floor, huddles close up to a small lake. The hills are smaller and ever smaller; there is scarcely a tree to be seen. Here it is at last—the boundless, untrodden steppe."[1] The steppe was originally a rolling expanse of tall grassland. On its moister fringe was open woodland; on its drier, the grass became thinner and poorer as it merged into scrub desert. The natural vegetation cover has long since been destroyed, at least in the more favored parts, to make way for crop farming. The soil on the steppe is known as "chernozem." The growth of tall grass gives

[1] Turgenev, S., The Forest and the Steppe, from "Sportsman's Sketches," New York, 1885.

rise to a rich humus in the upper layer of the soil, which is characteristically black in color. The chernozem conserves plant food and is thus among the richest and most productive of soils. In Europe it occurs in Hungary and in the steppe which stretches from southern Russia into Central Asia.

Where, on the desert margin of the steppe, the vegetation is thinner, the supply of humus less abundant, the chernozem gives place to dark brown and chestnut soils. These nevertheless have some agricultural value, and if they are not cultivated, it is because the rainfall is inadequate rather than because of deficiencies in the soil.

Mediterranean. The period of prolonged drought, coinciding with that of great heat, has produced a woody vegetation which is characteristically evergreen, with thick, leathery leaves, woody stems, and deep roots. Such vegetation is described as "sclerophyllous." The trees include evergreen conifers, such as the southern and Aleppo pines and cypress, and also broad-leaved evergreens like the ilex or holm oak, the cork oak, and Spanish chestnut. Thick woodland is not common. There is, however, an abundance of shrubs and small trees, some of them bearing brilliant flowers, some highly aromatic, and all evergreen. The olive, now rarely found wild, is one; the laurel (bay), oleander, tamarisk, myrtle, and mimosa are others. The ground is often covered with a thick mat of low spreading thicket, made up of thyme, sage, and lavender. There is a wealth of small bulbous flowering plants—the tulips, narcissi, and asphodels. All combine to produce a blaze of color in spring and die back to the prevailing gray-green which characterizes Mediterranean lands through the heat of the summer.

The wasteland is usually covered with one of two characteristic types of vegetation. The first is the *garrigue*, a sparse covering of low-growing plants which root in the crevices of the rock. This is characteristic of the limestone. The *maquis*[1] is somewhat richer and consists generally of almost impenetrable thicket in which men can hide with considerable ease. The resistance movement in France during the Second World War was called the *Maquis* because many of its members used to hide in this thick vegetation.

The low and seasonal rainfall and the generally sparse vegetation developed a soil that is shallow, poor in humus, and generally of low fertility and more suited for trees than crop farming.

Desert. The rainfall is in general too low for much plant growth. Over large areas there is little vegetation, and much of the surface is bare rock, gravel, or sand. A small, irregular rainfall leads to the growth of a thin grass or of scattered, drought-resisting shrubs. Such land may provide sustenance for wandering flocks but without irrigation is not capable of intensive use. In most desert regions are small areas in which water is available, either from springs or from rivers which enter the region. Here the date palm is grown, along with other palms, the olive, and such crops as barley and wheat. Such intensively cultivated areas occur in the valley of the Nile, in the river valleys of Turkestan, and in the oases of North Africa.

The sparsity or even complete absence of vegetation in the desert does not favor the formation of humus, and frequently there is no

real soil. At the same time, owing to the low rainfall, whatever elements of soil fertility are present are saved from being dissolved and removed. Thus the desert soils may be highly fertile where irrigated.

The mountainous areas of Europe form an exception to the distribution of vegetation as it has been described here. The diminution of temperature with increasing altitude on the mountain causes a zoning of the vegetation. The Alps, for example, which lie mainly in the

Terraced agriculture in the south of France. Note the small area of cultivated land added and the immense labor involved in constructing the terraces.

region of broad-leaved deciduous forest, have coniferous forests on their intermediate slopes, succeeded on their higher slopes by stunted trees and low-growing plants, such as characterize the tundra. Mountains, such as those of Norway and Sweden, which are within the coniferous forest belt, rise, if they are high enough, directly into the tundra.

Settlement. Everywhere in Europe is evidence of man's work. The landscape is "humanized," and very few areas—high mountains, tundra, semidesert—have not been fundamentally altered by his occupance. Irrigation in the arid regions of the south and southeast, the reclamation of fens as in the Fenland of England, the draining of the Polders of the Netherlands and of coastal marshes in France, Italy, Germany are all evidences of constructive use of the land. Even more conspicuous are the terraces on the hillsides of southern France, of

Italy, and of other Mediterranean countries, laboriously made so that man can grow his vines, olives, and his patches of wheat and vegetables on a hillside that would otherwise be too steep for successful use. Examples are not lacking, however, of destructive land use. Deforestation has been accompanied by soil erosion, the silting of rivers, and spread of disease in southern Europe. It was customary at one time to ascribe the spread of malaria and even the fall of the ancient civilizations to this cause. There are severe soil wash and gullying in parts of the Mediterranean lands, of the French Alps and in Scotland, but in most of northwestern Europe soil destruction is very much less serious than in most other continents. This is partly because of the less torrential rains.

It would be surprising if human influence were not profound in Europe. Man lived there perhaps during the warm phases between the advances of the ice during the Ice Age. The sod was first broken in northwestern Europe and crops first taken by Neolithic man 4,000 years ago. He cultivated first the dry, warm soils. Prehistoric hill camps and burial mounds are generally on high ground. Then with better tools, axes first of bronze and then of iron, he advanced into the forest and thicket-covered plain. Heavy was the task of man in spreading from the hill to the valley, from the dry limestone and gravel soils to the damp clay. Yet this expansion of settlement was made necessary by his growing numbers. An ancient religious play reflects the hardship:

> "Strong are the roots of the briars,
> That my arms are broken,
> Tearing up many of them."

The conquest of the woodlands and the extension of settlement were the great achievements of European man during the early and Middle Ages.

Such an extension was necessitated by the growing population. We are accustomed to regard the present-day birth rates of India, China, and Japan as exceptional. However, the rate of growth of European population in recent centuries was quite as rapid. It created a great land hunger. It cleared and colonized much of Europe and later helped to people the New World. The adversity which accompanied it stimulated man to physical and mental efforts.

The earliest advances were in Mediterranean Europe. Here the climate and the open nature of Mediterranean woodland favored his efforts. Western Europe presented greater difficulties—a harsher climate and denser woodland—but also a greater prospect of reward. The soils were in general better, and the distribution of rainfall throughout the year favored a wider variety of crops and the development of pastoral husbandry on a larger scale than had been possible in Mediterranean lands.

Settlement and agriculture spread eastward from western to central Europe. Areas of better soil were cleared and broken up for cultivation by the cooperative effort of the peasants. They laid out their arable fields, made up of long narrow strips. Every peasant family had strips in each field to ensure equal opportunity. Efficiency was sacrificed at the altar of equality. Swamp and heath were circumvented and brought into production only as necessity and opportunity arose. Many such areas have had to await the coming of modern techniques of drainage and land reclamation. The cultivation of some has depended on the modern use of artificial fertilizers.

One of the most promising of the vegetational regions of Europe—the steppe—was the last to be widely brought under cultivation. Its climate is severe, but its black chernozem soil is rich. The obstacle lay partly in the exposure of the steppe to the nomadic peoples, the Tartars, who at intervals came raiding across the steppe from the borders of Asia. The "planting" of the steppe followed the Russian conquest in the seventeenth and eighteenth centuries.

But man has made little impression on the northern coniferous forests and the tundra. Harsh climate and poor soil have deterred the agriculturalist. Cultivated land occupies a relatively small proportion of the whole, and over most of the area, forestry and mining are of greater importance than agriculture.

BIBLIOGRAPHY   *55605*

Brooks, C. E. P., The Role of the Oceans in the Weather of Western Europe, *Quarterly Journal of the Royal Meteorological Society*, LVI, 1930, 131–140.

Garnett, A., The Loess Regions of Central Europe in Prehistoric Times, *G.J.*, CVI, 1945, 132–143.

Hardy, M. E., "The Geography of Plants," Oxford, 1925.

Kendrew, W. G., "Climate of the Continents," London, 1944.

Köppen, W., "Die Klimate der Erde," Berlin, 1923.

Miller, A. Austin, "Climatology," London, 1944.

Newbigin, M. I., "Frequented Ways," London, 1922.

———, "Plant and Animal Geography," London, 1936.

Pardé, M., "Fleuves et rivières," Paris, 1933.

Praeger, Robert Lloyd, "The Way That I Went," Dublin, 1937. (This is a delightful book mainly on the plant geography of Ireland.)

Schimper, A. F. W., "Plant Geography," translated by W. R. Fisher, Oxford, 1903.

Shackleton, M., "Europe," London, 1950.

Sverdrup, H. U., M. W. Johnson, and R. H. Fleming, "The Oceans, Their Physics, Chemistry and General Biology," New York, 1942.

U. S. Department of Agriculture, "Climate and Men," 1941.

Von Hann, J., "Handbuch der Klimatologie," 3 vols., Stuttgart, 1908–1911.

Wills, L. V., "The Physiographical Evolution of Britain," London, 1929.

Wright, W. B., "The Quaternary Ice Age," London, 1937.

CHAPTER 3: *Europe: Race, Language, and Nationality*

RACE

Europe was peopled by groups which moved in from Africa and Asia. Man may have existed there before the beginning of the Ice Age. It is certain that he was present during the intervals between the successive advances and retreats of the ice. It is probable, too, that the changing physical conditions of the Pleistocene stimulated man to make mental adaptations which allowed him not only to achieve a position of superiority in the animal world but in some measure to control his environment. It is uncertain whether the present population of Europe contains any of the descendants of these Pleistocene inhabitants. Individuals have been found, however, having physical traits similar to skeletal remains of the earliest known Europeans.

As the ice retreated and the climate ameliorated, peoples moved northward from Africa. Hunters also invaded Europe from the east, along the belt of open grassland which was probably much more extensive then than now. Throughout prehistoric time, the population of Europe was sparse. Contact between one group and another was probably infrequent, and knowledge of inventions and discoveries traveled slowly. Agriculture seems to have been discovered at the end of the Stone Age or the beginning of the Bronze. The discovery may have been made in the Middle East, but it was presumably many centuries before agriculture was practiced in the eastern Mediterranean and longer before it reached northwest Europe. Early settlement was in areas which were free of dense vegetation. The dry chalk and limestone uplands, the belt of porous loess soil, and the areas of sand and gravel were the early sites of human settlement by virtue of the fact that

primitive man sought areas of open grassland or parkland and avoided the forests. The expansion of settlement from the dry soil to the moist, from the limestone and the chalk to the clay, from the upland to the lowland came later and has occupied the whole of historical time. This extension in the area of settlement accompanied an increase in population.

The many human groups which settled in Europe possessed characteristic physical traits, but intermixture with other groups spread and diluted these qualities. In Europe the intermixture of groups has gone far to break down homogeneity or purity of race. There are now no races in the strict sense of the word. No groups of people show uniformly similar physical traits.

Nevertheless, partly because certain traits tend to be "dominant" and others "recessive," there are regional characteristics. Broadly, brunettes, or people with a dark skin and hair color and brown eyes, tend to predominate in southern Europe. Fair coloring is regarded as characteristic of more northerly lands. Stature is, in general, greater in the north of Europe than the south. The northern peoples are relatively long headed. The Mediterranean peoples share this characteristic, whereas in central Europe is a belt, from west to east, of broad-headed peoples.[1]

The prevailing "brunetteness" of the Mediterranean region does not exclude many small groups of medium-colored and fair people. In the predominantly blonde regions of the north there are, similarly, many who display brunette qualities. There is nowhere any uniformity in

[1] See C. S. Coon, "The Races of Europe," New York, 1939, for detailed consideration of European racial types.

these racial characteristics, though certain qualities may be said to predominate in certain areas.

The United States contains descendants of people from all parts of Europe. From the racial point of view, the American people display an exceptionally great mixture.

It is idle to talk about the existence of a race or races in Europe. European peoples are too much interbred for clear-cut racial groupings. The statistical material on which a survey of racial characteristics of the Middle East and North Africa might be based does not exist. The evidence available suggests that here, too, the mixing of peoples has reached a point only a little less extreme than that in Europe. Traits which we commonly associate with northern Europeans sometimes are manifest in the native peoples of Algeria and Tunis, a relic perhaps of the invasion by the Germanic Vandals in the fifth century. Similarly, the "African" trait appears locally in France and Spain, left there by the Saracen or Berber invasions of the eighth and later centuries. In Egypt, Palestine, and Syria there are also mixtures of racial elements from differing parts of Asia and Africa, as well as the European blood in the veins of Jewish settlers in Israel and in the Egyptian landowner and Syrian Christian.

To summarize, the peoples of Europe display great racial mixture and are descended from immigrants from both Asia and Africa. Nevertheless, the peoples of northern Europe are in general of a bigger build than those of the south and are lighter in skin and hair coloring than the peoples of the Mediterranean area. In no instance do the people of one nation or of one country have consistently similar stature, head shape, and skin and hair color. No nation can fairly claim to be of a pure race.

LANGUAGE

Linguistic divisions in Europe have an importance and in many cases a precision that is wholly lacking in the racial. They constitute deep-rooted barriers between peoples and play a role of great significance in the policies and actions of the states of Europe. There are, in Europe alone, over 30 languages, which are spoken by large numbers of people, each having a literature of its own, each recognized as a distinct and separate vehicle for the expression of ideas and conduct of affairs. In addition to these there are numerous "sublanguages" and dialects, having close affinities with one of the major languages, but not generally having a separate literature. Many such dialects have died out in modern times or remain only as a patois spoken by country folk. The *langue d'oc* of southern France and the High German of South Germany are examples.

Linguistic groups are often, though erroneously, termed "races." With the exception of the Lapps, a rather primitive people who have come into northern Europe from the east, there is almost no group of people who display a separateness both in language and in physical or racial characteristics. There is not and never has been such a thing as a "French race" or a "German race," though for perhaps a thousand years there has been a French-speaking, as distinct from a German-speaking, people.

Most European languages are of fairly recent origin. Certain European languages, such as Basque and Albanian, are very old, relics perhaps of an early group of languages that has since been obliterated in other areas. Most other European languages belong to a single language family, the Indo-Aryan. There are similarities in syntax and frequently in vocabulary throughout these languages, which appear to have had a common origin. The Indo-Aryan languages are divisible into five groups, within each of which there is even greater similarity. These groups are the following:

Celtic Languages. These were brought from the east, possibly in the second millennium B.C. At the time of the spread of the Roman Empire over western Europe, a Celtic language was spoken in much of Spain and Gaul (France) as well as in the British Isles. In Gaul and Spain it was replaced by the Latin language of the Roman provincials, and it died out completely. In the British Isles, however, the Roman influence was less profound. Though Latin was used in the towns, the rural districts appear to have

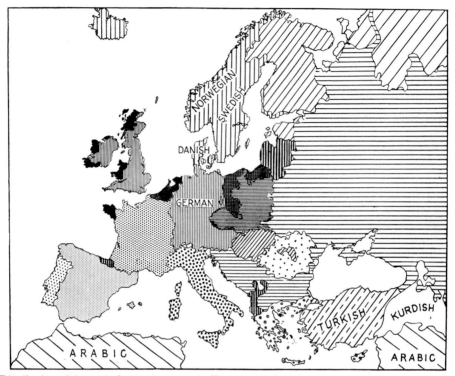

Fig. 18. Distribution of the main language groups in Europe and the Mediterranean. Romance languages are indicated by dots, Germanic by vertical shading, Slavonic by horizontal shading, Finno-Ugric by diagonal. Celtic is shown black, and Basque, Albanian, and Lithuanian by heavy vertical lines. Areas of Poland and Czechoslovakia from which the Germans have recently been expelled are indicated by both vertical and horizontal shading.

continued Celtic in speech. After the decline of the Roman Empire and the withdrawal of its legions from Britain, the Anglo-Saxon invaders came, bringing with them their Germanic language. This replaced Celtic over the lowlands of England, but in the highland districts of Scotland, Wales, and Cornwall, as well as in Ireland, Celtic languages survived. Bands of Celtic-speaking Britons even crossed at this time to Brittany, the northwestern peninsula of France, and reintroduced the Celtic tongue.

Gradually, however, the English language, which developed from the speech of the Anglo-Saxon invaders, penetrated the highlands of the "Celtic fringe." The Celtic language disappeared from Cornwall and the Isle of Man. Welsh was spoken only in the mountainous district of North Wales, and Gaelic only in the Highlands of northwestern Scotland. Even in Ireland, the English language made progress. More recently there has been a Celtic revival.

The number of Welsh-speaking people has increased (see page 107), and the decline of Celtic has been retarded in Ireland.

Classical Languages. These consisted of Greek and Latin. Greek survives, much altered in grammar and vocabulary, as the language of Greece and the Aegean area. Latin has disappeared as a living language but remains the language of the Roman Catholic Church, whose services are performed and documents published in Latin.

Romance Languages. These have grown from the Latin which was carried by the Roman settler and soldier throughout the Empire of Rome. In some of these lands the Latin language has survived in modified form. In each region it has tended to assume gradually a new shape. In Gaul, Latin ripened into French; in Spain and Portugal, into the Spanish, Catalan, and Portuguese languages; in Italy, into Italian; and in Romania, into Romanian.

The family resemblance between the Romance languages is very close. During the Middle Ages additional languages emerged, including the *langue d'oc* of southern France and the Romansch of the Engadine Valleys of Switzerland. Others were just strongly developed dialects. It was probably the invention of printing, the translation of the Bible into the more strongly developed languages, and the spread of literacy and education that checked the development of many of these lesser languages. *Langue d'oc* disappeared before the spread of French; Catalan before Spanish; the Walloon dialect of parts of Belgium before French. In Spain, a country where education has made little progress among the masses, there remain today a number of strongly marked local dialects, distinct from the standard or Castilian Spanish in many ways.

The boundaries between these Romance languages in western Europe are generally fairly clearly marked. A sharp line, approximately the national frontier, separates Portuguese from Spanish; the Pyrenees and the Alps separate, respectively, Spanish and Italian from French.

Romanian is spoken by a people remote from the main body of Romance speech. It is supposed that Roman settlers and Romanized provincials were driven, after the collapse of the Empire, into the mountain fastnesses of Transylvania and the Carpathians. Here they preserved their language, while Hungarians and Bulgar and Slav peoples settled the plains around. In more recent times they have spread outward to occupy much of the Romania of today.

Germanic Languages. The Germanic languages similarly constitute an interrelated group, which appears to have originated in the region of the Baltic Sea. They attained their present limits in the west in the course of the invasions which brought the Roman Empire to an end. The Franks crossed the lower Rhine, advancing the limits of their intensive settlements to a line which ran (Fig. 19) from a point near Boulogne, on the French coast, eastward through the future site of Brussels, then southward across the Ardennes and Lorraine and along the crest of the Vosges Mountains; thence across the Jura Mountains and the Swiss Plateau to the Swiss Alps.

The limits of the German tongue have receded only a little. In northern France it has been largely replaced by French. French has also made small gains in Lorraine. Elsewhere the

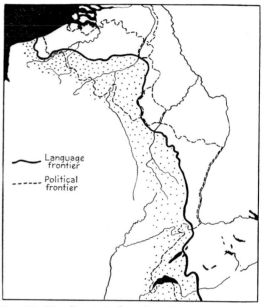

FIG. 19. The linguistic boundary in western Europe between areas of Romance (French) language to the west and Germanic to the east. On the French coast the language frontier has retreated from near Boulogne to near Dunkirk.

language frontier has shown a remarkable fixity and sharpness for a period of over 10 centuries.

The expansion of the German language eastward occurred later and was achieved by the advance of Germanic settlers into the then sparsely populated Slavonic territories. The advance was made at first on a broad front, but afterward followed three significant lines: along the Baltic coast toward what is now called East Prussia, up the Oder Valley and along the loess belt of Silesia and southern Poland, and, third, down the Danube toward the Hungarian Plain.

Between the limits thus defined the German language consisted of a large number of related dialects, which have been grouped into Low,

Middle, and High German. The Low German tongue of the northern plain survives in the dialects of Mecklenburg and Pomerania and in the Dutch and Frisian languages. High German of the south survives as a patois in certain rural areas, such as Alsace. It was a Middle German dialect that eventually spread over the whole of Germany as standard German. This spread was aided by Luther's translation of the Bible in the early sixteenth century into Middle German, thereby establishing a model for German prose.

Small "islands" of German-speaking peoples established themselves farther east, in Poland, Hungary, Romania, and Russia (see Fig. 124). In these outlying areas, German speech and culture were jealously and successfully preserved. Since 1945, however, most of these advanced posts of German language have been rolled back toward the fatherland, and most, if not all, of these "islands" have disappeared. The Volga Germans of Russia were forcibly moved into Siberia. Most of those in Poland, Czechoslovakia, and the Danubian lands have been driven back to Austria or Germany. Furthermore, Germans living to the east of the rivers Oder and Neisse, in Prussia, Pomerania, and Silesia, have mostly been forced westward into what remains of Germany.

The German language is spoken throughout Austria and in about half of Switzerland.

Dutch and Flemish are so similar that they may be considered as the same language. This is a Low German dialect which has crystallized in the region of the lower Rhine and Zuider Zee into a distinct language. Frisian, spoken on the Frisian islands and along the north German coast, is related to Dutch.

English is also fundamentally a Germanic language brought to Britain by the Anglo-Saxons and extended gradually over the whole British Isles and, from the sixteenth century onward, to the North American continent, Australia, New Zealand, and several other parts of the English-speaking world. It has, however, incorporated a very great many words of French, Latin, and Greek origin.

Danish is spoken in Denmark. Its southern limit in Schleswig has never coincided closely with the political limits of Denmark, and there is today a Danish-speaking minority on the German side of the frontier. Swedish is spoken in Sweden, in the Aland (Ahvenanmaa) Islands, and on parts of the west coast of Finland, where it was taken by Swedish emigrants in the seventeenth century. Norwegian is closely akin to Danish and is spoken in Norway and the Norwegian dependency of Spitzbergen.

Slavonic Languages. These form a closely related group and appear to have spread from eastern Poland. In the isolation of mountain valleys and forest clearings, many dialects evolved. Some have become extinct; others have attained the rank of distinct languages, though the family resemblances remain. The Slavonic group of languages can be divided into three, each having three or more subdivisions. The western Slav group consists of Polish, Czech, and Slovak; the southern Slav group, of Slovene, Serbo-Croat, and Macedonian; and the third, or Russian, group, of Great Russian, which is the official Russian literary language, and Ukrainian, with its subsidiary Ruthene and White Russian dialects.

Polish is the prevailing language of the Vistula Basin. In historical times it has lost ground in the west to German, but until recently it advanced in the east. The boundaries of Polish speech are not sharply defined and have given rise to disputes and bitterness. Czech, by contrast, is the language of the valley of the upper Elbe, where its area of distribution is the plain of Bohemia and the Moravian area to the east. As with the Polish settlement area, the Czech has also been intruded by German-speaking peoples who settled in the mountain fringe of Bohemia. Since the Second World War many of these Germans, whose ancestors had been here for many centuries, were sent back to Germany. Slovak is akin to Czech. It is spoken in the Carpathian Mountains of eastern Czechoslovakia.

Slovene, a southern Slav language, is spoken in the Sava Basin of Yugoslavia. On the north the Slovene area adjoins the German of Austria; on the west, the Italian. The boundary is indistinct and is the cause of frequent political disturbance. Serb and Croat are so similar as to be spoken of as Serbo-Croat. Their difference lies chiefly in the use of the Greek Cyrillic alphabet by Serbs whereas the Croats use the Roman alphabet. Macedonian is often classed as a provincial dialect of Serb. It has, however, incorporated many non-Serb elements and has affinities with Bulgar.

The third Slavic group is the Russian. Great Russian was the language of Moscow and has spread with the expansion of the Russian state. It was the official language of the Tsars and was used by the Russian literary masters of the eighteenth and nineteenth centuries. Ukrainian resembles Great Russian. It is spoken over the steppe of southern European Russia; appears in northern Romania, in the east of the former territory of Poland; and, as Ruthenian, is spoken in the Carpathians. Other Russian dialects, including White Russian, are spoken locally in west European Russia.

Non-Indo-European Languages. Basque was formerly spoken widely in northern Spain and southwestern France. For many centuries, it has been of diminishing importance. It is still spoken near Bilbao, but most who speak it also speak Spanish.

Albanian has survived in the mountains of Epirus but has absorbed elements of the Greek and Serbian languages spoken nearby. It is still a vigorous language and is the chief unifying force in the otherwise disunited state of Albania. The limits of the language do not correspond to those of the state, and there is a considerable Albanian minority in Yugoslavia.

Another group of non-Indo-European languages was brought into Europe by invaders from the East after the principal language groups of Europe had developed. They belong to the Asiatic or Ural-Altaic group. The speakers of these languages followed three routes. One group followed a northern route westward through the coniferous forest belt to Finland. With the exception of the Lapps, these peoples have largely become Westernized, though their ancient language survives as Finnish and Estonian. The second route is via the steppes of southern Russia. Some invading groups, in-

cluding the Huns, have left only the memory of their ferocious raids. Others have settled in Europe and have intermarried with the Slavonic-speaking peoples to such a degree that only their language remains to indicate their eastern origin. They now compose the Hungarian (Magyar) peoples. In the sixteenth and seventeenth centuries the Turks expanded across southeastern Europe to the gates of Vienna. From the end of the seventeenth century to the beginning of the twentieth they have been in slow retreat. Small groups of Turks have remained behind in the Balkans, but the only considerable Turkish population lies in the vicinity of Constantinople (Istanbul). There are three important Ural-Altaic languages.

Finnish and Estonian are confined to the republic of Finland and to the former independent state of Estonia. Hungarian is the chief language of the people of the plain of the middle Danube, while Romanian and the Slavonic languages are spoken in the surrounding hill country. An isolated group, known as the Szeklers, speak Hungarian and inhabit the mountain-rimmed basin of Transylvania.

Turkish is the most widely spoken of these languages. Its European area is Constantinople and the small area of Turkey to the west of the city, but it prevails in Asia Minor and in some of the islands off the Turkish coast. Cyprus, however, is Greek in speech.

Arabic Languages. A confusion of languages is found in the Middle East, the traditional site of the Tower of Babel. Basically the language is Arabic, but this has suffered mutations and distortions, and upon it have been superimposed other languages. In the Syrian republic, in addition to Arabic, the Armenian, Aramaic, Turkish, and French languages are spoken (see page 378). In Israel, in addition to the original Arabic, there have been introduced the languages of the Jewish immigrants. Of these Yiddish, basically a German dialect, and English predominate. Hebrew is also spoken, as well as European languages. In Egypt, Libya, and French North Africa the language of the native peoples is largely Arabic. The languages of the imperial powers, France and Italy, have

TABLE OF THE CHIEF EUROPEAN LANGUAGES

Language group	Language	Approximate number of people speaking language*	Chief countries in which the language is spoken
Celtic	Gaelic	140,000	N. W. Scotland
	Welsh	800,000	Wales
	Erse	500,000	Ireland (Eire)
	Breton	—	Brittany
Romance	French	46,000,000	France, S. Belgium, W. Switzerland
	Spanish	26,000,000	Spain, Spanish Morocco
	Portuguese	8,300,000	Portugal
	Romanian	13,000,000	Romania
	Italian	47,000,000	Italy, S. Switzerland, S.W. France, Corsica, Yugoslav coast
Germanic	German	76,000,000	Germany, Luxembourg, E. Switzerland, E. France, Austria, N. Italy
	Norwegian	3,000,000	Norway
	Swedish	7,000,000	Sweden, Finland
	Danish	4,000,000	Denmark, S. Schleswig
	English	53,000,000	Great Britain, Ireland
	Dutch, Flemish	14,500,000	Netherlands, N. Belgium
Slavonic	Polish	26,000,000	Poland, U.S.S.R.
	Czech	7,500,000	Czechoslovakia
	Slovak	3,000,000	Czechoslovakia
	Slovene	1,000,000	Yugoslavia, Austria
	Serbo-Croat	11,000,000	Yugoslavia
	Great Russian	92,000,000	U.S.S.R.
	Ukrainian	35,000,000	Ukraine, U.S.S.R.
	Bulgar	7,000,000	Bulgaria
	Macedonian	750,000	Bulgaria, Greece, Yugoslavia
Classical	Greek	8,500,000	Greece, Albania, Cyprus
Others	Basque	700,000	N. Spain
	Albanian	1,000,000	Albania, Yugoslavia, Greece
	Lithuanian	2,500,000	Lithuanian S.S.R.
	Finnish	4,000,000	Finland, Karelo-Finnish S.S.R.
	Estonian	1,250,000	Estonian S.S.R.
	Hungarian	10,000,000	Hungary, Czechoslovakia, Romania, Yugoslavia
	Turkish	16,000,000	Turkey, Bulgaria

* Note that the totals are only approximate. For few countries are there postwar statistical data on languages spoken. Many people, *e.g.*, most of those speaking Celtic and Basque, are bilingual.

also been introduced by colonists and acquired by some of the native peoples. Malta has a peculiar language, derived from Arabic.

The large majority of the population of Europe speaks one of a group of related languages, known as the Indo-Aryan or Indo-European. Though these languages have certain similarities in their construction and vocabulary, they are not in general mutually intelligible. The Indo-European language group is divisible into five. Most widely spoken of these is the Slavonic, with about 185 million, including the Russians; next comes the Germanic, including English, with about 160 million, and the Romance languages, with about 140 million. Greek and the Celtic languages are Indo-

European but are spoken by relatively small groups. The other non-Indo-European groups are also comparatively unimportant; the most widely spoken are Hungarian and Turkish.

RELIGION

Religion introduces a further element of complexity into the human geography of Europe. The distribution of religious groups and sects bears little relationship to that of either linguistic groups or racial characteristics. Religious differences are becoming of diminishing importance, yet the church still has political significance. Most Poles and Irish are Roman Catholic. The Scandinavians are Lutheran. Europe is fundamentally Christian, and the code of morals and respect for the individual which we regard as western European owe much to Christian teaching. The only other important religions are the Jewish and Mohammedan. The latter is significant along the Asiatic and African shores of the Mediterranean rather than in Europe itself. The divisions of the Christian faith that are important are the following.

Catholicism. The Roman Catholic Church has more members than any other in Europe. In Portugal, Spain, and Italy it has no rivals.

France, though a secular state, is predominantly Catholic. In Belgium also Catholicism is supreme. In Switzerland, Germany, and Czechoslovakia there is a long tradition of Protestant revolt, but in each of these countries, large and important sections of the population are Catholic. All of south Germany and much of central Germany, most of the rural areas of Switzerland, much of Czechoslovakia, and all Austria are Catholic. Poland, Hungary, and Ireland are also largely Catholic countries.

Protestantism. This is a general term covering a large number of distinct and sometimes conflicting religious groups which have in common chiefly their detachment from the Roman Catholic Church. Small Protestant groups are found in many Catholic countries. In France, Hungary, and Poland these groups are of considerable size. The British Isles with the exception of Ireland, the Scandinavian countries including Finland, and North Germany are predominantly Protestant. The Netherlands, Switzerland, and Czechoslovakia have large Protestant groups. The more important and extensive divisions of the Protestant faith are the Calvinism of Switzerland, the Netherlands, and Scotland; Lutheranism of Germany

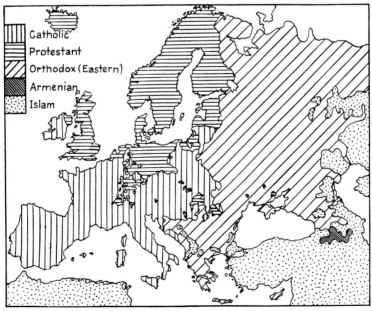

FIG. 20. Distribution of the main religious groups in Europe and the Mediterranean.

and Scandinavia; and Anglicanism (Episcopalianism) of England. All three are of considerable significance in America.

Orthodox Church. This, otherwise known as the Eastern, the Greek, or the Russian Church, is, like the Roman Catholic, a direct growth from the primitive church of the early Christians. The differences between it and the Roman Catholic Church developed during the formative early Middle Ages. Then the Roman Catholic Church, with its center in Italy, dominated western Europe. The Orthodox Church, its center in Constantinople (Istanbul), received the allegiance of Christians in the Balkans, Asia Minor, and the Aegean area. Between lay pagan lands from the Dinaric coast northward to the sparsely peopled forests of northern Europe. Each church expanded. The Serbs became Christians of the Orthodox Church; Croats and Slovenes in large measure Catholic. The Romanians were brought into the Eastern Church; the Hungarians into the Western. The Czechs were first converted by missionaries from the east but were later converted to the Church of Rome. Poles and Lithuanians became Catholic; Russians and Ukrainians, Orthodox.

The line of division between these two branches of the Catholic Church was generally sharp. Only in eastern Poland was it blurred. Here the Polish state expanded and came to include many Russians of the Orthodox faith. The latter were induced to form the Uniate Church, Roman Catholic in doctrine, Orthodox in ritual, which continued to exist until recently, when it was suppressed by the Russian government and its members absorbed into the Orthodox Church. The Maronite Church of Syria presents a similar compromise between the Catholic and the Orthodox Churches.

Islam. Islam, or Mohammedanism, was formerly more extensive in Europe than it is today. During the eighth century the Arabs carried Islam into Spain, where it survived in the south into modern times. It was similarly carried by Turkish invaders into the Balkans, but here, too, it disappeared with the disappearance of Turkish rule. But the long period of Turkish rule has left a deep impression on the Balkans. Islam made many converts among the native peoples, and some groups of Moslems have survived the retreat of the Turks. Particularly in southern Yugoslavia and in Albania the mosque and the minaret are still conspicuous features of the towns, and in Turkey, Islam has remained the dominant religion. Through the Middle East, Mohammedanism prevails. In Turkey it is no longer protected and assisted by the state but nevertheless is still an important force in the lives of the people. In Syria and Lebanon are small Christian groups, and in Israel, both Christian and Jewish. Throughout North Africa Mohammedanism is dominant except where it has been replaced by Roman Catholicism. As in Christian Europe, however, there are certain Reformed branches of the Moslem faith which enjoy a small following. Some such groups, the Senussi of Libya, for example, are of some political importance.

NATION AND STATE

The peoples of Europe are divided into groups each having some degree of homogeneity. This may show itself in a common language, common history and traditions, or a common respect for certain political principles and traditions. Most nations are also held together by an allegiance to a common government. The Poles did not cease to be a nation when they were partitioned between Prussia, Russia, and Austria. The Germans in the past were emphatic in their claims that a German is a member of the German nation by virtue of his language and culture whether he lives in Germany or not. In modern times there has been a strong tendency for the nation group to try to become a political unit or a state. At the end of the First World War several nations achieved the status of political units, some of them for the first time. In the erection of these new political units and in the demarcation of their boundaries, language was generally taken as the criterion of nationality. The political scheme set up in 1919–1920 proved neither successful nor permanent. The nation is an important division of the peoples of Europe, and the desire of most national groups to become independent, self-governing political units is obvious and natural. On the question of how to distinguish one nation from the next there has been no agreement. The following bases of division have been used:

Language. This seems the most reasonable basis. Germany has been foremost in urging that language is an adequate basis of the nation. Germany, according to J. G. Fichte,[1] should embrace all lands where the German language is spoken. This doctrine, carried to its extreme, resulted first in German territorial demands on her neighbors and then in the war of 1939. Frontiers in the Danubian and Balkan lands, on the borders of Belgium and Luxembourg, of Germany and Poland have been made to follow, as nearly as possible, the linguistic divisions. Rarely, however, especially in eastern Europe, was the division between neighboring language groups sufficiently clear-cut to be followed. More often the use of one language passed gradually into the use of another, and an equitable division on a linguistic basis was impossible.

Tradition and History. These have also provided a basis of definition of the nation-state. The state of Switzerland is the political expression of the Swiss people, who speak collectively four languages. Three of these, French, German, and Italian, are the principal languages of neighboring political units. Clearly language is neither bond of union nor basis of definition of the Swiss State. The Swiss are distinguished from their neighbors by their history and traditions, by a long established mode of government, and by their way of life.

In the United Kingdom, France, Switzerland, the Low Countries, and Scandinavia, tradition rather than language is the basis of the nation. In Germany, Poland, and the central and eastern European countries, language tends to be the more important.

Many of the political ambitions of European nations remain unsatisfied; some are mutually exclusive. Certain groups, some of them linguistic such as the Catalans, have for many years demanded a degree of local autonomy

[1] See particularly his famous "Addresses to the German Nation," delivered in Berlin in 1807.

which, if granted, would break up an established political unit. France's long-cherished dream of extending her frontiers to the Rhine conflicts with the Germanic conception of a state embracing all for whom German is the mother tongue. Other nation-states have ambitions to include territories which they possessed, perhaps only for a short period, at some remote time in their history. These sterile imperialisms are mutually incompatible. The Greater Bulgaria, reminiscent of the medieval state of Simeon the Great, would include part of Yugoslavia and Greece. Yugoslavia has its memories of a Greater Serbia, which included parts of what is now Bulgaria. Some Poles still dream of the Greater Poland which once extended into the Ukraine, Lithuanians of the ancient kingdom of Lithuania, and Germans of *Grossdeutschland*. The problems of the nation-state are not near solution; the ambitions and aspirations of nations will perhaps again play a vital part in the affairs of Europe.

POLITICAL DIVISIONS

On the mainland of Europe are today no less than 24 political units which claim to be sovereign. In addition to these, the United Kingdom of Great Britain and Northern Ireland with the Republic of Eire occupy the British Isles. The political units of Andorra, Monaco, San Marino, and Liechtenstein are too small to be of great political importance but are in most respects independent of the larger states which surround them. Gibraltar, politically distinct from Spain, is a dependency of Great Britain. To these might be added the three Baltic States Lithuania, Latvia, and Estonia, which have been absorbed into the U.S.S.R. In the Middle East are, in addition to Turkey, five independent political units. North Africa, west of the frontier of Egypt, is made up of dependencies of European powers. The fate of the former Italian empire is still, in 1953, undecided, while Algeria counts politically as part of "metropolitan" France.

The student should attempt to familiarize himself with the political map. He should be able to visualize each political unit, to see its shape and size in the setting of its neighboring states, as well as to superimpose the political frontiers onto the framework of mountain, valley, and plain. In the following chapters Europe and the Mediterranean countries are, as it were, taken to pieces, and each political unit or, in certain instances, group of political units is looked at separately. It is most convenient to base this regional study on the political divi-sions, but the student must always bear in mind that there are few abrupt boundaries in nature. The regions of one country are often continuous with those of the next. Frontiers are boundaries of political obligation, but in Europe they are artificial, perhaps lines of white posts or barbed wire. Fields, villages, and people are often similar, almost the same, on each side of these lines.

BIBLIOGRAPHY

Ancel, J., "Manuel géographique de politique euro-péenne," 2 vols., Paris, 1936.

——, "Slaves et Germaines," Paris, 1947.

Bowen, E. G., "Wales," Cardiff, 1941.

Bowman, I., "The New World," New York, 1928.

Chabot, Georges, "Les Villes," Paris, 1948.

Chadwick, H. M., "The Nationalities of Europe," Cambridge, 1945.

Coon, C. S., "The Races of Europe," New York, 1939.

Cornish, Vaughan, "Borderlands of Language in Europe," London, 1936.

Dickinson, Robert E., "The West European City," London, 1951.

Dominian, L., "The Frontiers of Language and Nationality in Europe," American Geographical Society, New York, 1917.

Entwhistle, W. J., "The Spanish Language," London, 1936.

Fitzgerald, Walter, "The New Europe," London, 1945.

Fleure, H. J., "Human Geography in Western Europe," London, 1918.

——, "The Peoples of Europe," Oxford, 1935.

Golding, Louis, "The Jewish Problem," New York, 1938.

Hadden, A. C., "The Races of Man," Cambridge, 1929.

——, "The Wanderings of Peoples," Cambridge, 1911.

—— and J. Huxley, "We Europeans," London, 1935.

Hartshorne, R., "A Survey of the Boundary Problems of Europe," Geographic Aspects of International Relations, pp. 163–213, University of Chicago, Chicago, 1938.

Hawtrey, R. G., "Western European Union," Royal Institute of International Affairs, London, 1949.

Hertz, Frederick, "Nationality in History and Politics," London, 1944.

Hope-Simpson, Sir John, "The Refugee Problem," Royal Institute of International Affairs, London, 1939.

Huxley, Julian, "'Race' in Europe," Oxford, 1939.

Janowsky, Oscar I., "Nationalities and National Minorities," New York, 1945.

Kirk, Dudley, "Europe's Population in the Interwar Years," New York, 1946.

Kohn, Hans, "The Idea of Nationalism," New York, 1945.

Kulischer, Eugene M., "The Displacement of Population in Europe," International Labor Organization, Montreal, 1943.

Lorimer, F., "The Population of the Soviet Union," League of Nations, Geneva, 1946.

Morant, G. M., "The Races of Central Europe: A Footnote to History," London, 1939.

"Nationalism," Royal Institute of International Affairs, London, 1939.

Notestein, F. W., et al., "The Future Population of Europe and the Soviet Union," League of Nations, Geneva, 1944.

Parkes, J. W., "The Jewish Problem in the Modern World," London, 1939.

Peake, H. J. E., and H. J. Fleure, "Corridors of Time," 8 vols., Oxford, 1927.

Population Changes in Europe, 1938–1947, Economic Bulletin for Europe, I (1) (1949).

Pounds, N. J. G., "An Historical and Political Geography of Europe," London, 1947.

Watson, H. Seton, "Eastern Europe between the Wars," Oxford, 1945.

"Western Union," United Nations Association, London, 1948.

Wilson, Francesca M., "Aftermath," New York, 1947. (This is a short, popular study of the postwar refugee problem.)

Wright, John K., "The Geographical Basis of European History," American Geographical Society, New York, 1943.

CHAPTER 4: *Europe: The Economic Basis*

In the next 27 chapters the continent of Europe will be divided into its many political pieces, each of which will be examined separately and with little reference to its neighbors in the European mosaic. Political boundaries are of far greater importance in Europe in separating different uses and developments of the land than are the "state lines" in the United States. But despite the particular slant given to agriculture, industry, or transportation by the

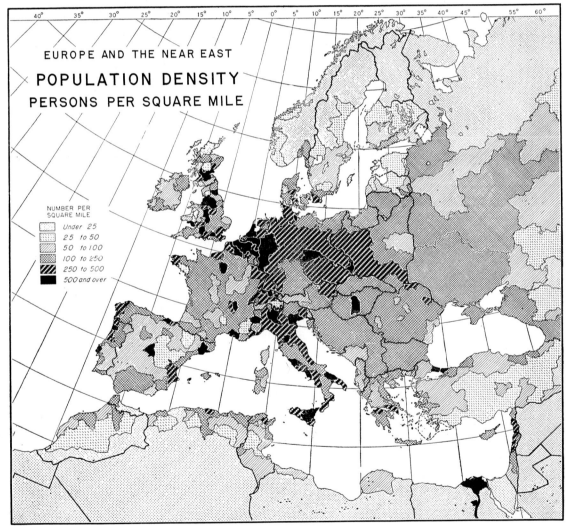

FIG. 21. Population density of Europe and the Mediterranean. (*From Agricultural Geography of Europe and the Near East, U.S. Department of Agriculture, 1948.*)

41

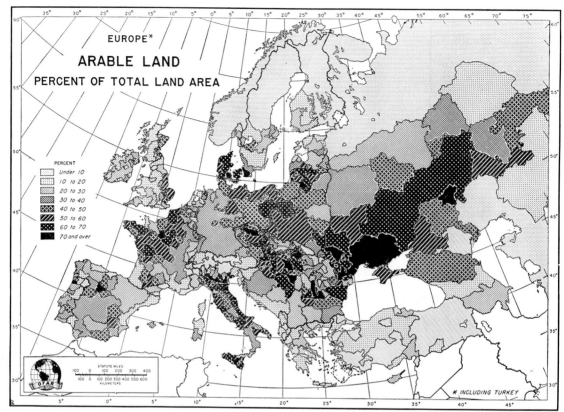

Fig. 22. Arable land in Europe as a percentage of total area. (*From Agricultural Geography of Europe and the Near East, U.S. Department of Agriculture, 1948.*)

policies of national governments, it is, nevertheless, possible to see a *European* pattern of agriculture and industry. It is important that we should have a view of Europe as a whole. As a European Union gradually takes shape, it will be the continental, not the national, patterns of economic activity that will be of importance.

European Agriculture. There are few areas of Europe where crop cultivation is not practiced, and in most parts it is the predominant type of agriculture. Forest and pasture prevail over large areas of the north and also in mountainous areas of central and southern Europe. Crop husbandry is relatively unimportant in the Mediterranean region of summer drought. The map (Fig. 22) shows the distribution of arable land as a proportion of the total land surface. Three areas are outstanding as regions of crop husbandry: (1) northern France, the Low

Countries, and eastern England; (2) Italy; and (3) a large area between the Black Sea and the Baltic including eastern Germany and the Ukraine. This high proportion of land under the plow may be due, as in eastern England and parts of northern France, to the excellence of the soil and the suitability of the climate. But in parts of Romania and Poland, it is due to the poverty of the peasants and the need to cultivate even poor or mediocre land with but small return for their labors. This map exaggerates the significance of national frontiers because the statistics upon which it is based have necessarily been collected upon a national basis. Figure 23 shows a more uniform distribution of cropland farming over the continent.

There are few strong contrasts in the crops grown. In general about half the cropland is devoted to cereal crops—more than half in the Balkans, very much less in the cold climate of

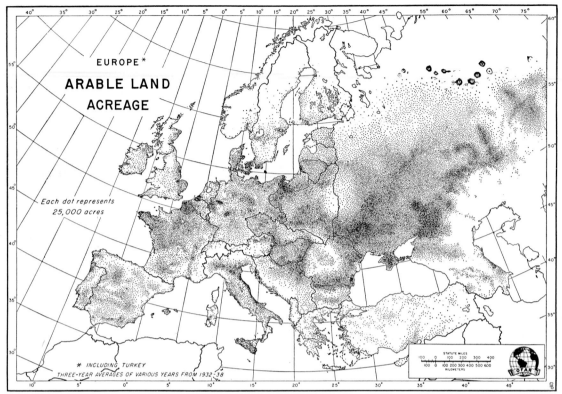

Fig. 23. Acreage under cultivation in Europe. (*From Agricultural Geography of Europe and the Near East, U.S. Department of Agriculture,* 1948.)

northern Europe. Wheat is the most important cereal in western Europe, rye in eastern, corn in the Balkan peninsula, oats in the cool damp north, and barley on the desert margin. A relatively large percentage of the arable land in northern Europe is under grass, suited to the damp climate and leached soils.

The greatest dependence upon agriculture as a means of livelihood is found in eastern and southern Europe. In Bulgaria 75 per cent of the working population are engaged on the land, and the percentages in Albania, Yugoslavia, Romania, and Poland are similar (see page 274). The countries in which the smallest proportion of the population is engaged in agriculture are England and Scotland, the Low Countries, France, Germany, Switzerland, and Austria. The population of western Germany and northern France is dependent to only a small degree on agriculture, while eastern Germany and southern France are heavily dependent on cultivation.

As a general rule crop yields decline from the west toward the east. In eastern Europe farm equipment is least adequate, farming methods most backward, and improved seeds and fertilizer, both organic and artificial, least used.

There is a steady progression from the scientifically managed and well-equipped farms of eastern England or northern France through the Low Countries and Switzerland to less well-conducted farms in Germany. Within Germany, methods were much superior in the west to those in the east, while eastern Germany was better in these respects than Poland, Romania, and the Balkans. A similar transition occurs in Italy between the relatively good agriculture of the Lombardy Plain in the north and the backward south and Sicily—similarly between northern Spain and southern. Conversely there is a decline northward from the good farming country of eastern England to northern Scotland, Wales, and Ireland.

	Bread grains, tons			Coarse grains, tons	
	1934–1938, average	1950	Output per head in 1950, pounds	1934–1938, average	1950
Norway	70,000	70,000	44	320,000	290,000
Sweden	1,110,000	980,000	353	1,720,000	1,610,000
Finland	480,000	530,000	264	830,000	900,000
Denmark	650,000	640,000	353	2,910,000	3,320,000
United Kingdom	1,750,000	2,620,000	66	2,800,000	4,200,000
France	8,910,000	7,920,000	463	6,190,000	5,110,000
Belgium	870,000	840,000	220	750,000	840,000
Luxembourg	50,000	50,000	375	50,000	50,000
Netherlands	930,000	700,000	198	480,000	620,000
Switzerland	190,000	230,000	88	30,000	100,000
Western Zones of Germany	5,590,000	5,640,000	287	4,880,000	4,370,000
Soviet Zone of Germany	3,620,000	2,950,000	375	2,620,000	1,660,000
Poland	8,820,000 *	7,870,000	661	4,460,000	3,530,000
Czechoslovakia	3,080,000	2,840,000	551	2,490,000	2,570,000
Austria	960,000	700,000	331	900,000	520,000
Hungary	2,920,000	2,960,000	661	3,180,000	3,320,000
Romania	2,770,000	2,810,000	375	5,160,000	4,950,000
Bulgaria	1,960,000	2,190,000	617	1,400,000	1,380,000
Yugoslavia	2,570,000	2,040,000	397	9,210,000	5,390,000
Albania	40,000	50,000	88	150,000	150,000
Greece	810,000	950,000	243	560,000	570,000
Italy	7,400,000	7,700,000	375	3,760,000	2,600,000
Portugal	580,000	720,000	154	430,000	630,000
Spain	4,920,000	3,290,000	353	3,770,000	2,830,000

* Postwar territory of Poland.

Agriculture is most backward and least productive in those areas where most people depend upon it and where cropland forms the greatest proportion of the total area. Here the pressure of population, with no important alternative employment, encourages the cultivation of inferior and marginal land. As long as the return to the cultivator for his efforts is barely enough to sustain life, there is no surplus for the accumulation of agricultural capital. It is highly desirable to grow less cereals and more fodder crops and rotation grass, but this reduces the total *volume* of food produced and hence fills fewer stomachs. Volume, not quality, of the crop is the most important consideration in the agriculture of these poorer areas. Animal husbandry, which gives less food per acre, is the least important.

Europe as a whole is far from self-sufficing in agricultural products. Most of the industrial countries of western and northern Europe have a considerable import of foodstuffs which is far from balanced by the export of a few delicacies and specialities of local production. In 1949 Europe, excluding the Soviet Union, imported from overseas 21 per cent of its bread grains, 42 per cent of its fats and oils, 34 per cent of its sugar, 30 per cent of its oil cake, and 11 per cent of its meat.[1] The United Kingdom was the most heavily dependent upon imports, but Belgium, the Netherlands, the Western Zones of Germany, Switzerland, and Italy also imported heavily. France was the least dependent of the

[1] *Economic Bulletin for Europe*, United Nations, Geneva. 2 (1), 21 (July, 1950).

industrial countries of western Europe, owing to her strong agricultural development (see page 163). Greece, owing to the importance of her specialized agricultural products such as olives, tobacco, and currants, was more dependent on imports than other east European countries.

The east and south European countries import little, and some, such as Bulgaria,

per cent above the average of the years 1934 to 1938.

Mineral Resources. Europe is comparatively well endowed with coal and iron ore but has comparatively few resources in nonferrous metals and in petroleum. The total European (excluding Russian) production of these commodities is shown in the accompanying table.

	European production, tons		As percentage of world output in 1950	Net exports (E) or imports (I) 1950
	1938	1950		
Coal.	579,600,000	543,000,000	49	1,500,000 (E)
Lignite (brown coal).	232,089,000	132,445,000	47	
Petroleum.	8,100,000 *	8,600,000	2	24,700,000 (I)
Iron ore (metal content).	32,400,000	28,700,000	32	2,600,000 (I)
Bauxite.	2,150,000	1,400,000	19	
Lead ore (metal content).	302,000	260,000	18	80,000 (I)
Zinc ore (metal content).	540,000	490,000	29	210,000 (I)

* 1 metric ton = 7.3 barrels.

Romania, and Hungary before the Second World War, actually exported more than they imported. But, we have seen, the relative self-sufficiency of these countries implies, not the abundance and variety of their domestic production, but rather their lack of purchasing power with which to live better.

The accompanying table (see page 44) gives the output of (1) bread grains and (2) coarse grains mostly fed to stock.

There is little international trade in fruit and fresh vegetables, most countries producing as much as they consume. There is, however, a movement of "earlies" and of certain fruits from Italy, southern France, and Brittany to more northerly countries. All European countries produce potatoes for their own needs, and most supplement the import of sugar by growing sugar beets. In the United Kingdom, France, Belgium, the Netherlands, Germany, Czechoslovakia, Poland, and Italy the production of beets is relatively considerable. Difficulties in the way of paying for the import of sugar have brought about a sharp increase in the growing of sugar beets, the production in 1950 being 28

Other metals are produced in only small amounts. Europe has, however, a large number of smelting works and refineries for nonferrous ores and metals, which are imported from other continents. The output of some of these smelters is far greater than is necessary to satisfy Europe's needs. The maintenance of these smelting and refining works clearly depends, however, on the import of ores and metal concentrates.

In addition to many iron-ore deposits of small or medium size, Europe has two reserves of exceptional size and importance. These are the high-grade ores of Swedish Lapland and the low-grade *minette* ores of Lorraine. Both ores are phosphoric and require that steel made from them be prepared by a special *basic* process. Both are, furthermore, of great importance to the heavy industries of northwestern Europe. The United Kingdom also has large reserves of low-grade ore, with much smaller reserves of ore of good quality. In addition to the Lorraine deposits, France has a number of small deposits of good ore. Spain has numerous deposits, and those of the Basque province were once of considerable European importance. Germany has many small deposits, most of poor quality, and Czechoslovakia, Austria, Italy, and the Balkan countries also have small but locally significant reserves.

CHIEF EUROPEAN PRODUCERS OF IRON ORE, 1948, IN METRIC TONS*

France	23,020,000
Sweden	13,330,000
United Kingdom	13,310,000
Germany	7,270,000
Luxembourg	3,400,000
Spain	1,630,000
Czechoslovakia	1,430,000
Austria	1,200,000
Italy	540,000
Poland	500,000
Hungary	200,000
European total	66,320,000
Production in United States	101,092,000

* These figures are tonnages of ore, not of metal content.

Coal is more widely distributed. There are few countries which have none. The only large fields, however, lie along the northern edge of the central hilly belt—in England, France, Belgium, Germany, and Poland. Most of it is "soft" coal. "Hard" coal is important only in the South Wales coal field, in the United Kingdom, and in the Ruhr area of Germany. The United Kingdom and Germany both have large reserves of coal suitable for making metallurgical coke for the blast furnace, but France, Belgium, and Luxembourg are wholly or in part dependent on Germany for coking coal.

COAL-PRODUCING COUNTRIES OF EUROPE, IN METRIC TONS

	1937	1949
United Kingdom	244,267,000	212,754,000
Germany	171,149,000	103,238,000
Poland	66,012,000	74,081,000
France	44,346,000	51,199,000
Belgium	29,859,000	27,850,000
Czechoslovakia	16,776,000	17,003,000
Netherlands	14,316,000	11,705,000
Saar Territory	13,365,000	14,268,000
Spain	2,084,000*	10,642,000
Italy	1,272,000	1,104,000
Hungary	912,000	1,238,000 (1948)
Yugoslavia	450,000	1,289,000

* Very low, owing to the Civil War.

In addition, Austria, Eire, Norway, Portugal, Sweden, and Romania each produced less than half a million tons. The figures in the accompanying table refer to "black" coal. Europe is also a large producer of lignite, or brown coal, obtained chiefly from large, open workings in Germany and Poland. Lignite is of low heating quality, and most of it is used locally to generate power or is compressed into briquettes for more economic handling.

Europe is overwhelmingly dependent on imports of petroleum and oil. Only Romania produces much. Small quantities are obtained in Germany, Austria, eastern France, Poland, and the United Kingdom.

EUROPEAN PRODUCTION OF OIL, IN METRIC TONS*

	1937	1947–1949
Romania	7,153,000	3,810,000 (1947)
Austria	33,000	1,213,000 (1944)
Germany	452,000	841,000 (1949)
Poland	501,000	128,000 (1947)
Total European production	8,244,000	7,270,000 est.
Total production of the United States of America	177,661,000	252,000,000

* 1 metric ton = 7.3 barrels.

The imported petroleum is brought in by sea, and there are refineries at many ports, especially in northwestern Europe. The heavy dependence on imported petroleum has led to the preparation of fuel oil from coal in Germany and, on a much smaller scale, in the United Kingdom.

Manufacturing Industry. All Europe carries on manufacturing industries, but in most of the continent it is on a domestic or small-factory basis and employs only a small proportion of the working population. The greater part of the factory industry of Europe is concentrated in the United Kingdom and in a narrow belt of country which stretches from the coast of northern France through Belgium and the Netherlands to Germany. Within Germany, it covers Westphalia and Saxony and extends into Polish Silesia and Czechoslovakia. Away from

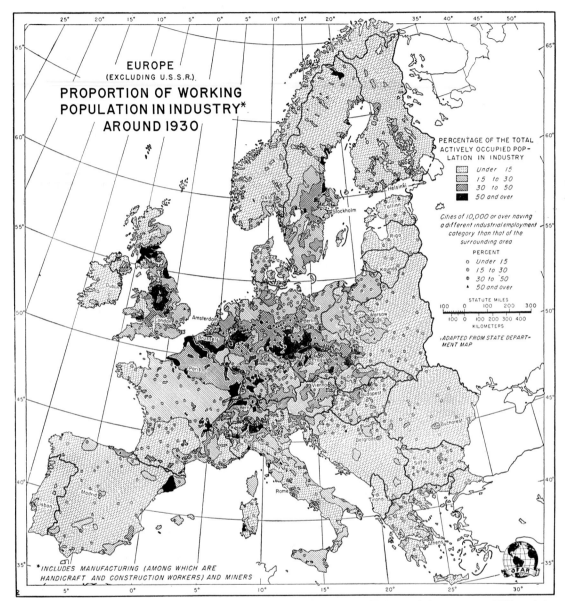

FIG. 24. Distribution of the industrial population in Europe west of Russia. This map is based on pre-1939 statistics, and the prewar frontiers are shown. (*From Agricultural Geography of Europe and the Near East, U.S. Department of Agriculture, 1948.*)

this axial belt are the industrial areas of Great Britain, of the upper Rhineland and Switzerland, of northern Italy, of Catalonia, of central Sweden, and of Russia.

The primary reason for the location of this belt of industry is the occurrence of coal along the northern edge of the hills of central Europe. The factory industries of Italy and Spain have

not been located with reference to fuel reserves, but in recent years they have drawn heavily on the hydroelectric power from the nearby mountains.

This industrialized area is the most densely populated part in Europe. It is an area (compare Figs. 22 and 24) where a relatively small amount of the land is under crops. This is due chiefly to the fact that factory industry affords an alternative employment and permits the purchase of imported foodstuffs.

The metallurgical industries of France, Belgium, Luxembourg, and Germany have come in recent years to form a group of closely related units. The German coal field of the Ruhr supplies coke to its neighbors; France and Luxembourg send iron ore to Belgium and Germany. These countries form a single industrial region. The student, in studying each of these countries, must always be aware of their interdependence. This is emphasized by the recent acceptance of the Schuman Plan for a single market in coal, iron, and steel by France, Belgium, Luxembourg, the Netherlands, western Germany, and Italy.

While most European countries have an iron and steel industry of some kind, production is dominated by Germany, France, and the United Kingdom, the only countries which have the raw materials—ore and metallurgical coke—in quantity. The steel production of western Germany, previously the most important producing area in Europe, has been curtailed as a result of Allied policy since 1945.

PRODUCTION OF CRUDE STEEL, IN METRIC TONS

	1938	1949
Germany:		
Western Zones	17,904,000	9,156,000 *
Soviet Zone	1,692,000	696,000
United Kingdom	10,560,000	15,816,000
France	6,216,000	9,120,000
Saar Territory	2,556,000	1,764,000
Belgium	2,280,000	3,852,000
Poland	1,896,000	2,304,000
Luxembourg	1,440,000	2,268,000
Sweden	972,000	1,356,000
Other European countries	4,476,000	6,876,000
Total European production	49,992,000	53,208,000
Total production in the United States of America	28,800,000	77,978,000

* The production from the Western Zones of Germany in late 1951 was at a rate of over 14 million tons a year. The United States production was, in 1952, at the rate of over 100 million tons a year.

The textile industries are more widely distributed than the metallurgical. All European countries are textile producers, but only the United Kingdom, France, Belgium, Germany, and Italy are exporters. Most other countries import more than they export.

TEXTILE-PRODUCING COUNTRIES, 1949, IN METRIC TONS

	Cotton yarn	Woolen yarn	Rayon yarn
Belgium	84,330	35,600	9,260
Czechoslovakia	75,800	35,400	5,570
France	228,000	123,000	46,460
Germany	228,000	65,100	49,900
Italy	209,000	*	49,980
Netherlands	61,000	22,000	19,210
Poland	91,000	38,600	9,040
Spain	59,600	8,800	6,760
Switzerland	*	*	8,620
United Kingdom	372,700	94,500	77,800
United States	1,715,000	312,000	362,600

* Figures not available.

The chemical industry is similarly widely scattered, though only the United Kingdom and Germany manufacture chemicals on a large scale.

From these brief remarks it is seen that a few European countries have developed manufacturing industries and a large foreign trade. They import raw materials for their industrial processes and, in varying degrees, foodstuffs and export mainly manufactured goods.

OUTSTANDING INDUSTRIAL COUNTRIES

	Value of export of manufactured goods, millions of dollars at 1938 prices	
	1938	1949
United Kingdom	1,738	2,949
Germany (Western Zones)	1,255	417
France	521	815
Belgium and Luxembourg	460	597
Italy	281	334
Netherlands	265	265
Sweden	212	239

Industrial Power. European industry is based primarily on power derived, either directly or indirectly, from coal. Petroleum production is small, that of natural gas is negligible, and hitherto an extensive use of hydroelectric power has been limited to a very few countries. There are facilities for the further development of hydroelectric power, but installations are expensive and not likely to be undertaken on a large scale in many countries until the price of coal becomes higher than it is at present. Much electric power is generated by burning coal. In Germany much of this is from lignite-fired plant. Countries in which hydroelectric power has been greatly developed, such as Norway, Sweden, Switzerland, and Italy, are those in which coal deposits are very small.

areas, relatively high incomes and good living standards.

3. A northern belt of harsh climate and sparse population, engaged in part in specialized occupations, such as mining and lumbering.

4. A large southern and eastern area of dense rural population, backward agricultural methods, and low living standards.

A highly important economic problem in Europe today is to remedy the conditions of widespread poverty which exist in the fourth of these regions. The basic problem is to broaden the basis of agriculture, to remove labor from the land, where much of it cannot find

ELECTRIC POWER GENERATED IN 1948 IN MILLIONS OF KILOWATT-HOURS*

	Hydroelectric power	Thermoelectric power
Norway	2,578,000	106,000
Sweden	2,958,000	951,000
Finland	491,000	474,000
Denmark	....	787,000
United Kingdom	343,000	13,424,000
France	5,321,000	7,430,000
Belgium	23,000	2,672,000
Netherlands	....	2,275,000
Switzerland	 2,881,000	
Germany:		
Western Zones	1,736,000	4,220,000
Soviet Zone		
Poland	 2,504,000	
Czechoslovakia	 2,505,000	
Austria	 1,598,000	
Yugoslavia	281,000	424,000
Italy	5,929,000	941,000
Spain	1,914,000	575,000
Portugal	145,000	189,000

* Separate statistics for hydro- and thermoelectric power are not available for certain countries. In Switzerland and Austria, however, almost all the power production is hydroelectric.

Population and Living Standards. A picture thus emerges of a Europe divisible into four economic regions. The boundaries of these regions are indefinite and are not all related to national frontiers.

1. An industrial core stretching from Great Britain to Upper Silesia, within which is the densest population and the highest average income and living standards.

2. A northwestern area of scientific agriculture and, despite small and more backward

employment, and to employ it in some other productive form. Any reforms along these lines require much capital, which only the United States or the countries of western Europe could supply. In recent years much publicity has been given to a suggested Tennessee Valley Authority for the Danube, by which the more advanced nations would invest capital in this underdeveloped region. It is significant that at present communism is strongest in these underprivileged and underdeveloped areas.

Overpopulation is a relative term. Expressed in terms of population per square mile it means little. The Balkan countries, with a population density which is numerically less than that of the Low Countries or England, are in fact very much more densely peopled. Overpopulation varies not only with the area and quality of the land but also with knowledge and capital to use the land, with factory equipment, and with transportation. In these terms overpopulation is acute in the countries of southern and eastern Europe. For a picture of these conditions far from overdrawn, the student is advised to read the novels of the Italians Carlo Levi and Ignazio Silone (see Bibliography).

The following table shows the degrees of dependence upon agriculture. It will be seen that as a general rule:

1. Countries in which only a small proportion of the total population is engaged in agriculture

	Population in thousands *	Percentage of population dependent on agriculture	Agricultural production per male engaged in agriculture. European average = 100 †	Yield of seven important crops per unit area. European average = 100 †
Northern Europe:				
Norway..........................	3,199 (1948)	27	111	133.1
Sweden...........................	6,842 (1947)	31	134	132.8
Finland..........................	3,989 (1948)	57	70	103.6
Denmark.........................	4,045 (1945)	30	323	177.8
Western Europe:				
United Kingdom....................	50,065 (1948)	‡	240 §	143.2
Eire (Ireland).....................	2,955 (1946) ‖	53	89	160.2
France...........................	41,744 (1950) ‖	29	160	105.0
Belgium..........................	8,625 (1949)	15	181	176.9
Luxembourg.......................	291 (1947) ‖	28	103	109.0
Netherlands.......................	10,027 (1949)	18	237	168.5
Switzerland.......................	4,401 (1945)	22	167	148.4
Central Europe				
Germany (all zones).................	64,619 (1946)	20	191	133.9
Poland...........................	24,160 (1949)	60	56	82.9
Czechoslovakia.....................	12,164 (1947) ‖	33	115	116.7
Austria...........................	6,653 (1939) ‖	26	128	109.6
Danubian and Balkan Countries:				
Hungary..........................	9,317 (1941) ‖	51	75	96.2
Romania..........................	15,873 (1948) ‖	72	53	67.4
Bulgaria..........................	6,977 (1945)	75	55	84.6
Yugoslavia........................	13,934 (1931) ‖	76	43	88.9
Mediterranean Europe:				
Greece...........................	8,025 (1949)	46	48	60.5
Albania..........................	1,003	80	25	95.9
Italy............................	45,540 (1947)	44	68	107.5
Spain............................	25,878 (1940) ‖	50	94	77.0
Portugal..........................	8,271 (1947)	46	53	62.7
Turkey...........................	16,157 (1935) ‖		39	63.5

* Population figures are taken from the "Demographic Yearbook, 1949–50," United Nations, New York. 1951.

† From Moore, Wilbert E., "Economic Demography of Eastern and Southern Europe," League of Nations, Geneva, 1945. Figures relate to the years before 1939.

‡ England and Wales, 5 per cent; Scotland, 8 per cent; Northern Ireland, 30 per cent.

§ England and Wales only.

‖ From census reports.

show a relatively high yield for each unit of labor.

2. In these countries the yield per acre is also high.

3. In eastern and southern Europe, where a half or more of the working population is engaged in agriculture, the yield for each unit of labor is relatively small.

4. In these countries of eastern and southern Europe crop yields are generally low.

5. The densest agricultural populations are found in those countries which are least able to support them.

Transportation. The development of manufacturing industries and the maintenance of a high standard of living would be impossible without a well-developed system of transportation. Over all the countries of northwest Europe there is a very close rail network, and the train service in all countries is both fast and frequent. This net is less developed in Spain, southern Italy, the east European and Balkan countries, and most of Scandinavia, areas in which the population is much sparser and industries less developed.

All significant European railroads, except the Russian, are on the standard gage of 4 feet 8½ inches. This enables through trains to be run across national frontiers. There are a number of transcontinental express trains, though these are neither so numerous nor so important as they were before the Second World War. The division of Europe by the "Iron Curtain" also limits the operation of long-distance trains. There are express trains from Paris to Madrid, Rome, and the larger cities of western Germany and also to Copenhagen and Stockholm. It is again possible to travel from Paris to Constantinople by train, though without the smoothness and speed of the prewar Orient Express. Train ferries operate between England and the packet stations (see page 168) of northern France and across the larger waterways of the Danish archipelago.

The road system of Europe is similarly developed. It is very close in the more populous and industrial countries of the northwest, less so in the south and east and extreme north. In northwest Europe most of the more important roads have a good metaled surface. In some countries, notably Belgium, northern France, and parts of Germany, the road surface is made of small squared blocks of hard stone. Unless carefully maintained, these roads quickly degenerate and become uncomfortable and dangerous. Some of the less important roads in northwest Europe and even of the more important in the south and east have only a dirt surface and are sometimes closed in bad weather. There is a tendency to supplement the local road systems with a planned national network of fast motor roads. The German *Autobahn* and the Italian *autostrada* are examples.

The rivers of much of Europe have the advantages of regular flow and comparatively little ice in winter, but most are too small for the larger and more economical modes of water transportation. They cannot be navigated by the larger barges. Some rivers, especially the Seine, Rhine, Vistula, and Danube, are large enough for parts of their courses. Others have been made navigable by deepening and straightening them. But few rivers are greatly used for transportation. They are supplemented by a system of canals. Many of these are old and small and, as in England, have largely been abandoned. But the canals of France and the Low Countries and the recently constructed canals of Germany are in regular use and play an important role in the economy of these countries.

Europe is particularly well blessed by the number and excellence of its ports and harbors. There are hundreds of small ports along the coasts between the Russian Arctic and the Middle East. Some were once important but have silted, like Fréjus and Aigues-Mortes in the south of France. Others have failed to develop as great commercial ports because of the inadequacy of their communications with their hinterlands; such are Lorient, Brest, Falmouth, and Vigo. A few have grown to be giant ports, equipped with all the modern devices necessary to handle the great ocean liners and cargo vessels. Liverpool and London, Le Havre, Marseille, Genoa, Antwerp, Rotterdam, Amsterdam, Bremen, and Hamburg are some of these. All had the advantages of being near thickly peopled and industrially developed areas and of having good landward communications. These ports handle most of the great foreign trade of Europe.

European Union. Europe west of Russia is smaller than the United States. It lacks the American advantage of a common language and unrestricted trade. It has a much smaller variety of environment than has the United States. Its population is more than twice that of the United States. It has few uninhabited or sparsely peopled areas, and to that extent the problem of communications and transport is less. Its major industrial and agricultural regions span the national frontiers as those of North America do the state boundaries. The contrast in living standards between England and Bulgaria is not vastly greater than the difference between New York State or Pennsylvania and Louisiana or Mississippi. There is no reason in the facts of geography why Europe should not become another union of states.

Opposition to the achievement of this end comes from two sources. The political divisions of Europe are nation-states. The original 13 colonies of the United States had much in common; they spoke the same language, had common ideals, and fought together for their independence, yet it was only after long debates that even they agreed to subordinate their local loyalties to a greater loyalty to an American Union. The states of Europe have a long history of independence and a long record of mutual opposition. The hand of history lies heavy on Europe. It will take long to eradicate the traditions and prejudices left by past wars. The European mind is conditioned to regard other national groups as former and still potential enemies. To the more backward peoples of Europe this incipient hostility appears natural and inevitable.

A second threat to the achievement of European unity comes from Russia. The U.S.S.R. has succeeded in the years since 1939 in annexing the Baltic States and parts of Finland, Poland, and Romania and in dominating and controlling all the Slav lands except Yugoslavia. Russia has succeeded by methods which at present are peculiarly her own in countering the nationalist aspirations of the Slav peoples. Let us hope that the free Europe which remains will so subordinate its national aspirations and forget its past discords that it can present a united western Europe to the threat that the Union of Soviet Socialist Republics now presents. In such unity lies the only way to both political security and economic well-being. But let us also remember that the sense of national sovereignty is strong and there are deep objections to sacrificing any of it. The American observer must be patient and must realize that the Schuman Plan, the North Atlantic Treaty Organization, and the Organization for European Economic Cooperation are important steps toward European economic and political union.

BIBLIOGRAPHY

"Agrarian Problem from the Baltic to the Aegean," Royal Institute of International Affairs, London, 1945.

"Agricultural Geography of Europe and the Near East," U.S. Department of Agriculture, Misc. Pub. 665, 1948.

Basch, A., "The Danube Basin and the German Economic Sphere," London, 1944.

Cavaillès, Henri, "La Houille blanche," Paris, 1946.

Committee of European Economic Cooperation, Vol. I, General Report, Vol. II, Technical Report, London and Paris, 1947.

"Economic Development in Southeastern Europe," Political and Economic Planning, Oxford, 1945.

"Europe's Trade," League of Nations, Geneva, 1941.

Jonasson, O., Agricultural Regions of Europe, *E.G.*, I, 1925, 277–314; II, 1926, 19–48.

Kish, George, TVA on the Danube, *G.R.*, XXXVII, 1947, 274–302.

"The Land Tenure Systems in Europe," European Conference on Rural Life, Document 2, League of Nations, Geneva, 1939.

Long-term Trends in European Agriculture, *Economic Bulletin for Europe*, Vol. III, No. 2, 1951.

Motive Power in European Industry, *Economic Bulletin for Europe*, Vol. III, No. 1, 1951.

Moore, Wilbert E., "Economic Demography in Eastern and Southern Europe," League of Nations, Geneva, 1945.

Mutton, Alice F. A., Hydro-electric Power in Western Europe, *G.J.*, CXVII, 1951, 328–342.

Notestein, Frank W., *et al.*, "The Future Population of Europe and the Soviet Union," League of Nations, Geneva, 1944.

Recent Developments in Trade between Eastern and Western Europe, *Economic Bulletin for Europe*, Vol. III, No. 2, 1951.

"A Survey of the Economic Situation and Prospects of Europe," United Nations Association, London, 1948.

Warriner, D., "The Economics of Peasant Farming," Oxford, 1939.

Weaver, John P., and Fred E. Lukermann, "A World Statistical Survey of Commercial Production: A Geographic Sourcebook," Minneapolis, Minn., 1950.

In recent years a vast amount of material, both statistics and reports, has been produced by such organizations as United Nations, the Organization for European Economic Cooperation, the International Labor Office, and the Economic Commission for Europe. In the reports of these bodies the student can find the latest information upon the economic recovery and development of Europe. The following list contains the more important of such works published hitherto. Those specific to a country are listed later in this book in the bibliographies of individual countries. The following are of a more general nature.

STATISTICS

Annual Bulletin of Transport Statistics, Economic Commission for Europe, Transport Division, Geneva, published annually from 1951.

Demographic Yearbook, United Nations, published annually.

Economic Bulletin for Europe, Economic Commission for Europe, published quarterly from July, 1949. (Also contains articles of the highest value.)

Economic Survey of Europe, Economic Commission for Europe, published annually.

Foreign Trade, Statistical Bulletin, Organization for European Economic Cooperation, Paris, published monthly.

Monthly Bulletin of Statistics, United Nations, New York.

Quarterly Bulletin of Steel Statistics for Europe, Economic Commission for Europe, quarterly from December, 1950.

Statistical Bulletins, Organization for European Economic Cooperation, Paris.

Statistical Yearbook, United Nations, published annually.

A Survey of the Economic Situation and Prospects of Europe, Economic Commission for Europe, 1948.

Yearbook of Food and Agricultural Statistics, Vol. I, Production; Vol. II, Trade, Food and Agriculture Organization of the United Nations, published annually.

Yearbook of Forest Products Statistics, Food and Agricultural Organization of the United Nations, published annually.

REPORTS ON DEVELOPMENT PROJECTS

Coal and European Economic Expansion, Organization for European Economic Cooperation, Paris, 1952.

Committee of European Cooperation: Vol. I, General Report; Vol. II, Technical Reports, London and Paris, 1947.

Economic Progress and Problems of Western Europe, Organization for European Economic Cooperation, 1951.

European Recovery Program, Annual Reports, Paris.

European Steel Trends, Economic Commission for Europe, Geneva, 1949.

Fertilisers in Agricultural Recovery Programs, Organization for European Economic Cooperation, Paris, no date.

First and Second Report on Coordination of Oil Refinery Expansion, Organization for European Economic Cooperation, Paris, 1949 and 1951.

General Memorandum on the 1950–51 and 1951–52 Programs, Organization for European Economic Cooperation, Paris, 1950. (Contains reports on Austria, Iceland, Portugal, Trieste, Turkey, the United Kingdom, Belgium and Luxembourg, Denmark, France, Germany, the Netherlands, Italy, Greece, Sweden, Norway.)

Interconnected Power Systems in the U.S.A. and Western Europe, Organization for European Economic Cooperation, Paris, 1950.

Interim Report on the European Recovery Program, 2 vols., Organization for European Economic Cooperation, Paris, 1948.

Interim Report on the European Recovery Program, Organization for European Economic Cooperation, Paris, 1948. (Reports of committees on coal, iron and steel, chemical products, textiles, timber, nonferrous metals, oil, etc.)

Tourism and European Recovery, Organization for European Economic Cooperation, Paris, 1951.

AGRICULTURAL CONDITIONS

Agricultural Advisory Services in European Countries, Organization for European Economic Cooperation, 1950.

Consolidation of Fragmented Agricultural Holdings, Food and Agriculture Organization, Washington, D.C., 1950.

Farm Advisory Methods for Grassland Improvement, Organization for European Economic Cooperation, Paris, 1950.

Food Consumption Levels in O.E.E.C. Countries, Report of the Food and Agriculture Committee, Organization for European Economic Cooperation, Paris, 1950.

PERIODICALS

A number of periodical publications, both official and unofficial, contain material that is relevant to the study of economic conditions in Europe. Among these are:

Economic Bulletin for Europe, Economic Commission for Europe, Geneva, quarterly.

Economic Review of Food and Agriculture, Food and Agriculture Organization of the United Nations, quarterly from January, 1948.

The Economist, London, weekly.

Foreign Affairs, New York, quarterly.

Foreign Agriculture, U.S. Department of Agriculture.

Foreign Commerce Weekly, U.S. Department of Commerce.

The Statesman's Yearbook, New York, published annually. (A privately published work of great value.)

The World Today, Royal Institute of International Affairs, London, monthly.

CHAPTER 5: *Northern Europe*

The chapters of this book have been grouped with short introductions into northern, western, central, southern, and eastern Europe. These divisions are all in some degree vague, and it proved difficult to decide in certain instances whether some marginal territory lay in one or another. But with northern Europe there was no indecision. Northern Europe is made up of Norway, Sweden, Finland, and Denmark. If the author had been writing 20 years ago, he would probably have considered including the so-called Baltic States of Estonia, Latvia, and Lithuania, but on the eve of the Second World War these territories were absorbed into Soviet Russia, from which it seems unlikely that they will be severed, at least in the near future.

This part of Europe has in common a high latitude and cool, moist climate. The most southerly island of the Danish archipelago lies in the latitude of Labrador, Stockholm lies as far north as Alaska, and the North Cape of Norway is as near the pole as any point on the mainland of North America. Yet the climate, at least of the more westerly and more maritime parts of Scandinavia, as the countries of Norway, Sweden, and Denmark are often called, is moderated by the Gulf Stream (see page 13), and all its Atlantic ports are ice-free. But only a short distance inland from the west coast the climate becomes more severe. Parts of the Baltic Sea are icebound in winter and even ports like Stockholm are accessible only with the aid of an icebreaker. Rainfall or snow may occur at all seasons. Much of the rain falls like a thick mist rather than heavy rain.

A consequence of the high latitude is the great length of the day in summer and of the night in winter. A considerable part of Norway and Sweden lies within the Arctic Circle. Here the sun does not rise at all for a period about midwinter but betrays its presence only by a glow that hangs over the southern horizon at midday. At midsummer the sun does not set but swings low along the northern horizon. Farther to the south the summer days are long, even if not of 24 hours duration, and the winter night is interrupted by only a short period of sunlight. In these high latitudes the light is more suffused than farther to the south. The sky is a pale, opalescent blue, and the coloring of trees and mountains is softer. These northern lands have a beauty not found in other parts of Europe, unless it be in the north of Scotland, where somewhat similar conditions are produced.

The inhabitants of these northern lands have in common a stability and moderation which is lacking in most countries farther to the south. Some would say that the cool climate has induced a slowness in thought and action and a freedom from passion which makes their history so quiet and well ordered. But the peoples of northern Europe were not always so. They have had their period of violence and aggression. During the early Middle Ages, the Vikings from Norway raided the coasts of northern England; Danes invaded England and France and even went so far as to settle in southern Italy; while the Swedes crossed the Baltic, sailed up the Russian rivers and down to the Black Sea, founding the earliest Russian state. In the sixteenth and seventeenth centuries the Swedes made the Baltic Sea a Swedish lake, conquering Finland and lands around the eastern and southern shores. Swedish troops were the terror of northern and central Europe, and only the rise of Prussia and Russia set a limit to their conquests. Early in the eighteenth century the Swedish star paled before that of Russia, and the period of Swedish military glory ended when Russia and Prussia interested themselves in the affairs of the Baltic.

It would probably be correct to say that the northern peoples have grown to political maturity and have learned to live together

Sogne Fiord, on the west coast of Norway. Settlement is limited to the narrow strips of flat land between the water and the steep slope of the mountains. Notice that even the main roads have rough surfaces. (*Norway Travel Association.*)

earlier than some others. They have their problems and disputes, but these they have settled peacefully and reasonably. The peace and reasonableness which characterize their relations with one another distinguish also their internal government. They have made democracy work more easily, more smoothly, and more effectively than almost any other nation that calls itself democratic. Their willingness to compromise, their reluctance to adopt extreme ideas and policies are in part the source of their success. They display that foremost character-

istic of educated people—reasonableness and moderation in all things.

The peoples of northern Europe have attained a very large measure of material progress. They have achieved a compromise between the evils of the planned and regimented economy and that of unbridled free enterprise. Their living standards are above the European average, and the expectation of life is long. Public health is good, and a long list of writers, artists, and musicians show how these countries excel, despite their small population, in the creative arts. But they have been fortunate. Sweden and Norway had been free from invasion and war for a century and a half until Norway was attacked in 1940. Apart from the short and by no means destructive war with Germany and Austria in 1864, Denmark had been similarly free until the German invasion in the Second World War. Finland's history is more disturbed. She came into being by revolt against Russia following the First World War and since then has twice had to defend herself against the Russians. In recent times these northern countries have not maintained large armies or spent large sums on national defense.

They have been fortunate, furthermore, in the size of their populations. None is really overpopulated, and none is faced with a population increasing in number faster than it can be absorbed. Each has achieved a balance between agriculture and industry which contributes to economic stability. Norway has too small an extent of agricultural land, Denmark is heavily dependent on the export of the products of its dairy farms, and Finland on that of its forest products, but these difficulties are small compared with those of southern and eastern Europe.

COMPARATIVE STATISTICS OF THE NORTHERN COUNTRIES

	Population, 1949 estimates	Percentage in agriculture	Percentage in industry
Norway........	3,239,000	35	27
Sweden........	6,956,000	41	31
Finland........	4,016,000	63	14
Denmark......	4,230,000	35	27

Geographically the whole of northern Europe has been influenced by the Ice Age; all its higher ground has been scraped bare of soil; its lower, covered with drift. In consequence, large areas are covered with infertile sands and gravel. Some areas, particularly eastern Denmark, the Danish islands, and southern Sweden, are marked off by their good dairy land. Elsewhere soils are generally poor. Wheat is rarely grown, and the commonest bread cereal is rye.

Manufacturing industries are well developed in Sweden but in most parts of the country are subsidiary in importance to agriculture. Resources for modern industry are not great. There is no coal of adequate quality, though the strong relief and high rainfall make the generation of hydroelectric power very important. There is a wealth of iron ore and of certain other metals, but in general these countries are situated too far from the sources of raw materials, except softwood timber, ever to become producers of factory goods on a large scale. Instead, their inhabitants produce goods of quality: high-grade steel, light machinery, farm equipment, and the refined products of a highly developed and most efficient farming industry. Both agriculture and industry have been developed in the face of natural difficulties. The northern peoples take the "middle way." They compromise with nature as they do with one another.

CHAPTER 6: *Norway*

The Scandinavian peninsula consists of a mass of ancient, crystalline rocks which extends for some 1,250 miles southwestward from the coastline of Arctic Europe. Norway is the northwestern or seaward edge of this peninsula. For much of its length of 1,400 miles from the Finnish border to the shores of the Skagerrak it has a width of no more than 75 miles. This expands in the extreme northern province of Finnmark to 150 miles, and in the south Norway broadens into a tabular mountain mass with eastward-flowing streams which converge in a small area of lowland close to the Swedish border. For most of its length the boundary with Sweden follows high mountains. It rarely coincides with the watershed except in the north; even less frequently does it traverse a clearly defined line of peaks. In general it follows the surface of a high and undulating plateau on which the drainage is sometimes indeterminate and the population always sparse.

Norway extends through over 13° of latitude, and in this distance the climate changes quite considerably. But the whole of Norway belongs to the moist, mild region of western Europe. Climatic conditions are strongly influenced by the North Atlantic Drift, which influences directly the whole Norwegian coast. The prevailing westerly winds blow from the ocean, carrying both warmth in winter and abundant rainfall to Norway. Conditions vary, however, within short distances. The mountains are responsible for the formation of strongly marked rain shadows in valleys parallel with the coast. At one point in southwestern Norway, the rainfall on the coastal mountains is about 100 inches in the year. Only 15 miles to the east, in Hardanger Fiord it is only about half this. The eastward slope of the plateau of southern Norway is very much drier than the western. There are many sheltered valleys where the rainfall sinks to less than 20 inches and some where it is less than 12. In some places Norway is obliged to resort to irrigation. The heaviest rainfall is experienced on the westward-facing coast of southern Norway. To the north it

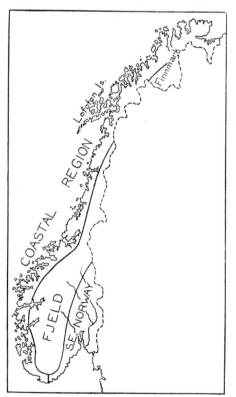

Fig. 25. Physiographic regions of Norway.

Hjelledalen in western Norway. This is a good example of a glacially eroded valley. There is grazing land in the foreground, but over most of the ground the soil is very thin and poor and bare rock outcrops over large areas. (*Norway Travel Association.*)

gradually diminishes and around the North Cape is only about 25 inches. Temperatures show a similar range. Along the coast the range of temperature is everywhere small. Winters are mild, and sea ice does not form. The difference in temperature between the extreme north and extreme south is far less than the difference in latitude would suggest. Within a short distance of the coast, however, the temperature range increases sharply. The number of days with frost rises near the Swedish border to almost two-thirds of the year, and the snow cover is similarly prolonged.

Norway falls into three major physical divisions:

Fiord Coast. To much of the world this is the characteristic region of Norway. Economically, however, it is very much less important than the lowlands of the southeast. The ancient plateau, of which much of Norway and Sweden is composed, here comes close to the coast. Its steep, irregular edge has been eroded to form the deep, narrow, branching fiords. Off the coast is a line of islands, most of them small and low, exposed to the Atlantic gales and almost devoid of soil, vegetation, and human life. These islands form the skerry guard. In general, they are not unlike the islands off the coasts of northern and northwestern Scotland. Off the coast of northern Norway, however, in the Lofoten group, they become very much larger and higher.

In general, the fiords have a rectilinear pattern. Arms or branches tend to join the main fiord at right angles, and the fiord itself tends to make sharp bends. The floor of the fiord shallows, especially near its mouth, where a "lip" may often occur. Similar submerged bars may interrupt the course of the fiord, and land-

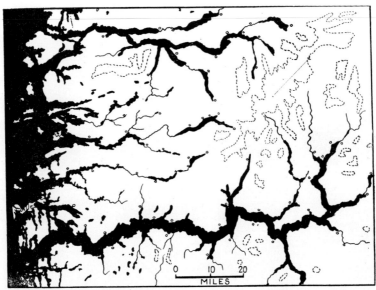

Fig. 26. Fiord coast of Norway. Note the rectilinear pattern formed by the branching waterways. The large fiord to the south is Sogne Fiord. Small circles indicate the position of villages. The dotted line indicates the outline of the ice field.

locked lakes frequently continue up the valleys the direction of the fiords, from which they are cut off by low, flat areas of rock or alluvium. The sides of the fiords are generally steep. Most often they rise directly from the water. Sometimes narrow strips of flatter land, in places only a few yards wide, lie between the cliffs and the water and support a small village settlement. The consensus at present appears to be that the fiords of Norway have been eroded by the action of water and ice in a land mass that has suffered extensive faulting and shattering, that the course of erosion was in large measure "fault-guided."

The coast is in places bordered by a rock-cut terrace, known as a "strand flat." It lies only a few feet above sea level and often provides a site for human habitation. It is generally narrow and exposed but, along with the small flats and alluvial deposits at the sides and heads of the fiords, contains most of the population of the coastal region.

The fiords are little more than deep clefts in a high, barren, and undulating plateau. Its surface is almost devoid of vegetation except low-growing arctic plants and peat. Tree growth is almost wholly absent except in

sheltered depressions, and here it is limited to stunted conifers and birches. Woodland occurs, however, on the gentler hill slopes around the fiords. In places, the upper slopes of the fiords serve as summer grazing, and here, on the *saeters*, or pastures, are huts inhabited by dairymen during the summer months. Villages are in general small, as areas of cultivable land are not extensive enough to support a large community. Most towns are situated on the coast and include Bergen and Trondheim. Smaller towns are important as fishing ports and as centers of the industries that have recently developed on the basis of hydroelectric power.

Bergen (109,300) is built on a small area of flat land, protected from the ocean by a group of low islands. During the Middle Ages it was an important trading center and a member of the Hanseatic League. From its earliest times it has been a center of the fishing industry and is today Norway's most important fishing port. Trondheim (57,100) is a smaller town, situated on the shore of the deep and sheltered Trondheim Fiord. The surrounding area is less mountainous than most of the Norwegian coast, and Trondheim serves as a center for its agricultural and forest industry. Stavanger (50,300)

Saeters on the high *fjeld*. These are inhabited only during the summer months, when animals are brought up to graze the scanty pastures. (*Norway Travel Association.*)

is a fishing port lying south of Bergen, but other urban settlements are very small. Narvik, the terminus of a railway which crosses the mountains to northern Sweden, is a highly specialized port handling the export of Swedish iron ore.

In the past, the fiord coast of Norway suffered from overpopulation. The small area of cultivable land along the sides of the fiords could not be extended, and migration became the alternative to starvation. The Norwegians became sailors and developed a large and important merchant marine. Today, factory industries, based on the abundant and cheap supply of electric power, are providing employment. Bauxite is made into aluminum, copper is smelted electrolytically, and electrochemical industries are carried on in many factories, established close to the generators, along the shores of the fiords.

The Fjeld. This is a barren plateau, built of ancient crystalline rocks and reaching an altitude of over 4,000 feet over most of the area. The region has been largely swept clear of soil by the glaciers, and its summits are rounded and polished. Hollows in the rock surface are now filled with water or peat. The deep valleys cut into the plateau surface are in part clothed with coniferous woodland, and their floors form the only significant areas of crop farming. Rising above the plateau around the head of the Sogne Fiord are the rugged peaks of the Jotunheim, where survives the largest ice field in Norway.

Southeastern Norway. On the east the high fjeld drops gently to the hilly country drained by the Glomma and its tributaries. The hill slopes are more gentle, the rivers broader and slower flowing, the climate drier, and the sunshine more abundant than in the hills and fiords to the west. The higher ground is forested with pine and spruce, but the lower and gently sloping land is well cultivated. Fields are small and enclosed by hedges or fences. The settlement pattern is dispersed, and farms lie at intervals along the bottoms of the valleys. Though near the effective limit of cereal cultivation, an appreciable area is under crop husbandry. Rye, oats, and barley are grown, as well as potatoes and fodder crops, but wheat is important only in the warmer area close to the Oslo Fiord.

Not only is this region important for its agricultural development, it is also the outstanding industrial area. Along the margin of the *fjeld* are timber, pulp, and paper mills, and close to Oslo Fiord are metallurgical, chemical, and engineering industries. Communications are good by Norwegian standards. The natural focus of this region is the town of Oslo, lying at the head of Oslo Fiord, where many of the valleys of the *fjeld* and of the southeastern lowland converge. Oslo is a town of medieval origin and is now a city of 418,450 inhabitants. Its industries, in addition to those associated with the local agricultural and forest products, are concerned with the working of imported raw materials for consumption in Norway.

Economic Development. Agriculture gives employment to about a third of the working population. Cattle rearing is the most important branch, and crop farming is devoted largely

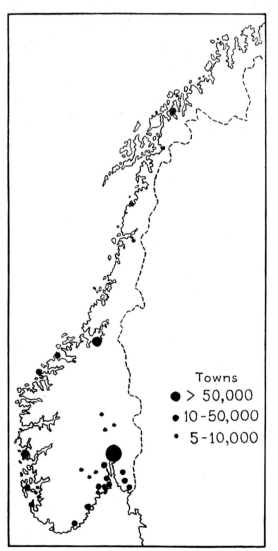

FIG. 27. Distribution of towns in Norway.

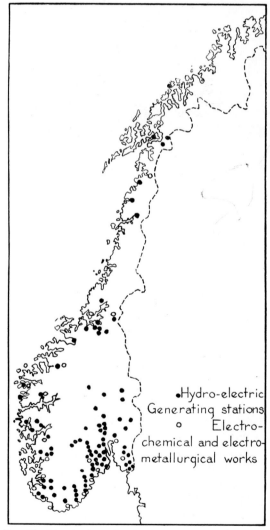

FIG. 28. Distribution of hydroelectric power stations in Norway.

Bergen. This important fishing port lies on a narrow strip of flat land between the mountains and the sea, protected by a fringe of small islands. (*Norway Travel Association.*)

to the production of animal feed. Domestic agriculture is unable, however, to supply the food requirements of Norway. The practice of transhumance, whereby the animals are grazed in summer on the higher pastures of the Saeter, is evidence of the marginal nature of agriculture.

The mineral wealth of Norway is varied, but with the exceptions of pyrites and copper, deposits are small and not of great importance. Pyrites is mined in central Norway; copper and iron in the extreme north.

Norway is lacking in all forms of mineral fuel but has abundant resources in hydroelectric power. The rainfall is well distributed through the year, and in the coastal districts at least frost interferes little with use of this power supply. Hydroelectric developments have been greatest in the southeastern lowland area and on the margins of the *fjeld*. Little power is generated in the north, where there is as yet small industrial demand. The domestic production of hydroelectric power is supplemented by the import of coal and oil fuels.

Industry is heavily dependent upon electric power, and Norway has tended to develop especially those industries which require large amounts of electric power. Prominent among these are the refining of minerals and manufacture of certain chemicals. The refining of aluminum requires particularly large quantities of electric power, and it is economical to import the purified alumina and to smelt it electrically in Norway, where the current is relatively cheap. Nickel and zinc are also smelted electrically, as well as certain metal alloys such as ferrosilicon and ferrochrome. Electroplating is carried on, and certain chemicals, such as calcium carbide and various nitrogen compounds, are manufactured.

Large stands of softwood occur only in the area of comparatively low-lying land around Trondheim and in the southeast. The latter is by far the more important, and here is concentrated the greater part of the Norwegian timber industry. The dominant species are Scotch pine and Norway spruce. The timber is logged for export, but the greatest part of the cut is consumed in the pulp mills.

Fishing is of great importance. The poverty of the land has driven a large proportion of the

Hallingdal in southeastern Norway. The climate is drier, the topography less rugged, and the land more productive than to the west. Note how the hay is hung on wooden stakes to dry. (*Norway Travel Association.*)

working population to adopt a life at sea, either in the fishing fleet or in the merchant marine. Norwegian fishing boats work the North Sea, Iceland, Newfoundland, and Arctic fisheries. Cod, herring, and brisling are caught and exported, either fresh or preserved, to countries of western and southern Europe. Related to the fishing is the whaling industry, now carried on by Norwegians in most oceans of the world. There are innumerable fishing ports, with factories which preserve the fish and process the fish oil, fish manure, and similar products, along the coast between the North Cape and Oslo Fjord.

Trade and Commerce. The problem of internal communications is a serious one. Both road and railway development is adequate in the lowland region of the southeast, but communication between this and the west coast is limited to the few railroads across the *fjeld.* Farther north the railway network is even less developed. There is no railway which extends the whole length of the country. Roads are more fully developed, but in the north these,

too, are few and blocked by snow for long periods in winter. There are times when the only communication between the more northerly ports is by boat through the islands of the skerry guard or by way of the more developed railway system of Sweden.

Foreign trade is large in proportion to the population. The prosperity of Norway depends heavily on it. Most valuable are the exports of timber and timber products, followed by minerals, fish, fish products, and chemicals. Imports are largely the foodstuffs which Norway is unable to produce, together with the raw materials of the limited manufacturing industries.

In time of peace Norway is prosperous and contented. Her merchant ships earn money, and she can carry on her trade, which, in proportion to her population, is very large indeed. War, which prohibits these activities, does great harm to Norway. Norway suffered heavily between 1940 and 1945, not only from the direct results of the fighting, which took place in many parts of the country, but also from the indirect consequences, the loss of trade and the inability to import foodstuffs and export pulp and paper, metals, and chemicals.

Norway is not naturally a united country. It is broken by its strong relief into compartments, fiords, and mountain valleys, cut off from one another by high and often impassable mountains. For this reason its political independence is itself recent in date. Norway had not a sufficient degree of unity to break with Denmark and Sweden, which had in turn controlled it, until the early years of this century. Even now, the country tends to function as a group of local and in part self-governing units rather than as a unified state.

Spitzbergen (Svalbard) is an arctic possession of Norway, lying between the latitudes of 77° and 80°N, about 730 miles northwest of the North Cape. The island group is irregular in shape and heavily glaciated. Most of it is covered by a permanent ice cap. It has a strategic value which may be expected to increase rather than diminish. Its economic importance is limited to its quite considerable deposits of coal, which are worked and exported despite the very unfavorable physical environment.

Jan Mayen Island, small and glaciated, is a Norwegian possession lying between Iceland and Spitzbergen.

ICELAND

This island of 39,700 square miles lies in the stormy North Atlantic. Its northern coast is almost on the Arctic Circle. The island was colonized by Viking peoples in the early Middle Ages and remained until 1944 under the Danish Crown, but in that year it became an independent republic.

Iceland is a rugged, glaciated island. Its coast is fringed with high cliffs and deep fiords, which provide shelter for its fishing fleet. The climate is cool and wet. Snowfall is heavy, and the island contains Vatna-Jökull, the largest ice field in Europe. Most of the surface is waste and treeless, sheep are reared in large numbers, but climate and soil are unfit for agriculture. There is grazing land in some of the valleys, but crop cultivation is confined to lowlands of the southwest.

The chief occupations are agriculture and fishing. The surrounding seas afford a rich harvest, which is taken not only by the Icelanders but also by several other peoples of western Europe.

The capital and largest town is Reykjavik, situated on a fiord of the southwest coast, but its population is only about 44,300. The population of the whole island is only 110,000.

Until recent years the significance of Iceland in the affairs of Europe had been slight, but its position where the Atlantic Ocean is narrowest gives it a greater importance, and as long as there is discussion of transpolar warfare, the significance of Iceland is not likely to be underrated.

BIBLIOGRAPHY

Norway

"Conference on Rural Life: Norway," League of Nations, Geneva, 1939.

Gathorne Hardy, G., "Norway," London, 1925.

"Géographie universelle," Vol. III, Etats scandinaves, Paris, 1933.

Gregory, J. W., "The Nature and Origin of Fjords," London, 1913.

Heiden, Noland R., Odd and Rjukan: Two Industrialized Areas of Norway, A.A.A.G., XLII, 1952, 109–128.

Hubbard, George D., The Geography of Residence in Norway Fiord Areas, A.A.A.G., XXII, 1932, 109–118.

Lund, D. H., The Revival of Northern Norway, G.J., CIX, 1947, 185–197.

Mead, W. R., Sogn and Fjordane in the Fiord Economy of Western Norway, E.G., XXIII, 1947, 155–166.

"The Northern Countries in World Economy," Copenhagen, 1937.

"Overseas Economic Surveys: Norway," London, 1949.

Strom, K. M., The Geomorphology of Norway, G.J., CXII, 1949, 19–27.

Thomson, Claudia, Norway's Industrialization, E.G., XIV, 1938, 372–380.

———, Norwegian Agriculture, Foreign Agriculture, Washington D.C., IV, 1940, 65–94.

The Norges Bank Bulletin, published every 2 months in Oslo, contains much material on the current economic development of the country.

Iceland

Axel Anderson, S., Iceland's Industries, E.G., VII, 1931, 284–296.

Mead, W. R., Renaissance of Iceland, E.G., XXI, 1945, 135–144.

CHAPTER 7: *Sweden and Finland*

The Baltic Sea is a large expanse of shallow water which within historical times has been becoming steadily shallower and less salty. Its shores bear evidence of the rise of sea level and "drowning" which followed the ending of the

Fig. 29. Political boundaries in Scandinavia and the Baltic. Pre-1939 boundaries are shown as solid lines. Post-1945 boundaries are shown as dotted lines.

Ice Age and also of the uplift of the land which has occupied much of the time that has since elapsed. To the west of the Baltic Sea is Sweden, to the east Finland and the territories which, until their annexation by the U.S.S.R., were

known as the Baltic States. To the south are Germany and Poland. The earliest of these to appear in modern times as an integrated state was Sweden. In the sixteenth and seventeenth century Sweden came to dominate the whole sea. Finland had for centuries been dominated by Sweden, and Swedish colonists had settled on its coast, where their descendants still remain. Sweden acquired ports on the southeastern and southern shores. This Swedish hegemony, which gave a certain cultural and economic unity to the Baltic region, was terminated by the rise of the Russian state of Muscovy and of the kingdom of Brandenburg-Prussia in Germany. Each sought an opening on to the Baltic Sea. Peter the Great established Saint Petersburg (Leningrad) in 1703 and later broadened his control to Courland and Livland (approximately Estonia and Latvia). The Hohenzollerns of Prussia drove the Swedes from their last foothold on the German coast in 1815. With the ending of the period of Swedish domination there has followed an uneasy balance between the political strength of Germany and Russia. Until recent years German control has been dominant, but the defeat of Germany in the Second World War has exposed the Baltic region to a renewed pressure from Russia. The Baltic States together with part of East Prussia have been absorbed into the Soviet Union. The U.S.S.R. has on two occasions, 1940 and 1945, taken small areas of Finnish territory and now exercises a strong political influence on Finland and, less directly, on Sweden.

Denmark formerly exercised over the islands at the entrance to the Baltic and over parts of southern Sweden a political control such as

Sweden possessed over the Baltic Sea itself. In the course of the seventeenth century Denmark lost her possessions in southern Sweden, though she retained until early in the nineteenth the control of the Sound and with it the right to levy dues on vessels passing in and out of the Baltic Sea.

SWEDEN

Sweden is the larger, eastern part of the Scandinavian peninsula. Much of the country consists of a dissected plateau whose general level sinks from the watershed, close to the Norwegian frontier, to the Baltic coast. South of this dissected plateau region is one of glaciated and lake-studded lowland, in which are most of the towns and a majority of the Swedish population. On the southern margin of this lowland rise the rounded, forested hills of Små-land. All the regions of Sweden mentioned hitherto are built of ancient rocks, much folded, faulted, and planated in earlier cycles of erosion. In the southernmost region of Sweden, however, the older rocks are buried beneath younger limestone and chalk. The landscape and economic development of this southernmost province of Scania (Skåne) greatly resemble Denmark, of which it was once a part.

Northern Sweden. This region makes up about two-thirds of the entire country, but of the total population of about 6,956,000 in 1949 little more than a sixth lives here. Toward the west it is made up of sharp, isolated peaks, whose summits reach heights of over 6,000 feet. East of these, however, there is a long and narrow belt of softer and more easily eroded rocks, but toward the east these give way to the crystalline mass which composes the greater part of Sweden. The belt of softer rocks has been excavated to form a depression between the folded mountains on the west and the crystal-line plateau on the east. It is irregular and far from continuous. On the physical map it is recognized more clearly by the large number of lakes that occupy hollows excavated in its surface than from the contours themselves.

Both the region of the lakes and the crystalline region to the east of it are undulating country.

Most of the many rivers of this region of Sweden rise in the mountains close to the Norwegian frontier and cross these more easterly belts of country in broad valleys sunk quite deeply below the plateau surface. The level of the plateau itself drops toward the east and close

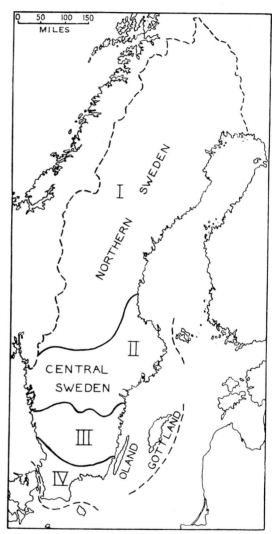

Fig. 30. Physical regions of Sweden.

to the Baltic Sea is covered with recent marine sediments which are fertile and would be productive if the climate were less rigorous.

The north of this region lies within the Arctic Circle. Its winters are long and severe, and snowfall heavy. The summer is cool and bright, but too short for most cultivated crops to grow

Kiruna in Swedish Lapland. The hill in the middle distance consists of iron ore, which is slowly being cut away. In winter artificial lighting is necessary even at midday. (*Swedish Tourist Traffic Association.*)

and mature. Some agriculture is practiced along the coastal belt, where soils are better and the climate moderated somewhat by the proximity of the Baltic Sea. But the amount of agriculture diminishes both northward and westward from the coast. Hardy cereals—barley, oats, and rye—are grown, but wheat is a rare crop. Vegetables, fodder crops, and cultivated grasses make up the rest of the produce of this region. Dairy farming is carried on only where climate and soil make it practicable and where communications are sufficiently developed to permit the movement of milk to the dairies or consuming centers. This is a region of hamlets and scattered farmsteads, though much of it is uninhabited. Buildings are made almost wholly of wood, the cheapest and most abundant material, and styles of farm buildings are adapted primarily to the climate and to the building material. A form of transhumance is still practiced, though on a diminishing scale. The cattle are sometimes taken in the summer months to the *fäbod*, a forest clearing or stretch of treeless, higher ground, in order to leave the home pastures free for making hay. Hay is a precious commodity; it is cut and dried with great care, a matter of some difficulty where the summers are humid and cool.

The higher land, in the mountainous belt to the west, is covered with short grass or bog. In places, the glaciers have scraped away the soil, leaving only bare rock. Forests, however, cover the lower ground, though in the north this is thin and stunted. The region lies to the north of the limit of most broad-leaved trees, but the birch is still conspicuous in its beauty, contrasting to the somber coloring of the spruce forests, which predominate. Lumbering is the most widespread industry of this region. The logs, cut in the forests, are floated down the great number of rivers to the sawmills near their mouths. Many small ports along the Swedish coast handle the export of timber and pulpwood.

Mining is the only other important industry. Iron is scattered widely through the ancient crystalline rocks, together with a number of other minerals. Of these, copper was formerly of outstanding importance, though now almost exhausted in central Sweden. It was mined at Falun, close to the southern edge of the region, and its export brought wealth and importance to Sweden in early times. The production of iron ore in the southern part of this region is now also small, though its nonphosphoric quality gives it some importance and it is the basis of production of high-grade steel in central Sweden. The ores of Lapland have come in the past half century to play a very important role. They are easily worked. Those at Kiruna are taken from open cuts, rising in steps up the sides of the steep hills which are themselves composed largely of iron ore. Shafts, where they are used, are not deep. The ores themselves, generally magnetite or hematite, are of a relatively high grade, usually over 60 per cent iron, though phosphoric. The production of ore in Sweden in 1950 reached over 13 million tons. Ore production had been quite small, less than a million tons a year before 1891, when a railroad was at last completed between the mines of Swedish Lapland and the Baltic coast port of Lulea. At once the volume of export increased. Lulea is icebound and inaccessible to ore ships in winter, and the seasonal nature of the export led to the continuation of the railroad from the orefields across the high *fjeld* to the Norwegian port of Narvik, which is ice-free. This railroad was completed in 1902. Elaborate ore-loading devices were erected. Narvik quickly grew to be a town of over 10,000 inhabitants, and the volume of export of both Lulea and Narvik increased steadily.

The mineral wealth of Norrbotten, as this northern province is called, is not limited to iron ore. At Kristineberg are large reserves of copper, which are now being worked. Gold is obtained at Boliden, and there are reserves of lead, zinc, and nickel in northern Sweden. The production of the nonferrous metals is still insufficient, however, to meet home demands.

In contrast to the settled Swedish inhabitants of this region are the seminomadic Lapps. These people, now few in number, constitute one of the most distinctive racial groups in Europe. They are of Asiatic origin, having come into northern Europe from Asiatic Russia. Until recently they had not practiced agriculture, living wholly on the produce of herds of reindeer, which they follow through the wastes of Lapland. The Lapps have never ob-

A Lapp camp in northern Sweden. The Lapps are a migratory people. Tents made by spreading skins or canvas over birch poles are their most permanent form of habitation. (*Swedish Tourist Traffic Association.*)

served political frontiers, moving freely between Norway, Sweden, and Finland.

This region is the "pioneer fringe" of modern Sweden. It lacks the long-settled character and the traditions of the south. Money is made easily in its booming mine towns and its lumber and pulp mills and is spent recklessly.

Central Sweden. Central Sweden is gentler in relief and milder in climate than northern. It was the nucleus of the Swedish state from which the kings of the House of Vasa moved outward in the sixteenth and seventeenth centuries to the conquest of both northern Sweden and the southern extremity of the southwestern peninsula.

The crystalline rocks which make up so large an area of northern Sweden are continued

southward but in central Sweden have undergone extensive faulting. Central Sweden is
several hundred feet lower than the region to
the north. The faulting has produced shallow
trenches, many of them lake-filled, and low
ridges with steep sides which follow the lines of

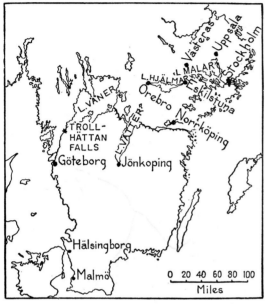

Fig. 31. Central Sweden. The Göta Canal joins the
lakes with the east coast.

faults. The relief is low but broken up by
these lesser land forms. In postglacial times,
before the recovery of the Scandinavian region
from its depression under the ice, the North
Sea joined the predecessor of the Baltic across
this region. Marine deposits, which now yield
fertile soils, were laid down at this time. There
are numerous lakes. Lake Vätter is wholly enclosed by faults; Lake Väner is in part bounded
by the lines of ancient faulting, in part by
glacial deposits. The complex waterway, formed
by Lakes Hjälmar and Mälar, which stretches
almost halfway across the region, is fundamentally due to faulting, but much modified by
glacial deposits. The northward retreat of the
ice left in its wake a series of eskers, or narrow,
sinuous ridges of morainic material. These lie
generally in a north-south direction. They
sometimes provide dry roadways above the
damp surface of the land. A considerable num-

ber of conspicuous eskers cross the lakes, producing islands in their midst and causing abrupt
narrowings of the waterway. For this reason,
the lakes are not important as navigable highways, and the towns on and close to their shores
make little use of them.

Central Sweden experiences a milder climate
than northern. The snow cover is less prolonged,
and the growing period longer. Broad-leaved
trees, the oak and ash in particular, are found
among the conifers. Much of the woodland has
been cleared, and a high proportion of the land

Fig. 32. The situation of Stockholm. Note how the lines
of converging railroads have been influenced by the
numerous lakes.

is under cultivation. Not only the hardy cereals
that are produced farther to the north but also
wheat are grown. Much of the land is under
grass, and dairy farming is here almost as important as in Denmark. In contrast to the region
to the north, this has a pattern of compact

Lake Mälar, central Sweden. This beautiful waterway stretches 140 miles inland from the coast. Its shores are well wooded and dotted with villages and small towns, such as Strängnäs, shown in this picture. (*Swedish Tourist Traffic Association.*)

villages, always a sign of greater productivity and prosperity, and small towns.

On the northern border of central Sweden is the ancient mining region of Dalarna. There are numerous iron workings. Many are ancient, and all of them have for centuries yielded a high-grade ore used in the Swedish steel industry. Until the nineteenth century Sweden produced from this area a large proportion of the world's output of steel, which was refined in small furnaces with the charcoal from the neighboring forests. The Swedish philosopher Swedenborg wrote in the eighteenth century a treatise on iron smelting and steelworking. Sweden retains today only a small steel industry, reckoned in terms of output, distributed over a number of small towns, amongst which are Eskilstuna (51,700) and Bofors. These lie close to the former sources of ore and charcoal. The steel produced today is of a very high quality. Sweden is famous for the production of ball bearings. Eskilstuna is a center of the cutlery industry, and there are many towns engaged in mechanical and electrical engineering.

With the exceptions of Göteborg (344,000) and Stockholm (725,700) the urban settlements are small. Uppsala (60,400), to the north of Lake Mälar, is an ancient castle and cathedral town, where a university, the oldest in Sweden, was established in the fifteenth century. The older buildings are clustered on the ridge of an esker, below which the modern town has grown up. Norrköping (83,300), Örebro (64,700), and Västerås (55,800) are other small centers of woodworking and textile industries. Göteborg, on the estuary of the Göta Älv, was established early in the seventeenth century as the port of central Sweden. The Göta Älv drains Lake Väner. A few miles below the outlet of the lake are Trollhättan Falls, where a small industrial town gathered around the source of power. The river is navigable for small craft, and the Göta

Canal has been cut to join it with Lake Vätter and the Baltic Sea. This canal is too small to have any great commercial significance.

Stockholm grew up on an island in Lake Mälar, where one of the eskers not only provides an easy approach to the lake but also narrows it and makes the crossing easy. The town has spread from the island to the main-

A street in the old city of Stockholm. In the distance is the cathedral. (*Swedish Tourist Traffic Association.*)

land on each side. It is now a city of about 725,700 inhabitants and has a varied range of textile, engineering, and timber-using industries. Its island situation and the beauty of many of its buildings, including the much photographed town hall, have earned it the title of "Venice of the North." Lake Mälar is tidal, and the port of Stockholm has uninterrupted connection with the sea. The waters freeze in winter, however, though vessels continue to use the port with the help of icebreakers.

Göteborg, by contrast, is ice-free. In size it is second only to Stockholm and in the volume of its shipping has begun to exceed Stockholm. These two cities, Stockholm in the east and

Göteborg in the west, focus the activities of central Sweden. No other city has been able either to attain any great size or to rival them.

Småland is a fault-bounded massif of old, crystalline rocks. On most sides its boundaries are sharp, separating it from the lower and more fertile country. Its surface is plateaulike. Much is forested with conifers, and there are stretches of sour and unproductive bog. The population is small, and agriculture but little practiced.

Skåne (Scania) is the southernmost province of Sweden. Geologically it resembles Denmark rather than the rest of Sweden and was for many centuries in Danish possession. The young rocks of this region are in part mantled with glacial drift, in part with the marine deposits left during the postglacial period of high sea level. The climate is milder than that in other parts of Sweden and closely resembles that of the Danish islands. Skåne has always been agriculturally the most productive of all regions of Sweden. Grain cultivation, formerly as important here as in Denmark, has given place in part to dairy farming, which is conducted on a cooperative basis. At the same time crop farming remains of great significance, and wheat, oats, barley, rye, and sugar beet are of importance. The region is flat or rolling. Farms are large, and settlement is generally in compact villages.

Towns are not large in this region. Many were once fortresses erected in the course of the wars between Denmark and Sweden, and all serve as market towns for this rich agricultural region. Malmö (185,950), on the coast opposite Copenhagen, is the largest city, the terminus of the ferry across the Sound, and an industrial center.

The islands of Öland and Gotland, the former a mere strip of lowland off the coast of Småland, the latter a large, more compact island, are now of little significance. Both are covered with glacial and recent marine deposits and are now devoted primarily to dairy and mixed farming. They were once, however, important commercial centers both of the ancient Swedish trade of the Dark Ages and later of that of the Hanseatic League in the Middle Ages. Ancient

Harvesting in Skåne (Scania). This is the low, undulating, and fertile southern tip of Sweden, where landscape and agriculture are similar to those of Denmark. (*Swedish Tourist Traffic Association.*)

The island of Öland, off Sweden's east coast. There is a shallow and stony boulder-clay soil, the boulders from which are gathered into the walls between the fields. The island is bleak and wind-swept. In the distance is Borgholm Castle. (*Swedish Tourist Traffic Association.*)

coins from the eastern Mediterranean have been dug up at Visby, evidence of the commerce that was once carried on between the Baltic Sea and the Black and Mediterranean Seas. On Gotland is the town of Visby, whose ruined walls and towers witness to its former wealth and prosperity.

Economic Development. Despite the prominence of its mining and specialized manufacturing industries, Sweden is an important agricultural country. Of its working population, 41 per cent are engaged on the land. The majority work small holdings and practice a mixed agriculture. Farming is carried on chiefly in the

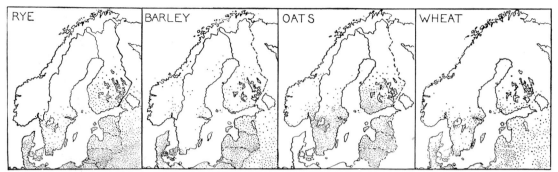

FIG. 33. Distribution of the more important crops in the Baltic area. Each dot represents 5,000 acres. (*From Agricultural Geography of Europe and the Near East, U.S. Department of Agriculture, 1948.*)

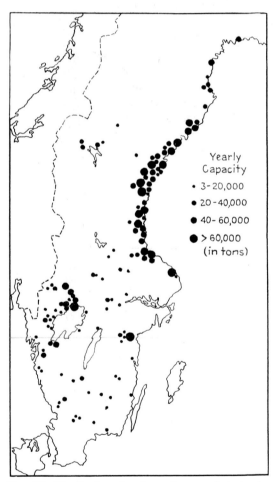

FIG. 34. Distribution of pulp and paper factories in Sweden. Most are placed to take advantage of water transport for the lumber. (*From Sweden Past and Present, Swedish Tourist Traffic Association.*)

southernmost region and in central Sweden. Elsewhere lumbering and, in places, mining are more important than agriculture. Lumbering predominates in the nonagricultural areas. The dominant species is spruce, which is cut for pulping. The sawmills are scattered along the rivers of the forested region. Originally they were driven directly by the force of the stream, but as the rivers come more and more to be used to generate hydroelectric power, this more convenient source of energy is increasingly used. Sweden's rivers form her only source of power. There remain, however, vast unused potentialities, especially in northern Sweden, where the demand for power is least.

After timber and timber products, iron ore constitutes the most valuable export of Sweden. Almost all comes from the extreme north and is exported from the ports of Lulea and Narvik. The ore consumed in Sweden's domestic steel industry is obtained from the lesser ore fields of central Sweden.

Despite the importance of its agricultural industry, Sweden is not normally self-sufficing in foodstuffs though the country made do without significant imports during the Second World War. A small quantity of grain has to be imported as well as animal fodder and foodstuffs of tropical origin. The limited industrial development of Sweden necessitates the import of textile materials as well as rubber and nonferrous metals. The nature of Sweden's exports has already been indicated. They are made up of timber products, ores, agricultural and especially dairy produce, and a limited range

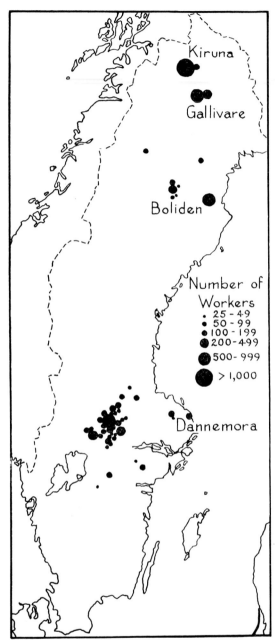

Fig. 35. Distribution of iron mines and iron concentration plants in Sweden, 1945. Note the few large units in the north and the many smaller ones in the center and south. (*From G. Löwegren, "Swedish Iron and Steel."*)

of specialized manufactures, which include high-quality steel and ball bearings.

Sweden's resources are her forests, her ores, her water power, and the patience and industry of her people. These have fitted her to become a producer of specialized goods for other countries. She must import foodstuffs and certain raw materials; she must export the products of her forests, mines, and factories in order to live. She is heavily dependent on trade, like her neighbors Norway and Denmark. Her geographical position makes her situation a precarious one. She has only a short coastline facing onto the ocean, and Germany and Russia are in effect her neighbors to south and east. Like Switzerland, in a somewhat similar position, Sweden finds refuge in neutrality, though less consistently than Switzerland. Sweden has avoided alliances and tried to remain on good trading terms with all countries. Today she is not represented in the North Atlantic Treaty Organization, while Denmark and Norway are both members. The apparent harmony between the Scandinavian countries, which leads them to act jointly on many issues, nevertheless disguises certain differences. When all is said, they remain commercial rivals, and there are apparent differences between their foreign policies.

FINLAND

Both geologically and culturally Finland is closely related to Sweden. The "shield" of ancient rocks which composes much of northern Sweden is continuous over the whole of Finland and extends beyond the eastern limits of Finland to a line which runs from the White Sea through Lakes Onega and Ladoga to the Gulf of Finland. Finland is low-lying, and its greatest heights, in northern Finland, rise to little more than 1,500 feet. Over most of the area the ancient rocks are covered and hidden by a deep mantle of boulder clay and morainic material. During postglacial times, however, marine deposits were laid down over parts of the country, similar to the marine deposits of southern Sweden.

Finland falls naturally into three distinct regions: the low, moraine-covered plateau, which composes all central Finland; the low hills of northern Finland; and the narrow coastal belt of the south and west.

Central and Northern Finland. The thick glacial deposits which cover the whole of this region have been modified somewhat by the sea when it extended over this region, but it remains fundamentally an uneven, clay-covered surface. The hollows have been filled by water to make the 40,000 lakes of Finland. The hills

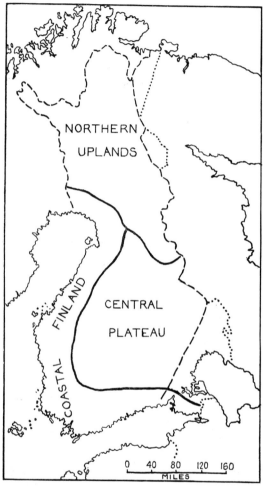

FIG. 36. Physical regions of Finland.

are mounds of boulder clay, esker ridges, and embankments of clay and gravel left by the retreating ice. Villages are often no more than lines of houses drawn out along the crest of a morainic ridge or an esker. Railways and roads often follow such ridges. The railway from Helsinki (Helsingfors) to Leningrad follows for a considerable distance the crest of the Salpauselka, a terminal moraine. The multitude of lakes is interconnected, making a complex system of waterways, sometimes used for floating

timber. At least 40 per cent of the area of this region is actually water. The land surface is mostly forested with spruce and pine, though birches lend some color to the dark forests. Small areas have been cleared for cultivation, but the climate is harsh, the growing season short, and the soils often poor. The central plateau of Finland lies very close to the northern limit of cultivation. Barley, oats, rye, and wheat are grown, but only in the southern part. Grazing is possible, and dairy farming is, over much of this region, the only important branch of agriculture.

The landscape is monotonous. In detail the surface is uneven, but the small irregularities rise to about the same height, and the skyline is level. The still, shallow lakes and the dark woods have a beauty of their own. The somber and continuous forest cover has shed an air of mystery over the country and its people, and this atmosphere, as powerful in its way as that of the Western Isles of Scotland, the Finns have tried to recapture in their literature and music, above all in the music of Sibelius.

To the north of the lake-studded plateau the underlying ancient rocks come to the surface and rise northward into the bare and rounded hills of northern Finland. These have been severely glaciated and are in many places bare of soil. The heavy forest cover thins away, the conifers become stunted and valueless, and the land is uncultivable. Northward, toward the Arctic Ocean, this semblance of forest passes into the tundra. The region is valuable chiefly by reason of its mineral deposits. There are deposits of minerals similar to those of Sweden and small but valuable deposits of nickel, pyrites, copper, lead, and zinc. The copper of Outokumpu, a state-owned mine, is the most extensive deposit of its kind in Europe.

Until recently northern Finland extended to the shores of the Arctic Ocean, where the Finns had established the port of Petsamo. This port, with the narrow strip of land which joined it to the rest of the country, was annexed by the U.S.S.R., part after the "Winter War" of 1939–1940 and part at the end of the war of 1939 to 1945.

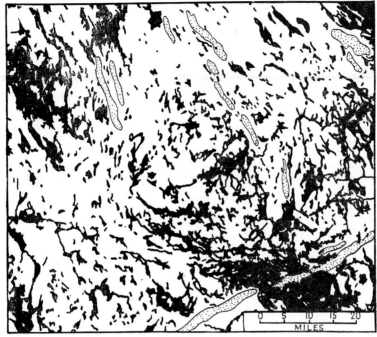

FIG. 37. Part of the Finnish lake plateau. Water is shown in black. Long thin dotted areas are the ridges of eskers or moraine.

Central and northern Finland, like northern Sweden, is the pioneer region, where settlement and economic activity are expanding into the wilderness of tundra, forest, and lake. The harsh environment has called forth the best in the Finns. Centuries of effort have brought this waste into production and have enabled it to send its timber, its timber products, and its minerals into the world market.

Coastal Finland. The central plateau, which lies at a height of about 300 feet above the level of the sea, drops gently through the narrow coastal belt to the shore of the Baltic Sea. This region, like much of the rest of the country, is covered with boulder clay but has patches of marine silt. The rivers, as they discharge from the lakes of the plateau, flow more swiftly, scouring their beds and deepening them to the underlying platform of ancient rock. The coast is deeply indented; forest-fringed creeks and inlets reach far into the land. Offshore is a "guard" of small islands, generally washed free of their boulder-clay cover by the sea.

The coastal belt had a similar forest cover to

A typical landscape in southern Finland. Note the undulating terrain and the clearing in the coniferous forest. (*Finnish National Travel Office.*)

Logs being floated down the Kyminjoki, one of the larger rivers of Finland. Note the strip cultivation along the banks of the river. (*Finnish National Travel Office.*)

that of the interior, though much of this has been cleared, and this is now the most settled and best cultivated region of Finland. Offshore, between the mainland of Finland and the Swedish coast, are the Åland (Ahvenanmaa) Islands, a group of low, rocky islands between Finland and Sweden. The whole of the Finnish coast, from Viipuri (Viborg), now within the frontier of the U.S.S.R., to the head of the Gulf of Bothnia, was formerly settled by Swedes, and extensive areas on the west and south coasts are today predominantly Swedish in speech.

The larger settlements of Finland are almost entirely coastal. Of these Helsinki (Helsingfors, 381,500), the capital, is the largest, lying partly on a peninsula, partly on the neighboring bay and islands. It is the most important port of Finland, but there are many lesser ports. Helsinki is but little impeded by ice in winter, and Hangö (Hankö), to the west, is open throughout the year. On the coast opposite the Åland Islands is Turku (Åbo, 102,322), a medieval fortress town and now a port and university city. Viipuri, once the second city

of Finland and now in Russian Karelia, grew up around a castle built by the Swedes in the Middle Ages. A short distance inland from Viipuri the Vuoksi River, draining the lake plateau of eastern Finland, descends from the higher level to that of Lake Ladoga by the Imatra Falls, one of the largest single power resources.

Political and Economic Development. The republic of Finland appeared on the map of Europe after the First World War, when the Finns, with German help, revolted successfully against the rule of Russia. As a result of the two wars, ending, respectively, in 1940 and 1944, Finland lost to Russia, in addition to the Arctic Coast and port of Petsamo, a large area in the "waist" of Finland, the Karelian isthmus, with the port of Viipuri and the Porkkala peninsula, near Helsinki. These losses were more significant than their territorial extent would suggest. About 11 per cent of the cultivated land, about 13 per cent of the forest resources, a quarter of the pulpwood factories, and about 13 per cent of other timber factories

An aerial view of the city of Helsinki (Helsingfors). The coastline here is "drowned" and bordered by a large number of small and often wooded islands. The city occupies a small peninsula. (*Finnish National Travel Office.*)

The Punkaharju, an esker ridge of glacial material in the Finnish lake region. This ridge is followed by a railroad, which can clearly be seen to the left. (*Finnish National Travel Office.*)

passed into Russian hands. Altogether 342 industrial establishments were lost. Yet more serious was the effect of the territorial changes on the supply of electric power. In all, 32 per cent of the hydroelectric-power capacity under exploitation or in process of development was lost. Finland has no solid fuel except peat, so this loss was felt the more severely. With the loss of Viipuri, Finland lost a considerable part of her grain-milling and seed-crushing plant, as well as part of her small steel industry. Furthermore Finland was burdened with a heavy reparation payment to Russia and with 35,000 refugee families to be resettled in the parts of Finland that remain. Despite these hardships and handicaps, Finland continues to present a bold front to her overpowering neighbor, and there is perhaps less fear of Russia in this little country than in any other west of the "Iron Curtain."

Since its liberation from Russian rule in 1918 Finland has developed stable, democratic political institutions and a prosperous agricultural economy. The population of Finland is only 3,989,000 (1948), of whom about 52 per cent are dependent upon agriculture. Indus-

tries other than the preparation of timber and the manufacture of timber products, such as plywood, pulp, paper, and matches, are of small importance. Textiles and light metal goods are made, and Finland has even a small blast-furnace and steel industry. Hydroelectric power is generated from the rivers of the coastal belt, where they drop from the plateau of the interior to the sea. The lakes form natural reservoirs, thus regulating the discharge of water. The exports of Finland consist overwhelmingly of timber and dairy products; her imports of manufactured goods, raw materials, and such foodstuffs as Finland is unsuited to produce. Over 80 per cent of Finland's "free" trade, that is, other than reparation deliveries to Russia, is with the nations of western Europe and the New World. Her economic ties are almost wholly with the West.

Finland, like Turkey, is a bridge between West and East. Scandinavian in its moderation and in its vigorous "social democracy," it is territorially part of eastern Europe. Its growth to political and economic maturity has been slowed down by a long period of Russian rule. It is still really a "democracy in the making."

BIBLIOGRAPHY

GENERAL

"Géographie universelle," Vol. III, Etats scandinaves; Vol. V, Etats de baltique, Paris, 1932–1933.
"Northern Countries in World Economy," Copenhagen, 1937.
Reddaway, W. F., "Problems of the Baltic," Cambridge, 1940.
Simon, Sir E. D., "The Smaller Democracies," London, 1939.
Woods, E. G., "The Baltic Region," London, 1932.

SWEDEN

Ahlmann, H. W., The Economic Geography of Swedish Norrland, *Geografiska Annaler*, III, 1921, 97–164.
Childs, Marquis W., "Sweden: the Middle Way," New Haven, 1938.
Collinder, Bjorn, "The Lapps," Princeton, N.J., 1949.
"Conference on Rural Life: Sweden," League of Nations, Geneva, 1939.
De Geer, Sten, Greater Stockholm: a Geographical Interpretation, *G.R.*, XIII, 1923, 497–506.
———, A Map of the Distribution of Population in Sweden, *G.R.*, XII, 1922, 72–83.

Hjulstrom, F., The Economic Geography of Electricity, *Geographica*, XII, Uppsala, 1942.
Jonasson, O., The Relation between the Distribution of Population and of Cultivated Land in the Scandinavian Countries, Especially in Sweden, *E.G.*, I, 1925, 107–123.
———, et al., "The Agricultural Atlas of Sweden," Stockholm, 1938.
Lowegren, G., "Swedish Iron and Steel," Stockholm, 1948.
Rickman, A. F., "Swedish Iron Ore," London, no date.
"Sweden: Review of Commercial Conditions," London, 1945.
Swedish Yearbook, published annually in English, contains statistical and other information.
Wiklund, K. B., The Lapps in Sweden, *G.R.*, XIII, 1923, 223–242.
William-Olsson, W., Stockholm: Its Structure and Development, *G.R.*, XXX, 1940, 420–438.

An admirable small atlas of Sweden, produced for the Swedish high schools, but of value to advanced students, is "Sverige Nu Atlas over Sveriges Folk, Land och Naringar," Stockholm, 1949.

The publications of the Swedish banks allow the student to keep abreast of developments in the field of economic geography, particularly the following:

Skandinavska Banken Aktiebolag, Quarterly Review, Stockholm.

Swedish Economic Survey, Aktiebolaget Göteborgs Bank, Göteborg, published monthly.

FINLAND

"Atlas of Finland," Helsinki, 1925.

Collinder, B., "The Lapps," Princeton, 1949.

Finland, "European Conference on Rural Life," League of Nations, Geneva, 1939.

Finland, "Overseas Economic Surveys," Board of Trade, London, 1949.

Finland Yearbook, Helsinki, 1947.

Freeman, T. W., and M. M. Macdonald, The Arctic Corridor of Finland, *S.G.M.,* LIV, 1938, 219–230.

Jackson, J. Hampden, "Finland," New York, 1949.

Kekoni, K., Ports of Finland, *E.G.,* VIII, 1932, 217–244.

Mead, W. R., Agriculture in Finland, *E.G.,* XV, 1939, 125–134, 217–239.

———, Finland and the Winter Freeze, *G.,* XXIV, 1939, 221–229.

———, The Finnish Outlook, East and West, *G.J.,* CXIII, 1949, 9–20.

———, The Cold Farm in Finland, *G.R.,* XLI, 1951, 529–543.

———, Finnish Karelia: An International Borderland, *G.J.,* CXVIII, 1952, 40–57.

———, Viipuri: Its Importance in the Political and Economic Geography of Finland, *S.G.M.,* LVII, 1941, 120–127.

Nordenskiold, E., Finland, the Land and the People, *G.R.,* VII, 1919, 361–376.

Van Cleef, E., "The Republic Farthest North," Columbus, Ohio, 1929.

———, Finland, Bridge to the Atlantic, *J.G.,* XLVIII, 1949, 99–105.

Wanklyn, H. G., "The Eastern Marchlands of Europe," London, 1941.

Wuorinen, John H., "Nationalism in Modern Finland," New York, 1931.

CHAPTER 8: *Denmark*

Denmark belongs geologically to the plain of north Germany, but from the point of view of history and culture Denmark is Scandinavian. The Danish peninsula stretches about 250 miles northward from the German coast, and all except the southernmost third belongs to the

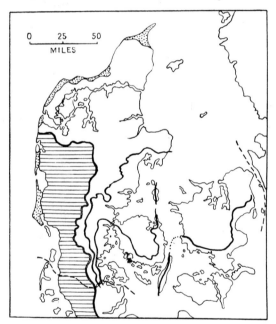

Fig. 38. The terminal moraine and the outwash area in Denmark. Solid black lines indicate terminal moraines; the shaded area is outwash; the dotted area, sand dunes.

kingdom of Denmark. East of the Danish peninsula and between it and the southern extremity of Sweden lies the Danish archipelago, a group of islands similar in relief and composition to the peninsula itself. Largest of these is Sjælland. Next in size comes Fyn (Fünen), then Lolland (Laaland) and Falster. Fyn is separated from the Danish peninsula, known as Jylland or Jutland, by the Little

Belt. This waterway narrows to only half a mile and is spanned by a rail and road bridge. The Great Belt, between Fyn and Sjælland, is at its narrowest 14 miles wide, and the only means of crossing it is by ferryboat. The Sound lies between Sjælland and Sweden. This is 3 miles wide at its narrowest point and is also crossed only by ferryboats.

Denmark is to a very large degree the creation of the Ice Age. During each of its major advances the ice sheet extended over the site of Denmark, but the last advance did not reach so far as its predecessors. The terminal moraine, which marked its maximum extent in north Germany, is continued northwestward through Mecklenburg and Holstein and then northward through Slesvig (Schleswig) and Jutland. The moraine forms the backbone of the Danish peninsula and, with its related drumlins, comprises the highest hills in the country. These glacial deposits were laid down upon a land that was built mainly of chalk. This is almost everywhere deeply covered, and its nature is known only through borings that have occasionally been put down. Here and there, however, this "solid" geology comes to the surface and a chalk cliff breaks the monotony of the generally flat and featureless coast of Denmark. On the basis of the glacial deposits Denmark can be divided into western Jutland, eastern Jutland, and the islands.

Western Jutland. The western half of the peninsula was covered only by the earlier glaciations. The moraines which were then laid down have been much eroded, and their remains have been surrounded and in part covered by the outwash of sand and gravel from the terminal moraine of the last glaciation. The

One of the older Danish farmsteads. Note the use of local materials in the timber frame and thatched roof. Compare with photograph on page 84. The picture was taken in Fyn. (*Royal Danish Ministry for Foreign Affairs.*)

surface of the land is undulating. There is marsh on the lower ground, and the higher consists generally of porous and infertile sand. Western Jutland is thus a relatively unproductive region. Its population is sparser than that in eastern Jutland and the islands; farming is less intensive; dairies less frequent. There are relatively large areas of heath and swampy moor. Villages are few and small, and settlements here are on the whole more recent than in other parts of Denmark. The only exceptions lie in the extreme north and extreme south. The limit of the last glaciation curved to the west, so that northwestern Denmark was included and is now largely covered with a clay loam. In the southwest, fen peat has accumulated, and this, together with the deposits of clay that formed here, gives this small region a very much greater productivity than the rest of the west coast, though much is too wet for crop farming and is under permanent grass.

Except in this southwestern area, the coast of Jutland has been smoothed by the current. Beach deposits have been drawn out into spits which partially or completely close the openings, and throughout its length the westerly winds have piled up a wide belt of sand dunes. Esbjerg (43,500), the only port on this coast, lies to the south of this belt of dunes and is protected by the sandy island of Fanö, which continues their direction southward. Esbjerg, established in the nineteenth century to handle the growing trade between Denmark and Britain, lies on one of the very few points along the coast where firm, dry land reaches right to the sea. Other towns in the region are few and small.

Eastern Jutland. This region is little different in relief from west, but the difference of soil has resulted in a different pattern of land use and a very much denser population. Within the limit of the terminal moraine is a hummocky area of ground moraine. The valleys are frequently marshy, and patches of infertile sand occur, but the region as a whole is covered with a productive clay or clay loam. In contrast to the western region the land here is almost wholly under the plow or used as permanent grazing. Villages are larger and more closely

One of the newer farmsteads in Sjælland (Zealand). (*Royal Danish Ministry for Foreign Affairs.*)

spaced. Dairies are more numerous, and there is a large number of small market towns. Western Jutland is exposed to westerly winds. It is a bleak and unfriendly region. Trees are few and frequently bent by the strength of the wind. Eastern Jutland has the luscious appearance of the English Midlands. Its small fields are surrounded by hedges, with hedgerow trees and small wood lots. The settlement pattern of Jutland as a whole has undergone a marked change in modern times. The earlier pattern was one of large and compact villages, each surrounded by its cultivated fields. In modern times settlement has become more dispersed. As land reform divided the open fields and allocated to each farmer a compact holding, he tended to leave the village and live in a separate farmstead on his land. The settlement pattern of Denmark is still in process of changing from one of large villages to one consisting mainly of scattered farms.

There are many small towns in eastern Denmark. With the exception of Aarhus (107,000) on the east coast and Aalborg (61,000) on the Lim Fiord, the largest has only about 30,000

inhabitants. They are market towns, and their primary purpose is to serve the requirements of the rural areas in which they lie.

The east coast of Jutland, in contrast to the west, is irregular in the extreme. The rise in sea level which has followed the retreat of the glaciers has drowned the coast, and there has been no strong current on this side, as there is on the west, to smooth out the irregularities. The deep inlets of the coast have low slopes, and at the heads of the larger are small ports, whose functions are now gradually passing to Copenhagen (København) and Esbjerg.

The climate of Jutland is similar in many respects to that of northern England but is less modified by the proximity of the Atlantic Ocean. Winters are a little more severe; summers a little hotter. The western coast is ice-free, but ice may form in winter over the sea between the islands of the archipelago. Denmark lies climatically on the borders of the region with a winter rainfall maximum and that with a summer maximum. Precipitation is well distributed and is over 20 inches in most places and sometimes over 30 inches.

The Danish Islands. These are, with the exception of Bornholm, composed entirely of ground moraine broken by the sinuous ridges of terminal moraine left by the ice sheet at various stages in its retreat. The soil is almost wholly composed of a clay loam. The landscape

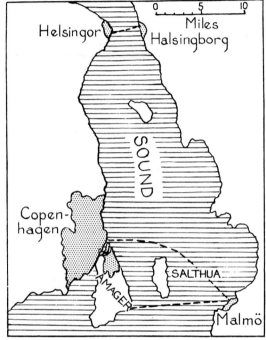

FIG. 39. Copenhagen and the Sound. The city is well placed to control the waterway and for many centuries was able to deny entrance to the Baltic to its enemies.

resembles that of eastern Jutland but is generally somewhat lower and less undulating. The islands of Sjælland, Fyn, Lolland, and Falster are almost wholly under cultivation. Their soil is among the most productive in Denmark and is mainly under crops. Wheat, barley, and sugar beet here take precedence over permanent grass.

The islands are irregular in shape and deeply indented. Fyn is linked with Jutland and Sjælland with Lolland, Falster, and Möen by bridges which carry generally both road and rail traffic. There are a number of small ports and market towns. The largest of these is Odense (92,500) in Fyn. The more easterly islands are dominated by Copenhagen, a city with a population, including suburbs, of 1,080,000. This is the only really large city in Denmark. It lies on the eastern shore of Sjælland, opposite Sweden. This unusual position for a capital city is to be explained in part in terms of the former extension of Denmark into the present territory of Sweden. A natural harbor was formed in the waterway which separated Sjælland from the small island of Amager, and the situation was one which commanded the Sound and the entrance to the Baltic. The prosperity of Copenhagen was firmly based in the Middle Ages on its control of Baltic shipping and on the trade of its merchants in the skins, furs, and metals of the Baltic region. Copenhagen still has an important entrepôt trade as well as handling a large part of the foreign trade of Denmark itself. Copenhagen handles much of the import trade in raw materials and has, partly as a result of this fact, built up a wide

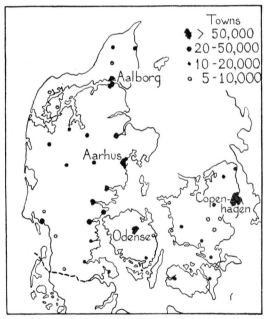

FIG. 40. Distribution of cities in Denmark.

range of manufacturing industries. It is by far the most important industrial center of Denmark and has engineering, pottery, chemical, textile, and foodstuff industries.

The island of Bornholm lies 120 miles to the east of Falster and closer to the Swedish than to the Danish coast. It differs from the rest of Denmark in being composed very largely of ancient granites, over which was spread only a thin and discontinuous layer of boulder clay. The island is devoted to agriculture except in the north, where rather rugged granitic uplands occur. The coasts are steep and straight and offer little refuge from the sea.

Copenhagen, general view of the city. (*Royal Danish Ministry for Foreign Affairs.*)

Problems of Economic Policy. Agriculture is the chief industry of Denmark, though the quality neither of the soil nor of the climate has greatly encouraged the developments which have taken place in recent years. An enlightened governmental policy encouraged Danish agriculture to break away from its medieval restrictions. Before the end of the eighteenth century most of the peasants owned compact holdings and enjoyed a security of tenure sufficient to encourage them to make improvements. The Danish government in the eighteenth century even planted trees as windbreaks in an attempt to cultivate and develop the exposed western coast of Jutland. During the nineteenth century

technical improvements were continually being made, but the basis of Danish agriculture continued to be the cultivation of grain. The change from a grain husbandry to a livestock husbandry came in the second half of the nineteenth century. The price of grain in the world market collapsed owing to the cheap import from the New World. Instead of protecting her agriculture by tariffs, Denmark introduced an intensive dairy farming, feeding the cattle on grain, roots, and other fodder crops grown in the country. Supplementary grain, purchased cheaply in the "new" countries, was admitted to feed the stock and, when they became available later, oilseed cake and other feeds were also imported.

The expansion of the Danish dairy industry was closely associated with the growth of the cooperative movement. During the last 20 years of the nineteenth century a large number of cooperative dairies was constructed and owned by the farmers themselves. Liquid milk was sent from each farm to its nearest dairy; the cream was separated, and skim milk returned to the farmer to be used as a pig feed. Pigs are also killed and cured at cooperative slaughterhouses. The farmer is freed from all obligations except that of rearing and tending his animals and growing fodder crops. The dairies are responsible for maintaining the quality of the product and for marketing it.

Crop farming is directed to producing fodder crops. Of these the most important in point of area are barley, oats, and root crops, which occupy together almost three-quarters of the cultivated area. Wheat is of some importance on the better soils, and rye is grown on the harsh soils of the west. In all respects the most valuable and the most intensively cultivated land consists of the islands and a narrow fringe along the east coast of Jutland from Randers southward to the German border. On the islands about half the total area is under cereals and a sixth under root crops. In eastern Jutland, the proportion under cereals diminishes somewhat and that under rotation and permanent grass increases. In western Denmark, grass covers up to half the total area and cereals are reduced to a third or even less.

The fisheries of Denmark, as of the other Scandinavian countries, are relatively important. Fishing is carried on in the inshore waters of the Skagerrak and Kattegat, as well as in the North Sea. Fish are landed at numerous small ports around the Danish coast.

Despite the predominance of agriculture, manufacturing industry is not unimportant and employs over a quarter of the working population. Shipbuilding, carried on in Copenhagen and Aarhus, is one of the most important. Fully a half of the ships built are on foreign account. Most are small, and many are driven by diesel engines, a form of power in the use of which the Danes have become highly skilled. Cotton and silk textiles are woven, chiefly for domestic use. There is a famous pottery at Copenhagen, and a small but important metallurgical and engineering industry, engaged chiefly in producing agricultural and dairy machinery.

The trade of Denmark is large in proportion to its population. Foremost amongst its imports are coal and liquid fuels. These are followed by iron and steel, both raw and manufactured, by machinery, and by grain and animal foodstuffs. The export trade is dominated by bacon, butter, cheese, and eggs. Before the Second World War animal products accounted for no less than about 70 per cent of the total exports. Denmark is always faced with the problem of securing a market for these commodities. Great Britain and Germany have been in the past the most important consumers of Danish produce, but Denmark cannot be certain that either will be as important in the future as they have been in the past.

Denmark, like all the Scandinavian countries, is concerned for its political independence. The military forces necessary to defend it would be far greater than the country could support. So it does not attempt to compete in armaments. Its army is small, and it hopes to protect itself by alliance with the North Atlantic Powers.

BIBLIOGRAPHY

Bergsmark, Daniel R., Agricultural Land Utilization in Denmark, *E.G.*, XI, 1935, 206–214.

"Conference on Rural Life: Denmark," League of Nations, Geneva, 1939.

"Géographie universelle," Vol. III, Etats scandinaves, Paris, 1933.

Hill, C. E., "The Danish Sound Dues and the Command of the Baltic," Durham, N.C., 1926.

Jensen, E., "Danish Agriculture: Its Economic Development," Copenhagen, 1937.

Jones, H., "Modern Denmark: Its Social, Economic and Agricultural Life," London, 1927.

Lamartine Yates, P., "Food Production in Western Europe," London, 1940.

Mead, W. R., Esbjerg, *E.G.*, XVI, 1940, 250-259.

———, Ribe, *E.G.*, XVII, 1941, 195–203.

———, Three City Ports of Denmark, *E.G.*, XVIII, 1942, 41–56.

Nielsen, N. (ed.), "Atlas of Denmark," Vol. I, Royal Danish Geographical Society, Copenhagen, 1949. (This Danish national atlas, which is in course of publication, is one of the finest works of its kind in Europe.)

"Northern Countries in World Economy," Copenhagen, 1937.

"Overseas Economic Surveys: Denmark," London, 1949.

Shaw, Earl B., Swine Industry of Denmark, *E.G.*, XIV, 1938, 23–37.

Woods, E. G., "The Baltic Region," London, 1932.

CHAPTER 9: *Western Europe*

Western Europe is less easy to define than northern. It embraces the British Isles and France. It is difficult to exclude Belgium, Luxembourg, and the Netherlands, but these are similar in the prevailing ways of life to the Rhineland, the Ruhr, and much of western Germany. Yet Germany as a whole cannot be considered as belonging to western Europe. If we consider in greater detail what characterizes the areas which are without dispute in western Europe, we may be able to define its limits more clearly.

From the physical point of view, western Europe is marked out by a varied terrain. There are no large, homogeneous regions, nothing resembling the prairies or the Russian steppes. The western European countries can be divided into small compartments, many of which can be crossed on foot in a day. Each has an individuality, and often each is more or less specialized in its productive activities. The French know these regions as *pays*. They have no generic name in Great Britain, but their reality is apparent to all who have studied the British Isles at first hand. Most of these small regions derive their individuality from their soil or relief. They may be on limestone or chalk or clay. The important feature is variety of resource and of environment within a small area.

Western Europe has a mild climate. Summers are cool, ranging in July from under 60° on the west coast of Ireland to over 70° except in the south of France. The winters are mild, over 40° in January on the west coast of France and the south and west of the British Isles. The range increases inland, but nowhere are summers really hot or winters cold. Rainfall is well distributed. The maximum comes in the winter months in regions closest to the ocean but moves to the summer as the borders of central Europe are approached. The rainfall is generally light, and torrential rains are rare. The atmosphere is humid. Fogs occur frequently, and the large number of factory towns, by pouring their smoke into the atmosphere, merely increase the liability to fog. All English towns have a reputation for fog that is not always deserved. Fog hampers navigation close to the shores of western Europe and holds up shipping in the estuaries and ports.

No place in western Europe is far from the sea. Marine influences go deep in the economic and social life. There are few people who are not familiar with the sea and its ways. The vacation is usually spent at the seaside. Tidal waterways reach far inland, ports are numerous and easily accessible, and sea-borne commerce is relatively very important. The sea which washes the shores of western Europe is tidal in greater or lesser degree. It sluices and cleanses the estuaries; it allows big ships to run with the tide far up the rivers to little ports many miles inland.

These physical characteristics are not confined to the countries listed in the first paragraph of this chapter. They are found also on parts of the Scandinavian coast, in northwestern Germany, and in northern Spain. Other qualities of western Europe will serve to define the region more closely.

Western Europe has a long tradition of civilization, of industry, and of urban life. This springs from its absorption into the Roman Empire. Gaul, or France, was conquered by Julius Caesar in the middle years of the first century B.C. He extended his frontier to the Rhine. Subsequent attempts by the Romans to advance farther to the east and to absorb western Germany into their Empire were defeated, and Roman civilization did not spread deeply into what we know as Germany. However, Julius Caesar led a brief raid into Britain, and this was followed up in A.D. 43 by a carefully planned conquest. The Roman conquest of Britain extended northward to the Scottish border. An invasion of Scotland was repulsed, and Ireland was left alone.

The Romans left over the area which they had conquered a legacy of good roads, of well-planned cities and a tradition of law, order, and good government. Throughout western Europe there are today the visible evidences of Roman occupation, from the south of France to the wall built by the Emperor Hadrian across the north of Britain to hold back the barbaric Picts and Scots. Much of the moral, as well as of the material, benefits of Roman civilization were lost, but western Europe retained through the Middle Ages and following centuries a distinct advantage over lands not favored by the civilizing hand of Rome.

This precocity of the west manifested itself during the Middle Ages in the development of trade and the revival of urban life. The spirit of nationality developed earlier in England, France, Switzerland, and the Netherlands than in lands lying farther to the east. A middle class, enterprising and commercially minded, arose, and the feudal structure of the Middle Ages yielded more rapidly in the west. Tradition lay less heavily on the agriculture and industry of the west. Change and technical progress opened the way to specialization and trade, and these to higher living standards.

Progress was far from regular or even. Some areas, particularly highland regions difficult of access, lagged behind. But over the good lands of England the open fields of medieval agriculture were giving place to enclosed. As early as the sixteenth century an English rhyming textbook on agriculture stated that:

"More profit is quieter found
    (where pastures in severall bee);
Of one seelie aker of ground
    Than champion maketh of three."

In the eighteenth century a four-course crop rotation was introduced. Animal breeding achieved great success, and sheep, cattle, and swine were bred for specific purposes, such as meat or milk or fleece. Agricultural reforms were also achieved early in Flanders and other parts of the Low Countries. They were slower to appear in France, and, except in the north, little progress was made before the French Revolution. But the agricultural progress of all western Europe was ahead of that of central and eastern.

It was the advance of western Europe in mechanical invention that was most marked. In most aspects of technology Great Britain was the most developed. Her wealth of easily worked coal, the existence of iron ore, and the great age of simple steelmaking practices gave Great Britain an advantage. Before the middle of the eighteenth century a form of steam engine had been invented and was applied to pumping water from the tin mines of Cornwall and the coal mines of the English Midlands. About the same time the process of making coke by heating coal and of using coke instead of charcoal in the blast furnace increased the scope of the iron industry. The puddling furnace for steelmaking was introduced toward the end of the century. The hot blast was introduced into the blast furnace. Crucible steel of high and uniform quality was invented and used for springs and the fine moving parts of machines. In the nineteenth century the Bessemer process for the large-scale and rapid manufacture of steel and the Thomas or basic process, which permitted phosphoric ores to be used, were all perfected in England and spread eastward through the continent of Europe.

In the sphere of textile manufacture, the west of Europe led the advance in technical progress. Improved spinning and weaving machines for cotton, wool, and silk; the stocking loom; and the Jacquard loom, which wove patterns into the cloth, were invented.

These developments in western Europe, and chiefly in Great Britain, brought specialization, trade, and wealth. They reacted upon other industries, encouraging the production of chemicals and dyestuffs. The growing industrial and urban population placed heavy demands on agriculture, which became increasingly efficient, while at the same time an even greater import of foodstuffs was necessary from overseas.

In the forefront of this industrial development stood Great Britain, but rivaling Great Britain were Belgium and France. Germany, which subsequently became the greatest industrial country of the continent of Europe, was later in developing. Its industry was organized on a craft basis well into the nineteenth century. King Frederick the Great of Prussia encouraged the development of the Silesian industrial area in the eighteenth century, but the Ruhr did not really develop until after 1850. Luxembourg and Lorraine did not become of great importance as iron and steel producers until the last two decades of the nineteenth century.

A large and specialized industrial output, combined with high standards of living, have made the nations of western Europe the most important in commerce of any. They have large merchant marines; their overseas trade developed early and led in turn to the foundation of colonial empires. Though the English have migrated in considerable numbers, this has not really been due, like, for example, the migration from Italy and the countries of eastern Europe, to overpopulation at home. The French, Belgians, and Dutch have emigrated and settled but to a small degree. The western European peoples have formed what the French call *colonies d'exploitation*, not *colonies de peuplement*, commercial colonies, not colonies for settlement. Uninterrupted access to raw materials and markets and secure control of the ocean routes have been their objects. The former Dutch empire of the East Indies and the late empire of Great Britain in India both sprang from semiprivate commercial undertakings, the Dutch and British East India Companies. Much of Britain's imperial activity in Africa was conducted under the guise of commercial companies, the British South African Company, the Royal Niger Company, and so on. The Belgian empire of the Congo was first the sphere of the semiprivate Congo Association.

The countries of western Europe owed their high living standards to this specialization and trade. Trade and markets were their lifeblood. By this means they built up overseas investments, the interest on which has helped very materially to balance their trade. They have merchant navies which carry their own exports and imports and earn foreign currency by carrying also for others. Great Britain, France, Belgium, and the Netherlands all earn considerable sums in this way. In the nineteenth century they could sell wherever they willed. In the twentieth they are finding increasing competition. Japanese and Indians, Brazilians and Russians have proved apt pupils, and they, too, look for the fruits of industrialization in better living standards and greater wealth. The competitive position of the west European countries has deteriorated, and two world wars within a generation have added to their difficulties. France, with a stronger agriculture and better economic balance, feels the difficulties least. Great Britain, which had given economic hostages as no other country had done, has been reduced to a serious economic predicament.

The west has lost its supremacy in the economics and politics of the world, but it cannot lose, except by the destruction of a third war, the advantages which it derives from its long cultural history. Those who succeed to the world position held by western Europe will, it is to be hoped, learn from it the art of living.

"Graecia capta ferum victorem cepit et artis intulit agresti Latio. . . ."[1]

Thus it seemed desirable to the author to draw the eastern limit of western Europe along the frontier of the Netherlands, Belgium, and France with Germany. Germany has the western qualities, though in a smaller degree, and eastern Germany can hardly be said to have them all. Switzerland bridges western and central Europe. Its possession of a large French minority, its political maturity, developed industry, and generally high standards of living separate it from its neighbor, Austria. It seemed desirable to conclude this section with Switzerland.

[1] Horace, "Epistles," Book II, No. 1. The lines may be translated: "Captive Greece captured her rough conqueror, and gave to Latium (Rome) her arts."

CHAPTER 10: *The British Isles*

The British Isles are a group of islands, two of them of considerable size, the rest small, lying close to the mainland of northwestern Europe. The total area is only about 120,000 square miles, less than that of New Mexico. The two major islands have an indented coastline, and many estuaries and bays carry the sea far into the land. No place is more than about 70 miles from the sea. In relation to the physical divisions of Europe outlined in the first chapter (pages 3 to 5), the British Isles embrace part of the low-lying plain of northern Europe and part of its highland margin to the northwest. Climatically the British Isles lie in the moist, cool, temperate area. Their temperature range is small. The winters are cool, though rarely cold, and summers are seldom hot. Rain occurs at all seasons and, except in the west, regularly amounts to more than 30 inches a year.

The most significant division of the British Isles is into a Highland and a Lowland Zone, the former being part of the mountainous region of the extreme northwest of Europe, the latter of the European Plain. The line of division between them extends from the coast of southwest England, near the mouth of the River Exe, northward to the northeast coast, near the mouth of the Tees. The line separates the southwestern peninsula and the whole of Wales from the English Plain, and the hills of northern England, the Pennines, and the whole of Scotland and Ireland lie on the highland side of the line (Fig. 41).

The *Highland Zone* is thus broken into four major divisions by the sea: the southwest, Wales, northern England and Scotland, and Ireland. All are composed in large measure of old, hard rocks, resistant to erosion and yielding only a shallow and often infertile soil. The rocks of the Highland Zone have, however, been exposed to erosion for a very long period of time. The hills are not high. Snowdon, the highest mountain in Wales, reaches only 3,560 feet. The hills of northern England are even lower, and in Scotland Ben Nevis is only 4,406 feet. The mountains of Ireland are not so high as those of Scotland. They all appear, however, to be higher and more impressive than they really are because they rise from near sea level and not from an area of plateau as do many of the higher mountains in North America.

During the long period of erosion to which this region has been subjected, valleys have been widened and gaps enlarged. The Highland Zone consists now rather of a large number of compact areas of hill, easily entered and yet more easily bypassed by the valleys and gaps that surround and penetrate them. Within the zone are extensive areas of lowland, such as the plain which occupies central Ireland and the Lowlands which separate the southern Uplands of Scotland from the Grampians. Anglesey, an island off the coast of Wales, is low and almost flat. Southwest England has few areas which are higher above sea level than the plains of Illinois.

All the Highland Zone, except southwest England and South Wales, was covered by the ice during the Ice Age (Fig. 2). The great ice sheet had the effect of smoothing and rounding the surface features of the land. In very few areas—chiefly in North Wales, the Grampians, and the northwest Highlands—has the ice fretted and etched the land into truly alpine forms, with steep precipices and sharp arêtes and peaks.

Fig. 41. Physical regions of the British Isles. The heavy black line marks the boundary of the Highland and Lowland Zones.

The *Lowland Zone*, by contrast, is built up of softer rocks. Limestone, sandstone, and clay alternate at the surface and are responsible for the major contrasts of relief in this subdued topography. Limestone extends from southwest to northeast across the plain, giving rise to the low, rounded hills of the limestone belt (Fig. 41). The chalk similarly produces an area of rolling hills. But the rest of Lowland England is a rich plain, sheltered, fertile, and densely peopled.

In the Midland Plain are several small areas of the harder rock which composes the Highland Zone, like islands of the older land surrounded by a sea of softer rocks. These "islands" are of no great altitude, but their different composition from that of the plain shows itself in their poorer soils and less well-developed agriculture.

The line which separates Highland from Lowland is not only important for the sharp break in the topography. It is a line along which coal measures occur. The geological deposits in which the seams of coal are found formerly extended over large parts of the Highland Zone but have been stripped away by erosion. Along the margins of the Highland Zone the coal measures have in parts been preserved, and, locally at least, they dip away underneath the Lowland Plain.

The British Isles lie in the moist, temperate region of northwest Europe. The main features of the climate have been reviewed (pages 15 to 22). The weather of the British Isles is changeable. Depressions move in from the Atlantic, bringing with them a sequence of weather types. The approach of the depression

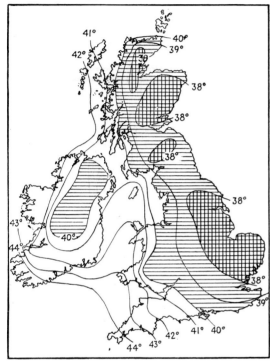

FIG. 42. Average temperature in the British Isles in January. Note the influence of the sea to the west in moderating the temperature.

is marked by southwest winds and mild, cloudy, and often wet conditions. As the depression passes, the wind changes to northwest, bringing cooler and drier conditions.[1] Despite the frequent changes in English weather, certain constant climatic characteristics may be noted.

Nowhere in the British Isles does the monthly average temperature exceed 65° or fall below 37°. Except on the high ground of the north, it is rare for the thermometer to remain below freezing point for more than a day or two. In winter the influence of the westerly winds is paramount. These have come directly off the warm waters of the Atlantic Ocean. The winter

[1] The sequence of weather types is fully considered in E. Gold, Aids to Forecasting, Air Ministry, Geographical Memoir 16, London, 1920.

isotherms tend to run, in consequence, from north to south (Fig. 42). The 40° isotherm runs close to and parallel with the west coast of Scotland, crosses Wales, and cuts off the southwestern peninsula. Lowest temperatures are experienced in the more easterly parts of the Scottish Highlands and in the eastern Midlands and East Anglia. In Ireland only in the center and northeast does the temperature fall below 40°. This mildness of the winters of western Britain has become almost proverbial, and the southwest of Ireland and Cornwall are well known for their almost subtropical vegetation.

In summer, on the other hand, the influence of direct insolation is more apparent (Fig. 43). Coastal areas are, in general, cooler than inland

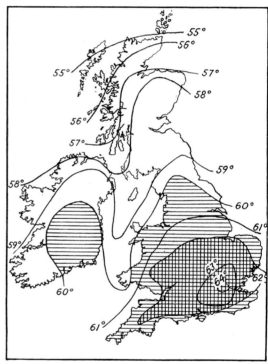

FIG. 43. Average temperature in the British Isles in July. The moderating effect of the ocean is very much less marked.

areas in the same latitude, but the south shows very much higher temperatures than the north. The greatest summer temperatures are usually recorded in the south Midlands and in the London area.

The rainfall of the British Isles derives from the sources that have already been considered (page 17). Rainfall is heaviest over the area which has been defined already as the Highland Zone (Fig. 44). A rainfall of over 80 inches

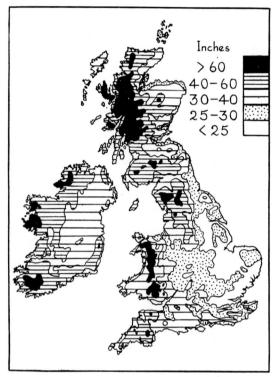

Fig. 44. Rainfall of the British Isles.

occurs in parts of this area, and most has over 40 inches a year. The precipitation diminishes in the central plain of Ireland and along the eastern coast of Scotland, where, locally, the fall is less than 25 inches. Over Lowland England, the rainfall is always under 40 inches and in much of the area under 30 inches. Humidity is generally high. This leads to the formation of fog. Fog forms in valleys on cool, still nights and in winter is likely to blanket cities and even counties and to bring movement almost to a stop. Sea fogs occur around the coast, with sometimes disastrous consequences for shipping.

With a relief as varied as that of the British Isles there are necessarily many local features and accidents of climate. These are now being studied as "microclimatology." In the still

conditions of anticyclonic weather, the cold night air concentrates in hollows and valleys, where fog and sometimes frost occur. It is usual not to plant tender crops, like the early potatoes of the southwest, in the bottoms of valleys. In such frost hollows night temperatures are sometimes recorded as low as those of a continental winter.

Rivers and the Sea. The heavy rainfall of the British Isles is carried to the sea by a multitude of rivers, few of them of a greater length than 50 miles, most of them so small as to be of no value for commercial navigation, almost all snaking their way through lush meadowland bordered by willows and serving at most to turn the mill wheel or to provide a harvest of trout. In parts of Scotland, the rivers descend from a greater height. They are swifter, cascading over rocks and babbling through shallows, clean and sparkling, while the rivers of the plain are heavy with the silt which they will lay upon the sea floor to build up new land.

Three rivers, each of considerable size by British standards, drain the Midlands. The Severn, after a circuitous course in Wales, turns eastward and then southward and finally westward to broaden into the Bristol Channel (Fig. 45). The second Midland river is the Trent, which rises in the southern valleys of the Pennines and receives tributaries from the Midlands before turning northward to mingle its waters with the Yorkshire rivers in the Humber. Lastly, the Thames flows from the Cotswolds, passing Oxford and the Chilterns, to London. The four "Wash" rivers, the Witham, Welland, Nen, and Great Ouse (so called to distinguish it from the Yorkshire and Sussex rivers), drain substantial areas of the east Midlands and discharge into the shallow and rapidly silting opening of the Wash. The east, the south, and the west are drained only by numerous short rivers. Much of the drainage of Wales is eastward by the Dee and Severn and then either southward to the Bristol Channel or northward to the Irish Sea. Only the Yorkshire Ouse has any pretensions to being an integrated and developed river system; it gathers together some half dozen Yorkshire rivers, which once had straight courses eastward to the sea, and discharges their waters into the Humber.

The rivers of the Scottish Highlands tend to follow the northeast to southwest grain of the

FIG. 45. Drainage basins of the rivers of England, Wales, and Scotland.

country. Only in the central Lowland area do these rivers assume any considerable size. The Tay and the Forth, which rise in the Highlands and flow southeastward into the Lowlands, are not long, but they are broad and navigable in their lower courses and thus of considerable economic importance. The Clyde, which discharges to the west, rises in the southern Uplands. The Scottish rivers are, with the exception of the three just mentioned, of negligible value

for navigation. They are potentially a source of hydroelectric power, and some have been dammed, and installations erected. But most are valued chiefly for the wild beauty of their valleys and the trout and salmon which live in their waters.

Ireland has one river of great length, the Shannon, the longest river in the British Isles (Fig. 46). This has gathered the drainage of most of the central plain. Only a few short rivers drain the mountain fringe.

No general review of the British Isles is complete without some reference to the British seas. The influence of the sea has been strongly marked in every aspect of British development. The sea has served "as a moat defensive to a house" to protect the British Isles from invasion. This added security has permitted a more gradual and continuous development of political and economic institutions than has occurred on

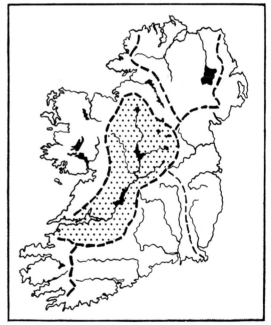

FIG. 46. Drainage basins of the Irish rivers. The basin of the river Shannon is stippled.

the continent of Europe. The proximity of the sea to every part has encouraged foreign trade. The estuaries of the rivers, running deep into the country, have permitted the growth of ports close to the inland centers of industrial activity.

Fig. 47. Britain and the British seas. Submarine depths are given in fathoms. The stippled area is shallow water. The chief fishing ports are named.

The sea provides the medium in which is carried on the fishing industry, one of the most significant from the point of view of both the numbers employed and its contribution to the nation's food supply. The sea, lastly, brings the warm North Atlantic Drift to warm the shores, to keep them free from ice, and to ameliorate the winds that blow eastward over Europe.

The North Sea is shallow. In its midst is the Dogger Bank, probably an accumulation of glacial material. Here fish breed in great numbers, and the shallow water provides conditions suitable for trawling, which is practiced from the east coast ports of Hull and Grimsby. The North Channel, Irish Sea, and St. George's Channel, which separate England and Wales from Ireland, are narrower and deeper. Their floor is more uneven, and fishing less important.

From 50 to 100 miles west of Ireland and north-west Scotland, the Continental Shelf ends; the sea floor steepens and sinks gently to the deep-sea floor of the North Atlantic.

All parts of the British coast are tidal (see page 13). The tidal range is as much as 40 feet in the Severn. The sea level rises and falls twice in a day but at Southampton is a complex double tide which has facilitated the movement of great liners in and out of this port. The tide ran formerly a considerable distance up each river, but its progress is now checked by a lock some distance above the mouth. The tidal movement is sufficient to keep the estuaries of rivers fairly clear of sediment. Silting nevertheless occurs along the coast of the Thames, Severn, and Humber estuaries and of the Wash, the joint estuary of a number of east Midland rivers, and here the land is gaining slowly at the expense of the sea. In most other places, however, the sea is battering the cliffs and slowly eating into the land. The losses on the coasts of East Anglia and of Yorkshire have been quite spectacular within historical times.

HIGHLAND ZONE[1]

Scotland. Scotland belongs wholly to the Highland Zone. It is, compared with England, a rough, sterile region, much of it thinly populated. The country consists of a mountainous region, occupying over a half of the total area, known as the "Highlands." South of this is an east-west belt of lower land, commonly called the central Lowlands, and south of this again another region of higher elevation and rougher terrain, known as the "southern Uplands."

Off the west and north coasts are a number of island groups, the Shetlands, Orkneys, and Outer Hebrides. They are complex and irregular in their geographical pattern (Fig. 48). The land surface is generally low and undulating. Areas of bare or almost bare rock alternate with glacial deposits and peat bogs. Isolated and steep-sided hills are all that remain of former mountains. The winds are strong and exercise a predominating influence on the location of settlement, and trees are rare except in sheltered hollows. Rainfall is heavy, and the soil acid and infertile. A small and now steadily diminishing population scrapes out a meager existence, growing potatoes, oats, and other hardy crops; fishing; and spinning and weaving the wool of the local sheep into the heavy tweed cloth.

The Shetlands are the most exposed and most northerly group. Here and in the Orkney Islands, which lie within sight of the Scottish coast, there is a strong Scandinavian influence, both in the physical make-up of the people and in their folklore and tradition. The Orkney Islands derive some importance from the fact that Scapa Flow, a stretch of sea almost com-

[1] The population of all cities of over 100,000 inhabitants is given. All cities of this size are named except the London boroughs (see Fig. 70). In Eire, where only Dublin exceeds this size, the population is also given of cities of over 50,000.

pletely surrounded by the islands of the Orkney group, has for many years been used as a base by the Royal Navy. Lewis, with its southern extension Harris, is the largest island of the Outer Hebrides. Its chief town, Stornoway, is a small fishing port.

Fig. 48. Physical regions of Scotland.

The extreme north of the Highlands is a high, rather monotonous, and generally wind-swept and treeless plateau which drops slightly toward the north and ends in cliffs of the greatest scenic beauty. Population is sparse; Wick and Thurso are small fishing ports. Agriculture is limited to simple pastoralism.

The Highlands of Scotland are divided into a northwestern region and a southeastern, the latter known as the Grampians, by Glen More, a rift valley which stretches from sea to sea. The northwestern Highlands are more rugged and wetter than the Grampians. Their valleys are steep and narrow, dropping westward to the long sea lochs of the Atlantic Coast. The population is very thin, and roads are bad, but tourists continue to be attracted by the wild beauty and the romantic associations of this coast. They come "By Tummel and Loch Rannoch and Lochaber" and cross "over the sea to Skye." Skye is the largest and one of the most rugged and beautiful of the islands lying close to the Scottish coast. Its mountains of red

The Caledonian Canal. The canal joins the several long, narrow lakes which occupy the Great Glen. The original purpose of the canal was to avoid the stormy and dangerous voyage around the north of Scotland, but it is now chiefly used by very small craft and by pleasure cruises.

gabbro are a paradise for climbers and provide some of the most entrancing scenery to be found in Europe. Few among those who know the northwest would be unwilling to take the risk of cloud, mist, and rain for the sake of the few days of rare beauty which it offers.

Glen More contains the two narrow lakes Lochs Ness and Lochy, whose altitude is only a few feet above sea level. The Caledonian Canal was cut to join them with each other and with the sea at each end and thus to provide a ship canal from Inverness to Fort William. It is now chiefly used by pleasure craft that bring holidaymakers from Glasgow and other large cities.

The Grampians are more massive but at the same time more gentle than the northwest Highlands. Relief is strongest in the west, where, as in the northwest, there are many deep sea lochs. Toward the east the landscape assumes a

more uniform aspect. The mountains, especially the Cairngorms, tend to be flat-topped, and the whole area has the appearance of a plateau in which the work of dissection by ice has made much less progress than farther west. It is possible that the mountain snow and ice fields received more sustenance in the west from moisture-laden winds than in the east and thus became more active as agents of erosion. The rivers Garry and Spey, the latter flowing to the north, the former southward to the Tay, have together carved an easy route through the mountains by way of the pass of Drumochter, which is used by the chief rail and road routes into the Highlands. A number of power installations have been erected at Glen Nevis, Kinlochleven, and Glen Tummel, and others are projected, both here and in the northwestern Highlands. For a long period now the population has been declining. In the Glens one finds only the ruins of the primitive crofts of the clansmen. The clans, the old tribal organization, are broken and dispersed, and their colored tartans, once hand-woven in their cottages, are now made in Lowland factories. Life was always hard in the Highlands; the climate severe, the soil poor and infertile, and the amenities of life were possible only for the few who could afford to purchase and bring them from a distance. When opportunity arose, the Highlanders drifted away to the factories of the Lowlands. The glens may be deserted, and the moors turned into deer "forest" and grouse moor, but Highland culture survives. Emigrant Scots, from Canada to New Zealand, retain their identity, wear their costume, practice their ancient dances, and hold their old festivals. Foremost among the cultural traits that survive in the Highlands is the Scottish language—Gaelic—which is spoken by some people in the northwest and in the islands.

On the east and north the Grampians drop gradually to an undulating belt of lowland, which begins near Stonehaven, widens into the plateau of Buchan, and again narrows. It lies in the rain shadow of the Highlands. Its temperatures are low at all seasons, and it is suited best for grazing and producing fodder crops. This has come to be a famous cattle-rearing

Dundee and the Firth of Tay. The city lies between the Sidlaw Hills and the coast. The factories seen in this picture are chiefly engaged in the manufacture of jute. The railway bridge across the Firth replaces that destroyed in the storm of 1879 and carries the main line to Edinburgh and London. (*British Information Services.*)

area, as the Aberdeen-Angus breed serves to show. A number of small towns lie along the coast, from which the fishing industry is carried on. Inverness is a route center for the northwest Highlands. Aberdeen (189,500) plays the similar role of local capital for the Grampians and east coast region.

The Scottish Lowlands form a belt up to 50 miles wide and bounded by faults. Between the faults, rocks of a younger geological age than those which appear in the hills to north and south have been preserved. These include the coal measures, which have here been folded to form three distinct basins.

The Ayrshire coal field lies near the west coast. It covers a large area but is not really of great importance, as its reserves of coal are small. A number of industrial towns have grown up on the field. The Lanarkshire coal field is the largest in its resources. It stretches from the Firth of Clyde to the Firth of Forth, and its presence has given rise to a large and varied industrial growth, which long since overflowed

the boundaries of the coal field. Miscellaneous iron and steel industries are practiced. On its margin are the cotton textile centers of Paisley (96,500) and Motherwell (70,500), and along the banks of the Clyde is the largest center of the shipbuilding industry in the British Isles. The Midlothian-Fifeshire field is small in area and divided by the Firth of Forth, here some 10 miles wide. This field has larger reserves than the others but has not yet attracted the industrial development which characterizes the other coal fields.

The economic and social life of the central Lowlands is dominated by two cities, Edinburgh and Glasgow. Edinburgh (489,000) is the titular capital of Scotland. It lies close to the south shore of the Firth of Forth and grew around a nucleus provided by a castle built upon an isolated volcanic plug. It has become a cultural and artistic center. It has many relics of Scotland's past, and the modern city is strikingly beautiful and well laid out. Glasgow (1,099,500) is a port. It has developed industries based upon its import of colonial goods and has added the building of warships and liners in the yards along the Clyde below the city. Greenock (79,000), near the mouth of the Clyde, is also a port and industrial city. There are a number of other centers of industrial activity: Dundee (81,000), on the northern shore of the Tay, is the seat of the jute industry; Kirkcaldy of linoleum.

The rocks of the Lowlands have been intruded by granite and similar igneous rocks, which have in turn been eroded into a line of hills, stretching from northeast to southwest. The towns of Perth, Stirling, and Dumbarton are set in the river gaps between them, as if to protect the Lowlands from incursions of Highland raiders.

The central Lowlands contain today the bulk of the population of Scotland, all its large cities, and most of its industrial activities. Neither the Highlands nor the Uplands, which lie to the south, can offer any important industrial resource except hydroelectric power, and movement in these hilly districts is difficult. The central Lowlands contain also the most extensive area of agricultural land in Scotland. The climate is cool and moist; the latitude is that of the Alaskan "Panhandle." Wheat is little grown, but oats, barley, and potatoes are important, and cattle rearing is practiced. Both the Ayrshire and the Aberdeen-Angus cattle originated in Scotland.

The southern Uplands and the Cheviot Hills are a broad upland region. The aspect of the country is more gentle than that of the Highlands. The hills are rounded and grass-covered. The valleys are broader, their sides less steep, and they open out in the southwestern district of Galloway and in the Tweed Valley into extensive areas of low, rich, and undulating agricultural country. The Uplands have been chiefly important for their sheep, which formerly nourished the tweed industry. The industry survives in the factories of Galashiels, Peebles, and Kelso, but it is now supplied with wool from overseas. The Merse, with lower altitude and lower rainfall than most of the region, is an agricultural region; the wetter, more westerly lowlands of Galloway are more

important as dairy and stock-rearing land. Stranraer in the southwest is the packet station on the shortest crossing to Ireland. The distance is 35 miles to Larne, near Belfast.

Scotland is part of the United Kingdom, as it has been since the Parliamentary Union of 1707. Scotland's population is only about 5,207,000, as against 43,595,000 in England and Wales in 1949. On the whole Scotland's population is poorer than that of England, which is not surprising in view of the conditions in which much of its agriculture is carried on. There has been a steady efflux of Scotsmen not only to England but to other parts of the Commonwealth and Empire, where their hardiness, frugality, and industry have enabled them to prosper. Scotland has become anglicized in many ways without losing its distinctive character. The Scottish language, Gaelic, has disappeared from the Lowlands, and there is little difference between the Scottish cities and the English.

Many Scots resent this assimilation of Scotland by England, and a small minority noisily demand home rule or independence. There is a minister in the British government specially charged with the supervision of Scottish affairs, but it is unlikely that complete independence would be desirable or practicable for either country.

Northern England. The Pennines form a north-to-south ridge, composed mainly of limestone. Geologically it is a domelike uplift. A hard sandstone, known from an earlier use to which it was put as "millstone grit," and coal measures occur along the flanks of the range and dip away both eastward and westward beneath younger and softer rocks (Fig. 49). The limestone surface of the Pennines is dry and has a cover of short grass, once grazed by numberless sheep. The millstone grit by contrast produces a soil that is sour and often waterlogged. Neither is of much value for crop husbandry, though grazing was formerly important. Lead and zinc were once mined from the Pennines, but the reserves are small, and this industry is now almost extinct. One of the most valuable uses to which the Pennines are now put is the catch-

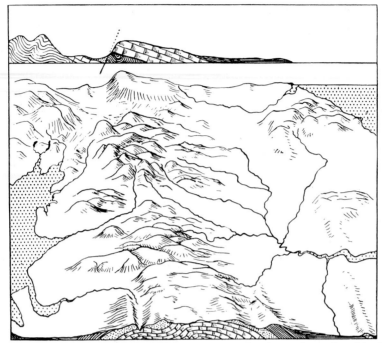

FIG. 49. Diagrammatic sketch looking north along the Pennine range. On the northern edge of the diagram the rocks of the Pennines are shown overlying the older rocks of the Lake District.

ment of water which is held in many reservoirs along their margin to supply nearby industrial cities.

The coal field is almost continuous along the eastern flank of the Pennines, though less so on the west. The Pennines are penetrated by wide, open river gaps, the Tyne Gap in the north, the Tees Gap, and the Aire Gap. These were formerly important in guiding movement and transportation. Castles were erected during the Middle Ages to control these gaps, but so many roads and railroads have been built over and through the Pennines that these gaps are no longer of importance. In the "Dales" of the northern Pennines and again in the Peak District in the south, the limestone moors have been much eroded and form regions of great beauty and attraction to tourists. This is particularly fortunate, because only a few miles to east and west are the industrial regions of northern England. The moors serve as "lungs" to the soot-blackened industrial cities.

Lying to the west of the northern Pennines is the so-called Lake District, a small, rounded area of ancient rock and strong relief that has come to be one of the most frequented of the resort areas of the British Isles. Long, narrow lakes of glacial origin lie in a radial pattern, pointing outward from the high central core of the area. Surrounding the Lake District is a narrow band of agricultural land. It is cool and damp and devoted more to pastoral than to crop husbandry. Sheep and cattle of the lowland farms often summer in the mountains of the Lake District. North of the Lake District, the deep inlet of the sea known as Solway Firth extends inland close to the Pennines. Road and rail are obliged to pass round its head, where has grown up the great route center of Carlisle, once a fortress protecting the way into England from the north, now a railway junction and industrial city.

Four of the most significant industrial regions of England have grown up along the flanks of the Pennine uplift, based upon the resources of coal that are to be had. East of the northern Pennines, the coal measures stretch out to the sea. Even in the Middle Ages coal was cut from the cliffs and exported. The port of Newcastle-on-Tyne (294,500), lying 8 miles up the river Tyne from the sea, handled much of the coal export. "Sea" coal was taken to London and other ports, and to "carry coals to Newcastle" entered into the English language. The earliest

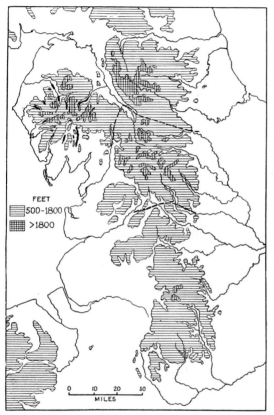

FIG. 50. Regional divisions of the Pennine range and of the Lake District. The broken line separates the Lake District and the northern, central, and southern Pennines.

coal workings were open cuts on the coast or valley sides. The first deep mines were sunk toward the west of the coal field, where the coal measures rise to the surface, and the oldest centers of industry were established here. With the gradual exhaustion of mines on this side, mining progressed to the east, and much of the mining is again near the coast. This field normally produces over 45 million tons a year.

Heavy industry is now chiefly located close to the tide-way, though a few inland works are still active. The lower course of the river Tyne, from Newcastle to the sea, is lined with ship-

building yards and factories. Opposite Newcastle is Gateshead (115,000), and at the mouth of the Tyne is South Shields (109,000). The Tyne is, after the Clyde, the most important shipbuilding area but, partly because the river is narrower, specializes in smaller craft. At the mouth of the river Wear is Sunderland (181,-000), iron- and steel-manufacturing center. On the estuary of the Tees are both Middlesbrough (146,000) and the Hartlepools. These lie within a short distance of the coal field, while to the south are the Cleveland Hills, from which bedded iron ore is obtained. The Cleveland ore formed the base upon which the steel industry of the northwest was built but is now being

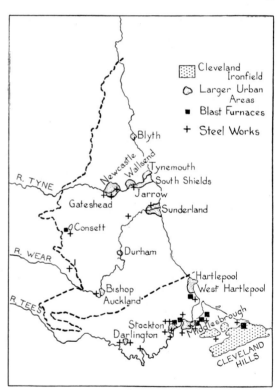

FIG. 51. The industrial region of northeast England. The broken line is the boundary of the coal field.

supplemented by import, chiefly from Sweden. The furnaces are located along the water front, in situations that in some respects resemble that of the Gary–South Chicago steel mills. The chemical industry has also grown to be important in this area, and at Billingham are the only significant works for the production of oil and gasoline from coal.

The Cumberland coal field occurs to the west, between the hills of the Lake District and the sea. Its output is small, less than 2 million tons annually, though its coastal location has given it a certain importance in the coal export. Iron- and steelworks are located here, and a small but now rather old and congested industrial region has grown up around the cities of Whitehaven and Workington. Iron ore of a high quality is obtained in the vicinity. A few miles to the south is Barrow-in-Furness, a city with engineering and shipbuilding industries.

Far greater importance attaches to the coal fields and industrial regions of Lancashire and Yorkshire. These lie on opposite flanks of the Pennines, and each has coal measures coming to the surface on the edge of the hills and dipping westward in Lancashire and eastward in Yorkshire beneath the younger rocks. In each, as in the northeast, mining was first carried on along the outcrop, but new mines are being sunk into the "hidden" coal field.

Little manufacturing industry was carried on in Lancashire before the establishment here in the eighteenth century of the cotton textile industry. The location of this industry in Lancashire is not easily explained. The region had no conspicuous advantages which other parts of England could not offer in a similar degree. Considerable opposition to the introduction of the cotton industry was raised, however, by the woolen industrialists, and Lancashire was an area where the influence of the latter was comparatively weak. As the industry developed, other advantages, not at first apparent, manifested themselves: the water power of the Pennine valleys, the coal of the Lancashire coal field, the port of Liverpool, and the Mersey estuary. The industry is divided geographically into a spinning, a weaving, and a finishing area, a division which derives from the earliest phases of the industry. The raw cotton is now largely imported through Liverpool (804,000); some passes up the ship canal to Manchester. Spinning is carried on in a semicircle of towns to the north and east of Manchester, from Bolton (169,000) through Bury, Rochdale, and Oldham (120,000), to Stockport (141,500). The weaving of the yarn into cloth is carried on in a group of towns lying to the north of the Rossendale Forest, a westward extension of the Pennines. The larger are Nelson, Colne, Burnley, Accrington, Blackburn (111,500), and Preston (120,000). The largest

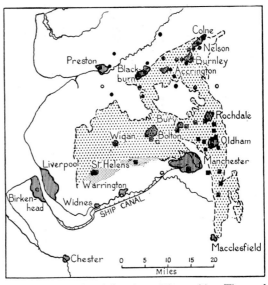

FIG. 52. The industrial region of Lancashire. The coal field is dotted. To the south it dips steeply beneath younger deposits. The small black squares indicate the position of groups of spinning mills; the small black circles, of weaving mills.

centers of cloth finishing are in or close to Manchester. The Lancashire cotton industry remains today of great international importance, though the rise of cotton manufacturers in other countries has greatly reduced the volume of exports since about 1914.

The industries of Lancashire are by no means limited to the manufacture of textiles. The availability of coal, the relatively easy means of communication, and the large local market encouraged the growth of iron- and steel-using industries. This is not a smelting area, but iron tubes, wire, and similar goods are made at Warrington, Runcorn, and other towns. The chemical industry, particularly in Wigan and St. Helens (112,000), has achieved an importance due partly to the local supplies of coal and

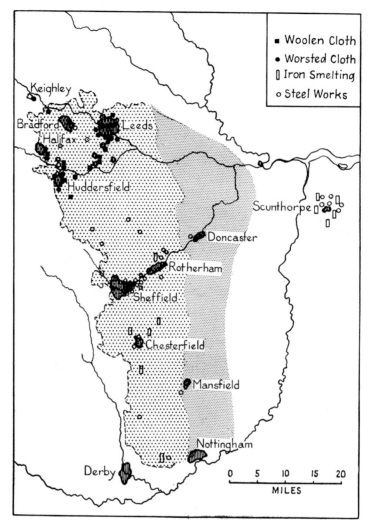

FIG. 53. The industrial region of Yorkshire. The exposed coal field is shown by coarse dots; the hidden, by fine.

salt, partly to the local demand for bleachers and dyestuffs.

Manchester (703,500) is the business and commercial center of the region. It lies just off the coal field. It had been the site of a Roman camp but throughout the Middle Ages was no more than a village in one of the most backward and least populous of counties. Its rise dates from the establishment here of the cotton textile industry. In the nineteenth century it grew fast. Its growth was unplanned, and it is today one of the least attractive of the creations of the Industrial Revolution. Close to Manchester is Salford (179,000). Liverpool, 30 miles

to the west, is the port for the Lancashire industrial area. It was of some small importance before the industrial age as a port of embarkation for Ireland but grew to be the second port in the British Isles only with the rise of northern industries. The broad Mersey estuary provides a sheltered waterway, along whose flat and marshy shores dock basins, warehouses, wharves, and railway yards could be built. On the west bank of the Mersey estuary are the industrial cities of Birkenhead (141,500) and Wallasey (101,500). The Manchester Ship Canal takes ocean-going vessels with their cargoes into Manchester, and a smaller canal stretches southeastward to the Midlands and to the region of Stoke-on-Trent.

The city of Stoke-on-Trent (275,000) lies on the small coal field of North Staffordshire, which is, in effect, a southward continuation of that of Lancashire. This small area has acquired a distinctive character and a world-wide reputation as the center of the English pottery manufacture. Its dominant industry derives from the fact that the eighteenth-century potter Josiah Wedgwood lived and worked here rather than from any conspicuous natural advantage. The area had coal and clay, though the materials of which pottery is made, china clay, barytes, and bone, are now largely imported. The city is dotted with the smoking beehive ovens in which the ware is baked; Stoke is inconceivable without its ovens. Every activity is dominated by the processing of clay. The atmosphere of this region is conveyed in the "regional" novels of Arnold Bennett, some of which give a profound study of life in the "Potteries."

On the eastern flank of the Pennines is a coal field which occupies part of the West Riding[1] of Yorkshire. The industry of Yorkshire is as firmly based on the manufacture of woolen cloth as that of Lancashire is on cotton. The woolen-cloth industry is much older than the cotton. When the traveler Defoe visited the region early in the eighteenth century, he found many small woolen mills strung along the small Pennine streams which provided water power. Yorkshire concentrated on the manufacture of the cheaper fabrics, for which in the eighteenth and nineteenth centuries the market was expanding the most rapidly. Older centers, like the southwest of England and East Anglia, declined in importance. When steam power was applied to cloth manufacture, Yorkshire was able to profit, and the industry grew steadily in size and importance. Local supplies of wool from the flocks of the Pennines and of the limestone hills of southern England proved inadequate at an early date and were supplemented by imports from Australia and other parts of the world.

[1] Riding, originally Trithing, is one of the threefold divisions of Yorkshire.

There is no distinction in the West Riding between the centers engaged in spinning and in weaving, nor is the manufacture of woolen cloth, worsted, and shoddy (an inferior fabric made from reused wool and the combings from better yarn) clearly distinguished. Leeds (507,500) is the focus of these industries. It is not primarily a clothmaking town, any more than Manchester is engaged directly in the cotton industry. It is rather a great cloth user, manufacturing ready-made clothing and similar goods, and is the business and commercial center of the region. Huddersfield (128,500) is the chief of several cities engaged in the manufacture of woolens; Bradford (292,500) and Halifax (292,-500) in that of worsted.

The woolen industry is concentrated in the valleys of the Aire and Calder. To the south, in the Don Valley, is the Yorkshire steel industry. This, like many others, developed upon the basis of local iron ore and charcoal from nearby forests. The substitution of imported ore and coke from the local coal came gradually. With these changes, however, the industry developed into one of the largest in Europe. Little smelting is now carried on here; pig iron is brought into the region from such smelting centers as Middlesbrough. Sheffield (514,500) retains the high reputation which it built up in the nineteenth century for the quality of its steel. The city lies in a narrow valley of the Pennines, but modern development has spread eastward on to the plain, where the steel-manufacturing towns of Rotherham and Doncaster have grown up.

The West Yorkshire industrial region is served primarily by the Humber ports of Goole and Hull (Kingston-upon-Hull, 298,000). The Pennines are, however, no serious barrier to communications, and the west coast port of Liverpool is also used. Canals and canalized rivers link West Yorkshire with the Humber, but the inland waterways are narrow and not of great importance.

The coal field of the West Riding is continued southward into Nottinghamshire but ceases to bear any large industrial concentration. Coal mining is carried on in villages rather than towns. Chesterfield, Mansfield, and Worksop have metallurgical industries, but manufacturing industries here are neither highly specialized nor geographically concentrated. Nottingham (303,500), formerly a center of the lace industry, is now important for hosiery, the raw materials

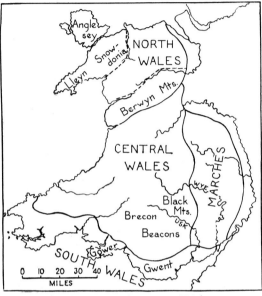

FIG. 54. Physical regions of Wales.

of which, cotton and woolen yarn, are obtained, respectively, from Lancashire and Yorkshire. The output of the whole coal field is generally about 70 million tons annually. It is thus the most productive in the United Kingdom.

Derby (143,000), located on one of the main railroads from London to the north, was adopted as a center of the railway engineering industry, and to this has been added more recently the important motor and airplane engineering industry of Rolls-Royce.

These great industrial cities lie close to the Pennines, overshadowed in some instances by the moors, in others, wrapped around by hills. To east and west is lower land. The plain of Lancashire is low lying and almost flat. Some is reclaimed marsh, and most of it is now intensively cultivated to supply the industrial cities with milk and vegetables. Along the coast are resorts, of which Blackpool (148,000) is the largest, where millworkers find relaxation. East

of the Pennines is the low, fertile valley of the Trent. Beyond this are low, swelling hills and rich farmland (see page 113) and then the coast of the North Sea.

Most of northern England is part of the Highland Zone. It has a character quite different from that of Midland or southern England. Its people are industrious, independent, grasping, even pugnacious. Southerners would describe the north as more raw and less civilized; certainly it lacks the ease and charm of the south. Its landscape has a darker and more rugged character. In literary terms, it differs from the south as the novels of the Pennine-born Brontë sisters differ from those of Wessex-born Thomas Hardy. The north is highly industrialized but has only a narrow range of industry: cotton and wool, iron and steel, and shipbuilding. When an economic depression strikes the north, it hits hard; the south, more diversified and more agricultural, takes the blow more easily. The north had "depressed" areas in the 1930's; not the south.

Carnarvon Castle. This castle was built by the English at the end of the thirteenth century. It lies on the coast of North Wales and was one of a group designed to enclose the mountains of North Wales, a center of Welsh resistance to the English. The small town of Carnarvon has grown up beneath the walls of the castle.

Wales. Wales has an individuality as strongly marked as northern England. Like the rest of the Highland Zone it is built of old, hard rocks; it has thin, poor soils, a wet climate, and a poorly developed agriculture. Like the Scottish Highlands, those of Wales have lost people by

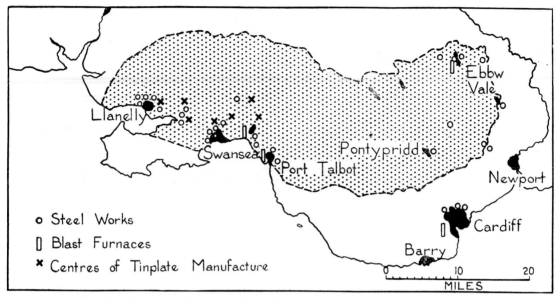

Fig. 55. The industrial region of South Wales. The area of the coal field is stippled.

migration in modern times. Along the border between Wales and England are the Marches, a beautiful region of hills and broad green valleys, where the mountains sink to the English Plain. Its border position between Wales and England made it once a very unsettled region. It is strewn with the remains of the castles of the "Marcher Lords," commissioned to hold back the Welsh who, from the austerity of their hills, loved to raid the "fat and fertile plain." Chester (once a Roman fortress), Shrewsbury, Ludlow, and Hereford are the cities of the Marches, now sleepy market towns; their castles and walls in ruins.

The Marches are a cattle-rearing, dairy-farming region which makes Cheshire cheese and breeds white-faced Hereford cattle. The region is protected by the hills from westerly winds and is drier and more sunny than the rest of Wales. Fruit and hops grow in the vale of Hereford and over the plain of Shrewsbury. It is a region of large farms; compact, brightly colored villages; and small market towns.

North Wales is the most mountainous part. The mountains of Snowdonia rise abruptly from a narrow coastal plain, and the summit of Snowdon, the highest mountain in England and Wales, is within 10 miles of the sea. The Snow-

don mass is a small but rugged area and attracts many climbers and others who wish to pass a vacation walking over its grassy slopes or climbing over its crags. They drop away to the west into the hummocky lowland of the Lleyn peninsula. Along the coast are resorts, and off the coast, separated from the mainland only by the narrow Menai Strait, is the island of Anglesey. This is a gentle, rolling area of green meadows, dairy farms, and villages.

North Wales and Anglesey have been a kind of stronghold of Welsh nationalism. The Welsh language survives in these hills; it is normally spoken in the home, though all who have to deal with tourists speak English. Welsh nationalism is fully as vociferous as Scottish, but no more effective. Welshmen often complain that their interests are neglected, but it is very doubtful whether an independent Wales would be politically and economically any more practicable than an independent Scotland.

The whole of Central Wales is a rolling upland or plateau. The valleys are wider and more open than those of North Wales. The hills are more rounded, and in every way the work of ice is less conspicuous. Agriculture, including the production of grain crops, is carried on in the valleys, and sheep and cattle are grazed over the

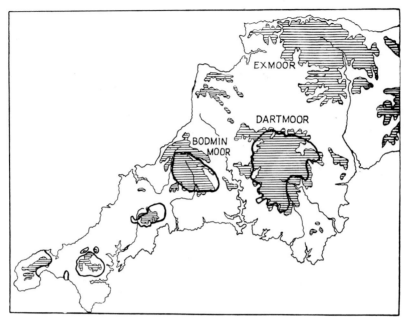

FIG. 56. Southwest England. Areas over 600 feet above sea level are shaded. The heavy line indicates the margin of the granite areas.

hills. Central Wales is easily penetrated by the broad valleys of the Dee, Severn, Wye, and Usk, which open out toward the English Plain. The English have penetrated the country by these routes, isolating North Wales. Central Wales is oriented toward the English Plain, not toward either North or South Wales.

A coal basin occupies part of South Wales, and its existence has given rise to an industrial region of great importance. The coal field reaches from near Newport and Cardiff (244,500) in the east to Swansea (161,000) and Llanelly in the west. On its northern edge the coal seams rise to the surface within the limits of the hills. Long, narrow valleys open southward, and along their bottoms are mines and mining villages. Smoke from the mines hangs in these narrow valleys and stains all buildings a dark-gray hue. The steel industry grew up here, as iron ore was obtained from the coal measures. Towns like Rhondda (112,500), Dowlais, Trede-gar, and Merthyr Tydfil developed on the basis of local coal and iron. But local ores have been almost exhausted. Ore from Spain and other countries is imported, and the iron-smelting and steelmaking industry has moved to the coast.

The inland centers are "depressed" and have been unable to develop new industries to replace the metallurgical. Most of the iron and steel plants are now near the coast, and a huge new works is being built near Port Talbot. A particu-larly important branch of the metal industry is the rolling of fine steel sheet and coating it with a thin covering of tin. The production of tin plate was probably encouraged by the fact that tin could formerly be obtained from the mines of Cornwall. This source of supply has been replaced by imports from Malaya.

The coal of the South Wales field includes the only really important British reserve of an-thracite and hard steam coal, suitable for ships' bunkers. It was formerly exported from the Welsh ports to ships' coaling stations throughout the world. In recent years the British coal export has declined very seriously (see page 130), though the South Wales production is still over 40 million tons a year. Cardiff (244,-500) focuses the activities of the eastern part of the coal field. It lies opposite the entrance to several mining valleys. It is a port handling coal, pit props, iron goods, and ore and has had a varied industrial development. Newport,

(106,000) at the mouth of the river Usk, is smaller. Swansea (161,000), also on the coast and having extensive docking facilities, similarly concentrates the activities of the western part of the coal field. Llanelly, Neath, and Port Talbot are chiefly engaged in iron, steel, and tin-plate manufacture.

South and west of the industrialized region of the coal field are small areas of rural and agricultural country. The vale of Glamorgan, to the south, is rich grazing land of the highest importance in supplying the nearby cities with milk. To the west is the low plateau which makes up Pembrokeshire. Much of it is windswept and treeless. At the coast it terminates in high cliffs, whose continuity is broken by deep branching inlets or drowned valleys. Milford Haven is the largest of these; its sheltered waters form one of Britain's lesser naval bases.

South Wales was occupied by the English at an early date. The region is dotted with the ruins of their castles, built to protect themselves and their routes from the Welsh of the hills farther north. This advance of the English along the plain between the hills of Central Wales and the sea took them to Pembroke, from whose craggy coast they sailed to the conquest of Ireland. The traveler today can also cross to Ireland from the Pembroke coast, where is the little packet station of Fishguard.

Southwestern England. The southwestern peninsula is, like Wales and northern England, a region of hard rock, of hills, and of distinctive local character. It was formerly, at least in Cornwall, a Celtic-speaking area, though the local language ceased to be spoken almost two centuries ago. It has been more receptive of English influences than has Wales, and its individuality has no political character. The peninsula has a backbone of high, granitic moorlands, largest in the east, where they form Dartmoor, smallest in the west, where the last of them runs out into the sea to form the massive boulder-strewn headland of Land's End. The southwest is nowhere mountainous, everywhere hilly. Before the days of modern transport, travel was not easy, and this gave a degree of isolation to the whole. The land west of Exeter,

which was the most westerly Roman city, was formerly as remote from the main stream of English life as were the mountains of Wales.

The southwestern peninsula was intruded by metalliferous veins, which supported the once important tin- and copper-mining industries. The reserves of copper are practically exhausted, and the tin mines of West Cornwall have almost all closed down. The extraction of china clay, formed by the decomposition of the granite by gaseous exhalations from the interior of the earth, is now an industry of great importance

The Cornish coast. This is bleak, wind-swept, and treeless. The building in the foreground is the ruinous pumphouse of an abandoned copper mine, Wheal (mine) Coates, near Newquay.

and is carried on chiefly in the St. Austell district of mid-Cornwall. Granite is quarried and exported from West Cornwall.

Agriculture is now the most important industry of southwest England. The rainfall is, in general, too heavy for intensive crop farming, though fodder crops are grown. Dairying is a more important branch of agriculture. The mild climate and the absence of severe winter frosts permit the production of early potatoes and vegetables for the London and other urban markets. The tourist industry is also of great significance. The magnificence of the coast scenery and the beauty of the deep, sheltered creeks have proved an attraction to tourists, and there are numerous resort towns on the Devon and Cornwall coasts. The largest town in the southwest is Plymouth (192,000), with which

is closely associated the naval base of Devonport. Falmouth, on the shores of the wide
Falmouth harbor, is a ship-repairing center and
is of some importance as the most westerly port
in England.

The southwest has an atmosphere as distinctive as that of any other part of the Highland
fringe. It has, like Ireland and parts of Wales
and Scotland, a continuity of history over a
long period of time. Ancient, pre-Christian and
even prehistoric practices and customs survive.
Stone monuments 4,000 years old are found on
its moors; its field boundaries and cottages and
its granite churches have an air of antiquity
more marked even than in the English Plain.

LOWLAND ZONE

Lowland England differs from the Highland
Zone in its gentler relief, in the younger age and
greater softness of the rocks of which it is composed, in its smaller rainfall and better soils. It
is a low plain ridged with hills. The plain is
developed generally on clay rock; its soils are
often heavy, though much improved by centuries of cultivation. Much of this lowland,
however, is still most important for its meadow
and pasture rather than its crop farming. The
ridges of higher land are built up of limestone
and chalk and, in a few areas, sandstone.
These areas are drier and in many parts are
cultivated.

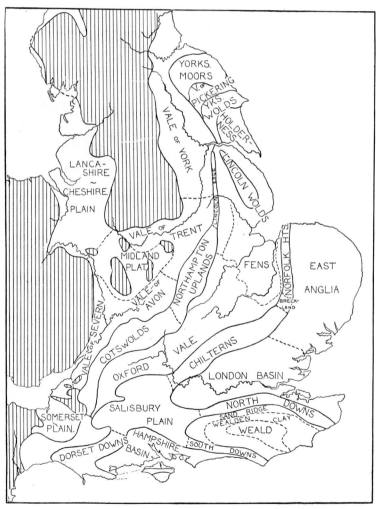

Fig. 57. Physical regions of Lowland England.

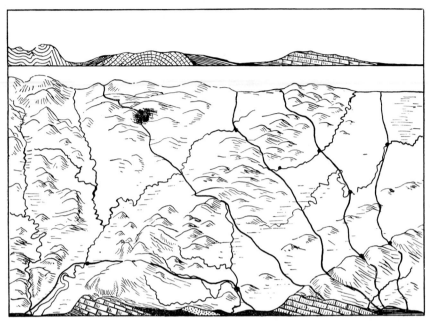

Fig. 58. Panorama across the English Midlands. The Cotswold and Chiltern scarps are seen in the foreground. Above the diagram is shown a section along its northern edge from the Welsh hills (*left*), through the Midlands, to the limestone uplands of Northamptonshire (*right*).

Lowland England has an aspect quite different from Highland. It has a richness, a lusciousness unknown in the harsh, sterile regions of the north and west. It is a land of tall meadow grass, of waving wheat fields, of clustered villages, orchards, and an infinity of small towns. Lowland England has been exposed, as Highland England has not, to invasion from across the narrow seas. Armies of invaders and groups of refugees have crossed to England, often bringing their peculiar skills and crafts with them. Flemings and Huguenots in the past, Poles and Jews today make their contribution to the variety of life and experience in Lowland England. In time of war the Lowland plain is exposed. From the time of the Romans until today there have been occasions when the peasant and farmer have prepared, with pike and musket, rifle and machine gun, to protect the shores. There are ruins on the Kentish coast of the Romans' forts. The Normans built castles here; towers, called Martello Towers, were built at the time of the Napoleonic invasion scare; and there are concrete pillboxes in the hedgerows, put up in 1940. The sea:

"Which serves it in the office of a wall,
Or as a moat defensive to a house,"

has in modern times protected England from all except the threat of invasion. Whether this happy condition can continue in an age of guided missiles and air-borne troops is at least uncertain.

The plain has coal and good fertile land, navigable rivers, and easy communications by road. It achieved a political and cultural unity long before the Highland region, and the variety of its resources have given it a broader economic basis and a greater stability than the hilly areas to west and north.

A knowledge of the geological structure of the English Plain is not necessary, though very helpful, for an understanding of its relief. The diagram (Fig. 58) shows the Cotswold and Chiltern Hills, which stretch from southwest to northeast across the plain. The geological section at the foot of the diagram shows the limestone, which makes up the Cotswold Hills, dipping eastward beneath the clay, shown black. The clay, its continuity broken by an outcrop

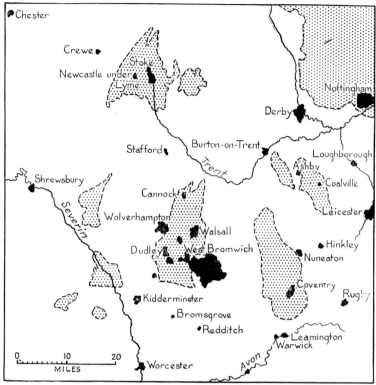

Fig. 59. The Midlands industrial region. Coal fields are stippled. Only exposed coal fields are shown.

of sandstone (shown by dots), dips beneath the chalk, which makes up the Chiltern Hills. The chalk in its turn dips beneath yet younger beds of clay, shown on the extreme right by horizontal shading. Both the limestone and the chalk form ridges, steep toward the west, gentle toward the east. The outcrop of the chalk forms a very unusual pattern. This is because the chalk which makes up the Chiltern Hills dips beneath the London Basin and rises in the North Downs. The chalk is similarly continuous from the Dorset Downs beneath the Hampshire Basin to the South Downs. Between the North and South Downs the chalk once formed a great upfold (Fig. 64), which has been eroded away, exposing the underlying rocks. If the student can only familiarize himself with these basic features of Lowland England, the following regional consideration of the area will become a great deal simpler.

The Midlands. The English Midlands form a region of lowland, triangular in plan and about 100 miles along each side. It is a region of soft rocks and rather heavy soil, of pasture rather than crop husbandry. There are, however, many areas of lighter, drier soil, where fruit and vegetables are grown. In the center of the Midlands, the old, hard rocks, which make up the Pennines and Wales and which everywhere underlie the plain, rise to the surface (Fig. 59). Coal fields occur and have brought about a transformation of parts of the rich agricultural lowland into closely built industrial cities and mining villages. On the west, the plain is drained by the Severn, on the north by the Trent, and on the southeast by the Avon, a tributary of the Severn.

To the northwest, the uneven deposition of glacial material has led to the formation of marshy, peat-filled hollows. Northeast, down the Trent Valley, part of the land has been drained artificially. All the land that possibly can now serves the neighboring cities, providing them with fresh milk and vegetables.

In the heart of the Midlands the land rises to a low, undulating plateau, where the older, coal-bearing rocks rise to the surface. The whole area has become highly industrialized. In a few areas, like Cannock Chase and Charnwood Forest, heath and woodland have survived, but generally, woodland and meadow have retreated before factories and mine tips, quarries and houses. Shakespeare's Forest of Arden has given place to Birmingham's suburbs. The spreading towns merge into one another, eating up the green countryside that once lay between. Birmingham (1,113,500) is the center of a "Black Country," made up of Wolverhampton (161,000), Walsall (114,000), West Bromwich, Smethwick and others.

The Black Country is the scene of a number of specialized and sometimes highly skilled metallurgical industries. The region lies in the center of England. It has no rivers of any useful size, and in the early days of its development, both raw materials and finished goods had to be conveyed by pack animals. This tended to limit their size, and the term "Birmingham goods" came to denote small ironware. Pins, needles, nails, locks, and chains were among the earliest of these specializations. The industry was based in the first instance on local supplies of iron ore, which was smelted with the charcoal from the Midland forests. Neither of these is available now, but the same industries are carried on on the basis of local coal and imported pig iron.

East of the Birmingham "conurbation," but still on or very close to one of the coal fields, are Coventry (226,000), with its mechanical engineering and automobile industries; Rugby, with its electrical engineering; Leicester (286,000), with hosiery and leatherworking; Burton-on-Trent, with brewing; and Derby and Nottingham, away on the border of the Pennines (page 106).

Around the industrial region is a very different world, one of small towns which come to life on market day, when the farmers bring in their animals and produce for sale. Stratford-on-Avon and Warwick, Evesham and Tewkesbury belong to this part of the Midlands. The low-lying and fertile plain reaches northward, down the Trent valley, past Newark and Gainsborough, and northward into Yorkshire, where the city of York (105,000) lies in the midst of the plain, route center and former capital and guardian of northern England. A great railroad depot and modern factories have been grafted onto the ancient core of the city.

Scarp and Vale in Southern England. Limestone hills, which reach all the way from the south coast to the coast of Yorkshire, make up a region of rolling upland. There is little

FIG. 60. Cottage architecture, the Cotswolds. The houses are built of the easily worked local limestone. The dominant styles have not changed for some 300 years.

surface drainage. Valleys are shallow, and woodland limited to small clumps of beech or ash. Fields are separated by the dry-stone walling which is a feature of limestone country. Buildings are also of the local stone and sometimes even roofed with thin limestone "slates." The stone works well under the mason's chisel and weathers to a gray or golden color. For centuries beautiful buildings have been erected throughout this "stone belt" and paid for, in the past at least, by the wealth earned in sheep rearing on the dry, grassy plateau. Towns like Chipping Camden, Stamford, Oakham, and Bath are museums of ancient architecture and among the most beautiful places in England. Sheep are still important on the limestone hills, but the region is now devoted mainly to mixed farming. In the clay-floored vales between the limestone ridges and in the valleys where the larger streams have cut down through the limestone cap to the softer beds beneath, there are meadows and dairy farming is practiced.

The city of Bath. Most of the buildings seen in this picture were put up in the eighteenth century. In the foreground is the Royal Crescent and beyond it the Circus, fine examples of planned eighteenth-century development. American students will notice the absence of planning over most of the area shown. (*British Information Services.*)

The limestone belt varies greatly in its aspect and development in the 300 miles that separate its southern from its northern limit. The Cotswold Hills form the most famous area of the limestone belt. A scarp rises steeply from the valley of the Severn, and from its crest the eye ranges over the plain at its foot to the hills of the Marches and to the Welsh Mountains beyond. Here are the "wool towns," whose newest houses seem often to have been built before the eighteenth century. Cirencester, Northleach, Stow-on-the-Wold, Chipping Camden. At the southern end of this region is Bath, lying in the deep valley of the Avon. It is built of the gray limestone and is rich in buildings of the eighteenth century and earlier. Twelve miles to the west is Bristol (442,000), an ancient city and now an important port with a varied industrial development. It was formerly of considerable significance in the trade between Europe and the New World and today carries on industries such as the preparation of tobacco, sugar refining and the manufacture of chocolate and soap, based upon its earlier colonial trade.

The region continues in the Uplands of Northamptonshire. Its scarp character is less conspicuous. It has the aspect of a rolling upland, with dry grassland and stone-built walls and cottages on the higher ground and meadow and hedgerow in the hollows. It is for the greater part an area of mixed agriculture, with dairy farming tending to predominate. Ironstone occurs in beds in the limestone and in recent years has come to be quarried extensively. Iron smelting is an old industry here, but in recent years has been greatly developed with the establishment of a large blast furnace and steelworks at Great Corby. The destruction of agricultural land consequent upon these operations has come to be a serious problem in a land as small and as densely peopled as England. Farther north, the limestone belt contracts to a narrow ridge. Where it is crossed by the river Witham lies the city of Lincoln, its great cathedral perched high on the edge of the limestone, overlooking the town and river. The belt is

The Avon gorge below Bristol. The river Avon is difficult to navigate here owing to the large rise and fall of the tide, and partly for this reason an outport has been established at Avonmouth. This photograph was taken at low tide looking upstream toward Bristol.

interrupted for a distance, to reappear and terminate in the Cleveland Hills of Yorkshire.

A belt of lowland reaches from Yorkshire almost to the south coast between the limestone hills and the chalk. It is not a level area; thin beds of limestone and sandstone come to the surface, producing smaller hill features. This clay plain is a land of heavy soil and slow, winding rivers. Fields are separated by thick hedgerows, and patches of woodland cover the less productive areas. Building stone is rare. The clay permits brick production, and brick is the most common building material. In the past timber was much used, and in many villages the familiar black timber structure with white clay and wattle infilling appears (Fig. 61). But the predominant coloring of the villages is the red and yellow of the local brick.

There is little variation in the aspect of this clay belt. Toward the south it is known as the Oxford Vale and consists of the upper valley of the Thames. A low and inconspicuous watershed separates the Thames Valley from the basin of the rivers which flow toward the Wash.

The whole region has a "parkland" appearance. The view is everywhere shut in by trees and tall hedges. The grass of the valleys is deep and green, and the countryside has a lusciousness and richness about it. Cows, pigs, poultry, fodder crops, and grain are the agricultural products. The land is dotted with little market towns, which come to life for the weekly market and appear to sleep for the rest of the time. A few of these, however, have grown to a considerable size and become places of more than local importance. Oxford (108,000) is the seat of a great university and also of an important automobile industry. Swindon, as a city, is the creation of the old Great Western Railway, which established its locomotive and carriage works here. Luton (110,000) manufactures automobiles and hats; Bedford, light machinery; Northampton (104,500), boots and shoes; Peterborough, bricks; and Cambridge, at the opposite end of the vale to its rival, has succeeded in remaining essentially a university town. In

Fig. 61. Cottage architecture, the Clay Vale. The houses are here built of timber, clay, and brick. The commonest style consists of a timber frame with panels filled in with wattle and daub. Modern building is usually in brick, which can be made locally.

their differing degrees, both Oxford and Cambridge preserve the atmosphere of medieval, cloistered, academic life in their colleges, each with its chapel and dining hall, where for centuries the life and work of the two older universities have centered.

In the neighborhood of the Wash, the clay vale passes into the Fens. The Fens of Cambridgeshire and Lincolnshire are a level expanse of peat and silt; above the surface rise "islands" of firmer rock on which the larger settlements have been made. The aspect of the Fens is not

Oakham, Rutland. The picture shows the market square and market cross, of medieval origin, beneath which much of the buying and selling took place. Behind are the tower and spire of the parish church.

unlike that of Holland; windmills, no longer of serious use, however, in draining and pumping, are still prominent features of the landscape. The land is new, trees are few, hedges small and thin or even absent, fields are large, and villages and farms occur mainly on the less productive ground which rises above the dark peaty soil.

The chalk downlands appear to radiate from the nuclear area of Salisbury Plain. The Downs, which reach out like tentacles to the southwest, southeast, east, and northeast, provided easy routes in primitive times. They were forest-free and dry under foot. Man could move easily over them, and Salisbury Plain became a meeting place where were built the prehistoric stone temples of Stonehenge and Avebury. Salisbury Plain is an area of rolling chalk downland, irregular in shape and going by different names in different parts. Woodland is rare and generally confined to the valleys; the natural vegetation is a short dry grass. Water is scanty; even the valleys, more often than not, are dry, and villages are clustered where water can be most easily obtained. Isolated farmsteads and houses are infrequent, though water now

can usually be obtained from deep wells. Crop farming is practiced. The moister soil of the valleys is good enough, but over the Downs the soil is thin, crops poor, and sheep rearing has always been important. The plain has in recent years became important as a military training area.

The town of Salisbury (34,000) at the convergence of several rivers of the plain is its chief town and market center. It is an open, spacious place. The rectangular plan of its streets, laid out in the thirteenth century, when its cathedral was built, anticipates the pattern of American towns. To the east is Winchester (28,000), a capital of Saxon England.

From this central area the chalk ridges reach out to form the Downs. The Dorset Downs

FIG. 62. A windmill of the Cambridgeshire Fens. These mills have been used since the eighteenth century for drainage, as in the Netherlands. They are now being replaced by steam or oil engines.

stretch southwestward to the coast; the South Downs, southeastward until they end in the white cliffs of Beachy Head; the North Downs, eastward to the Straits of Dover and the Chiltern Hills, northeast across England continued in the Lincoln and Yorkshire Wolds, until, they, too,

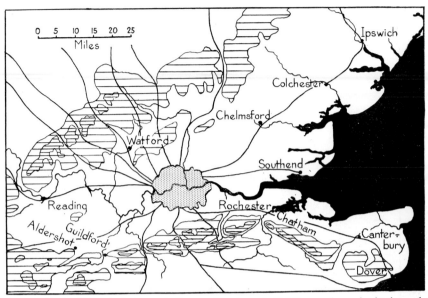

FIG. 63. The London Basin. The stippled area is Greater London, chalk hills are shown by horizontal shading. Note how the railroads use the gaps in these hills.

end at the coast in the cliffs of Flamborough Head in Yorkshire.

The Downs, the "blunt, bald-headed, bull-nose Downs," rise steeply from the lower ground, their rounded summits terraced by prehistoric hilltop camps and dimpled by ancient burial places. They are broken by numerous gaps, where rivers cross them through incised valleys. Many of these valleys are occupied by "gap towns," which grew up around a castle built to defend the gap and which now profit from the convergence of routes. Arundel and Lewes are gap towns in the South Downs; Guildford and Canterbury in the North.

Over the surface of the Chiltern Hills there is an extensive deposit of clay. However thin this layer may be, it serves to mask the underlying chalk and to produce a cold, heavy soil which holds water and supports a growth of damp woodland. But where this deposit has been worn away, the familiar grassy downland reappears. The Chiltern Hills are crossed by a number of low gaps (Fig. 63), all of them devoid of water except the artificial waterway of a canal. These, like the gaps in the North Downs, converge toward London and are of great importance in the trade and movement of the capital. Toward the northeast the chalk ridge becomes lower, its scarp character disappears, and it becomes merely a line of low rounded hills which continues northward to the Norfolk coast. It is covered with a patchy deposit of boulder clay, on which there is sometimes found a woodland cover. To the east this glacial cover becomes deeper and more continuous over the plateau of East Anglia.

The Weald is an area of older rocks set in a framework of chalk downland. It lies between the North and South Downs. In contrast to the chalk area, it has a wooded aspect. It has hedged fields and villages like those of the clay vale, of which it is, in effect, a kind of outlier. The Weald is on the dry side of England. It has more sunshine than most parts and has become important for its fruit-growing industry. Here also most of the hops are grown, and the oast house, with conical roof and wind vane, for drying the hops, is an essential part of the Kentish landscape.

There are only small towns in the Weald. Factory industry has not yet crept into this region on any considerable scale in spite of its nearness to London. Along the coast are resorts: Brighton (156,000), Eastbourne, Hastings, Folkestone, and towns that once were

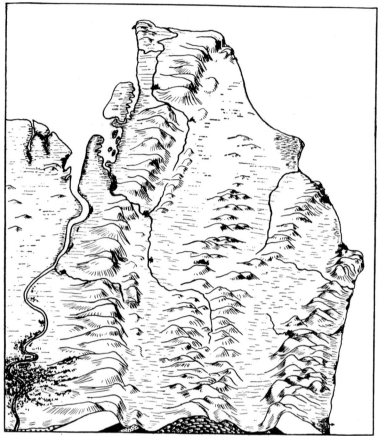

Fig. 64. Diagrammatic sketch of the North and South Downs and Weald, looking east. London and the Thames are to the left (north). The scarp slopes of the Downs face inward toward the hills of the central Weald.

fortresses built to protect Britain from invasion—Winchelsea and Rye, Hythe and Dover.

East Anglia. This is a low plateau, much of it covered with boulder clay, in which the rivers have cut broad shallow valleys. The landscape varies from flat and rather monotonous boulder-clay plateau and heathy end moraine to soft, rich valleys with the slow-flowing streams that Constable loved to paint. Here are patches of woodland and the small towns that have scarcely grown since, in the late Middle Ages, the wealthy merchants built their proud houses of half timber or brick and the superb East Anglian churches. The largest city of East Anglia and its regional capital is Norwich (120,000), a town with an unparalleled number of medieval churches and relics of its earlier history and now a center of the leather, boot and shoe, and food industries. Ipswich (104,-000) manufactures cranes and agricultural machinery. Chelmsford, on the margin of East Anglia, is important for electrical engineering and the manufacture of ball bearings. Between Norwich and the sea are the Broads, formed by the partial silting of the joint estuary of several rivers; they consist now of a number of irregular shallow lagoons, much frequented by yachtsmen.

East Anglia is primarily an agricultural region. The dry climate; the sunshine, which, for England, is abundant; and soils of moderate fertility have combined to produce the most important area of crop farming in Britain. There is a close network of little towns spread regularly over the region, providing the marketing facilities and amenities for the rural areas.

London Basin. This is a basin in the chalk,

filled in with later deposits of clay and sand. On the south it is bounded by the chalk of the North Downs, on the northwest by the Chilterns, and on the northeast by the margin of the drift-covered plateau of East Anglia. Both structure and topography are varied. Low, level areas

FIG. 65. A Kentish oast house. This is a familiar feature of the Kentish landscape. It is the building in which the hops are dried.

of the clay alternate with patches of gravel which form the caps of low hills. In the southwest the gravels are more extensive and produce broad areas of heathland.

London has grown up at the center of this basin. It lies at the present limit of ocean navigation on the Thames and at the lowest point at which the river could be bridged in early times. Routes from the Channel coast would be expected to make for a crossing of the Thames in this vicinity. The growth of a town in this situation was as nearly inevitable as is possible. The actual site was determined by the presence of gravel terraces which gave a dry approach to the river and a convenient place upon which to lay out houses. London grew up on a gravel-covered terrace on the north bank of the Thames. The Romans made London the center of their road system, and the Roman roads long continued to provide the basic road pattern of England. Trade moved along them to London. The government of the Plantagenet kings was located in London, and it came later to be the

headquarters of societies and the business center of industrial and commercial firms. Its theaters and other places of entertainment and amusement, its cultural societies and institutions, its shopping and commercial facilities led to greater numbers of visitors and, in turn, to a greater development of London's activities. The city spread outward (Fig. 66). At first only the more attractive sites, on the gravel terraces and above the damp, the fog, and the floods, were used; later the clay areas were themselves filled with factories, railway yards, and poor-class dwellings, which degenerated rapidly into slums.

Now, with a population of over 8,391,000, greater London appears to have reached a practical limit. New industries are still pressing to open up in London, and the housing of London's workers presents a problem. Satellite

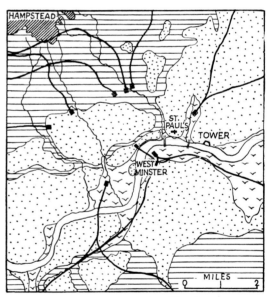

FIG. 66. The situation of London. The city grew up on the gravel terraces to the north of the Thames. The gravel terraces are shown by stippling: the London clay, by horizontal lines.

towns are being planned and built to satisfy this continued demand, separated from London by a few miles of green countryside, yet not too far away to enjoy the facilities which London offers.

The Pool of London. This is the stretch of the Thames below London Bridge, the second bridge from the bottom of the picture. To the right is the bomb-damaged roof of one of London's railroad stations and behind it St. Paul's Cathedral. In the right foreground are some of the towers and walls of the Tower of London, the castle founded in the eleventh century. (*British Information Services.*)

Other towns of the London Basin are dwarfed by the presence of London or have been engulfed by its expanding periphery. Reading (115,500) lies well up the Thames Valley; Watford beyond the city's northwestern margin. On the lower Medway is a small group of varied but contiguous towns: Rochester, with its cathedral and castle; Chatham, a naval base; and Gillingham. Farther to the east, on the Stour, is Canterbury. Along the shores of the muddy estuary of the Thames are resorts for London's dense population, of which the largest is Southend-on-Sea (150,000).

The Hampshire Basin resembles the London. It, too, is a downfold of the chalk, between the Dorset Downs and the South Downs, which has been filled in with sands and gravel. Alluvium has produced rich meadows along the banks of the Stour and Avon, another of the many rivers of that name, but a large area of infertile soil is occupied by the New Forest. This area was set aside for hunting by William the Conqueror in the eleventh century. In choosing for this purpose a region of low agricultural value he showed a deeper geographical insight than many have displayed in more recent years.

Within this region are the ports of Southampton (181,000) and Portsmouth (218,000). The former has a deep navigable waterway and a system of tides which greatly favors its use by the largest liners. It handles comparatively little cargo, but most passenger liners sail from here. Portsmouth is the home port of the Royal Navy. Bournemouth (139,500), Southsea, Worthing, and Brighton are resorts on this sunny and sultry coast.

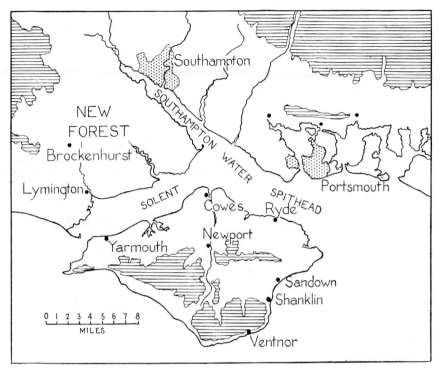

FIG. 67. Isle of Wight and the approaches to Southampton. Shaded areas are above 500 feet.

The Isle of Wight. The "island" is a microcosm of Lowland England. Within its small area of 147 square miles it contains a denuded anticline like the Weald, a small area of chalk downland, and, in the north, an extension of the Hampshire Basin. Its towns are very small. It has no significant industries except boat building, and agriculture and catering for summer visitors occupy the attentions of its people.

IRELAND

Ireland is a compact island, about 160 miles from east to west and 250 miles from north to south. Its coastline is rough and indented and on the west and north is bordered by high cliffs, where the mountains meet the sea. The island is made up of a large central plain, drained for the greater part by the Shannon (Fig. 46) and surrounded by a ring of hills. These are individually small in area and sharp in outline, rising steeply from the plain and from the areas of lowland which separate them.

The climate is damp and mild, the weather cloudy, and rain frequent. As in southwestern England, grass grows well and crop farming is not common except in the drier districts of the east. Ireland is a poor country, and its population (about 4,250,000) is small. Its manufacturing industries are confined to the northeast; the west is one of the most poverty-stricken areas in western Europe.

Ireland is divided politically into the republic of Eire and the province of Northern Ireland, which consists of the six northeastern counties. The latter is part of the United Kingdom and is represented in the Parliament at Westminster. The division of Ireland is artificial and derives from the settlement of Northern Ireland by Scottish and English Protestants early in the seventeenth century.

Northern Ireland. This region lies north of a line from Sligo Bay to Dundalk Bay and is larger than the political unit of the same name. It is a region of detached mountain masses between which meander the slow rivers on their way from the interior plain to the sea. In the northeast is the basaltic plateau of Antrim, with its "glens," deeply incised below the almost level plateau surface. To south and west are the damp lowlands of the Bann and the Lagan, in which lies Lough Neagh. This is the principal center of flax growing in Ireland, and the small towns of this region, such as Lurgan, Lisburn, and Portadown, are chiefly engaged in making linen. Belfast (438,000), at the mouth of the Lagan, is the capital of northern Ireland, the

Fig. 68. Physical divisions of Ireland.

largest center of linen manufacture and has in addition an important shipbuilding industry. To the west of the Bann the region is more hilly. Between the Bann and Foyle Valleys are the Sperrin Mountains, and beyond the Foyle, the mountains of Donegal, Leitrim, and Fermanagh. The last is a wild and sparsely populated region of great beauty but little wealth and prosperity.

Western and Southern Ireland. The mountainous areas of Connemara and Mayo resemble Donegal in their relief, their poverty, the sparseness of their population, and their wild beauty. South of a line from the Shannon mouth to Dublin is a region of isolated hill masses, separated by broad areas of rich lowland. Among these is the Golden Vale of Tipperary, famous for its dairy herds. To the east is the granitic mass of the Wicklow Mountains. In the southwest, the valleys become narrower and

the hills merge into the rain-sodden mountain mass of Kerry. The rivers Slaney, Barrow, Suir, and Blackwater, with their tributaries, drain the valleys between the hills, making broad gaps between the coast and the plain of the interior (Fig. 46).

Towns are few and small; Limerick on the Shannon, Tipperary, Kilkenny and Carlow are market towns and dairy centers. On the coast are the small ports of Wexford, Waterford (77,500), and Cork (81,000). The last lies several miles up the river Lee but has an outport in Cobh (Queenstown), at which the transatlantic liners sometimes stop.

Central Ireland. This is a plain which occupies the whole of central Ireland and reaches to the sea near Dublin. The river Shannon joins

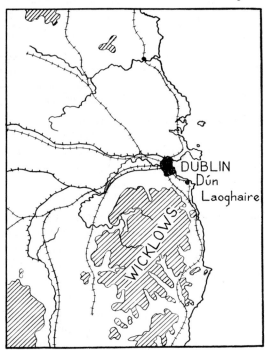

Fig. 69. The situation of Dublin. The city lies opposite a gap between the hills which bound the Irish Plain on the east.

together a number of lakes and gathers the slow drainage of much of this plain. Considerable areas are infertile glacial deposits, either hummocky drumlins or a sterile wash of gravel. More are covered with peat, which is cut for fuel but serves little other purpose. Away from the coast there are no towns except Athlone, itself little more than a village. Dublin (Baile Atha Cliath, 470,000) (Fig. 69) lies on the east coast, facing England. Behind it the land is drier and of some agricultural value, and here the barley is grown for Dublin's brewing industry. Dublin is the capital and largest city of Eire. It is a spacious city of great beauty but not really an industrial town.

All parts of the Highland fringe have a well-marked character of their own. Ireland stands apart, cut off from the rest by the sea, and its character is more individual than that of the rest. Ireland has a continuity in its history and a strength of local tradition greater even than in Cornwall or Wales. During the Dark Ages it developed a civilization, associated with its "Celtic" saints, of a higher level than that which prevailed in England. During the Middle Ages the English, under Norman leadership, established bases on the Irish coast but failed to conquer more than the hinterland of Dublin, the "Pale" of English settlement. The Irish strongly resisted English settlement and ownership of the land. The warfare between Saxon and Celt was very bitter and has left a legacy of hatred until today. England made good her conquest. English settlers owned the land, and the province of Ulster was "planted" early in the seventeenth century with a hardy colony of vigorous Presbyterian Scots. This region is the Northern Ireland of today, mainly Protestant in religion and Unionist in politics.

Ireland, or Eire, obtained home rule in 1920 at the end of a bloodthirsty war, and this has developed into complete independence. Eire remains Roman Catholic, while the rest of the British Isles is mainly Protestant. The political ambition of most Irishmen is to end "partition" and to reunite the whole island under the rule of Dublin. The Protestant majority of Northern Ireland resist this. Adjustments along the frontier in the counties of Armagh and Fermanagh would remove local difficulties and injustices but would not solve the problem of partition. Wholehearted cooperation with England, it may be said, is not likely while partition lasts.

Northern Ireland and Eire differ radically. Northern Ireland has a population of about 1,300,000; Eire has about 3,000,000 in an area about five times as large. Both are predominantly agricultural, but Northern Ireland has also large and well-developed shipbuilding and linen industries. The industries of Eire are more intimately connected with the country's agricultural activities. Eire is naturally a trading partner of Great Britain, yet repeatedly she allows her political prejudice to warp her economic policy. There have been times when the Irish would have preferred to starve in independence rather than to sell their butter to feed the English.

Unlike Scotland and Wales, Ireland has little coal. The Shannon barrage has been built to generate electric power, but resources are too small to be of much industrial value. But in Ireland conditions have been made a great deal worse by the inefficiency and the injustices of English rule; by the rotten system of land tenure which formerly existed, by which a handful of owners, usually absentee, owned much of the island; by the famine of the nineteenth century, occasioned by the potato blight; and by the large-scale migration of the more able and energetic Irishmen. It is an interesting comment on this that in the United States St. Patrick's Day is widely celebrated, and the sorry history of Britain's relations with Ireland does nothing to smooth Britain's relations with the United States.

Ireland lay formerly on the outer fringe of Europe. It is now a steppingstone in an Atlantic crossing. The development of a transatlantic airport at Foynes on the lower Shannon is giving Eire a large transit traffic. The small, rocky ports of the west coast, of little value for commerce, have a strategic importance, due to their situation far out in the North Atlantic. Britain formerly had small naval bases at Lough Swilly on the north coast and Berehaven and Queenstown (Cobh) in the south. These have been returned to Irish hands, but it is not difficult to envisage circumstances in which their possession again by one of the Allied and democratic powers would become desirable.

CHAPTER 11: *Britain's Economy*

The United Kingdom is the most highly industrialized country of Europe. No less than 62 per cent of its population lives in urban districts, towns of generally over 25,000 inhabitants, and some 45 per cent of its employed persons are engaged in factories or mines. This preeminence was achieved during the nineteenth century, when earlier trends of economic growth combined with a rich natural endowment to make possible the development of factory industries. At this time, too, agriculture, which had hitherto supported a majority of the population and had fed almost all of it, sank to a subsidiary position in the economy of Great Britain. It was considered wiser to allow the free importation of cheap foodstuffs from the "new" countries and so to permit industrial costs to fall than to protect the English farming community. Now, in the twentieth century, Great Britain is reaching a stage in her economic development when she is faced with foreign competition in the sphere of her industrial products and can no longer sell her manufactures as easily as she could a generation or two ago. Agriculture, neglected for the greater part of a century, is now again receiving advice and encouragement from the British government.

Industrial Development. From the Middle Ages England had been the scene of a vigorous industrial development. Her woolen cloth from East Anglia, the Cotswolds, and the west country was exported by the merchant adventurers. Iron was worked for local use, and nonferrous metals were mined and exported. A writer of the fifteenth century complained that the foreign merchants " . . . bare hence our best chaffare (merchandise), *Cloth, wool* and *tin.*"

To these goods, manufactured cottons and silks were added in the eighteenth century. The ancient iron industry received a great impetus at about this time from the introduction of smelting with coke. The invention by Cort of the puddling furnace and by Nielsen of the hot blast in smelting put England in the forefront of the world's metallurgical industries. At about this time, too, a revolution was taking place in the textile industries. The spinning industry, both woolen and cotton, came gradually to be mechanized, and mechanization spread to other stages in the manufacture of textiles. Above all, the steam engine was invented early in the eighteenth century and continuously improved during the years which followed. Early in the nineteenth century England was the scene of the first railroad to be built.

England was well placed to benefit from these developments. Her abundant coal provided cheap power for her machines and coke for her blast furnaces. The beginnings of certain industrial concentrations were apparent before 1800. After the end of the war with France in 1815 industrial development proceeded apace. As coal was the basic requirement, this development took place on or close to the coal fields. Ancient centers of the iron industry, such as the Forest of Dean and Shropshire, and the Cotswold and East Anglian textile areas either declined in importance or ceased to exist as centers of industry. During the nineteenth century other branches of industry became important: the chemical, paint, and paper industries as well as the processing of foodstuffs. In some instances these moved toward the older industrial centers; more often they were located at the great ports through which the raw materials were imported. During the

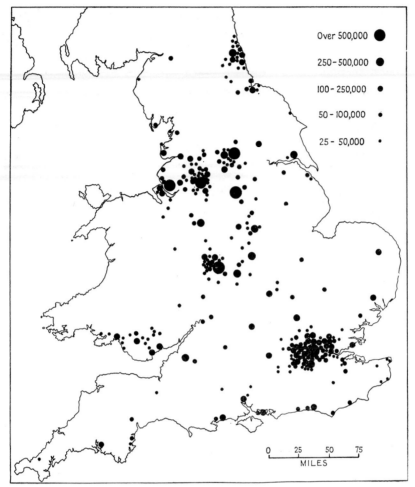

FIG. 70. The distribution of towns in England and Wales.

twentieth century a conspicuous shift in the centers of industry has become apparent. Those industries which were basic in the nineteenth century have declined in relative, some of them in absolute, importance. Reliance is no longer placed exclusively on coal for power. Instead, electric power, generated in the British Isles very largely by burning coal, is distributed by cable to places remote from the coal fields. The present trend is, then, toward both a dispersion of industries away from the coal fields and a concentration on the lighter industries.

The older industrial centers, located close to the coal fields, remain of importance: the industrial region of central Scotland, the Cumberland coast, the Northeast, Lancashire, York-

shire, the Midlands, and South Wales. But new industries are going elsewhere. The congestion and squalor of some of the older industrial areas discourage enterprise. New forms of power and new sources of raw materials have destroyed their advantages. Above all the decline in the export of some of the old staples, such as cotton, has brought unemployment and misery to several such areas. Such areas were the subject of special enquiry during the 1930's. New industries were deliberately located here, but this has not checked the movement of "new" industries to new and hitherto undeveloped areas. "Greater" London has become the most important, most varied industrial region in Great Britain. It is impossible to list its

The center of Birmingham. This is a good example of the unplanned development of an English industrial city. The student can distinguish a canal, railroad depot, and switchyards. He can also detect areas devasted by bombing. (*British Information Services.*)

industries. Even iron smelting has been established on the north shore of the Thames below the city. Ironworks have been set up at Great Corby, in the ironstone-producing area of the east Midlands, and at Scunthorpe and Frodingham, in the northward continuation of this same ironstone region in Lincolnshire. Factories have sprung up along the roads and railroads radiating from London. "Trading estates" have been formed where a group of similar or related factories can be established, sharing transportation and other facilities. In all this we see London, with its population of about 8,391,000 and its satellite cities, attracting industry more and more to its huge market.

The newest factories in England are models of industrial planning and are as efficient as any. But many industries, including the "basic" industries of coal mining and textile manufacture, are old. Their buildings and equipment do not conform with the best modern practice, and they compete with difficulty with the newer industries in other lands. The report of a commission which examined the comparative efficiency of the English and American cotton industries in 1944 concluded: "There need be no hesitation in saying that the U.S. industry is very far ahead of the Lancashire industry in production per man hour. At the same time it would be correct to say that there is no reason to suppose that the skill of the operatives of Lancashire is one whit inferior to that of the U.S.A. operatives. On the contrary everyone of us felt that the ability of the Lancashire cotton operative remains unsurpassed. The whole question at issue therefore resolved itself into one of mechanical efficiency or otherwise, and here we were quickly convinced that the U.S.A. has great superiority. The machinery employed throughout is more modern, methods about

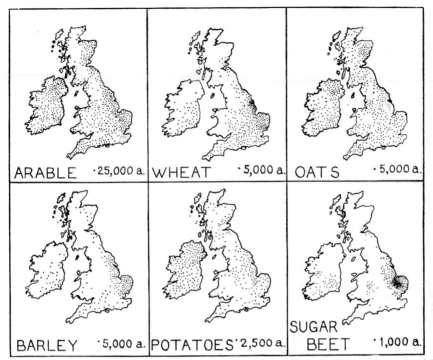

FIG. 71. Distribution of the more important crops in England and Wales. (*From Agricultural Geography of Europe and the Near East, U.S. Department of Agriculture, 1948.*)

which our industry is in doubt have become general practice, and automatic machines are far more readily adopted and absorbed."[1]

A report on the coal industry commented at about the same time that "the technical conduct of the British coal-mining industry seems to have been carried on without any radical changes in the practices long established in the various coalfields."[2] It added that "the individualism of a large number of self-contained units was unlikely to encourage major developments in the science of mining." It called for an integration and rationalization of production to meet the competition of Poland and other coal producers as well as the competition of newer forms of fuel.

These examples may serve to illustrate a general problem. The critic argues that British

[1] Report of the Cotton Textile Mission to the United States of America, Ministry of Production, London, 1944.

[2] Coal Mining: Report of the Technical Advisory Committee, Cmd. 6610, London, 1945.

industry formerly made large profits; more should have been plowed back in new capital equipment. This was not always possible, and in the full tide of success few pause to think of the hard times that may follow. Britain's position was deteriorating before the Second World War but was disguised by the "unearned" income from overseas investments. These were mostly lost during the war, and when it was over, Britain was left exposed to the harsh competitive situation from which she had hitherto been insulated (see page 130).

Population. The population of the United Kingdom is made up as follows (figures for 1949):

England............................. 41,007,950
Wales................................ 2,587,050
Scotland............................. 5,207,000
Northern Ireland..................... 1,371,000

It is still in process of growth, though the rate of growth is declining steadily, and a stationary population may be expected in the not too distant future. There has in recent years been a slow movement of population away from the older industrial centers and an increase of population in the London region and the east Midlands. Most of the larger cities have been described as lying within an hourglass figure, which expands over the southeast of England and over the Midlands, southern Lancashire, and the West Riding of Yorkshire (Fig. 70).

Agriculture. For a century agriculture has been of secondary importance. It now employs less than 6 per cent of the total employed persons, and the area under cultivation has visibly contracted in the less fertile areas of the north and west. An increasing proportion of the food requirements of Britain came to be satisfied by imports, which, in general, were cheaper than home-produced foodstuffs. The earlier emphasis on grain crops gave place to an emphasis on dairy, fruit, and vegetable farming, with which overseas countries could compete less easily (compare Denmark and France, pages 86 and 162). Two wars, during which Britain's food supply was gravely jeopardized, have demonstrated the folly of allowing agriculture to take its own course. Attempts are being made to support crop farming in Britain, though it is too early yet to assess the geographical results of such a policy.

The study of the agricultural geography of Britain is greatly assisted by the completion and publication of the Land Utilisation Survey (see Bibliography), a series of maps on a 1-inch scale, on which the land use is shown by distinctive coloring. As a general rule it may be said that the damp west together with parts of the damp, clay lowlands in the Midlands and the south are given up mainly to pastoral farming. Crop farming predominates in the drier east and on the lighter soils in other areas. There are, however, many exceptions to this generalization. The immediate neighborhood of large towns is likely to be devoted to trucking, whatever the soil and climate, owing to the heavy demand for produce. Essex, the county in England with the lowest rainfall, is an important dairy-farming area, because of the demand in London, which adjoins it to the southeast, for

liquid milk. Certain sandy areas, particularly in Bedfordshire and Cambridgeshire, are devoted to truck farming; the southwest of England is able, owing to its mild winters, to market produce earlier than other parts (*cf.* Brittany, page 134).

Farming in England is carried on in small, compact farms. The size of holdings, which are sometimes rented, sometimes owned by the farmers, varies with the region and with the type of farming carried on. They are smaller in the dairying country of the west than in the crop-farming region of the east. The over-all range of size of farms may be taken as from 50 to 250 acres, though individual farms may run to much greater sizes than this and there is a very large number of small holdings of much smaller size. There were, in 1946, 290,600 agricultural holdings, with an average size of 83 acres. The material equipment of English farms is generally good. There is a far greater use of tractors than in any other country of Europe. The combined harvester is making its appearance, though unsuited to the small size of English fields. Farm stock is usually good, and considerable care is given in all except the poorest farms to animal breeding and to the use of good seed. Mixed farming is general, and farmyard manure is available for the fields; in addition synthetic fertilizers are much used.

English farming has long since broken with the medieval system of intermixed strips in the open fields, which still obtains in many parts of Europe. Fields, on the other hand, are small and sometimes scattered. Much space is taken up by hedges and ditches, and with mechanized agriculture, an appreciable percentage of each small field goes uncultivated in the corners and close to the boundaries.

These remarks apply particularly to the Lowland Zone of England. They are less applicable to Wales and southern Scotland and not at all to the Scottish Highlands and Ireland. In the Highland areas crop farming is not generally of great importance. Its yields are small, and its material equipment less adequate. In the more remote areas, especially in Scotland, conditions are very primitive indeed, and some of the crofts, or small farms, are little removed from self-subsistence.

The nature of the agricultural practice in each region has been indicated in the previous chapter. The series of maps will serve to draw these facts together. Crop farming, it will be noticed, predominates in the east of England and in northern Ireland. Wheat and barley are grown on a large scale only in the drier east. Oats is a more widespread crop and is relatively important in Ireland and Scotland. Sugar beet is important only in East Anglia and Lincolnshire, where it is grown in rotation with grain crops and potatoes. Potatoes are more widespread. In the drier regions where the four-course rotation is employed, they are often grown as one course. In Ireland they assume a great importance as human food.

Animal husbandry is relatively very important. Sheep are reared on the hills of the Highland Zone and also on the river lowlands of the south and east. Cattle are very numerous, and there is no part of the United Kingdom where they are not important in the agricultural pattern. They are reared for beef purposes in parts of the Midlands. Dairying is practiced in every agricultural region but is of supreme importance only in the southwestern peninsula, in Somerset, Cheshire, and southwestern Scotland.

The Problem of Land Use. Great Britain is small and densely populated and, under present conditions of world trade, wants to get as much as possible out of its agriculture. The problem of the control of land use thus becomes important. It is desirable in the national interest to preserve good agricultural land for the farmer, to allocate only poorer quality land for housing or industrial works, to ensure the reconditioning of land that has been strip mined. This control is exercised through the Ministry of Town and Country Planning. It is itself the judge of what is the best mode of land use. It has had difficult problems. During a period of coal shortage, it has had to choose between the strip mining of coal and agricultural use of the land—similarly with the open-pit working of iron ore. Land is not nationalized, but it is no longer possible for the individual to do as he wishes with his land. The land is a resource that must be carefully husbanded. A small country learns this lesson before a large. The system of zoning land for the differing land uses works well, and this method of limited public control of land has been on all counts a success.

Transportation. The transportation system of Great Britain has been developed to a higher degree of efficiency and intensity than that of any other country in Europe. The railway system, consisting in origin, like that of the United States, of a large number of separate and privately owned railroads, has been absorbed into a state-owned "British Railways." A series of main lines radiates from London, and on these the service is frequent and sometimes fast. There is also a very great number of cross-country lines. Most of the tracks are double, though only a very small distance has more than two tracks. The network of main roads also radiates from London. The system of secondary roads is very close and of an excellent quality except in the remote areas of Wales and Scotland. Canal transport is now of little significance, though England still has a large number of canals. These peaceful waterways wind through the English Midlands, too narrow and too shallow for most modern river craft and rarely disturbed by any commercial activity, the resort of the angler and the naturalist. The Manchester Ship Canal and a few of the inland waterways of Yorkshire and the northwestern Midlands are exceptions to the general decay that has overcome canal transport in England.

Britain's Commercial Situation. Great Britain is an important exporter of manufactured goods and coal, but she is an even more important importer of foodstuffs, raw materials, and other factory goods. The volume of imports always exceeds that of imports. During the nineteenth century, when Great Britain was exporting manufactured goods to all parts of the world, a considerable part of this export was paid for by loans made by British financiers. Britain thus acquired overseas investments, the interest on which contributed to pay for the imports. For instance, Argentinean railroads were built with British capital and equipment, and until recently the interest from these undertakings was used to purchase meat and grain from Argentina.

Furthermore, the large merchant marine, before the Second World War the largest in the world, served the needs of many countries besides Britain and earned money in every port of the world. This also was used to purchase imports. Lastly, Great Britain performed services, carried on an insurance business, in Lloyd's, of international importance, and operated international commodity markets in tea, tin, and other commodities. Further sums were earned and spent.

BALANCE OF PAYMENTS OF GREAT BRITAIN, 1938, IN MILLIONS OF POUNDS STERLING

	Payments		Receipts
Imports	835	Exports	533
Government expenditure abroad.	16	Shipping	100
Shipping services	80	Interest, profits, and dividends	205
Interest, profits, and dividends earned by foreigners	30	Other receipts	100
			938
Film remittances	7	Deficit	70
Tourist payments by Britons abroad	40		1,008
	1,008		

By 1947 the balance of payments, as shown, had changed drastically. All figures were inflated. Changes in terms of trade were greatly to the detriment of Great Britain. The net earnings from shipping were reduced to small

proportions owing to the large losses of British shipping, and the income from overseas investments was smaller.

BALANCE OF PAYMENTS OF GREAT BRITAIN, 1947, IN MILLIONS OF POUNDS STERLING

	Payments		Receipts
Imports	1,574	Exports	1,125
Government expenditure	211	Shipping	180
Shipping	163	Interest, profits, and dividends	145
Interest, dividends, and profits	94		1,450
		Deficit	655
Film remittances	13		2,105
Others	50		
	2,105		

Britain's deficit on her overseas transactions in 1938 had been 7 per cent; in 1947, it was over 30 per cent. This unsatisfactory economic situation has been relieved by American monetary grants, by Marshall Aid, and also by the great increase in Britain's industrial activity and export of manufactured goods. The position is itself due in part to Britain's sacrifices during the Second World War. The condition of Britain's industries has made recovery difficult. The generosity of the United States is allowing Britain to re-equip many of her factories and mines, and the efforts of the nation have been rewarded by a far greater degree of recovery by 1951 than most American observers had thought possible. But the old condition of ease and affluence has passed; Britain faces a long period of austerity.

BIBLIOGRAPHY

GENERAL

Allen, G. C., "British Industries and Their Organisation," London, 1933.

"British Industry," British Council, London, 1944.

Committee on Industry and Trade, Reports, London, 1928.

Demangeon, A., "The British Isles," translated by E. D. Laborde, London, 1939.

Easterbrook, Laurence F., "British Agriculture," British Council, London, 1945.

Fleure, H. J., "The Natural History of Man in Britain," London, 1951.

Freeman, T. W., "Ireland," London, 1949.

Maxton, J. P. (ed.), "Region al Types of British Agriculture," London, 1936.

Ogilvie, A. G. (ed.), "Great Britain: Essays in Regional Geography," Cambridge, 1937.

Smith, Wilfred, "An Economic Geography of Great Britain," London, 1949.

Stamp, L. Dudley, "Britain's Structure and Scenery," London, 1947.

———, The Land of Britain, Reports of the Land Utilisation Survey of Britain (volumes on the agricultural geography of individual counties), 1936–1946.

———, "The Land of Britain: Its Use and Misuse," London, 1948.

——— and S. H. Beaver, "The British Isles," London, 1941.

LOCAL STUDIES

Allen, G. C., "Industrial Development of Birmingham and the Black Country," London, 1929.

Baker, J. N. L., and E. W. Gilbert, The Doctrine of an Axial Belt of Industry in England, *G.J.*, CIII, 1944, 49–72.

Beaver, S. H., Minerals and Planning, *G.J.*, CIV, 1944, 166–193.

Crowe, P. R., The Scottish Coalfields, *S.G.M.*, LXV, 1929.

Evans, W. David, The Opencast Mining of Ironstone and Coal, *G.J.*, CIV, 1944, 102–119.

Fawcett, C. B., The Distribution of the Urban Population in Great Britain, 1931, *G.J.*, LXXIX, 1932, 100–116.

Freeman, T. W., Farming in Irish Life, *G.J.*, CX, 1948, 38–59.

"An Industrial Survey of the Lancashire Area," London, 1932.

"An Industrial Survey of Merseyside," London, 1932.

"An Industrial Survey of the Northeast Coast Area," London, 1932.

"An Industrial Survey of South Wales," London, 1932.

"An Industrial Survey of Southwest Scotland," London, 1932.

Jones, L. Rodwell, The British Fisheries, *E.G.*, II, 1926.

———, "The Geography of London River," London, 1932.

Jukes, J., and A. Winterbottom, "An Industrial Survey of Cumberland and Furness," Manchester, 1933.

Lebon, J. H. G., The Development of the Ayrshire Coalfield, *S.G.M.*, XLIX, 1933, 138–154.

Manley, Gordon, "Climate and the British Scene," London, 1952.

Ministry of Fuel and Power, Regional Survey Reports, London, 1945–1946. (A series of reports on English coal fields.)

North, F. J., "Coal and the Coalfields of Wales," National Museum of Wales, Cardiff, 1935.

———, "The Slates of Wales," National Museum of Wales, Cardiff, 1927.

Pounds, N. J. G., The China Clay Industry of Southeast England, *E.G.*, XXVIII, 1952, 20–30.

Snodgrass, Catherine P., Map of Economic Regions of Scotland, *S.G.M.*, LIX, 1943, 15–18.

Williams, D. T., "The Economic Development of Swansea," Swansea, 1940.

———, The Economic Geography of the Western Half of the South Wales Coalfield, *S.G.M.*, XLIX, 1933, 274–289.

BRITISH GEOGRAPHICAL PERIODICALS

Geographical Journal, Royal Geographical Society, London, published quarterly.

Geography, Geographical Association, Sheffield, published quarterly.

Institute of British Geographers: Transactions, London, published annually.

Scottish Geographical Magazine, Royal Scottish Geographical Society, Edinburgh, published quarterly.

These frequently contain articles on the geography of the British Isles. There is also much geographical material in *The Economist* (weekly, London), *The Times Review of Industry* (monthly, London), and the periodical publications of the English banks, especially *Lloyds Bank Review* (quarterly, London), *Midland Bank Review* (quarterly, London), *Westminster Bank Review* (quarterly, London).

The *Government Publications Monthly List*, obtainable from the British Information Services in either New York or Chicago, lists many publications of considerable geographical value.

Valuable reports on those British industries which were not scheduled for nationalization by the postwar Labor Government, were prepared by "Working Parties" appointed by the Board of Trade and published at intervals in 1946 to 1948.

Some 20 sheets of the "National Atlas" have been published on a scale of 10 miles to the inch. They illustrate land use, types of farming, mining, iron and steel manufacture, movement of population, and other topics. The "Atlas" is very far from completion, but the sheets already published indicate that it may be the most perfect national atlas yet published.

CHAPTER 12: *France*

France is as varied in its structure and relief as the British Isles. All the east-to-west structural belts of Europe, with the exception of the Scandinavian Massif, are found here, and it has become a commonplace of French geographers that France is the meeting place of most, if not all, the physical and human elements of Europe. It is a compact country. Its greatest dimensions, about 600 miles, are from the extreme north, where the Franco-Belgian frontier runs down to the North Sea, to the Spanish frontier in Roussillon and from the Pointe du Raz in Brittany to the Rhine. Of the total periphery of present-day France, some 1,800 miles, 56 per cent, is bounded by the sea. For a stretch of many miles, the frontier follows mountain ranges, the Pyrenees, Alps, and Jura. It is far from true to say that the frontier here is unambiguous and admitting of no dispute. There have been prolonged quarrels regarding all of it, but these are insignificant beside the difficulties that have attended the formation of the frontier that runs from the northern end of the Jura to the north coast. For about 110 miles it follows the Rhine, then takes a course approximately in a northwesterly direction, skirting the valley of the Saar (Sarre) and the upland massif of the Ardennes to end in the populous plain of Flanders.

France is made up of a substructure of ancient rock, hidden over much of its area by the later deposits. Nevertheless, the older rocks are exposed by the denudation of the younger beds and appear in the Breton Massif, the Vosges, the Ardennes, and the large and complex Central Massif. Coal measures are associated with the ancient rocks and have been preserved in a number of small faulted basins in the Central Massif. Coal occurs on the edge of the Ardennes and in the Saar and Moselle (Mosel) Valleys, and in northern France the coal field of Belgium is continued beneath the shallow cover of later rocks.

Around and between the areas of older and harder rocks are younger, softer, and more fertile beds. These resemble closely the limestone, chalk, and clay of the English Plain, with which, in fact, they were once joined across the Channel. As in Lowland England, the beds of limestone and chalk tend to form ridges or plateaus, and the clay gives rise to the intervening valleys and plains.

Toward the southeast and south these younger beds are strongly folded. They rise first into the crumpled folds of the Jura Mountains and then into the folded and overfolded ranges of the Alps and Pyrenees.

Most of France belongs to the moist, temperate region of northwestern Europe, and only the coastal lands of the southeast fall within the Mediterranean region of summer drought. The range of temperature becomes greater toward the east, and the winters sharper. In the west the rainfall shows a winter maximum, but toward the east the summer maximum, characteristic of central Europe, begins to appear. The narrow Mediterranean region of the south has a light winter rainfall and summers which are dry and hot.

The aspect of France, as of England, is in large measure man-made. Little trace remains of its primitive vegetation cover. Most of France was once covered with deciduous woodland, with oak, elm, and beech and, on lower ground, willow and poplar. Conifers grew on the mountains and also on the dry gravel and sandy

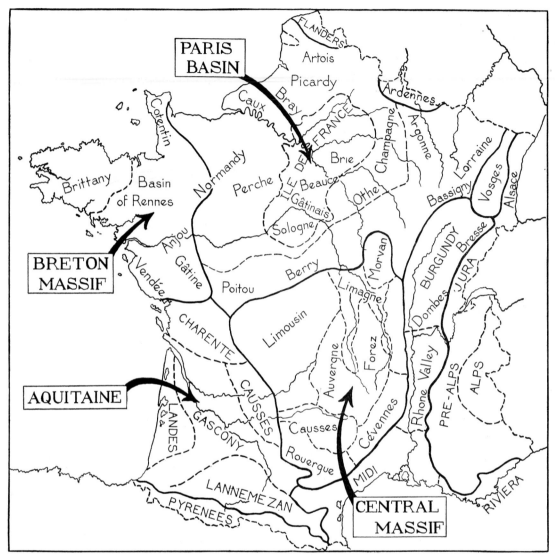

Fig. 72. Physical regions of France.

soils. Most of the forest has been cleared to make way for cultivation. A thin, coarse grass grows on the limestone, and in the mountains are large areas of rock outcrop without vegetation or soil. The Alps and Pyrenees have a vegetation cover which is characteristically coniferous woodland on the lower slopes and grass up to the limit of permanent snow cover.

In recent years considerable areas have been planted with trees. Forest now covers about 18 per cent of the total area. The largest stands are the pine plantations of the sandy and, in parts,

drained area of the *landes* of Aquitaine and the coniferous forests of the hills of eastern France. Little forest remains in the moist lands of the north and northwest. Here the landscape has the ragged appearance produced by small fields surrounded by thick hedges set with trees. This is what the French call the *bocage*. They contrast the *bocage* with the *champagne*, the rolling, treeless, hedgeless country, where fields are large, where fences are unsubstantial, and where the cultivated strips of the peasants are mixed in a medieval pattern. The *champagne* is found on the limestone and chalk and on the more recent deposits of the Paris Basin. It is good farming country. In the Middle Ages it was apportioned in large estates cultivated by serfs or other unfree workers. The *bocage* land of the west was harder to cultivate and yielded poorer crops. The open fields were few, and there were, instead, the small holdings of a poor but rela-

Fig. 73. Brittany and the Armorican region. The broken line indicates the margin of the massif of ancient rock.

tively independent peasantry. The medieval cycle, the "Roman de rou," contrasts

"Li paisan et li vilain,
    Cil des bocages et cil des plains."[1]

Breton Massif. This is a very much larger region than the ancient province of Brittany; it extends over western Normandy and southward into Anjou and La Vendée. On this account it is sometimes known, from the ancient name for this part of France, as the Armorican Massif. In its structure the region bears certain resemblances to the southwest of England. It is built up of ancient rocks, folded into a broad and complex trough, whose northern and southern margins give rise to lines of low, rounded hills. The land has no great heights or steep slopes. Granite and other hard rocks form hills which

[1] The peasant and the villein (*serf*); the former belongs to the bocage, the latter to the plain (*champagne*).

rise gently from broad, shallow lowlands. Unlike the more open *champagne* lands of the Paris Basin, the Breton region is characteristically one of *bocage*. Its fields are small and surrounded by hedges. Small plots of woodland are common, and the aspect is one of a rich and thick vegetation covering land forms that are predominantly rounded and mature. The coastal regions are more exposed to the Atlantic gales than is the interior. Trees are fewer, and many areas, such as Finistère, are virtually treeless on account of the violence of the wind. The sea cliffs are steep; the lower courses of the rivers are incised and frequently terminate in long branching estuaries or rias, such as the Rade de Brest, which form the harbors of the Breton fishing towns. The coastal region has a ruggedness which is in sharp contrast to the smoothness and maturity of the inland region.

The high rainfall and the mildness of the temperature render the region more suitable for pastoral than for crop farming. Although early vegetables are grown in sheltered areas near the coast for sale in the Paris market, dairy farming is the predominant agricultural pursuit. The south coast is warmer and more sheltered than the north, and more important in the production of "earlies." Fishing is carried on from the coastal villages. Along the south coast of Brittany the sardine fisheries are important, and sardine canning is practiced in certain of the coastal towns.

Brittany in the more restricted sense is the hilly western peninsula, where the ridge and vale topography is particularly strongly developed. Brest (75,000),[1] the French Atlantic naval base, is the largest town. Lorient, a small port at the mouth of the Blavet, was established in the seventeenth century to handle France's trade with the Orient but has long since been replaced by other ports more favorably situated in relation to the centers of French industry and population. Around the coast are innumerable small and picturesque towns, which depend for

[1] The population according to the census of 1946 is given for cities of over 50,000. Not all cities of this size, however, are named in the text. Many cities have increased considerably since 1946.

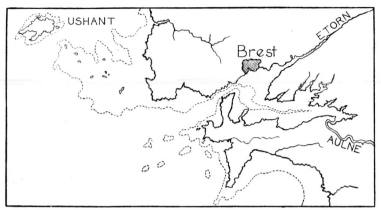

Fig. 74. The harbor of Brest. This admirable harbor is ill-placed for commerce but forms, like Devonport, an excellent naval base.

their existence on fishing, agriculture, and the tourist trade. At the base of the Breton peninsula the river Vilaine has excavated a broad, lowland plain, in which lies the Breton capital, Rennes (114,000). The climate is drier here than in the Breton peninsula, and crop farming becomes more important. Yet farther east, the relief is stronger and rainfall heavier. Dairying again becomes the more important branch of agriculture, towns are few, and population relatively sparse. To the north is the low Cotentin peninsula, like Brittany exposed along its cliff-fringed coast to the violence of the Atlantic. Cherbourg has developed on its northern coast as a port of call for Atlantic liners but handles very little cargo.

Near Angers (see page 142) the river Loire leaves the Paris Basin and enters this region of ancient rock. The aspect of the land changes. Viticulture disappears, and *bocage* replaces *champagne*. Angers (94,500) itself has, with its ancient fortifications, the character of a frontier town but has developed a number of modern industries. Nantes lies at the head of ocean navigation, but the Loire is a difficult river; only the smaller vessels succeed in reaching the town and then only with the help of lateral canals. Nantes (200,500), like Lorient, formerly had an important colonial trade. Saint-Nazaire has inherited certain of the commercial functions of Nantes but is not primarily a commercial port. It is the most important French center of the

shipbuilding industry. South of Nantes is La Vendée. In the center it rises to the infertile hills of the Gâtine but on the west and south drops to lowlands in which the vine and other crops which demand warmth and sunshine begin to appear. On this side the Breton Massif merges gradually and imperceptibly into the warm, rich lowland of Aquitaine, which is considered on page 146.

Paris Basin. Within the semicircle formed by the four massifs of Brittany, the Central Massif, the Vosges, and the Ardennes is the Paris Basin, equal in area approximately to West Virginia. Topographically the region is made up of a number of concentric rings of higher ground, built of limestone, chalk, and sandstone and separated from one another by clay-floored depressions. These beds dip toward the center of the Paris Basin and resemble in their structure a series of saucers of diminishing size, set one inside the other. The diagram (Fig. 75) illustrates both the topography and the structure and indicates the dependence of the former on the latter. Compare this diagram with Fig. 58, which illustrates the topography and structure of the English Midlands, and make frequent reference to the map of the regions.

On the southwest the Paris Basin extends into the valley of the Loire, on the east into those of the Meuse and Moselle, and the northern margin is drained by the Somme and by other short rivers which flow directly into the English

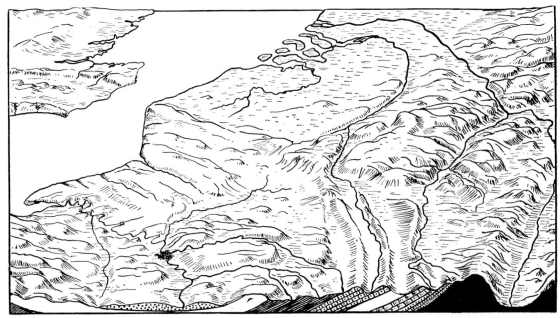

Fig. 75. Diagrammatic sketch of the northern part of the Paris Basin. The Seine is seen on the left; the Vosges Mountains and the Rhine on the right.

Channel. Nevertheless, the Paris Basin is essentially that of the river Seine and of its tributaries, the Oise, Marne, Yonne, and Loing. These have their sources near the margin of the basin and flow toward its center, crossing the alternate ridges and valleys. They unite in the neighborhood of Paris, and the Seine bears their water northwestward to the sea.

The Ile de France is the name given to the region in which the city of Paris lies. It is an island only in the sense that it is, at least on the southeast, east, and northeast, bounded by a scarp. This *falaise*, or "cliff," of the Ile de France is formed by the steep edge of a limestone plateau. On the south, this plateau thins away through Sologne, so that no physical feature marks its edge. Most of this region has the aspect of a low, dissected plateau, rarely exceeding 600 feet in altitude. Its sub-surface is formed generally of limestone, but not the same limestone bed over the whole area. To the southwest of Paris the limestone of Beauce forms a level, dry tableland, over which a thin loam has been dusted. It is a fertile, wheat-growing region. To the east of the Seine is Brie, similarly capped with limestone. The Brie Plateau is more dis-

sected than Beauce and is, furthermore, covered with a deposit of residual clay. Its soils are heavier, and Brie counts as a dairy-farming rather than as a crop-farming province. Between the two limestone beds already mentioned are the Fontainebleau sands which outcrop to the south of Paris, giving rise to a famous forested, resort area.

The larger rivers rise outside the region of the Ile de France and flow across it in deeply incised valleys. The Marne enters its valley at Epernay; the Aisne, above Soissons; the Oise, near Laon; the Seine, at Fontainebleau. These rivers converge in the vicinity of Paris. Settlements avoid the plateau surfaces, which are, as a general rule, made up of either dry limestone or infertile sand. They occur rather on the valley sides where springs are thrown out at the base of the limestone beds, and the larger towns lie where the rivers enter or emerge from their incised valleys across the plateau.

The towns of the Paris Basin are small and dwarfed by Paris itself. Paris (2,725,000) lies on the Seine a mile or two below the confluence of the Marne. The early town grew up on an island in the Seine, the Ile de la Cité. The site

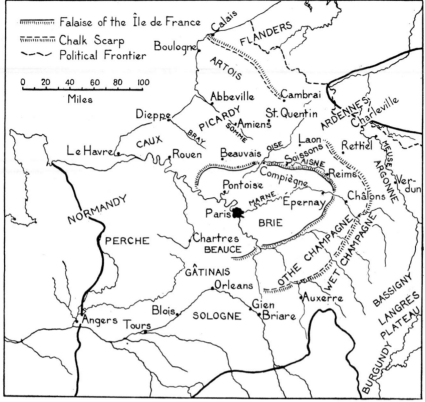

Fig. 76. The Paris Basin.

was occupied by the Romans, it was later fortified, and Paris was successfully defended against the Norsemen, who were able to sail this far up the Seine in their long boats. It then became the chief seat of the kings of France, and at the end of the twelfth century, the city embraced also a considerable area of land on both banks of the Seine. At this point a low hill, the Montagne Sainte Geneviève, advances close to the river from the south, while on the north, a flat semicircular plain—an ancient meander plain of the river—is bounded by a range of low buttes. The town spread quickly over the flood plain of the river, which, early in the seventeenth century, was almost wholly enclosed by the walls of the town. The nineteenth-century defenses embraced the whole of the buttes to the north of the city. Above Paris the river narrows; below it remains navigable today for the smaller craft. At a time when much of the commerce was river-borne, Paris

commanded a position of great importance. It acquired a commercial strength which it has been able to retain, even though the rivers are now of relatively small value. Paris also became a railway center. There are no less than seven railway termini, from which lines radiate to all parts of France.

The Ile de France region is well suited to support a great capital. The limestone of Brie and Beauce and the gypsum of Valois have contributed to its architectural beauty. Truck farming has spread up the Seine and Marne Valleys, dairy produce is obtained from the pasture lands of Normandy and Brie, and grain from the plateau of Beauce. Paris has been, since the Middle Ages, a center for skilled craftsmanship. It has now become the most important manufacturing area of France. With the location in Paris of the chief offices of government and the erection nearby of many of the palaces of the French kings and nobility,

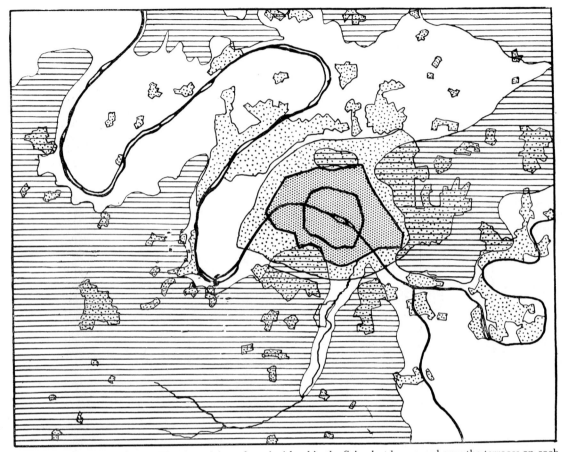

FIG. 77. The situation of Paris. The city originated on the island in the Seine but has spread over the terraces on each bank. The successive walls of the city show the stages in its growth. Fine dots indicate the area of the city built up at the time of the Revolution; the coarse, the present built-up area. The area shaded with horizontal lines lies at above 200 feet.

Paris developed as a manufacturer of "quality" goods. It is outstanding today as a source of clothing, jewelry, leather, skins, paper, glass, chinaware, and perfumery, much of high quality and destined for a luxury market. Many of the goods are handmade, but in recent years Paris has become also a center of heavy industry. The heavy industries are dependent upon cheap water and rail transportation, and many are of a kind that benefit from the publicity resulting from a location in the capital. Automobiles, airplane engines, machine tools, and electrical equipment are outstanding among its products. Paris is also a center of clothing manufacture and of the printing and publishing industry. Oil refining, rubber manufacture, and the preparation of nonferrous metals, cement, and artificial

fertilizers do not exhaust the catalogue of Paris industries but indicate their variety.

Paris has the advantage of excellent means of communication and transportation. Railways radiate to all parts not only of France but of western Europe. The Seine waterway has been deepened, made navigable, and supplemented by canals. It is in water communication not only with Rouen and Le Havre but also with the industrial regions of the north and east and with the Loire and Rhône systems. The luxury industries are in large measure located in the inner parts of the city. This is in itself an indication of their greater age. The newer industries have been established nearer the outer, expanding fringe of the capital. The aircraft, automobile, and chemical industries are carried on

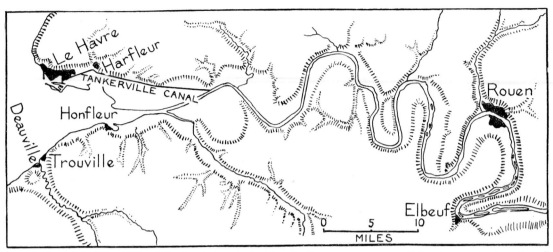

FIG. 78. The lower Seine Valley. The river is here incised in a chalk plateau, and along its banks are a number of small textile-producing towns.

very largely to the west and north, along the banks of the meandering Seine.

In acquiring its industrial significance Paris has lost none of its older charm and beauty. The cathedral of Notre Dame, the Sainte Chapelle, and the other old buildings of the island; the tree-lined banks of the Seine, where secondhand books and goods are sold in the little booths; the royal palace of the Louvre, set in the Tuileries gardens, and the other palaces, the Luxembourg on the Montagne Sainte Geneviève, and Versailles, a few miles to the west; then the spacious and dignified Paris that was laid out by Haussmann in the nineteenth century; the Champs Elysées and the boulevards which converge at L'Etoile all contribute to the fascination of the city.

The chalk region encircles the plateau in which Paris lies in a broad belt from the coast south of Calais through Artois, Champagne, Touraine, and Anjou to Normandy. In parts it forms a dry and dusty plateau stretching unbroken to the horizon; in others its true nature is marked by a superficial deposit of residual clay. Deep valleys have been cut into the chalk surface. A number of minor folds have produced low ridges in the northern part of the chalk area and have imparted a southeast-to-northwest direction to several of the rivers. In two places, the chalk has been stripped from the crests of such ridges. The "Weald" of Boulonnais reaches inland from the neighborhood of Boulogne (79,500) and appears to continue across the Channel from the Weald of Kent, which in structure and appearance it closely resembles. Bray is another example of such a stripped upfold.

The chalk of the northern part of the Paris Basin is drained by deeply incised rivers which flow in straight valleys to the English Channel. In the north is the dry ridge of Artois, where the chalk, covered by a fine loam, yields a rich dry soil and produces heavy crops of grain. To the southwest the chalk continues in Picardy and Caux. Along the coast are high, white, chalk cliffs; inland, the undulating tableland of Picardy lies open and bare of all except the growing crops. Caux has a richer vegetation, which announces the approach of the *bocage*. The villages lie in the valleys and in hollows of the ground; the strips of arable land are unfenced. This is true *champagne*, and its monotony is often broken only by the lines of tall trees that border the *routes nationales* as they run straight across the country. The heavier soils of Bray and Boulonnais support a richer growth. Here are hedges and patches of woodland, and the land has the *bocage* appearance that is common farther to the west. The valleys in the chalk often have heavy soils and are ill-drained·

the Somme Valley is particularly famous for its irrigated vegetable gardens. Towns lie in the valleys. Abbeville, Amiens (85,000), and Saint-Quentin lie on the Somme; Beauvais, with its spectacular Gothic cathedral, is in Bray. On the Seine, where it flows in broad meanders deeply incised in the chalk, lie Rouen and a number of lesser industrial towns that

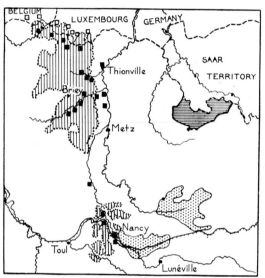

Fig. 79. The Lorraine industrial region. The iron and steel centers in eastern France are shown by black squares; those in Belgium and Luxembourg, by open squares. The iron-ore field is represented by vertical shading; the Lorraine extension of the Saar coal field, by horizontal; and the extent of the salt deposits, by dots. The Rhine-Marne canal is shown across the south of the map.

have grown up nearby. Rouen (107,500) is reached by seagoing vessels and was in the past an important coal port which handled the once-considerable import from England. It also imports cotton in large quantities not only for the mills of the district of Rouen itself but also for textile centers in the east of France. Along the river have grown up a variety of industries which depend upon the import of bulky goods and use the river as a source of power. But larger vessels and those making only brief calls to discharge or take on part cargoes dock at Le Havre. Le Havre (107,000) was founded by the French king François I early in the sixteenth

century, and it grew to importance with the increasing size of ships and the greater difficulty in navigating the tortuous Seine.

To the east of Paris the belt of chalk is narrower than in the north but is more dry, more regular, and less broken by valleys and hollows. This is the plateau of "dry" or "dusty" Champagne, *la Champagne pouilleuse*. On the west it is overlooked by the Brie Plateau; on the east it rises to a low scarp which overlooks the clay vale of "wet" Champagne, *la Champagne humide*. Reims (110,000) lies near its western edge; Châlons-sur-Marne and Arcis-sur-Aube in the valleys of through rivers; and Rethel, Vitry-le-François, and Troyes (59,000) where these rivers pass from the low plain of "wet" Champagne to the narrow valleys of "dry." The vintage for which Champagne is chiefly known is produced from grapes grown on the sunny, south-facing slopes of the deep valleys and on the edges of Brie. To the south the chalk beds rise in the Forêt d'Othe to a high scarp. They then thin away and are covered by beds of sand and clay, producing the damp, wooded slopes of the Gâtinais and the sandy, lake-strewn waste of the Sologne.

Northward from the Loire to the coast of Normandy is a broad belt of chalk, which rises in the hills of Perche and Normandy to heights of well over 1,000 feet. Patches of clay and sand lie scattered over the chalk surface. This, coupled with the heavier rainfall, renders the aspect of the region less dry and bare. In many parts it is *bocage* rather than *champagne*. Damp meadowland spreads over the lower ground, and even on the chalk heights there is often a heavy soil suited rather for dairy than crop farming.

The chalk region in its turn is partially encircled by the limestone. The limestone beds are separated by clay, and as, in the eastern and southern parts of the Paris Basin these beds all dip toward the center, erosion has produced a series of limestone ridges separated by clay-floored valleys. The ridges are steep toward the east and south, gentle toward the center of the basin, and their configuration has been of some importance in the military defense of the approaches to Paris.

French coal mine and mining settlement in the northern coal field. Note the level, treeless, and well-cultivated country-side, typical of northern France. (*French Embassy, Information Division.*)

The valleys are generally damp and poorly drained, more suited to pastoral than to crop farming. The limestone scarps are dry, with a poor soil, and the whole of this scarp-and-vale region is sparsely peopled. The Argonne, built of sandstone and more moist than the others, and the Côtes de Meuse form conspicuous ridges, but the highest and the most extensive is formed by the Côtes de Moselle. From southern Belgium it extends southward as a high, broken, and indented scarp front which rises like a wall above the Moselle Valley and the plateau of Lorraine and behind the cities of Metz (70,000) and Nancy (113,500). It broadens into the plateau of Langres, and its richly colored limestone rises in the steep Côte d'Or above the vineyards of Burgundy. The limestone plateau is exposed and bleak, the climate is more severe than on the lower plateaus farther west, and the region even less populous. It contains, however, in its northern part the rich deposits of minette iron ore which underlie the limestone. These constitute probably the most abundant resource of iron ore in Europe. In 1950 the mines of eastern France produced about 29 million tons of ore. The maximum production in any one year has been nearly 50 million tons. Lorraine now produces up to 40 per cent of the total European output of ore, but its relative importance is somewhat reduced by the low metallic content of about 31 per cent.

The metallurgical industry of eastern France is now concentrated in the Moselle Valley, between Nancy and Thionville, and in the neighborhood of Briey, a few miles to the west. This area produces about three-quarters of the total French production of both pig iron and steel. The furnaces lie either along the Moselle, at the foot of the limestone scarp, or in the valleys cut in the limestone plateau. The region produces mainly crude iron and steel, and the finishing industry in Lorraine is relatively small. Coal is obtained from the Saar coal field and its continuation in Lorraine at Saint-Avold, but metallurgical coke, for which this coal is only partly suited, is imported from the coal fields of western Germany. Since its rapid development in the later years of the nineteenth century, the Lorraine industrial area has suffered from an acute labor shortage, and numbers of Italians, Poles, and Czechs have been introduced to work the mines.

Between the limestone scarp and the Vosges Mountains is the plain of Lorraine, a damp, clay-floored region, sufficiently high above sea level for its climate to be appreciably cooler than in lower regions to west and east. Its surface is studded with small lakes. There are large areas of woodland, and agriculture is concentrated on animal rearing and growing fodder crops. Toward the south and west the limestone beds cease to form a regular and continuous scarp form. Instead, the whole region is one of rounded hills and broad, open valleys. Woodland occurs on the clay and sand, vineyards clothe the sunny slopes, and the more fertile areas are cultivated for grain.

The Paris Basin, as it has been described here, is larger than the area which is drained by the Seine and its tributaries. It embraces also the central valley of the Loire and part of the Meuse and Moselle Valleys. The Paris Basin has been the scene of numerous river captures. It is probable that the Loire formerly continued its northward course to join the Seine. At the same time the Seine and Moselle have drawn away tributaries from the Meuse, and the most striking example of river capture is that whereby a former tributary of the Meuse was tapped at Toul and made to flow east to join the Meurthe near Nancy and thus to make the river Moselle.

The Loire enters the Paris Basin near Nevers and flows directly across the limestone and chalk before making a conspicuous bend near Orléans (70,000) and flowing west through a broad and fertile valley. At Angers, the Loire leaves the Paris Basin and crosses an area of hard and ancient rocks to the sea. Along this rich valley is a succession of towns, many of them early centers of trade and wealth, which they show now in their cathedrals, castles, and rich domestic architecture.

The Meuse flows from its source in the limestone of the Langres Plateau across ridges and vales and then follows a deep, narrow valley along the Meuse hills, parallel with their scarp edge. It has few towns of importance. Verdun is a military center because it commands routeways across the ridges west of the city. The Moselle and its tributary the Meurthe rise in the Vosges, cross the plain of Lorraine, and after their junction near Nancy flow parallel with the limestone hills toward Germany and the massif of the Ardennes and Eifel. Nancy (113,500), on the Meurthe, is a former capital of Lorraine and is a city of great beauty and interest and a center of engineering, chemical, and other industries.

Flanders and the Northern Industrial Region. North of the downs of Artois the chalk dips beneath the sand, clay, and peat of the Flanders Plain. This low, flat region of intensive agriculture passes imperceptibly into drier land of slightly greater elevation, with a covering of loess. East of the city of Valenciennes this region rises gradually through the damp meadows, pastures, and woodlands of Thiérache to the Ardennes. Not only is the whole of this region one of rich and varied agriculture; it contains the richest coal field of France. Although the coal measures do not reach the surface they support a number of coal-mining and industrial towns, centers for textile and metallurgical industries.

In some respects the industries of this region are a continuation of the medieval cloth industry of Flanders. The region was well served by roads from early times. It produced flax and wool; it was richly productive, wealthy, and populous and had most of those natural advantages which help to locate a great industrial region. The northern industrial area has never shown a narrow specialization. Most branches of the textile and metallurgical industries are carried on, sugar is refined, pottery and glass are made, carpets woven, and a great variety of goods of lesser importance produced.

The textile industry is largely restricted to the vicinity of Lille, though there is a secondary center of cloth manufacture in the small towns of the upper valleys of the Scheldt and Sambre.

The woolen industry is carried on most actively at Roubaix (101,000) and Tourcoing (76,000), both now parts of a large conurbation

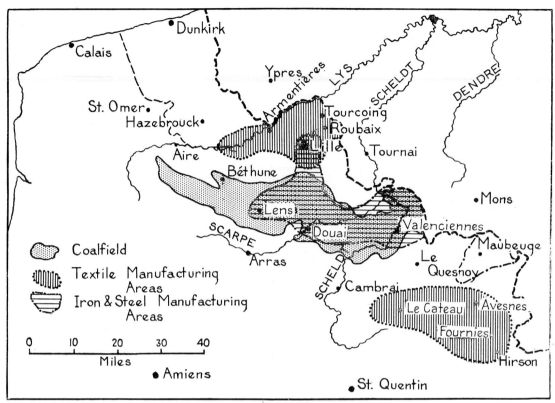

FIG. 80. The northern industrial region of France.

with Lille (189,000). Roubaix tends today to concentrate on dress fabrics, while carpets, tapestry, and harder wearing cloth for furnishings are made at Tourcoing. In the Thiérache and Cambrésis, which lie to the southeast, are a number of old but still very small centers of the woolen-cloth industry.

The cotton industry is modern in comparison with the woolen and was not present on any considerable scale in northern France until early in the nineteenth century. It has spread very largely at the expense of the linen industry, but its focus remains the town of Lille itself. Spinning is more important than weaving, and there is an export of spun thread to weaving industries in other parts of France. Lace, embroidery, and tulle are also made in a number of small towns of northern France. The cultivation of flax and manufacture of linen have long been staple industries of French Flanders. Though formerly widespread as domestic industries, flax

spinning and the weaving of linen cloth are now concentrated in Lille and its suburbs and in the small towns along the Lys Valley. The local production of flax is now supplemented by import from northern Europe.

The metallurgical industry, like the cotton industry, began in the nineteenth century. The region offers the advantage of coal and of easy communications, but iron and other ores have to be imported into the region. The Scheldt Valley, particularly the city of Valenciennes, has become the most important area within the north French industrial region for production of crude steel. The districts of Lille, Lens, and Douai produce finished-steel goods.

Coal mining is important from the most westerly extension of the coal field at Fléchinelle up to the Belgian border, but the principal area of exploitation is around Lens and Douai. Though this is by far the most important coal field of France, its annual output is no more than about 28 million tons, supplying less than half the needs of France.

It is difficult to set precise limits for the northern industrial region. The densely settled and highly industrial area shades outward through small towns and large, half industrial, half agricultural villages. Communications throughout the industrial region are good. The low-lying and very nearly flat land has facilitated the construction of railway lines and exca-

Fig. 81. Diagrammatic sketch of Alsace and the upper Rhine Valley, looking north. The Vosges are the left (west); the Black Forest to the right. S = Strasbourg; C = Colmar; B = Basel; M = Mulhouse; Bt = Belfort. The structure of the folded Jura is shown along the southern edge of the map.

vation of canals. Lying between the Ardennes and the sea, it is on one of the most used routeways in Europe, that from the Paris Basin northeastward through the north European Plain. Dunkirk (Dunkerque) is its chief port and imports the raw materials and exports the manufactured goods of both its French and its Belgian industrial hinterlands. Dunkirk is linked with Béthune, Lille, and other towns of the industrial north by a system of canals and canalized rivers, and a much-used canal through Cambrai to the Oise joins the north with Paris.

Eastern France. Along the eastern borders of France are areas of greater altitude and sharper

relief. The Ardennes Plateau, which lies chiefly in Belgium and western Germany, just extends within the French frontier. To the south is a broad tract of lower land, in which lie the German cities of Trier and Kaiserslautern. This has been one of the most used routeways between the Paris Basin and the Rhineland. In the seventeenth century the French built the fortress of Saarlouis at its western end, and on many occasions their armies have deployed over the Rhine Plain from its eastern end. Here also is the Saar (Sarre) coal basin. This small but rich and important region is German in speech and has always been considered German in sympathy. In 1919, the coal mines were occupied by the French for a period of 15 years, at the end of which it reverted to Germany at the will of its inhabitants. It has now, at the end of the Second World War, again been occupied by the French and now forms the autonomous unit of the Saarland (see page 238). The coalfield of the Saar can produce up to 15,000,000 tons of coal a year, and its steel production in 1950 amounted to 1,899,000 tons. Most of the industrial concerns are located in or near Saarbrücken.

The Vosges Mountains extend southward from this area of lower land to the Gap of Belfort, a distance of 130 miles. The northern half of the range, however, is low, rarely exceeding 1,500 feet in altitude. In the south the Vosges attain twice this height. The range here consists of crystalline rocks, which drop on the west to the sands and clays of Lorraine. The eastern face of the High Vosges is abrupt and follows a line of faulting. Stretched out before it is the flat floor of the Rhine Valley, and some 20 to 25 miles away rises the equally steep scarp of the Black Forest.

The Low Vosges are a rugged, dissected, and forested area of sandstone, drained very largely eastward to the Rhine. There are few routes across this hilly region; the easiest and most important is that which follows the Saverne Gap and links Strasbourg westward with the Paris Basin. A few miles to the south of Saverne the sandstone terminates, the altitude increases, and the bare grassy summit of the Vosges stretches southward until it drops abruptly to the Gap of Belfort. The flanks of the range are deeply grooved by the short torrents that rush to meet the Rhine. On the west the slope is more gentle, and on this side are a number of cotton- and other textile-manufacturing towns, which

The Vosges Mountains. This picture was taken near the head of one of the Vosges valleys. The agriculture here is mainly pastoral.

owed their rise in part to the availability here of water power.

From the foot of the Vosges scarp the slope eastward to the Rhine is so gentle as not in general to be perceptible. The Rhine itself is bounded by marshy alluvium and deposits of gravel and sand. This region, known in the south as the Hart, is forested and sparsely populated. To the west flows the river Ill, the river of Alsace. Along its banks are meadows, and between the Ill and the Vosges is a covering of loess. The land here is intensively cultivated, and on the sunny slopes are the vineyards where the Alsatian wines are produced. Settlements are mainly on the Ill or along this belt of warm, rich soil, close to the Vosges. Mulhouse (Mülhausen, 87,500), a cotton-manufacturing town, Colmar, and Sélestat lie on the river. Against the hills is a line of small, walled towns, each of them famed for its wines. Strasbourg (Strassburg, 175,500), on the Ill a short distance above its junction with the Rhine, was a large and important frontier town at the time of the Romans. It lay opposite the Saverne route and at a point where the Rhine marshes narrowed

and could be crossed with ease. It is now a focus of the commercial activity of Alsace and is not only a Rhine River port but also the terminus of canals which cross the Vosges into Lorraine and link the Ill with the Rhône through the Belfort Gap. Strasbourg, partly because of its French and German associations, has now become the seat of a parliament representative of the nations of western Europe. North of Strasbourg, the plain becomes less fertile, more thickly strewn with gravel, and more heavily forested. Potash deposits occur near Mulhouse, and small quantities of natural oil are obtained in northern Alsace.

Turkheim, Alsace. This small walled town lies in one of the best wine-making areas of the Rhineland. The grapes grow on the surrounding hills, and the wine is made in the cellars of the houses. Note the stork's nest on top of the medieval town gateway.

The province of Alsace is, with the exception of one or two of the upper valleys of the Vosges, German in speech. It was largely occupied by the French in 1648 and remained under French rule continuously until 1871. It was restored to France in 1919. Throughout this period the people of Alsace have generally demonstrated their desire to remain citizens of France, in spite of the barrage of propaganda that has at times been put up from beyond the Rhine. German is spoken in northern Lorraine, and this area also was annexed to Germany in 1871

The market place, Mulhouse, Alsace.

and remained German until 1919. At the same time the Alsatians have shown little disposition to absorb French characteristics and strenuously resisted the ill-judged attempts of the Paris government to impose the French language on them. They remain Catholic Rhinelanders.

The Basin of Aquitaine. The limestones of the Paris Basin extend through the so-called Gate of Poitou into Aquitaine. This broad gap, fully 40 miles wide, separates the Central Massif from the low hills, crossed by the Loire, which form the southerly extension of the Breton Massif. The plain, which broadens to the south, is floored with soft limestone which has been eroded into gentle hills and broad valleys.

In the district of Charente in the north, the chalk and limestone have been arched up in a low ridge which stretches northwestward across the north of Aquitaine and is continued seaward in the Ile de Ré and the Ile d'Oléron. The limestone and chalk produce a dry surface on which crop farming and viticulture are practiced, but on the areas of clay, meadowland and dairy cattle become important. This is a rich land of market towns. On the coast is the ancient port and center of the French Huguenots, La Rochelle, and a modern port, La

Pallice, has been built nearby. The region is important for viticulture, and the production of brandy, to which the town of Cognac bears witness, is a local specialization.

Between the plain and the high plateau of central France is a belt of hilly country consisting of chalk and limestone and crossed by the deep valleys of the many rivers which flow from the massif to join the Dordogne or the Garonne. The region is too hilly to be very productive, except for the grape vine which is grown on the terraced slopes. In the valleys are market centers such as Périgueux, Bergerac, and Cahors. Toward the south the limestone rises to high, bare, karstic plateaus, known as the "causses." In these regions there is little or no surface drainage. Vegetation is thin, resembling the garrigue that has been described earlier

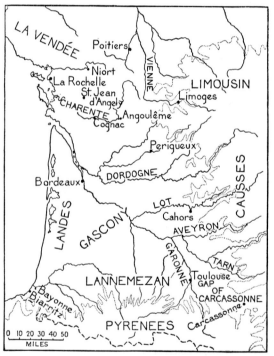

FIG. 82. Aquitaine. The contour shown is at 1,000 feet.

(page 27), and the aspect is wild and barren in the extreme.

The *landes* form the coastal region of Aquitaine between the mouth of the Gironde and the foothills of the Pyrenees. They consist of a wide belt of towering sand dunes, blown inland from the shore of the Bay of Biscay. Farther inland is an even wider belt of sandy soil where agriculture is in general impracticable and the sterile soils have been planted with pine trees or are grazed by sheep. The beach is straight and featureless. Most of the little rivers have been

The grape harvest in the Bordeaux region. The grapes are picked into large baskets which are emptied into ox- or horse-drawn carts and taken to the wine presses. (*Commissariat Général au Tourisme.*)

dammed back by the sand to make lagoons, and in the whole of this straight coast of 140 miles there is only one opening and only one small port, Arcachon at the mouth of the Leyre. The region is sparsely peopled; its products are pine logs and turpentine.

A vast flattened half cone, known as Lannemezan, is set against the northern flank of the Pyrenees. It has been built up in recent geological times by the torrents flowing northward from the mountains; it consists of coarse gravel and sand, becoming finer as it reaches lower land toward the north. The soil is poor and stony. The rivers have deepened their beds in the loose deposits and in doing so have lowered the water table. The Lannemezan is as dry as it is infertile, although fruit growing and viticul-

ture are important on the warm, sandy soils of Armagnac. The towns are small and serve mainly as markets for their surrounding districts.

Gascony is the broad undulating plain which occupies the center of Aquitaine and is drained

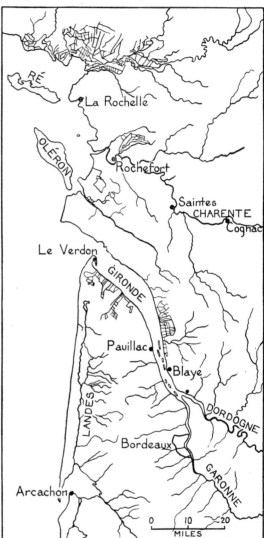

FIG. 83. The Gironde, estuary of the Garonne and of the Dordogne. Notice the obstructed drainage of the Landes and the artificial drainage of the marshland north of La Rochelle and along the Gironde.

by the Garonne, the Dordogne, and their tributaries. The soil is rich and is intensively cultivated, producing grain, tobacco, fruit, early vegetables, and, above all, the grape vine. The largest center of the region is Bordeaux (254,-

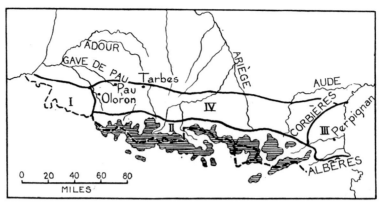

FIG. 84. The Pyrenees. The regions are: I, the Western Pyrenees; II, the Central Pyrenees; III, Roussillon; IV, the Pyrenean foothills. Shaded areas lie at above 6,000 feet.

000), lying at the head of the Gironde estuary and accessible to large ships. It has an important commerce with the French empire and with tropical lands and exports timber and wine. In the southeast, the basin of Aquitaine narrows between the Pyrenees and the Central Massif and passes into the Gap of Lauraguais or Carcassonne. At the western entrance to the gap is the town of Toulouse (264,500), a rail junction, route center, and industrial town.

The Pyrenean Region. The Pyrenees are like the Alps, a range of folded mountains, and like the Alps, they have a core of hard, crystalline rocks. The range increases eastward in both breadth and height. Toward the west, the mountains are formed wholly of soft sedimentary rock and are comparatively low and the land forms rounded. East of the Pic du Midi d'Ossau, the crystalline core comes to the surface and continues without interruption eastward to the Mediterranean. Most of the highest peaks, including the Puy de Carlitte, Maladetta, and Pic du Midi de Bigore, are carved out of granite and are rugged and precipitous. The range shows a quite remarkable continuity throughout its length of 250 miles. Passes are few and difficult. Best known of these is the Pass of Roncesvalles, through the low western Pyrenees, but more important, because the only easy crossing of the crystalline Pyrenees, is the Col de Perche.

The boundary between France and Spain, in general, follows the stream divide; the Garonne is the only north-flowing river which rises in Spain. On the French side, the range is drained by the Garonne, the Aude, and their tributaries. These rise in the snow fields and cirques of the crystalline core of the range and flow northward through valleys which broaden in the soft clays and narrow to pass through the belts of limestone. In some places, the approaches to the central region are guarded by difficult and narrow gorges, inside which the mountainous area tends to form an isolated and self-sufficing unit. The high Pyrenees tend to be a meeting ground for the inhabitants of the enclosed valleys to north and south, and many international treaties have been necessary to regulate the conduct of shepherds on the upland pastures which both sides share. The peculiar isolation and unity of the central area here encouraged the survival longer than elsewhere of small political units, of which Andorra has continued to exist until the present.

The French Pyrenees may be considered the western region, consisting of low dissected hills of limestones and clays. The rainfall is heavy, and the region is well forested with deciduous trees. The central Pyrenees display the features, such as cirques, overdeepened valleys, and arêtes, of an intensively glaciated mountain region. The region is one of sparse pastoral population, but in recent years the torrents which rush northward have been harnessed to generate hydroelectric power, and as in the Alps of Savoy, a number of electrochemical and electrometallurgical industries have been established. The crystalline Pyrenees continue eastward to the very shores of the Mediterranean. Between the eastern spurs of the Pyrenees lies the small, fertile plain of Roussillon. It has belonged both to Spain and to France in turn,

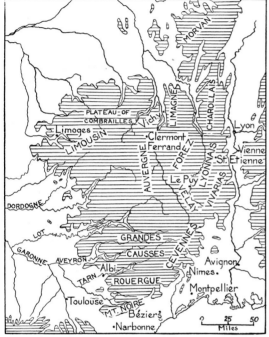

FIG. 85. The Central Massif of France. The shaded area lies at above 1,000 feet.

but since 1659 it has been French, though its language and customs are more Catalan or Spanish than French. The northern border of the Pyrenees consists of young, soft rocks. It forms a series of east-west ridges, usually of limestone, cut into sections by northward-flowing rivers. Some of these valleys, such as those of the Gave de Pau, the Adour, Garonne, and Ariège, have attained some reputation as tourist and vacation areas. The small towns, such as Oloron, Tarbes, and Pau, which each focuses the economic life of its valley, have developed small textile and metallurgical industries, and Lourdes, in the valley of the Gave de Pau, has become a place of pilgrimage for Catholics from all parts of western Europe.

The Central Massif. The Central Massif is the largest and most complex of the regions of

ancient rock in France and is made up of a number of distinct units, such as Morvan, the Causses, the Auvergne, and the Cévennes. On the west it represents a continuation of Brittany, and the hills here show the same northwest to southeast trend as the hills of La Vendée. On the east, the ranges of the massif run parallel rather to the direction of the Vosges and Black Forest. The whole region is one of the most varied in relief, aspect, and productivity of any in France. It has been intruded by igneous rocks which form extensive areas of rounded upland and has been the scene of volcanic action which has built up the range of *puys*, or extinct craters. On the west and south the region is covered by level beds of dry limestone, which compose the causses. Fault-bounded basins within the massif were once occupied by shallow

Ploughing in the Cantal. This is one of the poorer areas, with heavy rainfall, harsh climate, and infertile soil. Agricultural methods are primitive.

lakes and are now covered with sands and clays which contrast strongly to the surrounding uplands. The massif is made up of nine distinct physical units.

The Morvan is the most northerly extension of the massif. In size and configuration it closely resembles the Vosges. It is a forested region, with a heavy rainfall. To the south of the upland of Morvan is a faulted depression, known as the Autunois, where the coal measures have been preserved, and coal is mined at Le Creusot and Blanzy. This depression forms a routeway from the Loire Valley to the Saône Valley.

The Charollais, Beaujolais, and Vivarais stretch south of the Autunois. The coal beds are preserved in a faulted basin at Saint-Etienne and Rive-de-Gier. In the north these hills are not high, and they do not display the rugged and sharp-edged features which characterize their more southerly continuation. Along their eastern face the grape vine is grown, and the hills have given their names to famous vintages. South of the Lyonnais, the hills become higher and more rugged and form, in the mountains of Vivarais and of Coirons, a formidable barrier between the valleys of the Rhône and the headwaters of the Loire. The steep edge of the Cévennes overlooks the lowlands of the Rhône delta. It is a rugged, wooded region. The southeastern edge is straight and abrupt and follows, in part at least, a line of faulting. This faulting has preserved at the foot of the Cévennes scarp a small area of coal measures.

The Grandes Causses are formed of limestones which lie in horizontal beds on the surface of the crystalline rocks of the massif. The deep valleys of the Lot, Aveyron, and Tarn and their tributaries divide the causses into a number of barren and waterless plateaus. The causses display the erosional features commonly associated with limestone. Apart from the through rivers, there is little surface drainage, and most streams flow underground. The surface has little soil and little vegetation and is strewn with craterlike dolines and with smaller solution land forms. Agricultural potentialities are very small, and the population is sparse and diminishing.

Rouergue is the extreme southwest of the massif. It is cut up by the deep valleys of the Lot, Aveyron, Tarn, and Agout into a number of rounded and wooded or *maquis*-covered hills. Of these the Montagne Noire, the most southwesterly extension of the massif, is the most distinctive and most clearly defined. The valleys are wide and of some agricultural value. There are a number of small towns, in each of which industries traditional in these regions are carried on, such as the making of lace, woolen cloth, leather, and leather goods.

Limousin is strictly the name of the region about the town of Limoges (108,000). It is, however, used here to cover the whole region of rolling upland country which stretches from the plateau of Millevaches, north of the Dordogne Valley, through the region of La Marche to the plateau of Combrailles. Although coal is mined in a few small, down-faulted basins, the region is predominantly one of pastoral agriculture and sparse population. Towns are few, and only Limoges on the west and Montluçon on the north are of more than merely local importance.

Stretching from south to north across the center of the massif is an area of recent volcanic activity, known as the Auvergne. In the south is the basaltic massif of Aubrac, a now much-dissected region of basalt flows. This is continued northward in the Cantal, the huge base of a former volcanic cone in which recent volcanic activity has built up smaller cones, or *puys*. North of the Cantal is further evidence of recent vulcanicity in the Mont Dore and the chain of *puys* which lie to the west of the town of Clermont Ferrand (108,000). This vulcanism is very recent and was not quite extinct in the early Christian period. The landscape here is bizarre in the extreme. The steep, conical *puys* rise abruptly from the plateau in a closely spaced group. Their vegetation is sparse, and in places the rough scoria of recent eruptions still lies over the surface. The whole has the aspect of a lunar rather than terrestrial landscape.

Between the upper valleys of the Allier and Loire lies the steep, fault-bounded massif of Forez, continued southward in the volcanic mountains of Velay, on the margin of which lies the town of Le Puy. Here the volcanic stumps have provided pedestals for the exotic collection of churches and monuments which decorates this little town. The whole region is bleak and wet, and as in the mountains farther west, pastoral activities predominate.

The valleys of the Allier and the Loire were

the sites in earlier times of shallow seas, in which accumulated beds of sand and clay. The Allier, which rises in the Cévennes, flows northward through a number of small, mountain-rimmed basins and a few miles south of Clermont-Ferrand enters the broad flat plain of the Limagne. It is a productive and well-peopled region, dotted with villages and small towns. Amongst these, Vichy has a reputation as a spa and was the seat of the government of France during the German occupation of the Second World War. On the western margin of the basin is Clermont-Ferrand, a route center and seat of silk, textile, rubber, engineering, and chemical industries. The valley of the Loire was similarly occupied by a Tertiary lake, but the deposits which it left are smaller and, in general, less productive than those of the Limagne.

Despite the several fertile and sheltered basins that are contained within the massif, the region as a whole is one of thin, poor soil, of heavy rainfall, and cool, if not cold, winters. It has tended to be a kind of "poverty spot," where the people eke out a meager existence, growing hardy cereals and potatoes and rearing cattle and sheep. The more enterprising migrate to the lower and richer regions, and most parts of the massif have shown in recent times a diminishing population.

Burgundy and the Rhône Valley. The limestone plateau of Langres and the Côte d'Or sink eastward to the basin of Burgundy and beyond rise again in the long unbroken line of the Jura. Between the Vosges and the northern spurs of the Jura is the Gap of Belfort, a narrow strip of land some 15 miles wide, which links the upper Rhine Valley with that of the Saône.

The limestone of the Côte d'Or ends against the ancient rocks of the Central Massif, and from Mâcon southward to the boundary of Provence, the Saône and then the Rhône flow close to the steep edge of the massif. The plain is wider on the east, but at intervals hilly masses or narrow rocky ridges stretch westward from the Alps, dividing the Rhône Valley into a series of compartments.

The plain of Burgundy itself is a rich, well-

peopled agricultural region, through whose meadows and vineyards flow the Saône and its tributaries, the Ognon and Doubs. Viticulture is widespread, and along the slopes of the Côte d'Or, at Beaune, Nuits, and Chagny, are the vineyards from which is produced the wine of Burgundy. Dijon (100,500) is the center of the Burgundian wine industry and also the ancient capital of Burgundy. On the opposite side of the plain of Bresse is the engineering center of

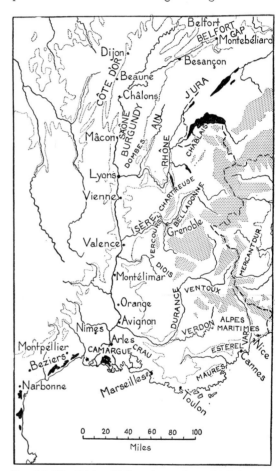

Fig. 86. The Rhône Valley. Areas above 6,000 feet are dotted. The contour shown is at 1,000 feet.

Besançon (63,500), almost enclosed by a meander of the Doubs. In the Belfort Gap are the towns of Montbéliard and Belfort. Belfort is a small town but of great military importance, guarding the route westward between the Vosges and the Jura.

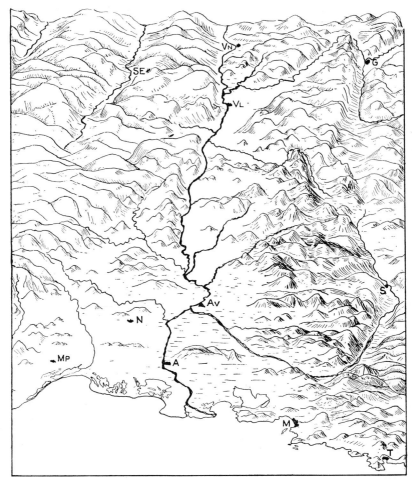

FIG. 87. Diagrammatic sketch of the Rhône Valley. A = Arles; Av = Avignon; G = Grenoble; M = Marseille; MP = Montpellier; N = Nîmes; S = Sisteron; SE = Saint-Étienne; T = Toulon; VL = Valence; VN = Vienne.

South of Chalons the plain narrows and the river is forced across to the western side of its plain by the discharge of the rivers from the Jura. The plain to the east, known as the Pays de Dombes, is covered with the boulder clay left by the Alpine glaciers. It is a region of cold, damp soil, and agriculture is little practiced.

The Rhône joins the Saône at Lyon (Lyons, 460,500). The town grew up on the right bank of the Saône and has since spread to the area between the two rivers, where is now the center of the city, and to the east bank of the Rhône, which is the present industrial suburb. The silk industry is the most important in Lyon. It was established here some four centuries ago. The rearing of silkworms was formerly important but is now largely discontinued, and raw silk is imported from Italy and from Asiatic countries. At first the industry was carried on by hand labor in and about the city itself, but in recent years it has spread into the surrounding country. Factories were established in the small towns of the Lyonnais, where labor was abundant and cheap, so that the town of Lyon is now the business center of the silk industry rather than the actual seat of its manufacture. With the decline in the demand for natural silk the Lyon area has developed the manufacture of the artificial substitutes that have been increasingly adopted. Lyon is now also a center of the chemical, metallurgical, and engineering industries.

To the northwest of Lyon are a number of towns, most of them small, in which is carried on a long-established woolen and cotton industry. In this rather sterile region there has always been a degree of poverty and of overpopulation sufficient to lead the peasants to take up domestic

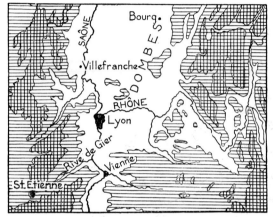

FIG. 88. The situation of Lyon. The city first grew on the high western bank of the Saône but has spread in modern times to the area between the rivers and also east of the Saône. Contours shown are at 1,000 and 2,000 feet.

industries and to offer their services at a low wage. The result has been the persistence of this manufacture in such towns as Roanne and Tarare.

A few miles to the southwest of Lyon is a depression between the Lyonnais and the Vivarais Mountains in which lies the Saint-Etienne coal field. In some respects this area is an industrial outlier of the Lyon area; it has a silk industry and has long been a center for the manufacture of ribbon. On the other hand its metallurgical industry is based on its local resources of coal. Iron and steel goods are made in the works of Saint-Etienne (178,000) and of the smaller towns of the coal field.

South of Lyon, the Rhône flows in a valley bounded on the west by the Central Massif and on the east by the foothills of the French Alps. Spurs from both east and west stretch out into the Rhône valley, dividing it into a number of compartments. The valley is thus made up of alternating basins and gorges. Below Lyon, the river occupies a narrow valley across a belt of

undulating hill country, where, shut in by steep hills, is the town of Vienne. Below Vienne the hills draw back and the river is bordered by a plain where, near Valence, the river Isère from the Alps joins it. Hills again draw in and separate the Valence Basin from that of Montélimar. A few miles below Montélimar, at the little town of Mondragon, a low ridge of hill runs out to the river and terminates in a castle-crowned crag. To the south is the plain of Provence.

The aspect of the land has been slowly changing from Lyon southward. In the Saône Valley the fields and meadows are those of northern Europe. Below Lyon the summer rainfall diminishes; the meadows become rarer and then disappear; southern fruits make their appearance. The vine is no longer grown only on land sloping toward the sun; vineyards now cover the flat valley floor and even the north-facing slopes. Tall cypress trees are dotted about the fields or are grown in straight rows as protection from the fierce *mistral*, which blows from the north. Small windbreaks of cane or wood are

The city of Avignon. Avignon lies on the high eastern bank of the Rhône. Its medieval walls, seen in the foreground, remain almost intact. On high ground within the city are the Château des Papes, the castle built and inhabited by the Popes, and the cathedral.

built to shelter the tender crops. The sunshine becomes more intense, the vegetation turns from green to gray and brown, and at Mondragon the first olive trees appear. This is the beginning of the Midi. Low ridges of dry, garrigue-covered hills continue to lie from east to west across the plain as if nature herself were erecting a barrier against the winds from the north. These ridges are infertile and uncultivated, but between them the alluvium of the Rhône makes for a profitable agriculture. The grape vine and the olive, interspersed with small groves of apricots and peaches and patches of corn, sunflower, or tobacco, cover the land.

Orange, a Roman town with many Roman remains, lies a short distance from the Rhône.

The Roman triumphal arch at Orange in Provence. This and the arena in the city show how great was the influence of ancient Rome in the south of France.

Avignon (60,000), with its ancient walls and its towering Castle of the Popes, rises from a bluff above the river, and in Arles, at the head of the delta, "as you walk along the tortuous land between high houses, passing on either hand as you go the ornaments of every age, you turn some dirty little corner or other and come suddenly upon the titanic arches of Rome."[1] The impress of Rome is strong in Provence; even its name is derived from the Latin Provincia.

The Camargue is the alluvial region of the

[1] Belloc, H., "Hills and the Sea," p. 72, London, 1918.

delta. Here the river is building forward quickly. Despite drainage, the region remains damp and in general unsuited for agriculture, though cattle are reared and crops of rice have recently been taken. To the east is the Crau, a stony wilderness, consisting of the detritus swept down from the Alps. Part is cultivated, though water for irrigation is scarce, and much of the land is used for the winter grazing of sheep, which in summer are taken by train to Alpine pastures.

In the Chaîne des Alpilles, which crosses Provence to the north of Arles, is the town of Les Baux. Here bauxite, the ore from which aluminum is obtained, was formerly extracted on a considerable scale.

West of the Rhône, the plain averages some 20 miles in width between Nîmes and the Pyrenees. The shore line is straight, smoothed by the currents that run westward along the coast. The mouths of rivers have been closed, lagoons formed, and ports cut off from the sea. On the inner side of the plain, the Cévennes rise steeply to their bare or scrub-covered summits. Nîmes (91,500), Montpellier (93,000), Béziers (64,500), and Narbonne are the more important towns of this rich agricultural region. Some of these were once ports, but their rivers have been choked, and their estuaries closed. The plain reaches westward to Carcassonne, the most perfect example of a medieval fortified town, before it is pinched out between the Pyrenees and the Central Massif. This is the most important wine-producing region of France, its volume of output greatly exceeding that of the more famous areas of vintage wines, but most of it is *vin ordinaire*, the cheap wine drunk by the Frenchman with his meals and not exported to other countries.

East of the Crau the mountains come down to the sea. Small areas of flat or undulating land alternate along this coast with precipitous cliffs in whose sides the French engineers have hewn the Corniche roads.[1] This stretch of coast, of no more than 150 miles from Marseille (Marseilles)

[1] Between Nice and Menton there are three *Corniches*, the uppermost of which is a spectacular routeway along the summit of the cliffs. West of Nice, there is a single road which bears the name *Corniche*.

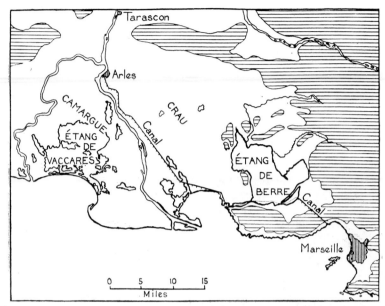

FIG. 89. The Rhône delta. The current runs toward the west, carrying the silt in this direction. Silt-free harbors lie to the east.

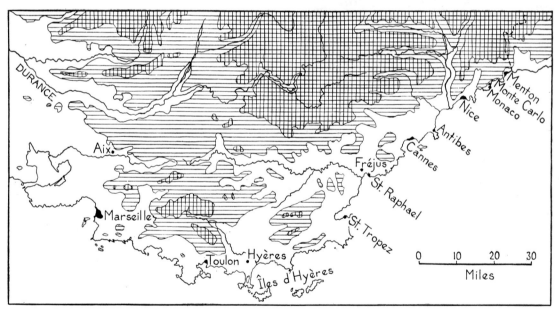

FIG. 90. The French Riviera. The coast is for much of the distance backed by mountains, which protect it from the northerly winds and suit it for the production of subtropical and early plants.

to the Italian border, is perhaps the most famous of the whole European periphery. Hills of limestone and of red granite, mantled with dark-green forests of chestnut, evergreen oak, and the even darker cypress and pine, drop steeply to the blue water of the Mediterranean. The small patches of cultivation bear mainly the vine, olive, and other fruits; vegetables and flowers are grown. The roads are lined with oleanders, and gardens are decked with the vivid colors of bougainvillaea and fuschia, scented with thyme, and lighted by the intense brilliance of the sun.

The harbor of Marseille. The site of the city is shut in by hills. Large vessels dock behind the mole; small vessels and fishing craft can sail up the river in the foreground. (*French Embassy, Information Division.*)

Marseille (636,500) lies to the east of the delta, protected by the westward run of the current from silting. It is shut in by high, bare, limestone hills, and the railways and even the canal enter the town by tunnels. It has a deep and sheltered bay which in some degree makes up for the inconvenience of its landward communications. Marseille is one of the chief commercial ports of France, importing "colonial" goods which have formed the basis for its manufacture of margarine, soap, and sugar.

East of Marseille is the naval base of Toulon (125,500), situated on a deep and sheltered harbor but joined to the rest of France only by a circuitous railway which follows the coast. East of Toulon, the Chaîne des Maures, a rugged massif, reaches the coast and produces spectacular scenery. East of the Argens Valleys and the little silted port of Fréjus, the Chaîne de l'Esterel rises steeply from the sea and separates the resort town of Saint-Raphaël from that of Cannes. Nice (Nizza, 211,000) is the largest

of the resort towns of this coast. To the east the Alpes Maritimes reach the sea in cliffs that rise more than 1,000 feet from the water between Nice and Menton. The principality of Monaco (population 24,000), a political enclave in France, lies between the cliffs and the sea and embraces the little rock-girt town of Monaco itself and also Monte Carlo. A mile or two beyond Menton (Mentone), a torrent bed forms the Italian boundary.

This is the Riviera, better known to the foreigner than any other part of France except Paris. Its warm and sheltered winters, its bright sunshine, the beauty of its coastal scenery, its attractive towns, coupled with judicious publicity, have made this a playground for much of Europe.

The Jura Mountains. The parallel ridges of the Jura run from the Rhône northeastward to the Rhine near Basel. The hills consist of beds of limestone and clay folded into a series of tight corrugations. These have been extensively eroded and reduced to a complex series of closely packed limestone ridges. The Jura rises gently from the plain of Burgundy but overlooks the plateau of Switzerland in a high steep scarp.

The drainage of the range is by rivers which flow between the ridges, breaking through by

Monte Carlo. The city lies in the little principality of Monaco, between the mountains and the sea. The short domed towers of the casino can be seen in the middle distance; the lower Corniche road can be seen part way up the hill. The upper Corniche runs over the tops of the hills seen here.

steep and narrow *cluses*, or gorges, from one valley to the next. The Doubs follows a circuitous course between the ridges of the northern Jura; the Ain and its tributaries drain the south. The only river that actually crosses the range is the Rhône, which, after leaving Lake Geneva, alternately breaching the limestone ridges and flowing between them, makes its way to the Saône.

The whole region is forested and sparsely peopled. Animals are reared, but only hardy crops are grown within the mountains. Hydroelectricity has been developed from the Rhône Valley, and further projects are being implemented in this region, where the narrow rocky valleys lend themselves to the construction of dams. Many of the valleys of the Jura are still difficult of access and likely to be cut off by snow in winter. Domestic crafts, especially woodworking and the manufacture of watches in small factories and workshops, are carried on in the recesses of the Jura.

The French Alps. The high ranges of the Alps reach southward from Lake Geneva to the

Mediterranean Sea near Nice. The core of the range is formed by the crystalline massifs of Mont Blanc and the Aiguilles Rouges, of Belledonne and Pelvoux. Each of these is a snow-covered and ice-fretted massif, a beautiful but pathless wilderness separating France from Italy. The valleys of the Isère, the Arc, and the Drac, which separate these masses from one another, lead up to the few passes across the range. The Little Saint Bernard Pass runs up from the Isère Valley, and the Mont Cenis, from the Arc. A railroad tunnel pierces the mountains a few miles from the Mont Cenis Pass and is the only connection between France and Italy through the mountains that is open throughout the year.

A depression borders the western edge of these massifs, from Martigny, at the bend of the Rhône, through Chamonix and Albertville until

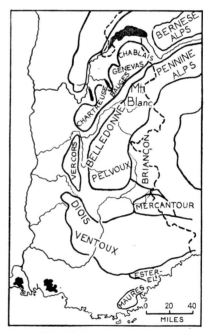

Fig. 91. The French Alps.

it opens into the broad, flat-floored trench of Grésivaudan. In the midst of this elongated plain is Grenoble (102,000), a city of considerable size and a center of electrical and other industries. The city is a focus of routes that radiate into the Alpine valleys, and it commands the Isère Valley as it opens westward to the Rhône. Hydroelectric installations are numerous in the Isère, Arc, and Drac Valleys, and around them have been developed electrochemical and electrometallurgical industries. The narrow, barren, and treeless valleys of the

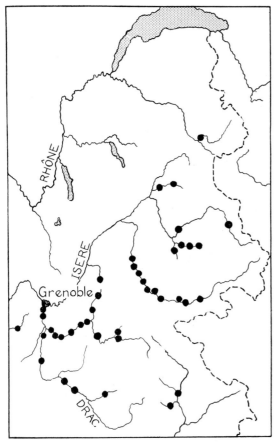

FIG. 92. Distribution of hydroelectric power stations in the French Alps.

Belledonne now contain smoking factories and workers' dwellings, in an environment that provides no amenities and no resource except power. The floor of the Grésivaudan is well cultivated. The grape vine is grown, grain matures and hay is made on moister land, but these conditions quickly deteriorate up the valleys. Fruit trees disappear; only hardy cereal crops and roots are grown; then these, too, give place to meadow and forest, until on the higher slopes no agricultural use of the land is possible. The high pastures are used only in summer,

when animals are brought up to them, some from as far away as the Rhône Valley, where the grassland is dried up by the summer heat.

West and south of the Alpine trench is a broad belt of mountainous country, less high and rugged than the crystalline Alps and without permanent snow fields. These mountains are built very largely of limestone. Rivers escaping from the Alpine trench have divided them by means of narrow gaps into a series of detached mountain masses. Most northerly of these is the Chablais, which rises in the north from the blue waters of Lake Geneva and reaches southward to the Arve Valley. The Genevois lie between the Arve and the valley of the Fier in which are Annecy and its lake. The Bauges continues the chain as far as Chambéry, beyond which rises the abrupt massif of the Chartreuse, in whose forested recesses the founders of the Carthusian order in the late eleventh century established the monastery which still survives at La Grande Chartreuse. The Isère breaks through the gap between the Chartreuse and the Vercors. The latter continues the direction of the more northerly folded blocks, but where it passes into the Diois, the folds begin to turn toward the southeast and in the Ventoux are running from west to east. The Durance crosses these ranges in the *cluse* at Sisteron, and to the east of the river the same easterly trend is maintained. These are barren, stony hills, where there is a sparse covering of southern forest and large areas of *maquis*. Rivers such as the Var and the Verdon cross them by gorges. Population is sparse and movement difficult in this broad southern part of the limestone Alps.

The French Alps are a region of contrasts. Over the greater part of the area it is one of poor agriculture and declining population. Its people melt away into the cities of the Rhône Valley and of Provence. The uppermost of the terraces on the valley sides are found abandoned, and in few valleys is there evidence of new building. The exception is found around Grenoble, in Tarentaise or the upper valley of the Isère, and in Maurienne or the upper Arc Valley. In each of these the generation of hydroelectric power has promoted industrialization. The electrochemical and electrometallurgical industries are carried on in little "boom" towns along the valleys, and an industrial population has settled high up among these austere mountains.

CORSICA

The island of Corsica was acquired by France in 1768. It is built of crystalline rocks. Its relief is rugged, and its soils shallow and poor. Much of its small area of 3,367 square miles lies at a height of over 1,500 feet. This considerable altitude moderates its Mediterranean climate and induces a considerable rainfall. Forests of chestnut cover much of the higher land and yield a food for man and beast. The valleys of the interior are deep and narrow, and movement is difficult. Settlements are small and very nearly self-sufficient. In their lower courses the valleys broaden and their agriculture becomes more extensive and more important. There is, however, little flat land. A narrow belt of plain, at most some 7 or 8 miles wide, fringes the east coast, but on the west the low-lying land is found only at the heads of the deeper bays. Ajaccio, the capital of the island, lies in such a position, and there are some small towns on the eastern coast. Most of the population, however, dwells away from the sea, in the mean and squalid villages of the interior, where poverty and backwardness of the people are extreme. The islanders in general speak Italian, and under the Fascist regime, the Italian government claimed the cession of Corsica. The natives, however, seemed undisturbed by such appeals to their earlier allegiance, and some derive a certain satisfaction from the fact that Napoleon was born a Corsican.

CHAPTER 13: *The Economy of France*

Everything in the human geography of France bears the stamp of antiquity. The fields that are now being cultivated have in many instances scarcely changed their size or plan since the Middle Ages. The cultivated strips of many owners lie intermixed in the open fields as they

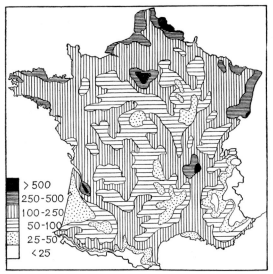

> 500
250-500
100-250
50-100
25-50
< 25

FIG. 93. Distribution of population in France. Density is shown per square mile.

did before the French Revolution. Many of the towns derive from Roman origins, and the Roman towns in their turn were often built to replace the prehistoric hilltop camps. The *bastides*, built by Louis IX in the thirteenth century, and the planned town of Vitry-le-François, laid out by Francis I in the sixteenth, are, for France, towns of recent origin. Really modern urban growth, such as that of Great Britain or Germany, is confined to a very few industrial areas, such as the northeastern coal field and the environs of Paris. Along with these

outward manifestations of a long history there go also a reverence for tradition, a respect for craftsmanship, and a degree of distrust of modern industrial development that may have served to protect a way of life which is essentially French but hardly serves to equip a nation for the fierce competition of modern industrialized societies. French agricultural holdings are small and, by English or American standards, ill-equipped and inefficient. French industrial undertakings are, with a very few conspicuous exceptions, also too small to compete on even terms with those of the other countries of the industrialized West. They tend to be family concerns, which have survived into an age of joint-stock companies and cartels.

Population. The population of France, including the island of Corsica but excluding the North African possession of Algeria, which is considered part of metropolitan France, was estimated in 1950 to be 41,744,000. The average density is about 197 per square mile. This density is not a high one for western Europe, and only the Scandinavian countries and the Iberian Peninsula are actually lower in density. A relatively large proportion of the total population, about 35 per cent, is engaged in agriculture and forestry. The description of the physical regions of France given in the previous chapter will have shown comparatively few large areas where agriculture is difficult and settlement sparse. A continuity of settlement pattern is one of the outstanding features of the geography of France. The population density is thin in only a few areas: the Alps and Pyrenees, the Cévennes, the Causses and the high volcanic region of the center of the massif, the sandy wastes of the *landes* and the Sologne, and parts of the high, dry chalk and limestone plateaus of the east of the Paris Basin. Few areas except the urban have a much greater density than 200 persons to the square mile. Only on the rich soils of French Flanders, in the plain of Alsace, in parts of the Rhône Valley, and in the vine-growing regions of Bordeaux and the Midi is there an agricultural population of greater density.

The population of France at the beginning of the nineteenth century was over 27 million. Since that date, its growth has been relatively slow, much slower, in fact, than that of Italy, Germany, and the British Isles. About the year 1800, France was the most populous country in Europe, with the possible exception of Russia; her population today is exceeded by that of all her great neighbors. The French birth rate, which had once been unusually high, began to diminish early in the nineteenth century. An important factor in this diminution of the birth rate lay in the law whereby the peasant holding had to be divided between the sons, each taking his share of his father's lands. The peasant desired above all things to maintain his land intact and to add to it rather than divide it. The alternative to a divided holding was a smaller family. The population declined in the richest agricultural lands, but it declined even more strikingly in those areas where the soil was poor and the climate harsh. From these labor migrated, sometimes seasonally, to gather the harvest in more productive regions, but more often permanently. The Alps, particularly in the *département* of Basses Alpes; the Pyrenees; much of the Central Massif, especially the Causses; the plateau of Langres; the damp hills of Normandy; much of the eastern part of the Paris Basin and the borders of the Ardennes; and the island of Corsica, all show continuous diminution of population over the past two generations. Much of the efflux from these regions went to maintain a more nearly static condition of population over the rest of France or to populate the growing industrial areas.

The number and size of French towns have increased quite markedly during the past century. A hundred years ago, less than a quarter of the total population was urban. Only 4 cities had a population exceeding 100,000, as against 22 in 1946.[1] Former French provincial towns, which had rarely counted more than 8,000 or 10,000 inhabitants, have grown to have 30,000 to 50,000.

France's deficiency in labor was made good by the immigration of Italians, Spaniards, Belgians, and Poles. Italians and Spaniards assisted in gathering the fruit harvest of the south. Italians labored on the road and railway works of the Alps and in the iron mines of Lorraine, Czech and Polish miners worked in the coal mines of the north, and in time of economic depression and unemployment, the temporary laborers could always be sent home to live on the charity of their native countries. It may not be more than a few years before the population begins to decline. The political and economic consequences of this fact are not without their importance. A sense of demographic and hence of military inferiority developed, and from this arose in the years between the wars a sort of defeatism and a desire not to engage in war, not even in self-defense.

France's Economic Position. Agriculture has been practiced in parts of France since Neolithic times, which, in this part of Europe, must have begun earlier than 2000 B.C. The oldest settlements were on the open or lightly wooded loess soils, the *terre de culture facile*, and on the dry limestone. From these regions it extended to the thickly wooded clays and the poorer sands. It is probable that the agricultural pattern had, in large measure, achieved its present shape by the end of the Middle Ages. Since then, the woodlands have receded somewhat and the marshes of Flanders and of the Biscay coast have been reclaimed. From very early times, agriculture was conducted on a two- or three-field system. In the south, half the land was under cultivation, while the remainder was allowed to lie fallow and recover something of its natural productivity. In the

[1] Paris, Marseille, Lyon, Bordeaux, Nice, Toulouse, Lille, Nantes, Strasbourg, St. Etienne, Le Havre, Toulon, Rouen, Nancy, Reims, Roubaix, Clermont-Ferrand, Rennes, Dijon, Grenoble, Limoges, Le Mans.

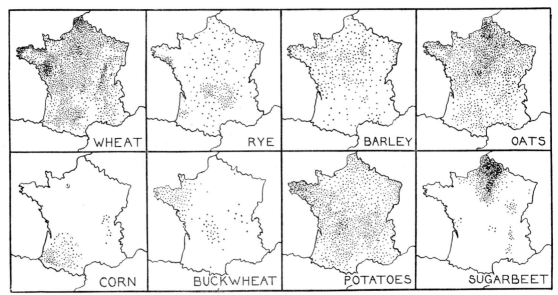

FIG. 94. Distribution of certain crops in France.

north, where a three-field system was more general, only a third of the land lay fallow in each year. In Flanders during the eighteenth century a more intensive cultivation, which admitted of no fallowing, succeeded to the three-field rotation and spread gradually into France. In very few places, however, had the practice of fallowing been abandoned at the time of the French Revolution. In the south, the maize, or corn, plant, introduced during the seventeenth century, spread and came gradually to be cultivated on land that had previously been allowed to lie fallow. Even today, however, there are farm holdings in the less accessible regions of the Central Massif where the ancient practice of two- or three-course fallowing is still maintained.

Even today the material equipment of French agriculture is in many ways quite inadequate. Artificial manures are used on an adequate scale only in a few limited areas. The grain-producing land of Artois in the extreme north, the lowlands of the Breton peninsula and the Biscay coast, where flowers and early vegetables are grown for the Paris market, and the irrigated plains of the lower valley of the Rhône may perhaps be considered adequately fertilized. For the rest, a line drawn from the western end of

the Pyrenees northeastward to the Ardennes separates a northwestern area where the use of fertilizer is considerable, if not adequate, from a southeastern area where its use is, except along the lower Rhône, quite inadequate.

Nor is enough use made of farm machinery, of electricity, and of piped water supply, although these are on the increase. Many are the regions of France where the grain is cut laboriously with the sickle and threshed by means of the primitive flail, swung above the heads of the farmers to beat the grain from the husk. Plowing with a wooden plow without even a moldboard and cultivating with a hoe are still far from unknown. This slowness to mechanize is not due to an abundance of rural labor that would make farm machinery superfluous; it springs from an innate conservatism, from a lack of capital, and from the smallness of both farms and fields. To the French peasant, agriculture is not a means of livelihood, but a way of life; to mechanize, even if he had the means, would go far toward destroying the *mystique* which surrounds the oldest and still the most respected occupation in France.

France is a country of peasant land ownership. The size of the holdings varies with the wealth and social standing of the peasant and also with the soil and the mode of agriculture practiced. A great many holdings are too small for economic exploitation. About 36 per cent of the cultivated area is divided into holdings of a size less than 25 acres. Only a quarter of the total area devoted to agriculture has really large farms of 250 acres or more. These lie either in the broad grain-growing lands of the Paris Basin or in the infertile mountains of the southeast. The numbers of farm holdings according to their size are as follows:

More than 125 acres.............. About 100,000
25 to 125 acres.................... About 700,000
Less than 25 acres................ About 4,500,000

At the time of the Revolution the peasants took over the land from their *seigneurs*. The change was one of legal and social status; the practices of agriculture scarcely altered. The peasants continued to cultivate the same strips of land as their ancestors had done, intermixed in the same open fields. This fragmentation of the holding has continued until the present in many parts of France. Attempts to gather the strips into a number of compact and economic holdings have met with only a moderate degree of success, but if the change continues only at its present slow rate, it is likely in the course of several generations to alter radically the appearance of the countryside.

Almost three-quarters of the farmers themselves own the land they cultivate. The rest pay rent in some form or other. The farmers pay a fixed money rent to a landowner; the *métayers*, or sharecroppers, receive from the landowner not only the holding itself with its buildings but also equipment, animals, and sometimes even the seed to sow, and by way of rent they return to the owner in kind a fixed proportion of the total farm income.

THREE TYPES OF LAND HOLDERS

	Per cent of total cultivators	Per cent of agricultural land
Proprietors......	74	60
Farmers........	21	30
Sharecroppers...	5	10

Each of the three types of tenure shown in the accompanying table has a clearly defined area of distribution. Sharecropping, which is of diminishing importance, was formerly widespread in the south and remains of significance in Aquitaine, Provence, and Berry. It seems to have been important in areas where either rural poverty was great or the prevailing agricultural activities, such as tree cultivation, required a considerable capital. Rent-paying farmers are most important and numerous in the north of France, from the Gate of Poitou to the Belgian border, where, in general, the farm holdings tend to be the largest. The owner-proprietor is most common in the southeastern half of France, where, in general, holdings are smallest and the material equipment and use of fertilizers least adequate. It is among the proprietors that the French agrarian problem shows itself most conspicuously and most seriously.

A line from the mouth of the Gironde to Alsace, which, as we have already seen, divides the area of larger, better manured, and more highly mechanized farms from the less well managed, serves also to demarcate the most important region of grain farming. Over most of the area northwest of this line, except the damp uplands of Brittany and Normandy and the plateaus of eastern France, wheat or grain cultivation is widespread. Oats and barley have a broadly similar distribution. Rye, however, is less widespread within this northwestern area except on areas of poorer soil and unfavorable climate, such as the Breton and Norman hills and the plains of Lorraine. On the other hand, rye is common in the Central Massif, where it is, by and large, the most important crop in the damp and chilly climate and on the acid soils of these uplands. Maize, or corn, has a very limited distribution. It is grown on a very small scale over most of France, but only in Aquitaine are there a sufficient heat in summer and an adequate rainfall during the crop's growing season for its cultivation to be really widespread.

Root crops are grown as a rotation crop in the grain-growing region of the north. Of these sugar beet is an important crop in Artois and Picardy. Potatoes are more extensive. In the north they are grown in rotation. In Brittany, Lorraine, and the hilly region of the center they are of considerable importance for human food, because, like rye, they are tolerant of the harsh environment.

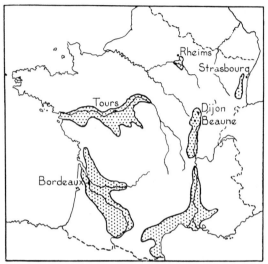

Fig. 95. Distribution of viticulture in France.

Animal husbandry is particularly important in the northwestern coastal region from La Vendée to Artois, in the Central Massif, and the Pyrenees. In the first of these, the mild and humid climate encourages the growth of pasture. Dairy cattle can be kept out of doors throughout the year, and hay and fodder crops grow well. This is the outstanding dairy region of France. Butter and cheese are made on a larger scale than in most other parts, and liquid milk is sent to the urban centers. The Central Massif is a region of greater altitude. Except locally, rich pastureland is not available, and in comparison with the north, little fodder is produced. Animals, particularly cattle and sheep, are grazed on the high moorlands. Many of these are transhumant, returning to the lower land for the winter months. Pastoral pursuits are the most important in the Alps and Pyrenees, but the total number of animals maintained is small. Milk and cheese production is of some importance in these regions, and sheep, which winter in the plains of the Midi and on the Crau and Camargue, are taken to the mountains in summer.

In many areas of suitable soil and climate, the grape vine is the most important crop in terms of both the area cultivated and the value of the crop. The greatest production by far is from the lowlands to the west of the Rhône delta, where wine of a poorer quality is produced and sold as *vin ordinaire*. The more famous French wines are produced in areas nearer the climatic limit of wine growing. Their excellence depends upon the skill of the viticulturalist, upon the care shown in pressing the grapes and fermenting the juice, and perhaps upon small and often unrecognized peculiarities of soil. Champagne is produced from the sunny slopes of the plateau near Reims; claret and the sparkling wines from the gentle hills of the Loire Valley; hock from Alsace; burgundy, châteauneuf, and other such heavy wines from the Saône and Rhône Valleys; and light wines, médoc, barsac, sauterne, and graves, from the region of Bordeaux.

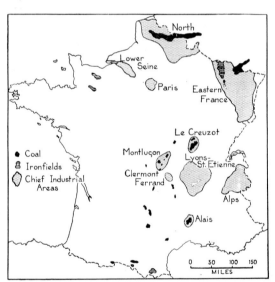

Fig. 96. Industrial regions of France and the distribution of coal and iron.

North of the limit of viticulture, beer and cider are more important. Normandy produces a raw cider from its apples, and beer is brewed and flavored with the hops that grow in the dry, sunny climate of Alsace.

Industrial regions frequently bear little relationship to physical. In the previous chapter reference was made to the many small towns of France in which factory industry is carried on, but any consideration of the more developed centers of French industry was postponed. The predominant characteristics of French agriculture are present also in French industry. It is old; it shows a deep respect for tradition; it is carried on in units that are often too small to compete with the corresponding industries of other countries; there are a love and respect for craftsmanship that are absent from the large-scale, mass-production industries of the West. The use of mechanical power was adopted slowly, almost unwillingly, in the nineteenth century, and throughout that century and into the twentieth domestic crafts in spinning, weaving, wood- and leatherworking and the production of jewelry, watches, and mechanical devices retained an importance that they had lost or were losing in Britain and the United States. The very great use of hand labor, which characterizes French industry, has made for a *finesse* and attention to style and detail in French products which have carried them into the markets of all the more wealthy countries of the world.

Not all French industries, however, are carried on in the cottages and homes of domestic workers. The cotton and woolen industries and the production and fabrication of steel are factory industries, but the scale of operations is smaller than in Germany, Great Britain, or the United States. Many of the steelworks and textile factories are small enough for production to be slow and less efficient and competitive than it might have been had it been carried on in larger units.

These two characteristics of French industry, its production of luxury or semiluxury goods for a select market and the relatively high-cost nature of its production, make the French industrial situation in some respects unstable. A luxury market, such as France enjoys for a wide range of her products, is one that is likely to decline most readily and most sharply in a depression. At the same time, the luxury product is always open to imitation and competition by substitutes, as has been the French production

of natural silk by synthetic; French wines by South African, Californian, and Australian; French fashions and millinery by those of London and New York.

Iron ore is the only metallic mineral of significance in France today. In Lorraine are the largest deposits of iron ore to be found in Europe. This is a bedded ore of low grade—rarely more than 30 per cent—but easily mined. It occurs in the Côtes de Moselle, where it was formerly mined in open-pit workings along the scarp, but now the ore is obtained either from drifts cut horizontally into the hillside or from shafts put down from the plateau surface behind the scarp. The ore is phosphoric. It could be worked into steel by the slow and laborious processes that were in use in the Middle Ages and in early modern times but was quite unsuited to the Bessemer converter, which was widely adopted in the 1860's. The ores were thenceforward considered of only slight importance until Gilchrist and Thomas, in 1878, introduced their basic method of producing steel. These deposits then gained steadily in importance. Being of a low grade, they do not readily stand the high cost of transport. While ore has been exported to neighboring countries, especially Germany and Belgium, a large part of it is smelted in Lorraine and in nearby Luxembourg.

The only other iron-ore deposits of significance in present-day France are those of Caen in Normandy, which are worked and in part smelted near the mines.

France's great reserves of iron ore are not in any way matched by her coal deposits. She has a number of small coal fields, individually of slight value. In the interwar years her total output rarely amounted to more than a half of her requirements.

The northern coal field is a continuation into France of the coal field of Belgium. The coal measures lie beneath a cover of later deposits and, on this account, were not discovered until the eighteenth century. The field extends from the Belgian border near Valenciennes eastward to Béthune, a distance of about 60 miles, and has a width of about 10 miles. The average depth of the mines is about 1,250 feet. In comparison with those of other coal fields of Europe, the seams are thin and separated by considerable thicknesses of unproductive rock. The coal seams have been much folded and faulted and are relatively difficult to work. The field is therefore a high-cost producer and retains its importance in the French economy, partly at least, only because it has been able to attract cheap foreign labor. On the other hand, much of its surface equipment is new and efficient, having been built in the 1920's to replace that which was destroyed during the First World War. The coal produced is mainly steam coal. Comparatively little coal suitable for metallurgical coke is mined, and there is no anthracite. The volume of output before the last war was in most years a little under 30 million tons, some 60 per cent of the total French output.

The small Lorraine coal field is a continuation of the deposits of the Saar Basin (pages 144 and 238). Its development, around the towns of Forbach and Saint-Avold, has been comparatively recent and has reflected the demand for fuel in the nearby steel-producing area of Lorraine. The coal produced here is not, however, of a coking quality.

On and about the Central Massif are a number of coal basins, all of them small and few of them of more than local importance. The basins themselves are generally bounded by faults and surrounded by rocks of a very much greater age. The most important of these fields (Fig. 96) are those of Le Creusot, Saint-Étienne, and Alès. Taken together, these fields do not yield much more than 10 per cent of France's coal output, but they are of considerable local importance, and each supports a small but significant mixed industrial area. The other fields of the massif are of even less significance.

The French deficiency in coal is to some extent met by the generation of hydroelectric power which is produced from the swift streams of the Alps, Pyrenees, and Central Massif. This development in the French Alps has been particularly great in the valleys of the Rhône, Isère, Arc, and Drac, where it is used in part by the railways, in part by electrochemical and electrometallurgical industries. In both the Alps and Pyrenees the current is generated from the streams which are impounded behind dams and released to flow through turbines. The most important of the dams and the largest in western Europe is at Génissiat, on the Rhône about 30 miles from the Swiss frontier, where the river cuts across one of the ridges of the Jura. Another great dam is now under construction on the lower Rhône near Montélimar. The effect of these dams will be not only to increase greatly the amount of electric power generated in France but also to make the Rhône navigable to above Lyon. Other dams are either built or projected elsewhere on the Rhône and along its Alpine tributaries.

The Pyrenees are at present less important than the Alps for the generation of hydroelectric power, in part because the rivers are smaller and their flow is less regular. The Central Massif and the Vosges are also the scenes of the development of hydroelectric power.

The electric current is distributed by overhead cable over much of eastern and southeastern France. The main railroad from Paris to Dijon has now been electrified. The hydroelectric stations, however, have generally to work in close association with steam-generating stations, which sometimes become necessary to supplement the low output of hydroelectric power in time of drought.

The previous discussion of French industry must not be allowed to detract from the very considerable expansion of French industry that has taken place in recent years. The development of hydroelectric power has encouraged the growth of the electrochemical and the electrometallurgical industries, especially in the French Alps and Pyrenees.

The coal field of northern France and the iron field of Lorraine are the scenes of large and vigorous iron and steel industries. At the present time the plant is being extended and modernized. The present output of steel is about 9 million tons a year, and if present plans are achieved, the output will rise to nearly 15 million tons a year. The French iron industry suffers, however, from an acute shortage of metallurgical coke, for which France has to depend heavily upon Germany.

Other industries which are carried on in factories and on a large scale are the manufacture of textiles, both cotton and woolen, in the

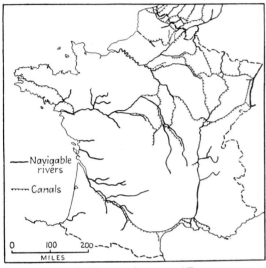

FIG. 97. The canal system of France.

northeast; the silk manufacture in the Rhône Valley; and the automobile industry in "greater" Paris.

France has never, like Great Britain and Germany, passed through a phase of intensive and rapid industrialization. But factory industries have been increasing steadily in importance since the later years of the nineteenth century. This continued growth of factory industries is in evidence today. They are increasingly important relative to the "luxury" industries, for which France is probably more widely known.

Communications and Ports. Communications were developed in France at a relatively early date, and they remain today probably more complete and of an over-all higher quality than those of any other continental European country. A network of Roman roads radiated from Lyon. This road system has been supplemented and reoriented so that it now focuses on Paris and serves to bind the provinces to the capital. The present magnificent network of

routes nationales is in large measure the creation of the nineteenth century.

Canal development also took place at an earlier date than in other European countries. Navigable rivers had been much used during the Middle Ages, and from the seventeenth century attempts were made to join up the rivers with canals and to establish a system of inland navigation. France is naturally suited for the development of canal transportation. The wide extent of low-lying country, the numerous gaps between the hills, and the high rainfall all make the construction and maintenance of canals easier than in many other countries. By the middle of the nineteenth century all the main natural waterways had been connected with one another by canals. In 1879, the French canal system was unified by Freycinet. Two standard sizes of barges were adopted, and canals were adapted and classified according to their ability to take the smaller or both. Certain rivers are much used: the Seine up to Paris, the lower sections of the Oise and Marne, the Rhine, and the lowermost course of the Rhône. The canals of northeastern France and the important waterway which links the Marne with Lorraine

The Rhine-Rhône Canal in southern Alsace. The canal is small, but can take the large French *chaland*, seen in the background.

and with the Rhine at Strasbourg all bear a considerable traffic. Other canals are but little used. Barge traffic is slow and unsuited to commodities for which there is not a steady demand. Some two-thirds of all goods carried in recent years have been coal and building

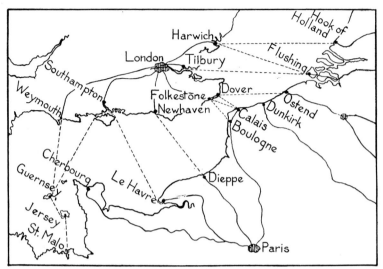

Fig. 98. The regularly used crossings of the English Channel and the chief packet stations.

materials such as stone, timber, cement, and gravel.

France has a dense railway network which is particularly well developed in the northern half of the country. Most lines are still operated by steam locomotives. Only lines in the south, near the Alps and Pyrenees, have been electrified, though the important and much-used route from Paris to Lyon has been converted to electric power. In France the railways are relatively important for the transportation of all manner of freight and merchandise. It was estimated that before the Second World War some 75 per cent of the total freight transported within the country was carried by rail, 13 per cent by the waterways, and 12 per cent by road.[1]

France is served by a small number of ports in relation to the length of its coastline and the volume of its trade. They may be grouped into those engaged primarily in the passenger traffic and those whose business is mainly in freight. The former group includes the packet stations of Dunkirk, Calais (50,000), Boulogne, and Dieppe, which handle the cross-channel passenger service and have good rail connections with Paris. Cherbourg is a passenger port but serves only the transatlantic liners, which pause here

[1] "Géographie universelle," Vol. VI, Part 2, Section I, p. 420, Paris, 1946.

to embark or disembark passengers. The port lies on the northern coast of the Cotentin peninsula and is linked with Paris by fast boat trains. In this way the transatlantic traveler can save many hours in reaching Paris while the boat sails to Le Havre. Marseille, primarily a cargo port, also has a considerable movement of passengers.

The most important French ports, in volume of merchandise handled, are Marseille, Rouen, Le Havre, Dunkirk, Bordeaux, Nantes, Saint-Nazaire, Caen (51,500), Boulogne, and Sète (Cette). The first three of these handle over a half of the total sea-borne trade of France. Several ports of France are grouped in pairs, one at the head of an estuary or near the limit of navigation and one close to the open sea: Rouen and Le Havre, Nantes and Saint-Nazaire, Bordeaux and the several small ports on the Gironde. The inland port is the older but has become gradually less accessible as the size of ships increases. Many such ports are visited only by the smaller coastal craft. Strasbourg plays an important role as an inland port on the river Rhine.

Foreign Trade. France is often cited as a country of varied resources and balanced development to which a degree of self-sufficiency is more natural than is the case of most industrialized countries of western Europe. Algeria, to be considered in a later chapter, is part of metropolitan France, and trade between French and Algerian ports therefore counts as domestic not as foreign trade, which gives the ambiguous effect of increasing the range of production within the French customs union.

The food imports of France are relatively small. France is near self-sufficiency in grain in good years. There is a large import of cheap wine, but this comes mainly from Algeria. Tropical fats, sugar, coffee, and cocoa are among the more important food imports. More important than foodstuffs are raw materials for French industry. In the past about half the total coal used has been imported, much of it from Great Britain, though the proportion mined in France has increased in recent years. Almost all the natural oil is imported, all the cotton, and much of the wool and flax and, in recent years, of the raw silk. Timber and wood pulp, nonferrous metals, except aluminum, and even some iron ore are brought into France.

Among the exports of France a foremost place is occupied by textiles, especially those of high quality, metallurgical goods, paper and books, the more highly priced wines and spirits, and a wide range of *articles de luxe*. In the French trade balance must also be included the not inconsiderable sums of money brought into the country by foreign travelers. France exports her culture and her scenery.

Conclusion. Within the memory of men and women still living, France has been three times invaded by the Germans, in 1870, in 1914, and again in 1940. On each occasion great material damage was done and the economy of the country was disrupted. Physical damage was greatest during the First World War, when for 4 years much of northern and northeastern France was fought over and its forests, villages, and factories destroyed. During the Second World War the material damage was localized: around Calais and Dunkirk, in the heavily bombed ports such as Brest and Le Havre, and where the Allied landings were made in 1944. The heaviest destruction was in Normandy, where the city of Caen is now being rebuilt completely from its ruins.

On the other hand, over 4 years of German occupation, with the Resistance Movement, or Maquis, conducting a civil war in many parts of the country, and general unwillingness of the population to assist the "Vichy" government because this, in its turn, was assisting the Germans, led to a slow impoverishment of the country. Plant and equipment were not maintained or replaced. French workers were conscripted to serve in German factories or to build the defense works of the German "Western Wall." The country was slowly "running down."

The rescue of France by the Allies in 1944 was by no means a painless process. The Germans retreated across the country, delaying as they went the advance of the Allies by destroying bridges and other means of transport and communication, occasionally halting to defend some strong point.

France has always shown an extraordinary vitality and power of recuperation. Her recovery from the war of 1870–1871 was fast enough to give the German Chancellor Bismarck serious cause for alarm. She recovered relatively quickly from the First World War, and her revival from the low ebb of 1945 has been no less marked.

This capacity in France derives in part from the balance which exists between factory industry and agriculture, from the relatively high degree of self-sufficiency of the country, and from the thrift of its people. It also owes something to the recognition that France has certain spiritual values which are worth retrieving. France is very conscious of being the most civilized country of Europe, and she will not readily abdicate her position.

Nevertheless, the postwar development of France would have been very much less marked without generous American economic and technical aid. The shattered transport system has been rebuilt, the coal mines are operating more successfully than before the war, and the productivity and efficiency of agriculture have increased. At the same time, a considerable capital investment is now being made in French industry. New steelworks are being equipped with American plant. A number of hydroelectric power projects are being implemented and navigation is being improved on the Rhône.

France is recovering from the blow struck by the Germans in 1940, but she is not a rich country, and elaborate and costly preparations to meet a possible Russian attack are scarcely within her means. Are the French to see their newly won prosperity dissipated in preparation for another war? A large number of Frenchmen would say no. The perpetuation of French culture is to them a primary obligation.

BIBLIOGRAPHY

GENERAL

Bell, J. F., Problems of Economic Reconstruction in France, *E.G.*, XXII, 1946, 54–66.

Cameron, Elizabeth R., "French Reconstruction," Yale Institute of International Relations, New Haven, 1948.

"Conference on Rural Life: France," League of Nations, Geneva, 1939.

De Martonne, E., "The Regions of France," London, 1933.

"Economic Conditions in France," Department of Overseas Trade, London, 1934.

Evans, E. E., "France," London, 1937.

Fleure, H. J., "French Life and Its Problems," London, 1943.

"Géographie universelle," Vol. VI, La France, Part I, France physique, Paris, 1947; Part II, France économique et humaine, Paris, 1946 and 1948, 2 vols.

Hunter, N., "Peasantry and Crisis in France," London, 1938.

Lamartine Yates, P., "Food Production in Western Europe," London, 1940.

Maillaud, P., "France," Oxford, 1942.

Ogburn, W. F., and W. Jaffé, "The Economic Development of Post-war France," New York, 1929.

Ormsby, H., "France," 2d ed., New York, 1950.

Siegfried, A., "France: A Study in Nationality," London, 1930.

Vidal de la Blache, P., "The Personality of France," London, 1928.

PAPERS AND SPECIALIZED STUDIES

Agnew, S., Rural Settlement in the Coastal Plain of Bas Languedoc, *G.*, XXXI, 1946, 65–77.

———, The Vine in Bas Languedoc, *G.R.*, XXXVI, 1946, 67–79.

Blanchard, R., The Natural Regions of the French Alps, *G.R.*, XI, 1921, 31–49.

Cowan, Laing G., "France and the Saar," New York, 1950.

Demangeon, A., and L. Febvre, "Le Rhin," Paris, 1935.

Fish, W. B., Population Trends in France, *G.*, XXV, 1940, 107–120.

Fleure, H. J., A Generalized Diagram of a City of the Paris Basin, *G.*, XXV, 1940, 34–35.

Gallois, L., The Origin and Growth of Paris, *G.R.*, XIII, 1923, 345–367.

Musset, R., The Geographical Characteristics of Western France, *G.R.*, XII, 1922, 84–99.

Mutton, Alice F. A., Hydro-Electric Power in Western Europe, *G.J.*, CXVII, 1951, 328–342.

Peattie, Roderick, The Conflent: A Study in Mountain Geography, *G.R.*, XX, 1930, 245–257.

Pounds, N. J. G., Port and Outport in North-West Europe, *G.J.*, CIX, 1947, 216–228.

Russell, Richard J., Geomorphology of the Rhône Delta, *A.A.A.G.*, XXXII, 1942, 149–254.

Shaw, Earl B., Land Use in the Upper Ardèche Valley of France, *E.G.*, XI, 1935, 357–367.

Veyret-Vernet, Germaine, "L'Industrie des Alpes françaises," Grenoble, 1948.

Vidal de la Blache, P., and L. Febvre, "La France de l'est," Paris, 1918.

There is an excellent geographical literature on the provinces of France, inspired in part by the work of P. Vidal de la Blache. Foremost among the many regional monographs are the following:

Baulig, H., "Le Plateau central de la France et sa bordure méditerranéenne," Paris, 1928.

Blanchard, R., "La Flandre," Dunkerque, 1906.

Demangeon, A., "La Picardie," Paris, 1905.

Sion, J., "La France méditerranéenne," Paris, 1934.

———, "Les Paysans de la Normandie orientale," Paris, 1909.

Sorre, M., "Les Pyrénées," Paris, 1922.

Vallaux, C., "La Basse Bretagne," Paris, 1907.

ATLASES

"Atlas de France," Paris, 1933.

Larmat, L., "Atlas de la France vinicole," 6 vols, Paris, 1941–1947. (A very detailed atlas of French viticulture.)

A number of maps, rather like those of the "British National Atlas," have been published by the Présidence du conseil, Direction de la documentation. Number 32, "Les Systèmes de culture de la France," is a good, detailed map of French agriculture.

Postwar developments in France are very well covered in the official publications of the United Nations and the Organization for European Economic Cooperation.

These have been listed on pages 53 to 54. The more important for the study of France are:

Coal and Steel Industries of Western Europe, *Economic Bulletin for Europe*, II (2), 1950.

Economic Survey of Europe, Economic Commission for Europe published annually.

European Recovery Program, Annual Reports, Paris.

Fertilisers in Agricultural Recovery Programs, the Organization for European Economic Cooperation, Paris.

General Memorandum on the 1950–51 and 1951–52 Programmes, the Organization for European Economic Cooperation, 1950, Report on France.

Interim Report on the European Recovery Program, Paris, 1948.

Rapport Général sur le Premier Plan de Modernisation et d'Équipment (Plan Monnet), Paris, 1946. (A plan for the postwar economic development of France.)

Quarterly Bulletin of Steel Statistics for Europe, Economic Commission for Europe.

GEOGRAPHICAL PERIODICALS

Annales de géographie, Paris.

La Géographie, Paris, ceased publication in 1941.

A very large number of articles on the regional geography of France has appeared in these volumes.

BIBLIOGRAPHIES OF GEOGRAPHICAL WORKS

Almeida, P. C d', Frankreich, *Geographisches Jahrbuch*, XLIII, 1928, 276–312.

Conover, Helen F., "France: A List of References on Contemporary Economic, Social and Political Conditions," Library of Congress, Division of Bibliography, Washington, D.C., 1944.

CHAPTER 14: *The Low Countries*

The three countries of Belgium, Luxembourg, and the Netherlands have been closely associated for many centuries. These territories were brought together in the fourteenth and fifteenth centuries by the dukes of Burgundy. The acci-

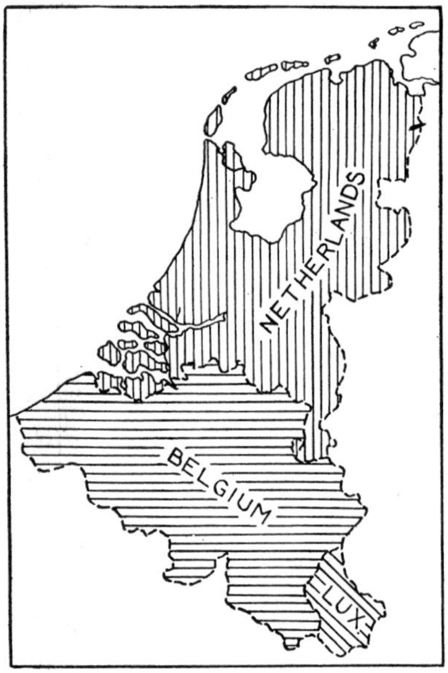

FIG. 99. Political divisions of the Low Countries.

dent of history split them apart, but now, in the aftermath of the Second World War, an attempt is being made to mold all three political units into a single economic unit. The three countries have much in common. The boundaries that divide them are arbitrary, their problems are similar, and their common fate during the years 1940 to 1945 has further strengthened the common factors which serve to hold them together.

The Low Countries together form a triangular-shaped territory, some 280 miles from the southern border of Luxembourg to the

coast of Friesland in the north and 150 miles from western Flanders eastward to the German border. This territory constitutes a cross section through the hilly region of central Europe and the northern plain. The strongest feature in the

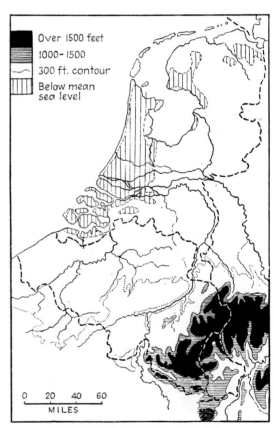

Over 1500 feet
1000–1500
300 ft. contour
Below mean sea level

0   20   40   60
MILES

FIG. 100. Relief of the Low Countries.

relief of the Low Countries is the Ardennes Plateau in the south, lying generally above 1,500 feet. On the south the hard rocks of the Ardennes dip beneath the younger and softer beds which make up most of Luxembourg. On

172

the north also the Ardennes Plateau sinks beneath the chalk, which here forms a low, undulating plateau. The chalk in turn sinks beneath the sands and clays of the low plain of Flanders and of the Netherlands. Much of this land has been reclaimed by artificial enclosure and drainage in modern times. Much, on the other hand, is overlain with sterile deposits of sand and gravel, the outwash distributed from the ice sheets.

LUXEMBOURG

The smallest of the three units that make up Benelux achieved its present shape in 1867, when an earlier and larger Luxembourg was divided into a French-speaking and a German-speaking part and the former annexed to Belgium. The grand duchy survived as a German-speaking sovereign state in customs union with Germany. After the First World War it entered into customs union with Belgium.

It has an area of only 998 square miles and a population of about 291,000. The capital and largest city of the grand duchy, Luxembourg itself, has a population of only 62,000. Luxembourg is rich and prosperous by virtue of her iron and steel industry (see page 174). This employs half the working population and contributes about 40 per cent to the total iron and steel output of the Benelux Union. Before the war the annual output of steel averaged about 2 million tons. Postwar production has been hampered by problems of reorganization and the supply of materials, but despite this, output had increased to 2,450,000 tons in 1950. Despite the possession of local low-grade ore, Luxembourg uses some ore imported from Sweden. Her most serious problem, however, lies in the supply of coke for the furnaces, and for this she is largely dependent on imports from western Germany.

Luxembourg is a peaceful and prosperous country, heavily dependent for her well-being on the export of her principal manufacture, steel, and on the import of foodstuffs to supplement her inadequate home production. Less than a quarter of the employed population is engaged in agriculture. Luxembourg has a small army but is alone quite incapable of defending her territory against aggression. She is an active member of the economic and political organizations that are seeking to bind the countries of western Europe together.

Luxembourg can be divided into two regions, almost equal in area. The more northerly is part of the Ardennes plateau. To the south is a region of low, rolling country, similar to that

Fig. 101. Physical regions of the Low Countries.

of northern Lorraine. In the south are several small fingers of limestone upland thrust northward from the Côtes de Moselle. They overlook an undulating plain in which rather sterile, forested, sandstone ridges alternate with more fertile, more intensively cultivated areas of limestone and clay. The region is a distinctive one and, in contrast to the Ardennes, has gained the name of *Gutland* (*le bon pays* or "good land"). Along the southern margin of Luxembourg there occur deposits of bedded iron ore similar to those of Lorraine, with which, in fact, they are continuous. These ores are mined, and some are smelted locally. In 1950, the production of ore was about 3,832,000 tons, with a metal content of not over 30 per cent. Some is sent northward to Belgium or to neighboring countries. Apart from the metallurgical centers along the southern margin there are few towns, but many large, rich, and picturesque villages. The city of Luxembourg (62,000) itself, capital of the grand duchy, is a small commercial city, picturesquely situated above the deep, winding valley of the Alzette.

The Ardennes of Luxembourg are a mass of rounded hills, separated by deep valleys. The area is forested. The climate is cooler and moister than in southern Luxembourg. The soil is thinner and poorer, and agriculture is little practiced and unimportant. The Ardennes of Luxembourg are continued without interruption in the Ardennes of southern Belgium.

BELGIUM

Belgium, like Luxembourg, is made up of two contrasted regions, the southerly, more hilly region of the Ardennes and a more northerly region of plain, in which lie most of the industrial cities of Belgium. The latter can be divided into the low, rolling country of Hainaut, Brabant, and Hesbaye and the almost level plains of Flanders. To the northeast is an area, known as the Campine, of outwash sands and gravels, which today constitute a rather infertile area of heathland.

Ardennes. This is a plateau, whose surface reaches heights of up to 2,000 feet. The massif ends abruptly on the south and west, where it just reaches into France; on the north it drops more gradually to a more dissected region known as the Condroz (page 175), while eastward it continues, as the Eifel, into Germany. Rivers have deepened their courses into the ancient rocks of the plateau, and the Meuse, which crosses the region from south to north, occupies a valley with deep, incised meanders. In the center of the region, however, the plateau has but slight relief and the small streams occupy shallow depressions. The area has a poor

The Ardennes Plateau. The surface is level or rolling, and the rivers deeply incised. The land has little agricultural value. Much is forested, though there is meadow and grazing land along the valleys. (*Belgian Railways and Marine.*)

The river Meuse at Dinant. Near here the river escapes from the uplands of the Ardennes. The citadel, replacing the castle, lies on the crag above the little town. (*Belgian Railways and Marine.*)

podsolic soil and a wet, chilly climate. Small peasant holdings are numerous, and agriculture is based on cattle rearing and the cultivation of hardy crops. The steeper slopes and the borders of the Ardennes are thickly wooded with oak and beech. It has been the forests, rather than the altitude or the relief, that have given to the Ardennes their reputation as a pathless and impenetrable waste.

On the northern edge of the Ardennes is the more broken and generally lower region known as the Condroz. It is also built of ancient rocks, among which limestone is conspicuous, and along its northern edge limestone comes to the surface. It is a region of greater scenic beauty than the Ardennes Plateau. The rivers have cut narrow gorges across the limestone ridges, and there are caves and underground streams characteristic of limestone topography. It is also more populous than the Ardennes; there are several small towns. Crop farming is more widespread and more productive, and the rye and potatoes of the plateau give place gradually

to the wheat and oats of the lowlands. In the Condroz hills are a number of resorts, such as Spa and Dinant, and the greater agricultural possibilities are reflected in the number of small market towns.

The Industrial Region of Central Belgium and Limburg. The river Sambre rises within France and flows eastward to join the Meuse at Namur. As far as Liége the Meuse keeps close to the margin of the Condroz and then swings away across the northern plain. The coal measures come to the surface along the valley of the Sambre and the valley of the Meuse between Namur and Liége. An industrial region has grown up here and spread both southward into the Ardenne foothills and northward on to the plain.

This industrial region is based on the local deposits of coal. It extends for about 100 miles from west to east. Coal does not, however, occur continuously throughout this belt, and the industrial, urban areas are interrupted by stretches of open country. In the west, the region of Mons (Bergen), known as the Borinage, is primarily a coal-mining area. Manufacturing industries are relatively less important, though the manufacture of earthenware and the coking and briquetting of coal are carried on. The Charleroi basin lies a short distance to the east

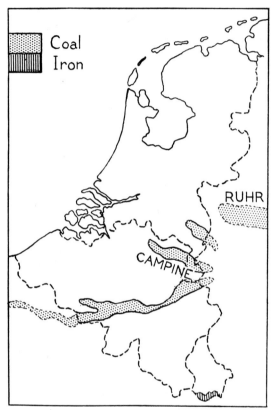

Fig. 102. Mineral resources of the Low Countries.

in the Sambre valley. Coal output is greater here than in the Borinage, and a vast number of manufacturing industries—metallurgical, engineering, chemical, pottery, and glass—have grown up. Charleroi itself is merely the center of a great number of small industrial towns which have grown into one another and reach westward along the Canal du Centre, the canal that traverses this part of the coal field, for a large part of the distance to Mons.

Between the Charleroi industrial area and that of Liége manufacturing is less developed. Liége (Luik, 156,500) lies on the Meuse, near its junction with the Vesdre and the Ourthe

and on the edge of the Ardennes, where, during the Middle Ages, iron ore was mined and worked. This early metallurgical industry later moved into the Meuse Valley where coal was available for the furnaces. The smelting and manufacture of zinc, mined in the Ardennes, were later added to that of iron. Liége was already an important industrial center when, at the end of the eighteenth century, the English industrialist Cockerill brought the techniques newly developed in England. The local coal proved to be suitable for metallurgical use. A modern iron-smelting industry was established, and an iron- and steel-finishing industry grew up. Liége now produces an immense range of

Fig. 103. Industrial regions of the Low Countries.

finished-steel goods, ranging from wire and nails to railway engines and automobiles. The zinc-smelting and galvanizing industry, which grew up on the basis of local materials, is now maintained by imports of zinc and zinc ore.

In the valley of the Vesdre, to the southeast

of Liége, is the town of Verviers, where was established at the end of the eighteenth century the manufacture of woolen cloth. This was the earliest mechanically driven textile mill to be established on the continent of Europe and owed its origin to that same Cockerill family which had largely been instrumental in developing the steel industry of Liége. Verviers and its surrounding villages now produce a great deal more than half the woolen cloth of Belgium and, in addition, wash and prepare the wool that is used in the spinning and weaving industries of other parts of the country. Verviers is also the site of an important glass industry.

The river Meuse formerly served as a means of communication between parts of the coal field and the Liége industrial area. The increasing size of barges rendered navigation difficult. A canal was first constructed in the nineteenth century from Liége to the Belgian port of Antwerp. This was too small for modern needs, and in 1940 the Albert Canal was opened. This is a large and modern ship canal between the Meuse at Liége and the navigable Scheldt at Antwerp (see page 179).

The territory of the Netherlands extends southward to the foothills of the Ardennes a few miles to the northeast of Liége. This area of South Limburg contains a small coal field which is similar to though geologically distinct from that of the Meuse Valley. This Limburg coal field is a continuation to the west of the Aachen coal field (see page 231) of western Germany. It is worked a few miles to the northeast of the Dutch city of Maastricht and then continues westward into Belgium. Maastricht (77,700), the largest city in the area of the Dutch coal mines, lies on the Meuse (Maas), very close to the Belgian boundary.

The Sambre-Meuse coal field of Belgium produces at present about 16 million tons of coal annually. But reserves are comparatively small, the mines are old and do not readily lend themselves to modernization, the seams are thin and steeply inclined, and firedamp is a serious hazard. These mines are among the least economic in Europe, and the Schuman Plan envisages closing down some of them.

The coal field of Dutch Limburg and its continuation westward into the Kempenland (Campine) area of Belgium have been developed very much more recently. The first of the present Dutch mines was brought into production at the beginning of the present century, and the first Belgian in 1917. Coal mining on a smaller scale is much older than this in the Netherlands. The mines are modern, well equipped, and efficient. The output of coal per worker is higher in the Netherlands than in any other European country. At present the Dutch output from Limburg is about 12 million tons and from the Belgian Kempenland, about 7 million tons.

Plateau of Hainaut, Brabant, and Hesbaye. A few miles to the north of the Meuse and Sambre the chalk overlies the coal-bearing beds. No relief feature marks this change, but the aspect of the land alters. The wooded *bocage* of the wet Ardennes and Condroz ends; the rolling plain of chalk, overlain in many parts by a shallow dusting of the fertile loess, appears to stretch without interruption or limit. Fields are large, open, and unfenced, divided into cultivation strips by unseen boundaries. Roads run straight to the horizon, bordered by their lines of trees. Villages are large and compact, and isolated settlements are as rare as the small patches of woodland, which sometimes break the monotony of the patchwork of cultivated fields. This is rich agricultural land, dotted with a close pattern of market towns, whose architecture bears witness to a long period of prosperity. Louvain (Leuven) with its richly decorated town hall, Tongeren (Tongres), Tirlemont (Tienen), and Tournai (Doornik) all lie near the northern edge of the region.

Brussels (Bruxelles, Brussel, 960,500) is the largest and most important city and the capital of Belgium. It lies in the shallow valley of the Senne where the river flows from the plateau of Brabant out on to the Flanders Plain. Brussels has all the appearances of a great capital. To the modern administrative buildings, museums, and palaces it adds the monuments of its great past: the town hall, lying in the center of the old city, and the cathedral of Sainte-Gedule, on the

Flax retting near Courtrai, Belgium. The flax, after harvesting, is fastened into bundles and allowed to soak in the rivers and canals in order to free the fiber from the soft vegetable matter. (*Belgian Railways and Marine.*)

edge of the plateau to the east. Brussels is a smaller city than Paris but has a similarly varied range of industries, many of them crafts which demand a high degree of skill and sell at luxury prices; in addition there are many textile and food industries.

Flanders. The transition from the plateau of central Belgium to the plain of Flanders is no less sudden and the contrast no less strongly marked than that from the Ardennes and Condroz to the plateau of Brabant. The change is not wholly due to the geological structure. Much of Flanders is floored with sands and clays and is low-lying and flat. The rivers, the Scheldt (Schelde, Escaut), Lys, and their tributaries, occupy valleys so shallow that the eye can scarcely detect the slope of their sides. The rivers wind sluggishly. Drainage from the land is slow and is assisted by drainage ditches cut around the margins of the fields. Even so, there remain small areas of bog, where rushes and osiers grow amid the stagnant, black, peat-stained pools. The sands and gravels which lie about the Flanders Plain in isolated patches often support poor woodland. Sometimes they have been cleared to make a dry site for a small, compact, red-roofed village, with a slender church steeple, visible for many miles across the flat land. All land that is capable of cultivation is under crops and is worked intensively. Holdings are very small, and only the most exacting labor can extract a livelihood from them for the peasant proprietors.

The faint undulations of Flanders disappear toward the north. The sandy beds thin away and along the coast give place to a belt of flat, alluvial land, cut off from the sea only by a range of sand dunes, supplemented by dikes, and in parts lying below sea level. Drainage is more difficult here, and crop farming less common. The grazing land is crossed by wide, straight canals, each flanked by low dikes. Villages are few and compact, gathered on outliers of the sandy soils for dryness and protection.

In Flanders are many of the oldest and most famous towns of Belgium, which in the Middle Ages established their fame for the manufacture of woolen cloth. In some, such as Ghent (Gand),

Alost (Aalst), Courtrai (Kortrijk), Ypres (Ieper), is to be found the modern textile industry. Others have preserved the outward mani-

Bruges. The ancient city is dominated by the thirteenth-century tower of its city hall.

Malines, the market place, dominated by the great Gothic cathedral. Note the very large area of the market place.

festations of this great past, such as Bruges (Brugge, 53,000), perhaps the loveliest medieval town in northwestern Europe, and Mechelen (Malines, 60,500). Ghent (167,600) has developed modern textile industries, especially the manufacture of woolen and cotton cloth, and is now connected with the Scheldt estuary by a ship canal along which factories have been developed. A number of towns of modern origin and growth, such as Lokeren and Sint-Niklaas, carry on the textile industry.

The largest city and greatest port of Flanders is Antwerp (Anvers, Antwerpen, 262,000), lying on the right bank of the lower Scheldt, close to the Dutch boundary. For a period of some 200 years the port was closed owing to the refusal of the Netherlands to allow vessels to and from Antwerp to pass through its territorial waters. Napoleon threw the port of Antwerp open to the commerce of the world at the beginning of the nineteenth century, and the city slowly regained its ancient prestige and importance. Its cathe-

Brussels (Bruxelles), the late medieval or renaissance houses of the wealthy merchants of the city.

dral, town hall, guild houses, and churches belong to its medieval past; its docks and canals to its modern development. Antwerp is now the port for the industrial regions of Liége and the Kempenland. The Albert Canal, completed in 1940, puts it into close contact with the middle

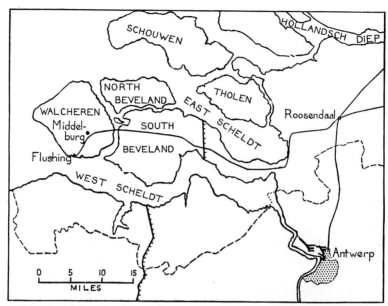

Fig. 104. The lower Scheldt and the port of Antwerp. Note that the political boundary crosses the Scheldt a few miles below the port. The railroad is shown running to the cross-channel packet station of Flushing.

Meuse Valley. The Scheldt is navigable up to Ghent, and the waterways of the lower Meuse and Rhine allow barges to pass from Antwerp to the Rhine Valley. A number of manufacturing industries, including the smelting of imported ores, have been established near the port.

Kempenland. East of the plain of Flanders is the sandy Kempenland, or Campine. The level of the land rises somewhat above that of the plain to the west. It is composed of sands and gravels laid down by the rivers. The soil is generally poor and infertile. In places, the sand blows into dunes when the surface vegetation is removed; elsewhere an impervious bed, a little below the surface, leads to the formation of springs, shallow lakes, and damp, peat-filled depressions. Much of the Kempenland has been cultivated but gives only a poor return. Crop farming has for many years been declining. Crop yields are in general below the average for Belgium as a whole. Some areas have never been cultivated and remain covered with a vegetation of dry heath; others have been planted with conifers. The aspect of the Kempenland is changing, however, with the opening of coal mines and the development of industries, particularly along the southern or Belgian margin of this territory.

The Belgian State. The kingdom of Belgium has had a chequered history. Its territory formerly was part of the Spanish Netherlands, the northern part of which revolted successfully in the sixteenth century. Belgium is that part which did not make good in its bid for independence. Its northern boundary was defined by the exigencies of war. Its port of Antwerp was cut off from the sea by the Dutch province of Zeeland. The territory passed from Spain to Austria. In 1815 it was reunited with the Netherlands but revolted and in 1831 established its own independence, which has since been endangered only by German aggression.

Two languages are spoken in the Low Countries. In the southern half of Belgium the prevailing language is French. At an earlier date the Walloon dialect of French was spoken, but this has gradually given place to orthodox French. In northern Belgium and in the Netherlands the language is Flemish or Dutch. There is no appreciable difference between them; they were both Low German dialects which crystallized into languages in the Low Countries. German is the prevailing language of the grand duchy of Luxembourg. The most important linguistic frontier in the Low Countries is that between Walloon and Flemish. From near Ypres on the

Antwerp (Anvers) and the river Scheldt. Antwerp lies on the east bank of the river, which is here a fine navigable waterway. In the distance can be seen the west front of the cathedral, and to the right a local business house, known as the "Skyscraper." (*Belgian Railways and Marine.*)

western border of Belgium it runs eastward through Brussels to the Meuse between Maastricht and Liége. From this point the boundary between Walloon and German extends southward across the Ardennes to the French frontier (see Fig. 110).

Within Belgium, the differences between the Walloon and the Fleming go very deep and have in the past aroused strong passions. From the early days of the Belgian state the French-speaking Walloons assumed an air of superiority and made no attempt to disguise their contempt for the less cultured Flemings. French was the language of government, of the courts of law, and of education. During the nineteenth century there was an awakening of Flemish consciousness, which developed into a vigorous nationalist movement. The hostility of the Flemings to the government in Brussels led some of them to become the willing tools of German imperialism. It should be emphasized that Flemish nationalism never received any overt support from the Dutch government. Generalization is difficult,

but as a rule, the Fleming is more likely to be Catholic and royalist; the Walloon, agnostic or, at least, anticlerical and republican. Although the population has increased over the whole of Belgium, the rate of increase has slackened markedly in southern Belgium. It has been pointed out that there is a "close correlation between the areas of relatively stable population and the areas in which French is the common language."[1] Those social and economic factors which in France may have had an adverse influence on the birth rate are not operative in southern Belgium (or in Romance Switzerland, which shows a similar trend), nor are there any economic factors which suggest reasons why the birth rate of the Walloons (French-speaking Belgians) should be lower than that of the Flemings and Dutch. Perhaps it indicates that the Walloons derive the pattern of their social behavior more from France than has been supposed. In Flemish-speaking Belgium

[1] Kendall, H. M., A Survey of Population Changes in Belgium, *A.A.A.G.*, XXVIII, 1938, 145–164.

the rate of population growth has continued with little interruption, and the Netherlands now show the highest birth rate of any country of western Europe. At present the total Belgian population of 8,512,000 (1947) is about evenly divided between Walloon and Fleming. The prospect of being outnumbered in the near future by the Flemings is not altogether pleasing to the Walloon, who has hitherto been in the majority.

Belgium was occupied by the Germans through both world wars. During the Second World War, Belgium was on the whole well treated. Her industries, already closely bound up with those of Germany, were to be integrated into the German system. They were thus able to continue production. The Allied campaigns at the close of the war swept quickly through Belgium, and very little damage was done either to industrial equipment or to organization. After the war Belgium enjoyed a period of high prosperity. Life was gay in Brussels. The shops were full and food was abundant when austerity and even starvation existed in the rest of Europe. The economic policy of the Belgian government was wise and successful, and though suffering from a shortage of coal and to some extent hindered by the slower recovery of Germany, Belgium has remained one of the most prosperous of European countries.

Belgium is primarily an industrial country, and about 42 per cent of the working population is employed in factories and mines. By contrast, only 17 per cent is on the land. Belgium is a considerable importer of foodstuffs for which she pays with the export of her manufactures. Agriculture in Belgium is conducted on small holdings, in contrast to that of the Netherlands.

Size of holding, acres	Percentage of the total holdings	
	Belgium	Netherlands
Under 25..........	96.35	66.5
25 to 125..........	3.4	32.0
Over 125..........	0.25	1.5

In Belgium the holdings are even smaller than the figures in the accompanying table

would indicate. In 1930, 74 per cent of the holdings were actually of less than 2 acres each and a further 17 per cent were between 2½ and 12½ acres. A very large proportion of these minute holdings, however, provides only a part-time occupation for industrial and town workers. These lie mainly in Brabant, Hainault, and Flanders, within easy reach of the urban centers.

Belgium lies where the hills of central Europe —here the Ardennes Plateau—approach to within a short distance of the coast. The Flanders Plain has tended to be used not only for the peaceful movement of goods between France and Germany but also for their military campaigns. It is not true that campaigns are not fought over the Ardennes. Rundstedt's offensive of 1944 took this course, but the majority have been in the lowlands between the Ardennes and the sea. Here are the fields of Ramillies, Jemmappes, and Waterloo, of Flanders and of Dunkirk. Belgium was from the start a small and militarily weak power in a position of great strategic importance. She defended herself by her policy of neutrality, of making no alliances, and of taking no sides until 1914, when she was invaded by the Germans. Since then she has been active in plans for western European defense. Only in union with her neighbors is she secure from attack.

Belgium has a vast and rich empire in Central Africa. She had no colonial ambitions and really acquired her empire by accident. This was the creation of an association of which King Leopold of Belgium was a leader. It became a personal possession of his and was passed on by him to the Belgian state. The Congo is a rich source of tropical timbers and other vegetable products. Copper and now uranium are among its products. Their sale within the free world brings large sums of foreign currencies into the hands of the Belgians. The dollar is not the "hard" or rare currency in Belgium that it is in France and Great Britain.

NETHERLANDS

The boundary between Belgium and the Netherlands traverses the Kempenland from east to west. Although this line was achieved almost by accident—it derives in the main from the course of the fighting between the Dutch and the Spaniards early in the seventeenth century—it has the merit of running through sparsely peopled areas.

The Kempenland, or Campine, of the Netherlands resembles the corresponding area of Belgium in having a poor soil and sparse population. A consequence of its slender natural endowment has been the poverty of its people. Their willingness to accept low wages has attracted industries to this area. Close to the Kempenland or along its northern edge are the cities of Breda (87,000) and Tilburg (118,000), both having cloth industries, and Eindhoven (138,000) with the important electrical engineering works of Philips.

East of the Kempenland is a southerly projection of Netherlands territory, known as South Limburg. It follows the Meuse (Maas) Valley and lies mainly to the east of the river. It extends into the Ardenne foothills and contains the only area of really hilly country in the Netherlands. South Limburg contains an important coal field, part of the coal field that extends from Aachen in Germany westward into the Belgian Kempenland. Large-scale coal mining is of recent origin in South Limburg. The mines are deep, but production is highly mechanized, and the Limburg field is probably the most efficient in Europe.

On the west bank of the Meuse, very close to the Belgian boundary, is Maastricht (76,500), an ancient city of Roman origin, at a crossing of the river Meuse.

The area of the Netherlands north of the Kempenland owes its present form in part to the work of the glaciers of the Ice Age and the postglacial sinking of the land surface, in part to the work of man in reclaiming the area and bringing it into agricultural use.

The ice extended southward to a line somewhat north of the course of the lower Rhine, which was itself diverted to its present westerly course by the ice. There are considerable areas of sand and gravel, remains of the terminal moraines and outwash fans of the former glaciers. After the Ice Age the land surface sank relative

to the sea. Toward the east alluvium was laid down by the Rhine and now constitutes the damp and level plains along each bank of the Rhine and of its distributary the Ijssel.

To the west of the present territory of the Netherlands many low islands were formed by the submergence. Wind, waves, and currents combined to build a natural barrier of sand and silt along their western margin, protecting the

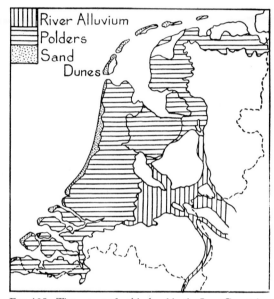

Fig. 105. The extent of polderland in the Low Countries.

lagoons and islands inside it. In the course of time the islands grew larger as a result of sedimentation and the lakes smaller. Most of the latter have filled with silt or peat and have been reclaimed by man for his use.

We thus have in the Netherlands a western region of low and almost level land, much of it actually below mean sea level, all of it kept dry for agricultural use only by careful drainage and the continuous pumping of water from the ditches that surround the fields. This is the polderland of the Netherlands.

To the east the land is somewhat higher. In part it consists of alluvium along the rivers, still low-lying and liable to flood in winter but generally a foot or two above the level of the polderland. But most of eastern Netherlands is covered with sandy and gravelly deposits left

Windmill drainage in the polders of the Netherlands. (*Netherlands National Tourist Office.*)

by the glaciers of the Ice Age. The soil over these areas is thin and poor. It formerly gave only small crops and the population was scanty and poor. In recent years, however, vigorous and successful attempts have been made, with the help of fertilizers and deep plowing, to bring considerable areas of the heathland into cultivation.

The Polderland. The contrast between the east and the west is dominant in the geography of the Netherlands. The western Netherlands is in large measure the creation of man during the past thousand years. It has been reclaimed from lake and swamp and shallow sea. This region formerly consisted of low, marshy islands, which made up the joint delta of the Rhine, Meuse, and Scheldt. The tide ran in and out between them, and along their outer, or seaward, margin the stiff winds from the sea piled up sand dunes, which gave some protection to the lagoons and islands. Nature was slowly modifying and, in general, enlarging the islands, but the process was immeasurably speeded up by man. During summer he built dikes around the drier patches, strong enough to withstand the storms and

floods of winter. He drained the land inside the dikes and preserved it for his own use. In time he added to it, enclosing adjoining areas of the mud with banks, freed it of its sea salt, and brought it into cultivation. In this way the multitude of islands grew toward one another, until only narrow channels, necessary to carry away the drainage, were left. The process was not uninterrupted; early in the fifteenth century there was a serious break-through of the sea, known as the Saint Elizabeth's Flood, which in part undid the work of centuries. But the task of diking and reclaiming continued vigorously through the later Middle Ages and modern times. The windmill, so typical a feature of the Dutch polderland, was used to lift water from the reclaimed fields. Certain large and deep lakes, such as the Haarlemmer Meer, were not drained until the nineteenth century, when the steam engine was employed for the purpose. The operation of the old windmill drainage is illustrated in the sketch (Fig. 107), but the rather unreliable windmill has generally been replaced by steam and oil engines.

The extensive cutting of peat for fuel had complicated the drainage, because it led to the formation of small lakes. When drained, the peat areas tend to contract in thickness, thus lowering the surface and increasing the difficulties of drainage.

The latest development of land reclamation has been the drainage of the Zuider Zee. This is an extension on a very much larger scale of a process that has been going on for centuries. The work began in 1919. A large dike was built, 18 miles in length, across the entrance to the Zuider Zee. The reclamation of four large polders was planned within the lake thus formed. The smallest, the Wieringermeer polder in the northwest, was completed first and was brought into cultivation in 1930. It is now mainly under crops—wheat, barley, oats, potatoes. It is a level area of about 80 square miles, lying in general 20 feet below the mean sea level at Amsterdam, crisscrossed by the narrow drainage ditches, such as are illustrated in Fig. 106, which carry the water from the fields to the pumps which raise it to the level of the sea.

The northeastern polder has also been reclaimed, but the remaining two are still incomplete. When finished, the drainage will have added about 875 square miles to the land area of the Netherlands and the Zuider Zee will have been reduced to the very much smaller Ijssel Meer. To the northeast of the Zuider Zee the polders extend into Friesland and Groningen.

Both the peat and silt areas of the polderland are very fertile and bear good crops of wheat and other grain crops. Crop husbandry depends

FIG. 106. Map of a typical Dutch polder.

upon the level of the water table. Where this is high, the land has to be left under grass. In certain areas there are local specialities, such as the bulbs, especially tulips, around Haarlem.

FIG. 107. Diagram of polder drainage. The water collects in the small drainage ditches and is lifted by pumps, many of them windmills, to the larger canals, which carry it to still larger canals and the sea.

These are grown on soil that has been lightened by an admixture of sand blown by the wind and brought by man inland from the coastal dunes. Along the western edge of the Polderland is a narrow belt of land along which sand, blown inland from the dunes, has been deposited.

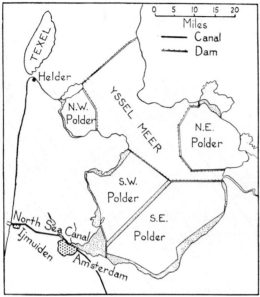

FIG. 108. Amsterdam and the Zuider Zee. Amsterdam is linked directly with the sea by the North Sea Canal.

This rather "warmer" soil is intensively cultivated for vegetables and other garden produce. A good deal of this area is built over with glasshouses for the cultivation of early and tender plants.

Most of the polderland is divided into individual holdings. These are generally small, and a majority are of less than 25 acres. The farmsteads are scattered and often protected by a few trees to break the force of the wind.

In Zeeland and Holland are a number of small, ancient towns, founded on areas of dry land and sometimes still surrounded by their ancient water defenses: Leiden (89,500), Alkmaar. Haarlem (161,000), Delft (64,000), Utrecht (190,500), Dordrecht (70,000), and Middelburg. Some have developed modern industries. All are closely grouped as if to conserve space. They are clean, with the red brick houses that the Dutch masters used to paint, tall

belfries, and richly carved and decorated town halls.

Three towns have outgrown their petty origins. The Hague (Den Haag, 's Gravenhage, 559,000) is a well-laid-out city with broad streets and large modern governmental buildings. It is not primarily an industrial city. It had been a residence of the counts of Holland before the formation of the United Netherlands and continued to contain the royal palace and seat of the government. Amsterdam (836,000) is the great banking and commercial city and the titular capital of the Netherlands. It grew up in the later Middle Ages where the little river Amstel was dammed as it flowed into the Ij. The rivers provided the growing town with a naturally protected harbor. The town was fortified, and its walls had at intervals to be moved farther out to enclose an expanding urban area. This became in the seventeenth and eighteenth centuries the port from which sailed the East Indiamen, and in the town were developed industries based on the products of the East which those ships brought back to Holland. Amsterdam had been approached by way of the Zuider Zee, but increasing difficulties of navigation led in 1876 to the cutting of the North Sea Canal from Amsterdam westward to the sea at Ijmuiden. Large vessels now can enter the canal by locks at its western end and sail across the polder to the city. The trade of Amsterdam is chiefly the domestic trade of the Netherlands. It has good canal communications with most parts of the Netherlands. A large canal from Amsterdam to the Rhine puts Amsterdam in connection with the Ruhr industrial area, and to a small extent Amsterdam serves as a port for the latter. A small steel industry has been established at Velsen, near the western end of the North Sea Canal. Ijmuiden is the chief Dutch fishing port. The fisheries are of great importance in the Dutch economy and make a valuable contribution to the nation's food supply.

Rotterdam (676,000) has achieved the position of a great port only recently. It serves western Germany, and its prosperity depends largely upon the industrial and commercial

The dam constructed across the mouth of the Zuider Zee in order to exclude the sea and to permit the drainage of the lake area behind it. (*Netherlands National Tourist Office.*)

The town of Sneek, Friesland. The canals provide an important means of communication in such small Dutch towns. (*Netherlands National Tourist Office.*)

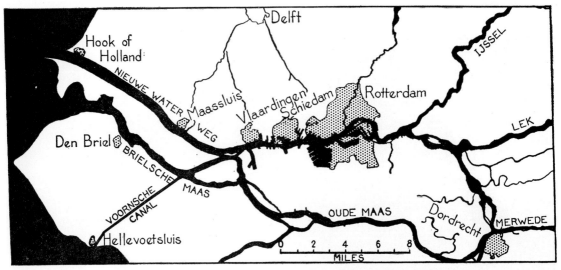

Fig. 109. Rotterdam and its connection with the sea and with the Rhine.

activity of the Ruhr. The Rhine divides into distributaries which branch and reunite. Rotterdam grew up on one of these, the New Meuse, some 20 miles from the sea. Its connection with the ocean was at first difficult, but the distributary of the Rhine on which it lies was improved, thus giving Rotterdam a straight, broad, and deep connection, known as the New Waterway, with the sea. Most of the imports are transshipped to Rhine barges, which are towed up the Rhine. Rotterdam has become an industrial town, but on a smaller scale than Amsterdam; the greater part of its traffic is in transit to or from Germany. Rotterdam was heavily damaged in the German air raids of May, 1940, but is gradually being rebuilt. It is ironic that a city which suffered so severely at the hands of the Germans should be dependent for its prosperity on a revival of the trade of the German Rhineland.

The area of polderland lying northeast of the Zuider Zee is partly under crops, partly grazing and dairy country. Leeuwarden (78,500) and Groningen (136,500) are important market centers. The region is protected by dikes, and offshore lies the chain of Frisian Islands which stretches from North Holland to the base of the Danish peninsula. These are low, treeless, and exposed and are partly dune covered. Cattle rearing is the most important occupation.

Valleys of the Rhine and Meuse. The broad flat valley which contains the Meuse (Maas) and the Waal and Lek branches of the Rhine extends eastward from the polderland of Zeeland and Holland. It lies above sea level but is nevertheless liable to flooding by the rivers, which sometimes mingle their waters over the intervening fields in times of severe flood. Most of this land is under crops. The valley of the Ijssel branches from the Rhine above Arnhem. This river no longer carries more than a small proportion of the discharge of the Rhine, but its valley, like the Betuwe, is chiefly under crops.

The Betuwe is not thickly peopled, but on the higher and drier land which borders it are a number of small cities, which include Nijmegen (110,500), on the southern bank of the Waal, and Arnhem (103,500), 10 miles away across the level Betuwe.

Eastern Netherlands. To the south and east of the Zuider Zee and east of the valley of the Ijssel are large areas of glacial sands and gravels. Outwardly these resemble the Kempenland, but the surface stands generally somewhat higher above sea level. Much of the surface is covered with heath or with newly planted stands of conifers. Hollows in the sandy surface fill with water and accumulate peat. Valleys are floored with a heavier and more productive soil, and around the margin of this region is marine or lacustrine clay. In recent years successful at-

The Rhine Valley near Nijmegen. The land is flat, fertile, and intensively cultivated. It is divided into small holdings, each with its dwelling house and outhouses. Trees are often maintained as a windbreak. (*Netherlands National Tourist Office.*)

tempts have been made to develop the higher moors for agricultural purposes, and with the use of lime and artificial fertilizers worth-while progress has been made. This region now produces considerable quantities of rye, oats, barley, and potatoes. Towns are few and small in this sandy eastern region. Most serve only to focus the agricultural activities of the surrounding country, but some have developed small industries. In the towns of Twente, particularly Enschede (107,000), Lonneker, and Almelo, a cotton industry developed in the nineteenth century whose local basis was the cheap labor and the skill in manipulating wool and flax of the local population. There is no fuel in this eastern region of the Netherlands, except peat or turf, which is cut and burned, and the small production of petroleum from a field near the German boundary.

The Kingdom of the Netherlands. The state of the United Netherlands came into being as a result of successful revolt against Spain in the late sixteenth century. Hitherto its territory had made up a group of distinct and often hostile units: the county of Holland, the bishopric of Utrecht, the duchy of Guelders, and so on. "The Dutch nation was born, coherent and distinct from other national units. It was born because, during the second half of the sixteenth century, a state came into existence, within whose territory men lived and strove together, and shared experiences so crowded and so intense that they found themselves overnight where it had taken the people of other nation states centuries to arrive."[1] The Netherlands thus achieved a unity such as Belgium has never known. In the course

[1] Renier, G. J., "The Dutch Nation," p. 10, London, 1944.

of the Dutch revolt a large part of the population became Protestant, generally Calvinist. In contrast to the Catholic tradition of Belgium, the Dutch tradition is Protestant.

The Netherlands are in many ways complementary to Belgium; they are more agricultural,

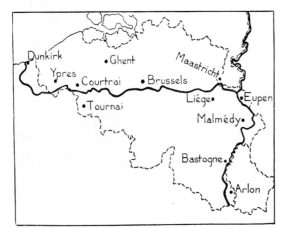

FIG. 110. The language frontier in Belgium. Walloon (French) is spoken to the south and west, Flemish (Dutch) to the north, and German to the east.

while Belgium is more industrial. Of the working population about 20 per cent is engaged in agriculture (as against 17 in Belgium) and 26 in industry (as against 42 in Belgium).

Dutch agriculture is on the whole somewhat better equipped than Belgian. Somewhat over a half of the agricultural land of the Netherlands is under permanent grass and is used mainly for dairy farming. The output of liquid milk and of butter and cheese is considerable, and pigs are widely kept as an adjunct of dairy farming. In Belgium the balance of agricultural practice is tipped in favor of crop farming; some three-fifths of the agricultural land is under the plow, though there has been in recent years a marked trend toward an increase in dairy farming. The rather larger average size of holdings in the Netherlands hides a more acute agrarian problem. Here a large proportion of the land has necessarily to be under grass because it is too damp for cultivation, and a large area of dry, sandy heath is too unproductive to be worth plowing. There is, in consequence, a very great pressure of population on the land.

Land values are high, and the cultivators make the most of their holdings by a very heavy use of fertilizers. The standard of rural housing is not always good, rural indebtedness is high, and mechanical devices are but little used on some of the farms.

This higher dependence upon agriculture, with the greater pressure of population, leads in the Netherlands, on the one hand, to the reclamation of land, on the other, to the development of industries which can absorb the surplus population. The textile industry of the Twente district, for example, has no conspicuous ad-

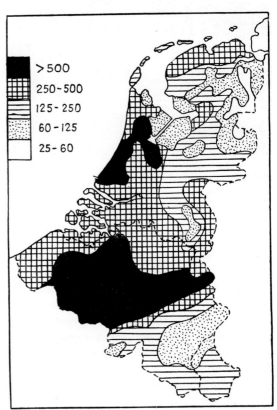

FIG. 111. Population density in the Low Countries per square mile.

vantage except the availability of labor in this region of poor agriculture. The manufacture of leather goods, of radios and other electrical equipment, of pottery requires large supplies of labor. The reclamation of the Zuider Zee was also part of a plan to alleviate rural overpopula-

The North Sea Canal between Amsterdam and the sea. The locks seen here are near Ijmuiden. The level of the canal is above that of the polders on each side of it. (*Netherlands National Tourist Office.*)

tion. The Dutch merchant marine and overseas commercial interests also provide an outlet for the population, and the Dutch act as middlemen in the commerce of Northwestern Europe.

Both Antwerp and Amsterdam are engaged primarily in handling the commerce of their immediate area, though both are to some extent engaged in the transshipment of goods either despatched from or destined for their German hinterlands. Rotterdam is, first and foremost, the port of the Rhine River system, and its livelihood depends largely upon the activity of the Ruhr industrial region. It exports Ruhr coal, coke, and steel goods and imports iron ore, timber, and other raw materials. The attempts of the German government in the years between the two great wars to divert much of this Ruhr traffic to the German ports of Emden and Bremen and the attempt of Antwerp to increase its share in the traffic of the Rhine have done little to diminish the trade of Rotterdam. More serious is the diminution in recent years of the industrial activity in the Ruhr and the falling off of shipments through Rotterdam.

In contrast to Belgium, the Netherlands suffered severely in the Second World War and their recovery has been slow. Ten per cent of the cultivated land was flooded by the breaching of the dikes; 20 per cent of the houses and buildings were damaged or destroyed. Great harm was done to dock and port installations, and over 3,000 ships were sunk in the coastal and inland waterways of the Netherlands. The German occupation, furthermore, was harsher and more destructive of life and prosperity than that of Belgium. Dutch recovery has been impeded by the changed relationship between the Netherlands, on the one hand, and Germany and Indonesia on the other. These supplied the Netherlands with a large and essential part of its foreign exchange. The lower level of industrial activity in Germany limits the services which the Dutch can perform for Germany, and this also limits the purchases which they may make. Much industrial equipment has been idle because replacements could not be obtained from Germany. The former Dutch possessions of the East Indies sold tin, rubber, petroleum, and tea into the world's market and received foreign currencies for the Netherlands,

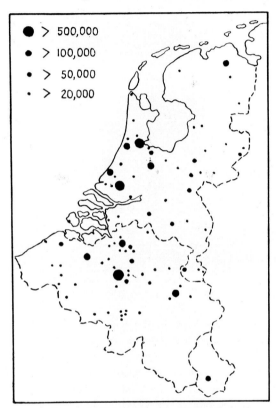

Fig. 112. Cities of the Low Countries.

while the Dutch supplied goods and services to the Indies. The Indonesian Republic is now independent and earns no dollars or sterling for the Netherlands. These changed circumstances necessitate a new approach to economic problems. "In the view of the Dutch authorities the ultimate solution of the problem requires a material change in the structure of Dutch economic life in favor of industrialization. . . ."[1] We may look for an extension of manufacturing, especially of lighter goods, such as textiles, leatherware, and light engineering. Coal reserves in the Campine are large and are now

[1] "Overseas Economic Surveys: Netherlands," p. 3, London, 1949.

being developed. There is a danger that this new turn in Dutch economic development may conflict more directly with Belgian interests. It would be unfortunate if such developments injured the prospects of the Benelux union, but in Europe it is not always easy to subordinate national interests to international.

THE UNITY OF THE LOW COUNTRIES

In November, 1947, a customs union was established between Belgium and Luxembourg on the one hand and the Netherlands on the other. This was regarded as merely the first step

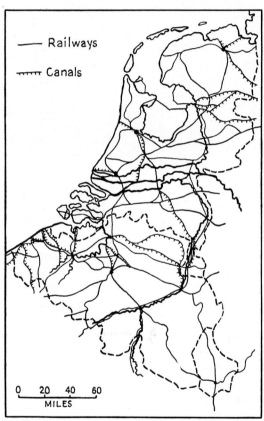

Fig. 113. Railroads, rivers, and canals of the Low Countries.

in the restoration of at least the economic unity of the Low Countries. Much remains to be done at the time of writing. The three countries contemplate the completion of their economic union in three stages, of which the customs union is only the first. Serious economic difficulies stand in the way of the completion of the union. The abolition of all obstacles to the internal movement of commodities would open the Belgian market to the vegetable produce of the Netherlands. This is produced in general more cheaply than that of Belgium, and the Belgian growers would suffer accordingly. Conversely, the small steel industry of the Netherlands is a high-cost industry and in its turn would suffer from competition with the larger and more efficient Belgian industry. On the other hand Dutch coal mining is more efficient than Belgian, and Dutch coal is cheaper. The creation of Benelux must necessarily be accompanied by much dislocation and not improbably by a considerable degree of ill-feeling. To some extent, these problems, in so far as they concern iron, steel, and coal, will be looked after by the organization of the Schuman Plan.

The time is not ripe to regard "Benelux" as if it were a single unit. It still consists of three states, with three elected parliaments and three governments, between which the possibility of disagreement cannot be wholly excluded. The boundary between Belgium and the Netherlands lies to the south of the Scheldt estuary, crosses the river a few miles below the port of Antwerp, and takes a somewhat irregular course across the Kempenland to the Meuse near Maasbracht. To the east of the Meuse the Dutch province of Limburg extends southward to reach, in the latitude of Maastricht, the border of the Ardennes. Thus does the Netherlands interpose a barrier between Belgium and Germany, only from 4 to 18 miles in width, but enough to prevent a low-level connection from being built from Belgium to the Ruhr. The Dutch possession of south Limburg and of the lower Scheldt has constituted vexing a problem in the relations of the two countries. Further problems have arisen because the Meuse flows from industrial central Belgium into Holland. The Dutch have at various times made improvements in the navigation of this river and along the stretch from Maasbracht up to Maastricht have built a parallel canal, the Juliana Canal, to take vessels for which the river was too narrow and difficult. It thus seemed in the early 1930's that the trade of Liége and of central Belgium might pass northward into the Netherlands and so to the port of Rotterdam. The Belgians' answer was the construction of the Albert Canal from Liége to Antwerp, a broad ship canal which served to open up the coal field of the Belgian Kempenland and to focus the trade of the whole of eastern Belgium on the port of Antwerp.

At the end of the Second World War the Dutch made certain very small and unimportant territorial gains along the frontier which runs northward from the Rhine estuary to the German Ems.

BIBLIOGRAPHY

GENERAL

The Coal and Steel Industries of Western Europe, *Economic Bulletin for Europe*, Vol. II, No. 2, 1950.
"Géographie universelle," Vol. II, Belgique, Luxembourg, Les Pays-bas, Paris, 1927.
Lamartine Yates, P., "Food Production in Western Europe," London, 1940.
Mance, Osborne, and J. E. Wheeler, "International River and Canal Transport," Oxford, 1944.
Sargent, A. J., "Seaports and Hinterlands," London, 1938.

BELGIUM AND LUXEMBOURG

"Belgium: British Survey Handbooks," London, 1944.
Bindoff, S. T., "The Scheldt Question," London, 1945.
"Conference on Rural Life: Belgium," League of Nations, Geneva, 1939.

"Conference on Rural Life: Luxembourg," League of Nations, Geneva, 1939.
Kendall, Henry M., A Survey of Population Changes in Belgium, *A.A.A.G.*, XXVIII, 1938, 145–164.
Monkhouse, F. J., "The Belgian Kempenland," Liverpool, 1949.
"Overseas Economic Surveys: Belgium," London, 1947.

NETHERLANDS

"Conference on Rural Life: Netherlands," League of Nations, Geneva, 1939.
Congres international de géographie, "Excursion Handbooks," Amsterdam, 1938.
Crone, G. R., Notes on the Rhine Distributaries and Land Reclamation in the Netherlands, *G.J.*, CIV, 1944, 92–101.
Hoffman, George W., The Netherlands Demands on

Germany: A Post-War Problem in Political Geography, *A.A.A.G.*, XLII, 1952, 129–152.

Jansma, K., The Drainage of the Zuider Zee, *G.R.*, XXI, 1931, 574–583.

Kampp, Aage H., Cultivation and Export of Netherlands Fruit, *E.G.*, XIII, 1937, 315–324.

Morgan, F. W., Rotterdam and Waterway Approaches to the Rhine, *E.G.*, XXIV, 1948, 1–18.

La Néerlande, études générales sur la géographie des Pays-bas, reprinted from *Tijdschrift van het Koninklijk Nederlandsch Aardrijkskundig Genootschap*, Leiden, 1938.

Tesch, P., Physiographic Regions of the Netherlands, *G.R.*, XIII, 1923, 507–517.

Thierry, J. W., The Enclosure and Partial Reclamation of the Zuider Zee, *G.J.*, LXXVII, 1930, 223–237.

The quarterly publications of two Dutch banks, the Rotterdamsche Bank and Amsterdamsche Bank *Quarterly Reviews* contain a great deal of material of geographical value.

The publications of the United Nations, the Organization for European Economic Cooperation, and Food and Agriculture Organization, listed on pages 52 to 54 are also valuable for the study of the Low Countries.

PERIODICALS

Tijdschrift van het Koninklijk Nederlandsch Aardrijkskundig Genootschap, Amsterdam, published every 2 months.

Tijdschrift voor Economische en Sociale Geografie, Rotterdam, published monthly.

CHAPTER 15: *Switzerland*

Switzerland belongs partly to western, partly to central Europe. The western part of the country is French in speech; its drainage by the Rhône is westward into France. The central and eastern parts are German in speech and are oriented rather toward the lands of the Rhine and Danube. In the south Switzerland reaches beyond the limits of the Alps to the margin of the plain of northern Italy. From the region of the Saint Gotthard, rivers flow southward to the Po, westward to the Rhône, and north to the Rhine. It is a country of hydrographic dispersion, of several languages, and it has no natural boundaries against any of its neighbors, yet it is one with no serious minority problems. It is without frontier difficulties and territorial ambitions.

Switzerland has been a country of slow growth and expansion. The confederation originated in the three cantons of Uri, Schwyz,

and Unterwalden, lying around the shores of Lake Lucerne (Luzern) and guarding the northern approaches to the Saint Gotthard Pass. The parochialism of the dwellers in these valleys, reinforced by the stimulus of Italian urban revolutions in the twelfth and thirteenth century, led to their revolt from their territorial lords, which included the Austrian House of Hapsburg. The trade which, from the first half of the thirteenth century, began to move across the Saint Gotthard Pass between Italy and Germany brought employment and profit to the mountaineers. They controlled one of the most frequented of European trade routes, and their friendship was sought by all who depended upon transalpine trade. Lucerne at the northern end of the lake sought their friendship and alliance and in 1330 entered their confederation. Lucerne was followed by trading cities to east and west: Zug, Zürich, and Bern. The southern

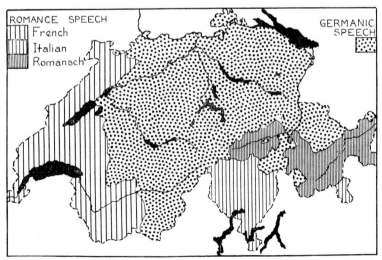

FIG. 114. Distribution of languages in Switzerland.

195

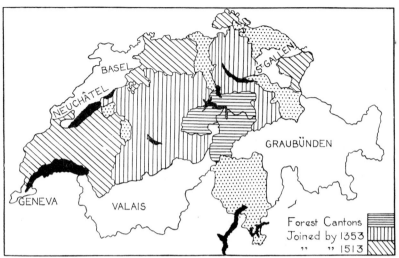

Fig. 115. The growth of the Swiss Confederation. Districts subject to though not formally part of the Confederation during the Middle Ages are stippled. The white areas were free allies of the Confederation until modern times.

approaches to the Saint Gotthard Pass were conquered, and although the Swiss failed to hold all their conquests on this side of the Alps, the Italian-speaking canton of Ticino (Tessin) remains part of the confederation. On the north the food-producing regions of Aargau and Thurgau were absorbed, a necessary step if the unproductive mountain regions and the populous cities were to be fed. Basel, Schaffhausen, and even Mulhouse, trading cities on the routes which ran northward across Germany, entered the confederation. The addition of the French-speaking regions to the west, the Vaud (Waad), Valais (Wallis), and Geneva (Genève), in the later Middle Ages and of the Grisons (Graubünden) and Neuchâtel more recently has completed the territorial growth of Switzerland.

The nucleus of Switzerland remains the German-speaking region. Here is the federal capital Bern, the two largest towns Zürich and Basel (Basle, Bâle), and the greater part of the engineering and textile industry of Switzerland. The German-speaking population is about 72 per cent of the total as against 21 per cent French-speaking and 5 per cent Italian-speaking. Romansch, like Italian, is a derivative of Latin. It survived when other similar languages, formerly spoken in various parts of southern Europe, disappeared, perhaps because of the

remoteness of the Engadine, in which it prevailed. The three major languages of Switzerland are each regarded as a national language and may be used anywhere within Switzerland in courts of law and on formal and public occasions. Romansch became in 1937 the fourth national language. Language differences have never constituted a serious political problem in Switzerland, though minor difficulties do occasionally arise over such matters as education and the seasonal movement of labor from one linguistic area into another.

Religion is another factor making for division in Switzerland. In the sixteenth century the Reformation was an affair of the towns, and it made little headway in the rural districts. Zürich, Basel, and Geneva (Genève, Genf) are predominantly Protestant. This division was in part the result of a social rift between town and country, which derived from the early stages of Swiss history.

The division of Switzerland by language and by religion bears no relationship to the physical divisions of the country. The latter consist of three belts which trend in a northeast-to-southwest direction. Smallest of these is the chain of the Jura Mountains, of which over a half lies in France. Along its straight and abrupt southeastern edge the Jura overlooks the misnamed

The Swiss Plateau. This is a very hilly region. The higher ground is often forested, but the gentler slopes are well cultivated. (*Swiss National Tourist Office.*)

Swiss Plateau, a country of rolling hills, deep valleys, and small lakes. Over half of Switzerland belongs to the third, the Alpine, region.

Jura Mountains. A brief account of the structure and topography of the Jura Mountains has already been given. They consist of a series of close, parallel ridges, lying from northeast to southwest. The limestone rock tends to produce a karst topography. Rivers flow along the valleys, breaking at intervals from one into another by means of the narrow and steep-sided *cluses*, or gaps. Without these the Jura could be crossed only with difficulty, and most of the roads make use of these gaps, which are often dominated by the ruins of a castle that may have served in turn to intimidate or to protect the medieval traveler.

The ridges of the Jura are usually forested. The valley floors have often been cleared, and agriculture is practiced. The climate is severe in the Jura. Altitude reduces the summer heat, and in winter snow lies for a period of many weeks and often closes the passes and cuts off towns and villages from the outside world. It is

in this harsh country that the Swiss watch and clock industry has been established. It grew from the crafts practiced by the peasants during the long periods of idleness in winter and has now become a factory industry of importance. Watch factories are scattered through the Jura, but the chief center of production is La Chaux-de-Fonds, a small town strung out along a high narrow valley of the central Jura.

In the main the Jura Range is drained by small streams which, after following a longitudinal course between the ranges, break through the *cluses* eastward to the river Aare, the main drainage system of the plateau. In the north, however, short rivers flow directly to the Rhine or join the Birs, which in turn joins the Rhine above Basel. The part of the Jura which is drained in this way to the Rhine is generally lower in altitude; its valleys have been more exposed to denudation and are in consequence more open and more thickly settled. There are many small walled towns, surrounded by vineyards and orchards, and prosperous villages, whose relative opulence stands in sharp contrast

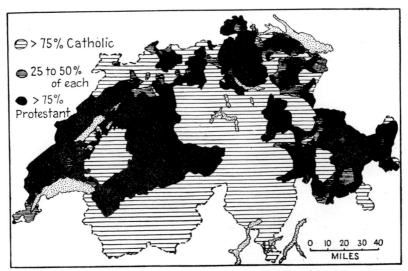

FIG. 116. Distribution of the religious groups in Switzerland. Protestantism is relatively more important in the cities and on the plain; Catholicism, in the hills and the rural areas.

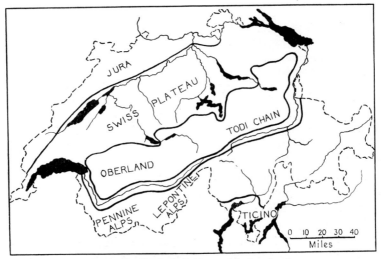

FIG. 117. Physical divisions of Switzerland.

to the poorer and more primitive conditions of the High Jura.

The valleys of the northern Jura converge on Basel (162,000),[1] which has for many centuries been the gateway to Switzerland. Here the medieval traders reached the Rhine after their weary journey over the Alps. Here the Rhine becomes a broad, navigable stream as it swings northward to enter the flat, fertile plain of the

[1] The population is given of all cities of over 50,000 inhabitants, and all cities of this size are named in the text.

rift valley. Basel is a route center on which ways converge from Burgundy, from Alsace and the middle Rhineland, from the Danube Valley, and from the Alpine passes and the Swiss Plateau. The old town lies clustered beneath a steep, sandstone bluff which rises sharply from the Rhine, with the modern town to the west, south, and east of the ancient nucleus. Basel is now an important center of the chemical industry and of the manufacture and finishing of silk cloth. It has no local source of power, except electric energy generated from the Swiss rivers.

Coal is, however, imported at the port of Basel by barges which bring it up the Rhine from the Ruhr and from coal fields even farther afield. Barges moving upstream commonly use the canal which runs parallel with the Rhine from Strasbourg through Mulhouse to Basel. The

A *cluse* in the Jura Mountains. Steep limestone ridges separate the valleys of the Jura. The *cluses* are gaps through the ridges, sometimes guarded, as in this picture taken near Solothurn, by medieval castles (see also page 157).

return voyage is often made with the assistance of the current of the Rhine. The river-borne trade of Basel is large, and the Swiss have for many years been asking their neighbors, France and Germany, to improve the navigation on the waterway which is their mutual boundary.

Swiss Plateau. The Swiss Plateau is an uneven and, in places, markedly hilly tract of country that lies between the Jura and the Alps, some 150 miles from Lake Constance (Bodensee) in the northeast to Lake Geneva (Lac Léman) in the southwest, and from 25 to 40 miles wide. The drainage is mainly by the Aare and its tributaries. These rise within the mountain mass which lies to the southeast and flow northwestward toward the plateau. Some flow through lakes created by glacial deposition in the valleys, where they pass from the mountain zone on to the plateau. The abundant discharge of the silt-laden streams from the Alps has forced the main stream of the Aare over to the northwest, so that it now flows for a significant part of its course along the very foot of the Jura scarp. In the Aare Valley are the

most extensive areas of level land in Switzerland, and here the proportion of land under crops is the greatest of any part of Switzerland The climate of the plateau varies but is, on the whole, fairly dry for Switzerland. Winters are cold, but summers are warm and bright. Along the steep slope of the Jura Mountains, as they rise from the Aare, vines are grown, from whose grapes the neuchâtel wine is made. In the lowlands of Solothurn (Soleure) and Aargau fruit is grown and ripens well in the bright warm summer.

Toward the southwest the plateau contracts in width as the Alpine chain extends farther to the west. The plateau drops gently to the warm and sheltered shores of Lake Geneva, and a narrow strip of low ground extends along the Jura foot and encloses the lower end of the lake, where lies the town of Geneva (124,500). The central and northern parts of the plateau are made up of a series of valleys and ridges. The region is built of the soft beds, formed from the material eroded from the Alps as they were being folded, but the structure is in many places deeply buried beneath glacial and riverine deposits, which derive from the last glaciation.

The Rhine at Basel. Basel is the effective limit of navigation on the Rhine and an important port for handling the German export of coal to Switzerland.

The terrain is hilly. The aspect is one of rolling hills which appear to have neither rhythm nor pattern. The higher and poorer slopes are often wooded. Crops—wheat, oats, rye, root and forage crops with here and there the grape vine and orchards—are grown, but agriculture is

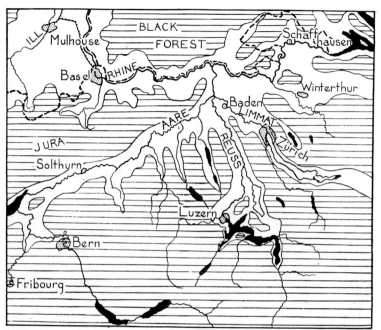

FIG. 118. The cities of Basel, Zürich, and Bern and the drainage of the Swiss Plateau.

based mainly upon the dairy herds. The region does not supply its needs in agricultural produce but makes and exports large quantities of cheese, of which the Gruyère and Emmentaler are among the more familiar.

Schaffhausen on the Rhine. The castle on its vineyard-covered hill overlooks the little town. The river is wide and navigable here, but a short distance downstream are the falls of the Rhine.

The plateau is by far the most densely populated area of Switzerland. Rural settlement is largely in compact and closely spaced villages. Small towns, many of them retaining their medieval walls and towers and the domestic buildings upon which has been lavished for centuries the artistic skill of their inhabitants, are spread over the land. Most of these are rural in their functions, serving as market

Morat (Murten) in Fribourg, the main street of the little town. In the distance is the east gate of the town.

centers; some have some small specialized industry, such as cloth weaving, embroidery, or lace making. Some are of more than local importance. Bern (130,500), the federal capital, was established within a meander of the deeply

Bern. The city lies within a sharp loop of the Aare, seen behind the trees in the foreground. In the middle distance is the spire of the Minster and beyond it the domed roof of the Parliament building (*Swiss National Tourist Office.*)

incised Aare. It preserved its old charm, while assuming the duties of a modern capital. Zürich (336,500) is its neighbor, 60 miles to the northeast. It lies on both shores of the river Limmat where it leaves the lake of Zürich. The ancient city lies close to the river, but the modern, industrial suburbs extend over the hills to east and west. The town is one of the most impressive in Europe; in its large public buildings it combines the massiveness and the strength of the German with the lightness and grace of the French. Although the town is wholly German in speech, it seems to display the finer characteristics of the two peoples who constitute the greater part of the population of Switzerland. Zürich is a center of the cotton and silk industry and has also an important mechanical- and electrical-engineering industry.

Lucerne (Luzern, 54,500), which lies between Bern and Zürich at the northern outlet of Lake Lucerne, is smaller, has no significant industries, and is dependent on the tourist traffic. Toward the northeast of the plateau are a number of small towns in which are carried on the engineering and textile industries. Saint Gallen (62,500) is a center for the cotton, lace, and embroidery industries, Winterthur (59,000) has cotton and engineering, and Schaffhausen, situated close to the falls of the Rhine from which it derives some of its power, has chemical industries. There are fewer towns in the more hilly southwest part of the plateau. Fribourg (Freiburg), a small textile-producing town, lies in a situation very similar to that of Bern, within a meander of the river Saane. Lausanne (92,500) lies upon a hill above the northern shore of Lake Geneva. A castle and cathedral were built here, and the town grew around them, extending gradually down the hill to Ouchy, 2 miles away on the water's edge. Lausanne is a tourist resort; it lacks the charm of the cities of German Switzerland but has a situation of great beauty, facing across the blue lake to the mountains of Chablais and the Mont Blanc Massif. Geneva lies, like Zürich and Lucerne, at the outlet of a lake. It is French in speech, is linked with the

Lucerne (Luzern). The city lies at the outlet of Lake Lucerne (*Vierwaldstättersee*). It was a walled city, and part of its ancient defenses can be seen in the foreground. In the distance is snow-capped Mount Pilatus. (*Swiss National Tourist Office*.)

rest of Switzerland only by the narrow strip of land along the northern shore of the lake, and entered the confederation as recently as 1815. The ancient core of the town lies on both banks of the Rhône as it leaves Lake Geneva. From the Middle Ages, it has been a focus of routes and an important commercial center. It has since been a center of international activities and a home for political and religious refugees. Here Calvin, who had fled from France, carried through his Reformation; here were established the headquarters of such societies as the International Red Cross; and here came, in 1919, the League of Nations. Geneva, in the neutral state of Switzerland, is one of the most cosmopolitan cities in Europe.

Alps. The Alps cover considerably more than a half of Switzerland and are commonly regarded as its most beautiful region. They contain, however, little more than a quarter of the population of Switzerland and a very small proportion of the country's industrial activity. Apart from agriculture, the most important occupation of this region is the maintenance of hotels and of other facilities and amenities for tourists.

The Swiss Alps are part of a mountain range which begins on the Mediterranean coast of France and fades out on the borders of the Hungarian Plain. They continue the divisions of the French Alps that we have already examined. The Swiss Alps are divided longitudinally by the valleys of the upper Rhône and the Vorder Rhine into a northwestern chain, which continues the line of the limestone Alps cf Chablais and Chartreuse, and a southeastern, which stretches east from Mont Blanc. Between is the broad Rhône-Rhine trench.

The Bernese Oberland and Tödi chain form a distinct physical unit, clearly defined by the

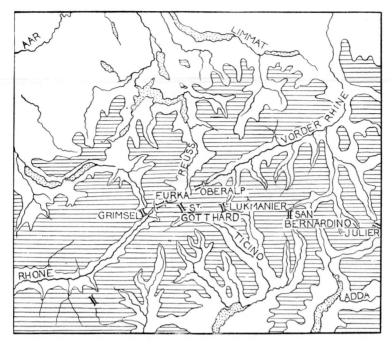

Fig. 119. The Saint Gotthard Pass and the central Alps. The Saint Gotthard Pass between the Ticino and Reuss valleys allows of a crossing of the range with only one ascent and one descent.

longitudinal and transverse sections of the Rhône and Rhine. The southwestern half of the range is the Bernese Oberland. The range drops steeply to the Rhône Valley and on this side is drained by a series of short valleys. The Lötschental is the largest and most populous of these. A few miles to the east is the Great Aletsch Glacier. On the northwest, the surface drops more gently toward the Swiss Plateau. The valleys of the north-flowing rivers are longer and frequently deeper and more spectacular than those on the southeast. They contain a number of tourist resorts, which include Grindelwald and Kandersteg. The Oberland rises eastward to a rugged and snow-capped massif of great beauty. The Breithorn, Jungfrau (13,668 feet), Mönch, Eiger, and Schreckhorn, with the Finsteraarhorn (14,026 feet) lying a short distance to the southwest of the main chain, raise their sharp, pointed summits, creating an impassable barrier to transportation and a great attraction to tourist and climber. On the east the Oberland ends abruptly as it drops to the Haslital, the valley of the upper Aare. The Aare rises on the northern slope of the Grimsel

Pass, one of the few significant crossings of the whole range. Flowing past the resort town of Meiringen, it enters the lake of Brienz and then the lake of Thun, which occupy one of the several longitudinal valleys of the Oberland. From Thun it flows northward to the plateau, to Bern and the Rhine. Between the two lakes and on the alluvial fan which separates them is the resort town of Interlaken. The river Reuss rises to the south of the Oberland-Tödi chain, crosses the range in the Schöllenen Gorge below Andermatt, and flows northward through the valley of Uri to Lake Lucerne.

The Tödi chain stretches from the gorge of the Reuss up to the broader transverse valley of the Rhine. It is lower than the Oberland. The Tödi reaches 11,887 feet, but the range is continuous and unbroken. At its eastern end is the Säntis (8,216 feet), which overlooks the Rhine and sends spurs northward to Lake Constance.

The Alpine region is both agricultural and pastoral. The valleys on the north are broad and gentle enough for crop cultivation. Wheat, oats, rye, and fodder crops are grown, but, in most parts, agriculture centers in the herds of cattle which are wintered in the barns attached to the farmsteads in the valleys and spend the summers on high pastures. But agriculture is difficult. The winter climate is severe, and in summer the warmth and sunshine are not always sufficient to ripen crops or even to dry the hay. The preparation of winter fodder for the cattle demands great care and labor. No

Chalets on an *alp* in the upper Rhône Valley. The buildings are roughly made of wood and are used only in the summer months when the animals are taken up on to the higher pastures. Compare with p. 154.

grass is allowed to go uncut, and hay is fastened to stakes or folded over strings to enable it to dry more easily out of contact with the damp ground.

The villages lie in the valley bottoms. On the high Alps are small and primitive chalets, the summer houses of the herdsmen, where they milk the cattle and make cheese, while crops are being taken from the fields in the valleys. The distribution of the village settlements is strongly influenced by insolation. In a region as mountainous as this, shadows are long and parts of most valleys are in the shade for a large part of each day. The Swiss distinguish between the *Sonnenseite* (sunny side) and *Schattenseite* (shady side) of the valley, and their settlements are often carefully located to obtain as much sunshine as possible.

The Rhône-Rhine trench is one of the most strongly marked features on the relief map of Switzerland. It is straight and continuous for some 140 miles from the bend of the Rhône at Martigny to the Rhine below Chur. For over a hundred miles the valley has a broad, flat floor, and the mountains to the north and south lie back from it. Villages and small towns lie at intervals along its course. Sion (Sitten) and Brig (Brigue) in the Rhône Valley and Chur in the Rhine are locally important.

Between the source of the Rhône and that of the Vorder Rhine, about 15 miles away, the longitudinal valley is drained by the Reuss, which breaks northward through the Schöllenen Gorge. This short tract, the Urserental, is bounded on the west by the Furka Pass (7,976 feet) and on the east by the Oberalp Pass (6,719 feet). Southward is the Saint Gotthard Pass, the most famous and historically the most important of all the passes of the Swiss Alps.

Below Chur the Rhine bends northward, and its plain widens as it approaches Lake Constance. In its valley lies the principality of Liechtenstein, a small, independent state which always acts in close harmony with the Swiss Confederation.

The Pennine, Lepontine, and Albula Alps. The Pennine Alps continue the general direction of the Mont Blanc Massif, from which it is separated by the Great Saint Bernard Pass. Its high and continuous crestline scarcely drops below 12,000 feet, and above this rise the Matterhorn (14,705 feet) and Monte Rosa (15,217 feet). The flanks of this broad mass are furrowed by deep valleys, in each of which the mountaineers live an almost isolated and self-contained life. Longest and broadest of these is the Zermatt Valley, which reaches from the Monte Rosa northward to the Rhône.

East of the Pennine Alps is the Simplon Pass (6,584 feet), and beyond this the lower Lepontine Range. The almost impassable crest of the Pennine Alps forms the boundary between Switzerland and Italy. The Lepontine Range is more broken; there are a number of passes, in addition to the Saint Gotthard, which present no difficulty. Between the Nufenen and the Saint Bernardino Passes the Swiss in the later Middle Ages pressed southward toward the Lombard Plain. They lost part of their conquests but have retained the Italian-speaking canton of Ticino.

The eastern parts of the Lepontine Alps are

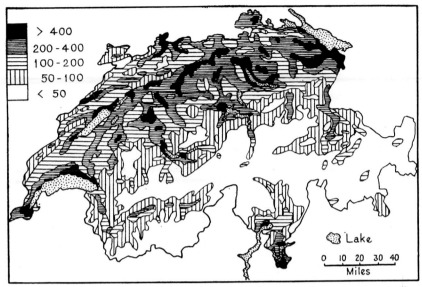

Fig. 120. Distribution of population in Switzerland. Density is shown per square mile.

drained by the Vorder and Hinter Rhine, and farther to the east the Albula Alps form the divide between the Rhine drainage and that of the Danube. The Engadine is the upper valley of the Austrian river Inn. It takes a direct course, roughly parallel with that of the Rhine, from the Italian to the Austrian fronter. At the source of the Inn the low and easy Maloja Pass gives direct access to Italy, and a number of passes lead from the Engadine across the Albula Alps to the Rhine Valley. The Engadine is easily accessible and, unlike the Rhône-Rhine trench, has long been a highway for trade and marching armies. It is now one of the most frequented of the Swiss resort areas. Here an Italian influence shows itself in the architectural styles, and much of the beauty of the farmsteads and houses of the Engadine is due to the way in which the Italian style, like the French, gives lightness and grace to the German.

Only in the canton of Ticino does Switzerland include any appreciable part of the drainage basin of the Italian Po. The canton embraces the Ticino Valley above Lake Maggiore, known as the Val Leventina, a small part of the lake itself, and much of Lake Lugano. It is, in comparison with Switzerland to the north of the Pennine and Lepontine Alps, a region of warmth

and sunshine, of the grape vine, and of southern fruits. The winters are nevertheless cold, and the soils of no high fertility. The drought of summer restricts the growth of grass, and pastoral activities are of much smaller importance than to the north of the Alps. The region is heavily dependent on the tourist traffic, which is attracted by its beauty. Locarno and Lugano are the most important lakeside resorts. The region is politically Swiss, but in all other respects it is Italian. Language, customs, and styles of architecture are those of Italy.

Economic Development. Switzerland has a population of 4,400,800 (1945) in a country of 15,940 square miles, of which little over a quarter is under cultivation. Some 40 per cent of the area is fit for grazing, and forests cover about a quarter. The roughness of the terrain, combined with the severity of the winter climate, has always made it difficult for the Swiss to support themselves in their small country. In the past they served in the armies of other countries. It was a Swiss Guard that defended the French King Louis XVI during the French Revolution, and at the Vatican there is still a guard of Swiss, dressed in their traditional sixteenth-century costume. The problem of overpopulation has been solved in modern times by

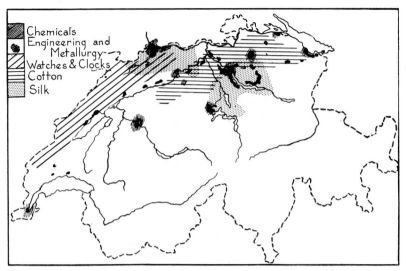

Fig. 121. Industrial regions of Switzerland.

industrialization, but agriculture remains of considerable importance, engaging about 26 per cent of the employed population. Grain crops— wheat, oats, barley, and rye—are grown, but in quantities far from adequate to support the population. There was an import of grain foods amounting to over 40 per cent of the total consumption before 1939. On the other hand, dairy produce, in particular cheese, is produced in excess of Swiss demands and is exported. Most of the agricultural activity is in the central plateau region and in the broader Alpine valleys.

Switzerland has become primarily an industrial country. Manufacturing industries engage about 37 per cent of the employed population. Switzerland lacks mineral fuel. Coal and oil have to be imported and are, in consequence, relatively costly. Switzerland depends heavily on hydroelectric power, which its steep swift streams are well suited to produce. There are few rivers that are not harnessed in at least one or two places and made to generate current. The production of electric power is restricted in the winter months, when, owing to the frost, the streams flow less readily, and at this time the hydroelectric power has to be supplemented by thermoelectric, generated with the help of imported coal.

Many Swiss industries derive from medieval

origins in the town and village crafts. These have been reinforced by numerous groups of refugees, who have each brought its own specialized trades. Electric power has been applied to ancient craft industries, the watchmaking of the Jura, the woolen of Fribourg, the cotton of Winterthur, the lace and embroidery of Saint Gallen. Some of these make little use of power, remaining predominantly handicrafts. The mechanical- and electrical-engineering industries are of a more recent origin. They have grown up in Zürich and Basel as well as in smaller centers such as Winterthur. They owe much to the encouragement given by the development and use of electrical power, but the kinds of mechanical engineering are also a consequence of the absence in Switzerland of the raw materials of the industry. Switzerland engages in the finishing industries. It imports pig iron, which it works up. A great deal of skill goes to the fashioning of only a small volume of metal, so that the cost of the imported raw material constitutes only a minute proportion of the total cost of the finished article.

A consequence of the use of electric power is that in Switzerland there are few factory chimneys and no black and smoke-stained industrial areas. The factories are scattered among the towns and villages, supplied with power by an overhead cable and with materials

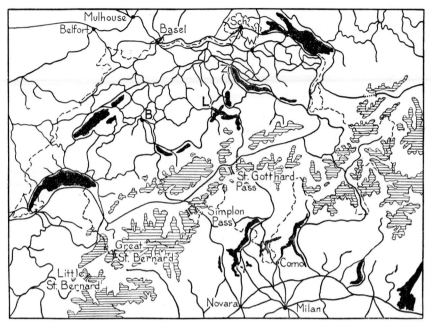

FIG. 122. Distribution of railroads in Switzerland. B = Bern; G = Geneva; L = Lucerne; W = Winterthur; Sch = Schaffhausen; Z = Zürich.

by motor vehicles or by the railway. The northern part of Switzerland, the cantons of Basel, Zürich, Appenzell, and Saint Gallen, is the most industrialized, but there are few cantons and few towns where some manufacturing industry is not carried on.

Transportation has always been difficult in a country as mountainous as Switzerland. This, however, does not mean that it is not important. It has been the volume of traffic crossing the passes from the Middle Ages to the present that has encouraged the building of the bridges, roads, railways, and tunnels. Basel, Zürich, and Bern are each the center of a railroad network which is spread thickly over the plateau. Even the Jura is crossed in several places, and the railways follow many of its narrow valleys. The Alps are penetrated by the valleys of the Rhône and Rhine, which are joined by a light railway that tunnels under both the Oberalp and Furka Passes. Little movement, however, takes place *along* this trough; transport rather moves *across* it. The Simplon Tunnel through the Lepontine Alps and the Lötschberg Tunnel through the Bernese Oberland shorten the route from Italy to the plateau. The Saint Gotthard Tunnel has

the advantage of allowing the whole Alpine Range to be crossed by only one tunnel. The track climbs the steep Reuss Valley, making use of circular tunnels in the hillside to hasten its ascent. Near the lower end of the gorge of the Reuss it enters its tunnel to emerge 10 miles to the south at Airolo in the Val Leventina. From the upper Rhine Valley railways ascend the valleys of the Graubünden, and one crosses the Albula into the Engadine. The railway net, however adequate on the plateau and in the Jura, has in the Alps to be supplemented by a system of *postes*, small buses which cross the passes and carry tourists, mail, and baggage to places which the railways could never approach. The higher passes are closed, however, for periods which vary, from one pass to another and from one year to the next, from 5 months to as many as 8.

Switzerland's geographical position, between France, Germany, Austria, and Italy, together with the stability and good government that have characterized the country, have combined to give it an importance in the financial world akin to that of Great Britain. Switzerland is a center for banking and insurance. Its currency, the Swiss franc, is as highly respected as the American dollar and is reckoned to be a safe currency to buy.

Like Sweden, Switzerland has avoided the commitments of war and the entanglement of alliances. She is recognized as a neutral and is not expected to take sides. There is thus a presumption that Switzerland will be free of invasion. Switzerland has preserved her neutrality inviolate from the time of Napoleon until today. She has, nevertheless, a small army and careful plans for national defense. These include the defense of the "national redoubt," a strategic term for the Rhine-Rhône trench, the approaches to which from Lake Geneva, Lake Lucerne, and Lake Constance are strongly fortified.

War in Europe constitutes a threat to Swiss neutrality. It is a danger even more to the Swiss economy. Switzerland has achieved a high standard of living on the basis of a large foreign trade, by entertaining tourists, and by performing financial and actuarial services for other nations. The flow of trade, of visitors, and of business is cut off in war. In the years from 1940 to 1945 Switzerland was faced with the loss of almost all these assets. A plan was devised for Swiss agriculture, and "in spite of the serious obstacles of poor soil, shortage of labor, machinery and fertilizers and adverse climatic conditions, the wholehearted support of the farmers and industry enabled the plan to be carried out with a success"[1] which greatly exceeded expectations. The proportion of total foodstuffs produced at home rose from 53 per cent in 1938 to 82 per cent in 1944. Certain small coal deposits were opened up and contributed in some degree to supply the deficiency left by the failure of Germany. The gearing down of Swiss agriculture to the postwar situation was not easy but has been achieved. "At

the beginning of 1948 Switzerland could lay claim to be one of the few countries which had emerged from the Second World War and its immediate aftermath with her economic structure unimpaired." Switzerland's position today is a very strong one indeed; the only cloud on the Swiss horizon is the fear that in another war belligerents may not be so scrupulous as in the past in recognizing Swiss neutrality. After all, Switzerland is a capitalist state.

Switzerland is the only European example—Russia and the new Federal Republic of Germany excepted—of a federal state. It was built up, like the United States, by the addition of fresh states, or cantons, to the original nucleus, the forest cantons of Uri, Schwyz, and Unterwalden. The 25 cantons have a high degree of independence both of one another and of the federal government which meets in Bern. At least one of the cantons perpetuates the ancient democratic practice of having a parliament consisting of all adult males meeting out of doors, not unlike the governments of ancient Greece. On vital issues affecting the whole country, resort is had to the plebiscite, in which the whole adult population participates.

The value of Swiss trade in proportion to her population is one of the highest in Europe. In 1938, half the oils and fats and almost two-thirds of the cereals as well as even larger percentages of sugar, tobacco, coffee, and cocoa were imported. All the solid fuel was imported, the coal chiefly from Germany and Poland, petroleum and heavy oil from overseas. Hardwoods and the materials of the textile and metallurgical industries are imported. Switzerland exports textiles, machinery, diesel engines, watches, and electrical equipment, for each of which she has a high reputation. She supplements her income by her tourist industry, one of the largest and best organized in Europe.

BIBLIOGRAPHY

Ammann, Hektor, and Karl Schib, "Historischer Atlas der Schweiz," Aarau, 1951.

Boesch, Hans, Basle, Switzerland: a Port Terminal, *E.G.*, XII, 1936, 259–264.

[1] "Overseas Economic Surveys: Switzerland," p. 13, London, 1948.

Bonjour, E., "Swiss Neutrality," translated by M. Hottinger, London, 1946.

Chapuis, Alfred, "La Suisse dans le monde," Lausanne, 1939.

Davies, Elwyn, The Pattern of Transhumance in Europe, *G.*, XXVI, 1941, 155–168.

Fleure, H. J., Notes on the Evolution of Switzerland, *G.*, XXVI, 1941, 169–177.

Fruh, J., "Geographie der Schweiz," 3 vols., St. Gallen, 1930–1938.

Garnett, Alice, Insolation, Topography and Settlement in the Alps, *I.B.G.*, London, 1937.

"Géographie universelle," Vol. IV, L'Europe centrale, Part II, Paris, 1931.

Herold, J. Christopher, "The Swiss without Halos," New York, 1948.

Lamartine Yates, P., "Food Production in Western Europe," London, 1940.

Mayer, Kurt B., "The Population of Switzerland," New York, 1952.

"Overseas Economic Surveys: Switzerland," London, 1948.

Peattie, Roderick, Height Limits of Mountain Economies, *G.R.*, XXI, 1931, 415–428.

"Schweizerischer Mittelschul-Atlas," Zurich (several editions).

Siegfried, A., "Switzerland," New York, 1950.

Unstead, J. F., The Lötschental: A Regional Study, *G.J.*, LXXIX, 1932, 298–317.

IMPORTANT REFERENCE BOOKS

"Dictionaire géographique de la Suisse," 6 vols., Neuchâtel, 1902–1910.

Statistisches Jahrbuch der Schweiz, Bern, published annually.

The official publications listed on pages 52 to 54 contain in general only incidental references to Switzerland.

BIBLIOGRAPHIES OF SWISS GEOGRAPHICAL LITERATURE

Hassinger, H., Schweiz, *Geog. Jahrb.*, XLIII, 1928, 236–275.

"Bibliographie der schweizerischen Landeskunde," Bern, 1927.

The chief Swiss geographical periodical is "*Geographica Helvetica, Schweizerische Zeitschrift für Länder- und Völkerkunde*, published quarterly in Bern.

CHAPTER 16: *Introduction to Central Europe*

Central Europe is that part of Europe, lying between France in the west and Russia in the east, which has been dominated by German political power and settled, wholly or in part, by people of German speech. In the west it includes the Rhineland and eastern Switzerland; in the east, Poland, Czechoslovakia, and Austria. It is a transition region between the relatively high

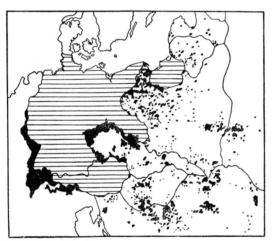

FIG. 123. The German settlement area of central Europe. This has contracted very greatly since 1945. Areas shaded black were inhabited by people of German speech outside the German Reich in 1938.

living standards of France, the Low Countries, and Switzerland and the conditions of poverty that distinguish eastern Poland and Slovakia in the east. It is further a region within which political frontiers have been very unstable. The eastern limits of Germany have advanced and receded on several occasions. Their greatest extension, the period of the Second World War excepted, was before 1914; their smallest, since 1945. No one dares assume that the present

frontiers will last longer than their predecessors, and any textbook that covers this area takes the risk of being out of date soon after it has been published.

This instability has derived in part from the nature of German settlement; in part from the physical conditions, which make west-to-east movement easy; and in part from the political traditions and ambitions that have been developed within the German ruling classes. German settlement has been spread, though increasingly thinly, all the way from the river Elbe in Germany to the Volga in Russia. Colonies of Germans stretched down the Danube to Romania and Bulgaria. This ancient German settlement has encouraged in recent years the assertion of German political control over this area. Austria and parts of Poland and Czechoslovakia were for a short period incorporated into Germany. These outliers of German speech have now in large measure been removed, and their members sent back to Germany. But Poland and Czechoslovakia nevertheless bear deeply the imprint of German civilization, and, however nationalistic may be their policies, they cannot wholly remove their debt to Germany. In this sense the region considered in this section of the book may be called the German realm.

But central Europe is closely bound up with the west. The industries of the Rhineland use the ports and serve the markets of western Europe. Rotterdam and Antwerp are the "natural" ports of western Germany, and the prosperity of the Low Countries is dependent in some degree on that of Germany. The plans at present under consideration envisage a gradual breakdown of the barriers between Germany and her western neighbors, with the coal mines and industries of the Ruhr ministering to the needs of France and the Low Countries.

Central Europe is made up of a series of west-to-east belts of territory. In the north is the Great European Plain, reaching from France to Russia and widening gradually eastward. South of the plain is a belt of hilly country, which stretches from the Ardennes in Belgium and France to Czechoslovakia. South of this again is a belt of varying width separating these hills from the Alpine Ranges. This latter region is drained in part by the Rhine, in part by the Danube. The Danube Valley, opening eastward toward the Black Sea, forms, like the northern plain, a route of eastward movement and expansion. Lastly the Alps shut in central Europe on the south.

Germany cuts across all these divisions from the northern plain to the Alps. Poland lies almost wholly within the northern plain; Czechoslovakia, within the central belt of hills; while Austria occupies the Danube Valley where it narrows between the Czechoslovakian hills and the Alps, and once defended the approaches to Germany from the southeast.

CHAPTER 17: *Germany in the Modern World*

The German state of 1953 is the product of a complex series of changes spread over 15 centuries. Most of Germany lay outside the limits of the Roman Empire. Part of it was inhabited at this time by Germanic tribes, some of which broke into the Empire in the fifth century, and some penetrated deep into Gaul, or France, and extended the limits of German speech roughly to its present boundary. During the centuries which followed, the Rhineland became the cradle of a Germanic state. Its chief cities were Aachen and Cologne (Köln), Frankfurt and Mainz. During the Middle Ages Germans moved eastward, settling new lands, building cities, and establishing trade. They spread along the loess belt to Saxony and Silesia. They moved down the Danube Valley, defeated the predecessors of the Hungarians, who tried to halt their progress, and established Austria as the Ostmark, or "eastern march." German traders and crusaders moved along the Baltic coast, carving out for themselves estates in what are today Pomerania and Prussia.

The Germany of the Middle Ages was theoretically the realm of the Holy Roman Empire but was never welded, as were France and England, into a unified state. The emperor was elected by his peers. At a critical period the emperors chose to squander their resources in a vain attempt to conquer Italy, while Germany fell to pieces, degenerating into a congeries of small, quarreling, and virtually independent states.

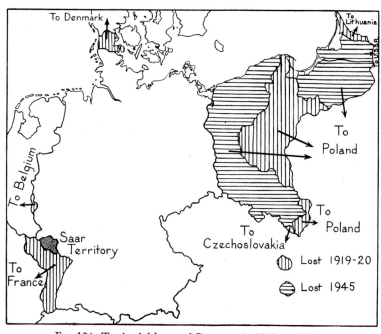

Fig. 124. Territorial losses of Germany in 1919 and 1945.

German unity was the creation of the nineteenth century. Germany still consisted a century ago of some 50 distinct units, jealous of their privileges and independence, though forward-looking young Germans were learning to sing *Deutschland über Alles*, not a hymn of conquest, but rather an aspiration, a dream of a Germany embracing all the little political units which territorially composed it. The German Empire was created by the diplomacy and power of the Prussian Chancellor Otto von Bismarck and sanctioned by liberal-minded Germans, happy to see the end of the political fragmentation of their country.

This was the "Second" *Reich;* the "First" had been the medieval empire. Its aggressive impulses took it into the war of 1914. It was defeated and by the Treaty of Versailles (1919) lost territory in the west, north, and east: in the west, small areas to Belgium, Alsace and northern Lorraine to France, and the Saar territory which was placed under the League of Nations; in the north, the territory of North Schleswig, which went to Denmark; and in the east a much more extensive area which went to the making of the new Poland.

Beginning in 1938 with the seizure of Austria, Germany began a new phase of aggression. This was excused in some quarters as a legitimate desire to incorporate into the *Reich*, the "Third" or Hitler's *Reich*, all areas of German speech and sympathy. When in March, 1939, the Czech lands of Bohemia and Moravia were also annexed, this apology could clearly hold no longer, and the German invasion of Poland in September, 1939, opened the Second World War.

Germany suffered a defeat more crushing than any she had known before. Her eastern provinces, which had been German since the Middle Ages, were added to Poland, and the rest of Germany was divided into zones and occupied by four of the victorious powers.

The study of a land so partitioned presents difficulties. During the past century Germany achieved political and economic unity at approximately the same time. The development of railways and canals, the establishment of factories, and the supply of minerals, fuel, and foodstuffs came in the later years of the nineteenth century to be organized on a national basis. Agricultural and industrial areas were integrated, each furnishing part of the requirements of the other. This pattern of internal trade was rudely shattered after 1945. Pomerania and Prussia no longer sent foodstuffs

FIG. 125. The occupation zones of Germany and Austria.

to the populous western districts; Berlin was cut off from its supplies of coal. In a hundred ways, the economy of the old Germany was disrupted by the inability to buy and exchange freely across the new zonal and national frontiers. Furthermore, there was a considerable internal movement of population, which further disorganized production.

Statistical data for present productive activities are inadequate, and for all eastern Germany it is difficult to discover even the nature of recent changes in the distribution of population and of agricultural and industrial activities. No picture of contemporary Germany can hope to be balanced, complete, and accurate. It is impossible to say what degree of permanence the division of Germany into an eastern and a western republic is likely to have,

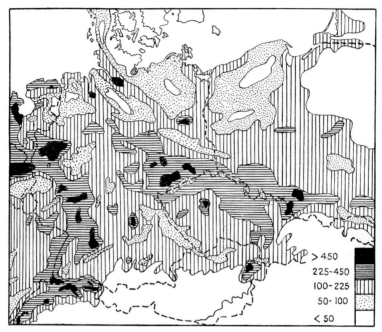

> 450
225-450
100-225
50-100
< 50

Fig. 126. Distribution of population in central Europe. Density is shown per square mile.

nor can it be said whether the Poles will make good their occupation of Germany east of the Oder and Neisse. The wholesale expulsion of Germans from this territory and the introduction of Poles from the Polish provinces ceded to Russia will not make future readjustments of the frontier easy.

The population of Germany in 1939 was 69,622,500. Its distribution was very uneven. Densely settled and highly urbanized areas lay close to sparsely populated heath, moor, and mountain. The most strongly marked feature of the distribution of German population was the belt of dense settlement which extended from Silesia to the lower Rhineland, along the Börde and the margins of the central highlands. Within this area population was particularly concentrated in four areas: Upper Silesia, Saxony, the Börde of Hannover, and the Ruhr. These regions were all highly industrialized, and the greater part of the population in all of them lived in towns and derived its livelihood from work in manufacturing or commerce. Nevertheless, these areas are all highly productive agriculturally, and employment on the land is not unimportant. A belt of dense population,

second, follows the river Rhine from the Ruhr area upstream to the borders of Switzerland, with extensions up the Main, Neckar, and Moselle. There are also a number of smaller areas, usually centering in a particular town, where population is dense: the districts round Nuremberg (Nürnberg), Bremen, Hamburg, and Berlin.

This pattern of population was not greatly changed by the war; only the density of population was increased. The population of the Germany of 1939 was 69,622,500; that of the Germany of 1946, 64,498,000, notwithstanding its diminution in area by about 25 per cent.

The German population is relatively highly urbanized. Berlin, the second largest city in Europe, had in 1939 a population of 4,332,000. In 1949 this was estimated to have been reduced to 3,307,900. There were, in 1939, 58 cities with a population each of over 100,000 as against 79 in England and Wales and 26 in France. Altogether 44 per cent of the German population lived in towns of over 20,000 inhabitants.

Though most of them had expanded greatly during the nineteenth century, most German cities had until the last war a nucleus which was medieval in plan and sometimes only a little younger in construction. The narrow winding streets; the tall, sometimes timbered buildings,

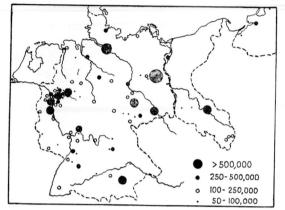

FIG. 127. Distribution of cities in Germany.

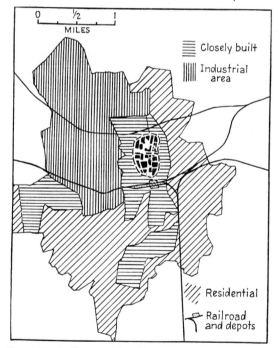

FIG. 128. A German city: Essen. Note the line of the ancient walls surrounding the old city, shown in black (compare photograph on page 216).

with highly decorated façades; the market place; guildhall; and the ancient walls, or at least the course which they once followed, were common to almost all. In some cities, these features were so strongly developed that they

became an attraction to the tourist. Even in the heart of devastated Dortmund and Cologne something of this ancient beauty can be discerned. On the coal fields of both the east and west a few nineteenth-century towns have grown up which are no less congested than the older towns and very much uglier.

Even the smallest towns of medieval Germany were enclosed by walls. Space within the walls was valuable. It was filled to capacity, and streets were narrow and houses tall. Only in modern times have the German cities burst through their confining ramparts and spread

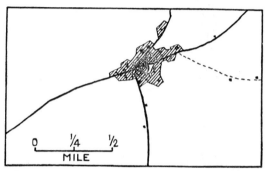

FIG. 129. A nucleated village of the German Plain.

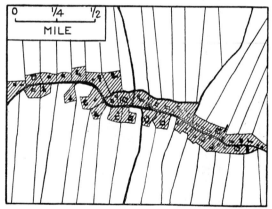

FIG. 130. A forest village of Germany. The houses and farm buildings are distributed along each side of the road cut through the original forest.

into the surrounding countryside. Most show today a sharp contrast between the older and more closely built area and the more recent spread of houses and workshops. With the greatest regularity the streets become a yard or two wider and the buildings a story or two

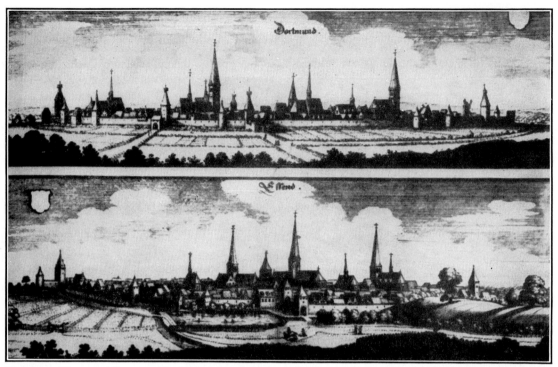

The cities of Essen and Dortmund in the seventeenth century. Note how the buildings, dominated by the churches, are enclosed by the city walls. The engraving appeared in Merian, "Topographia Westfaliae," published in the seventeenth century.

lower as the line of the town walls is passed. A feature of most European towns is the distance of the railway station from the town center. Only in exceptional cases was the railroad able

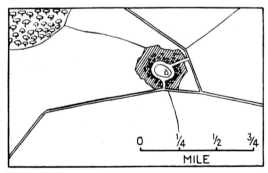

FIG. 131. A round village (*Runddorf*). This pattern is common in eastern Germany but is found elsewhere. The houses form a "ring fence" around a central "green."

to enter the confines of the ancient town; usually it kept to the outskirts.

Much of Germany was settled by colonists coming from the west. The pattern of their settlement was determined in part by their own traditions and social structure, in part by conditions imposed by the environment. The German village is generally nucleated, the houses lying close to one another. The nucleated villages are themselves divided into a number of distinct groups. The close group of brightly colored houses, surrounded by the unfenced and treeless open fields of the village community, is a familiar feature of the good agricultural lands of the Börde and Rhineland. In the forests settlements were more often made on each side of the trail as it ran through the woods, and each settler cleared a narrow strip of land reaching back from the road. In the marshland areas of the northern coast the village patterns resembled those of the "forest" villages, being drawn out along the sinuous lines of the protective dikes, which could alone ensure that the village remained beyond the reach of floods. In parts of central Germany a round, or ring-fence, village pattern exists, possibly derived

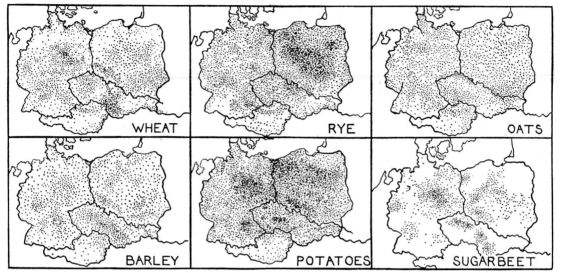

Fig. 132. Distribution of the chief crops in Germany, Poland, Czechoslovakia, and Austria.

from a Slavonic settlement plan adapted to a pastoral economy. The central space of the village may have served as a pound for the animals. Areas of poor soil, whether on the geest, or sandy areas, of the northern plain or in the hills of the center and south, are commonly distinguished by a settlement pattern which consists of isolated dwellings or at most of very small groups of houses.

While the German language is spoken in all parts of the German state, a number of distinct dialects survive, especially in the north and the south. During the Middle Ages there were three groups of German dialects. Of these Low German was spoken over most of the northern plain, though there were originally marked differences between the dialects of east and west. The Dutch and Frisian languages, the latter now nearly extinct, were related to Low German. Middle German was the language of the hilly country of central Germany. It was a Middle German dialect that became the basis of modern literary German. High German embraced the dialects of south Germany, Switzerland, and Austria. These dialect differences have by no means disappeared, though standard German is used throughout the country. Languages other than German were of no serious significance in the Germany of 1939,

though a small number of Danes lived and continue to live in the German area of Schleswig, and in the forested lakeland southeast of Berlin there remains a colony of Wends, who speak a language akin to Polish.

German Agriculture. Germany remains to a far greater extent than the United Kingdom an agricultural country. Before the Second World War about 20 per cent of all employed persons were engaged in agriculture.

During the nineteenth century much of the agricultural land of eastern Germany was farmed in large estates. After the end of the First World War some of these were broken up into smaller holdings, but on the eve of the Second, farm holdings east of the Elbe remained in general very much larger than the average, not only for Germany but also for the rest of Europe. West Germany, particularly the Rhineland and Bavaria, was distinguished, on the other hand, by the small average size of the holdings. The existence of large estates and of large farm holdings has been a feature of the eastern, southeastern, and southern margins of western Europe, areas in which the land was conquered and not always adequately settled in the later Middle Ages. It appears that since 1945 the large estates of what was formerly eastern Europe have been expropriated and either divided into small holdings or converted into collective farms on the Russian model. It should be added that the climate and soils of eastern Germany are not everywhere suited to intensive peasant agriculture and that generally far more agricultural capital is required for their development than the peasant is able to command.

Germany is a country of mixed farming, in which temperate cereals, fruits, and fodder crops grow well. The growth of a large industrial

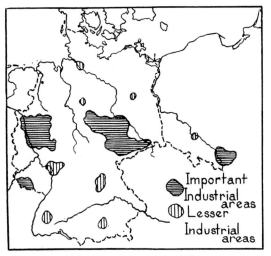

FIG. 133. Industrial regions of Germany.

population has created a demand for vegetables, milk, and meat. The relatively severe climate of central and eastern Germany and the sour soil of much of the highland area and of the geest greatly restrict the range of crops that can be grown in these areas. Rye is quite important over the whole of the northern plain of Germany and becomes the chief crop in certain of the ceded areas in the east. Animal husbandry is practiced in all parts of Germany and in some parts is more important than crop farming. Cattle are numerous on the damp, heavy soils of the north, ill suited to plowing. Sheep graze the hilly areas, and pigs are an adjunct to every type of farming.

In general German agriculture is neither highly mechanized nor very efficient. As in France, the wasteful practice of open-field husbandry continues. The plow and harrow are drawn sometimes by the horse or mule, sometimes by the ox. A crop rotation is used, and in many parts of Germany there is an adequate use of fertilizer. Indeed, many parts, especially the infertile, sandy heaths, would be quite valueless without large quantities of artificial fertilizer. Germany is fortunate in being able to supply this, both from her chemical industry and from the "Thomas slag," waste from the steelworks consisting partly of lime and phosphorus. The output of German agriculture is large by virtue rather of the great industry of the German peasant than of his use of machines and modern methods. It is very doubtful whether the agricultural output could be greatly increased in many parts of Germany, though with better equipment and improved methods a smaller labor force could probably obtain as great a yield as is obtained today.

Nor is it easy to extend the area under cultivation. Attempts were made under Hitler to reclaim heath and marsh, and some success attended these efforts. But such undertakings would have been impossible on a commercial basis. They were made possible then only because German youth contributed its labor as a patriotic duty.

Before the war Germany was, on balance, a small importer of foodstuffs. She could be self-sufficing in animal produce at the expense of sacrificing bread food or in the latter by importing fodder and fats. The result of territorial changes has been to reduce very considerably the German output of foodstuffs, without any comparable diminution in the number of mouths to be fed. It becomes all the more necessary that Germany should export her factory products in order to supplement her inadequate production of food.

German Industries. Germany is the most highly industrialized country on the mainland of Europe, though the proportion, 41 per cent before the last war, of the working population engaged in mining and manufacturing industries was slightly less than that in both Switzerland and Belgium. The modern industry of Germany derives in part from medieval crafts. Until a little over a century ago most of the manufactured output was from small, domestic workshops, and the craftsmen were organized on a guild basis. It was not until the latter half of the nineteenth century that a modern factory industry really developed, though there had for many years been an iron and steel industry in the Rhineland and in Upper Silesia. The rapid development of manufacturing industries accompanied and followed rather than, as in England, preceded the development of a railway system. A consequence of this has been that, despite the existence of certain heavily industrialized regions, German industries are less concentrated than are those of Great Britain or even of Belgium.

The rapid development of German industries came only after 1850, by which time a customs union had been established covering most of Germany. Thenceforward the German iron and steel industry expanded, quickly displacing imports of Great Britain, Belgium, and other countries. By the end of the century Germany had replaced Great Britain as the greatest steel producer in Europe. Bismarck had described his policy as one of "blood and iron." The English economist J. M. Keynes observed that "the German Empire has been built more truly on coal and iron than on blood and iron."[1]

The resources which Germany possessed within her prewar frontiers were very considerable. Germany was, after Great Britain, the largest producer of black coal in Europe. Her total output in the good years was about 180 million tons annually. About two-thirds of this came from the Ruhr district, and much of the remainder from Upper Silesia, now in Poland. The small coal fields of Saxony and Hannover accounted for the remainder. From 1935 until the conclusion of the last war the Saar Territory, with an output of about 14 million tons a year, was also part of Germany. In addition there was a large production of lignite, mined from open pits in the lower Rhineland, Saxony, Brandenburg, and Lower Silesia. Lignite has a low heating value and will not bear the cost of distant transport. Most of it is compressed

[1] Keynes, J. M., "The Economic Consequences of the Peace," pp. 74–75, London, 1919.

into briquettes, having a lower moisture content than the original coal, and either burned close to the pits to generate electric power or exported short distances for factory and domestic uses.

Germany is no longer well placed for supplies of iron ore. The reserves in the hills on each side of the middle Rhine, formerly of great importance, are still worked, but the output is small. A low-grade ore is mined in Hannover but cannot easily compete with imported ores,

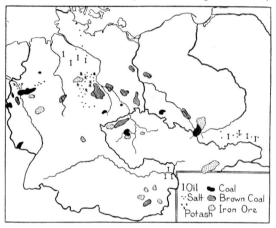

FIG. 134. Distribution of mineral resources in central Europe.

and its production and use had to be subsidized by the government in recent years. The production of nonferrous metals is also small and is practically limited now to zinc in Upper Silesia, lead and zinc in the Harz, and copper at Mansfeld in Thüringen. Common salt and potash are worked in the lower Rhineland and Saxony. Natural oil is found in Germany, particularly in Hannover, but the quantity obtained is very small and covers only a minute proportion of Germany's requirements.

It is a mistake to believe that German industry is always efficient in its use of machines. Much, indeed, is, but even more makes little use of mechanical devices and relies overwhelmingly on a supply of abundant, cheap, and skilled labor. A British inspector observed in 1946 that "the German manufacturers have remained competitive (in certain fields) rather through the low costs and the hard work of the operative, than from any special technical skill or pre-eminence in design of machinery and layout of plant." With a rise of wages to the English level—highly improbable at present—many of the smaller German firms would be obliged to close down. Even many of the largest and most famous concerns showed these defects. Krupp's works were well known for their obso-

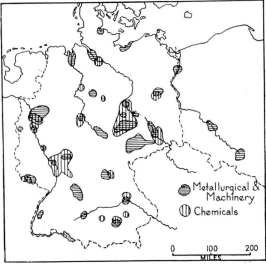

Fig. 135. Distribution of metallurgical and chemical industries.

lete equipment, and in many works and mines modern safety precautions were unknown or little used.

At the same time the Germans had achieved great economies through their industrial organization. The "vertical" combine was developed in the nineteenth century. The steel-producing firm reached back to the source of its materials, buying coal mines, building coke ovens, acquiring iron-ore concessions, owning docks and means of transportation. At the same time it also reached forward to control steel-using works and steel-marketing organizations. Thus were created such economic empires as Thyssen, Klöckner, and Krupp, with works and interests in all parts of Germany. Sometimes they were built too big—like Stinnes—and collapsed. Some little "empires" were amalgamated to form the greater combine of the Vereinigte Stahlwerke (United Steelworks). Such unions were not limited to iron, steel, and coal. The I. G. Farbenindustrie was a union of interests (*Interessen-*

gemeinschaft) of the chemical works of Germany. Siemens-Schuckert-Halske controlled a great part of the electrical-engineering industry.

After the end of the Second World War the Allies were determined to break up what they termed "excessive concentrations of economic power." These firms were "decartelized," though one may doubt how far this process of "unscrambling" may be carried without jeopardizing the efficiency of the industry. At the same time some plants and equipment were "dismantled." Germany's power to wage aggressive war was reduced, whatever the economic consequences might be for Germany. But the stupidities of this "pastoralization" policy were in the end removed, and in March, 1947, Herbert Hoover appealed for "policies which will restore productivity in Germany and exports with which to buy their [the Germans'] food. . . . "

In the geographical pattern of German industry is one area of exceptional importance, the Ruhr, but scattered over almost the whole of

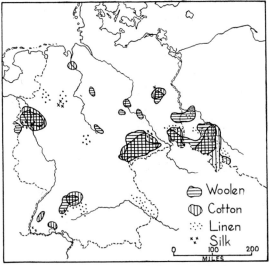

Fig. 136. Distribution of textile industries in Germany.

Germany are cities, large and small, each with its own specialized production, each deriving power and raw materials from a distance, each having good communications by road, rail, and canal with the ports, coal fields, and other towns. Berlin itself and the great ports of the

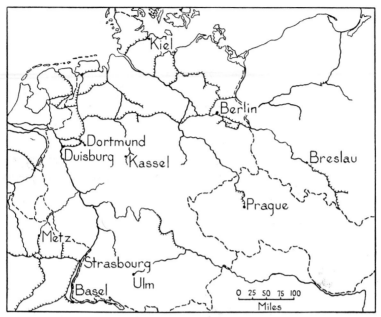

Fig. 137. Navigable rivers and canals of Germany.

north coast are very important industrial centers.

The textile industry is as widely scattered as the metallurgical. There is little tendency to concentrate in one locality or on a single type of product. If the lower Rhineland appears to stand out, it must be noted that the industry here is spread over cotton, wool, silk, and linen manufacture.

During the nineteenth century Germany built up an elaborate and efficient mechanism of transportation. The railway network was one of the most complete in Europe. Through routes connected all the important towns with one another, and the railway service before the last war was frequent and fast. The railway network is most dense in Saxony, the Ruhr, and the central Rhineland, but in no part of the country was any place more than 10 miles from the nearest railroad.

Railway transportation is supplemented by a highly developed system of canals. Germany had an advantage in this respect in the number of large and easily navigated rivers. In the later years of the nineteenth century, a number of canals was constructed and an ambitious scheme of future building put forward. The Dortmund-Ems Canal was cut to link the eastern part of the Ruhr with the North Sea port of Emden, and the Rhine-Herne Canal and the Lippe Canal were later cut to join it with the Rhine. In the

Essen, the Krupp works in 1950. The works, famous for the production of articles of high-quality steel, were almost completely destroyed by bombing during the Second World War.

present century the Mittelland Canal has been dug eastward through Hannover to the Elbe at Magdeburg. The Havel and Spree, tributaries of the Elbe, have been rendered navigable, and the Spree itself linked by a short canal with the

Oder. The Noteć, a tributary of the Oder, is joined by a short canal with the Vistula. In the south, an old and narrow canal joins the upper Main Valley at Bamberg with the Danube near Regensburg. This waterway is also small and incapable of being used by the larger canal vessels, and it is planned to replace it by a larger waterway. The existing canal network allows Ruhr coal to be distributed over a great deal more than a half of prewar Germany. A canal of a rather different nature is the Kiel Canal,

The Rhine near Duisburg. The barges, drawn by tugs, are used to carry coal, coke, and iron ore down the Rhine to the Netherlands and upstream to various ports in central and south Germany.

between the estuary of the Elbe and the town of Kiel, on the Baltic coast of Schleswig. Although it has a certain commercial importance, this canal was cut for essentially military purposes to join the naval base of Kiel with the North Sea.

The Rhine from the Dutch frontier up to Mannheim is the most used German waterway. It carries large quantities of coal, distributed from the Ruhr port of Duisburg-Ruhrort, and also iron ore, grain, and timber. Above Mannheim the river is more shallow, and the lowness of the water level in winter is a serious obstacle. It is nevertheless much used by upstream traffic as far as the twin ports of Strasbourg and Kehl. Much of the barge traffic for Switzerland uses the Alsatian Canal (page 199). The lower course of the Main as well as the Ems, Elbe, and Oder are also used. There is, however, little traffic on either the Weser or the Danube. Neither flows

through highly industrialized areas, nor do they flow close to important mineral resources.

The road network of Germany was in the past much less effective and efficient than the rail. The quality of the roads was in general not good and unsuited to heavy or fast traffic. During the 1930's, however, a system of motor roads, or *Autobahnen*, was designed. Its purpose was primarily a military one, but the system, incomplete as it is, is of considerable importance in German transportation.

Germany is linked by road, rail, and water communications with each of her neighbors, and much of her foreign trade is across her land frontiers. The ports of the Low Countries serve as outlets for the Ruhr. The German government tried during the interwar years to divert as much of this trade to the German North Sea ports as possible, and this was in part the objective of German canal construction. The North Sea ports are Bremen and Hamburg. Each handles a very large volume of shipping, and each has an outport, Bremerhaven and Cuxhaven, respectively, which handles passenger traffic and receives vessels unable to make the journey up river. The completion of the projected canal system would enable Bremen and Hamburg to serve more directly the needs of the Ruhr.

The Baltic Sea ports are relatively unimportant. Lübeck, Rostock, and Stralsund, of great commercial importance before modern times, now handle a negligible traffic. Stettin (Szczecin) was formerly the most important of Germany's Baltic Sea ports by virtue of the traffic of the river Oder which passed through it. It is now an outlier of Polish territory on a river which serves at present as an international frontier.

The future of no European country is less certain than is that of Germany. The division of Germany into four zones of occupation itself causes duplication and inefficiency in government services and limits the free flow of goods and the efficient functioning of the industrial system. In the past century Germany achieved a kind of balance between the industrial northwest and the mainly agricultural east and south.

The Western Zones have today an unduly large industrial production and a small agricultural, and the evils inherent in this situation have been intensified by the migration westward of Germans from east Germany, Czechoslovakia, and the Polish-occupied territory. Germany in the past sold much of her factory products in the markets of central Europe. She is now cut off from former markets by the Russian control of east Germany and central Europe. She must therefore compete more strongly in the markets of the west. Great Britain rightly fears the consequences of this renewed German competition. Western Germany has, for this reason, welcomed the Schuman Plan, which aims to create a single market for coal, iron, and steel in western Europe without the artificial barriers created by tariffs.

But the economic problem, serious as it is, is overshadowed by the political. The Western Powers have been torn between the desirability of reducing Germany's heavy industry and thus of limiting her capacity to make war and the need to assist her to rearm and thus to defend herself, should need arise, against Russia. There can be little question that the German hates the Russian, but the German has seen enough of war and does not want to make his country a battlefield between east and west. The Western Powers are now again slowly rebuilding German industry, but whole-hearted German cooperation in the defense of the west is by no means assured. Germany, defeated and outcast in 1945, sees in 1953 her favor solicited by east and west. What could not a Bismarck build on a situation such as this?

CHAPTER 18: *The Regions of Contemporary Germany*

The Germany of today is a small and crowded country. Since the end of the Second World War its eastern frontiers have been pushed back to the line of the river Oder, and into the area west of this river have been crowded refugees from former German territory and also from neighboring countries to the east. Germany now has a population of 64,500,000, scarcely less

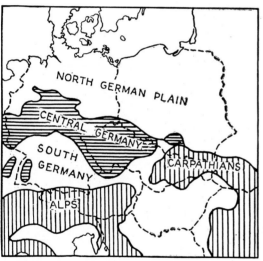

Fig. 138. Physical regions of the German settlement area.

than the population of the whole of Germany (69,622,000) before the war. Former German territory has been added to Poland, and a small part of the former province of East Prussia has been joined to the U.S.S.R. The Germany of today, furthermore, is divided into four occupation zones. The east is occupied by Russian forces, and its government in effect is controlled from Moscow. The west is occupied by the British, Americans, and French.

The British, French, and American Zones have been fused to make a single unit of government, with its capital in Bonn. The Saarland has been formed into an autonomous area closely linked with France. The Federal Republic of Western Germany has a population of 47,585,000, about 20 per cent more than this territory contained before the war. About 9,400,000 persons are refugees from the east; some 7,500,000 are *Vertriebenen*, Germans evicted from Poland, Czechoslovakia, and other non-German countries. Most of the remainder are refugees from the Soviet Zone.

The large number of refugees has been assimilated remarkably smoothly. Many are craftsmen and have set up in industries in parts of western Germany. In fact, in the American Zone a kind of industrial revolution is in progress. Only the farming community has proved difficult to absorb, because the area of farmland in the western zones cannot be expanded.

This dismemberment of Germany has had serious consequences. It broke up an area which over a long period of time had grown to be an economic unit. It cut off central and east Germany from their source of coal and west Germany from part at least of its supply of foodstuffs. The capital of Germany, Berlin, lies enclosed within the Russian Zone, inaccessible to the majority of Germans.

Most Germans look forward to a reunification of their country, and some cherish the ambition to take back again into the *Reich* the areas ceded to Poland and Russia. Some very small areas in the west, of slight economic importance, have been taken by the Netherlands, but this has not aroused German hostility as much as the separation of the Saar territory by France.

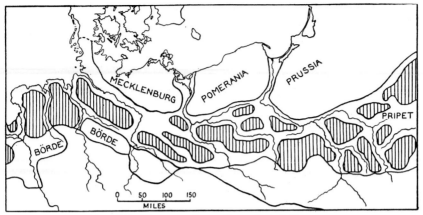

Fig. 139. The great river valleys of north Germany.

The Germany of today has one great resource, the Ruhr industrial area, but the rest of the country is far from rich. Much of it is poor agricultural land; large areas are forested. Germany cannot now feed itself without considerable imports, replacing the foodstuffs formerly imported from the ceded territories in the east. Nor can it easily employ all of its large population, swollen by the large influx of refugees.

The Germany of today is made up of four belts of territory, already referred to in the introduction to this section of the book. In the north is part of the plain of northern Europe; south of this is a belt of hilly country, which stretches from France to Czechoslovakia. Southward again is a rolling plain or plateau, rising in places to hilly ridges and making up most of south Germany. Lastly a small area of the Alps lies within the limits of Germany in the south. Very broadly, it may be said that northern Germany is low-lying and nearly flat, southern is made up of hills and plateaus. The account which follows is based on this fourfold division of Germany. Some unity is given to all these divisions by the course of the Rhine, which rises in the Alps of Switzerland, flows northward through southern Germany, and crosses the central hills by the famous Rhine Gorge before widening into the northern plain. The Rhineland could be regarded as a distinct unit within Germany, but it is here broken for convenience into sections, one of which, the Alpine, is considered in the chapter on Switzerland. The

Weser and the Elbe, other rivers of the northern plain, also rise in the hills lying to the south. The plain of southern Germany is drained partly by the Rhine and its tributaries, the Main and Neckar, partly by the Danube, by which it is joined with Austria.

The North German Plain. This plain broadens eastward from the borders of the Netherlands until it passes into Russia. Toward the west it is no more than 100 miles wide from north to south, but in the longitude of the river Rhine it widens somewhat as it sends fingers of lower land into the hilly region which lies to the south. Most of the plain is less than 300 feet above sea level, yet it is far from level or uniform. Most of it was covered by the ice sheets during the last glaciation, and these have laid down a deep covering of drift. As we see it now, the northern plain is the creation of the Ice Age. Most of the terrain is of glacial origin, moraine, outwash, or boulder clay, and the present courses of the rivers are in large measure a product of glacial interference with their drainage.

The glacial deposits represent several distinct advances and retreats of the ice, but their collective result was to push the Rhine mouth westward to its present position and to distribute moraine almost to the margin of the hills of central Germany. Water escaping from the ice spread gravel and sand over the plain, and a halt in the retreat of the ice led to the formation of a series of morainic ridges which constitute one of the strongest features of the northern plain. The sandy moraines of northern Germany make a complex pattern. They loop through the Danish peninsula and islands, deploy over north Germany, and stretch away eastward into Poland and Russia. They create a maze of small hills, separated by marshy, lake-studded depressions. During a late phase in the history of the glaciation, the rivers were forced to flow northwestward, parallel to the edge of the ice, to the North Sea. The river beds remain as conspicuous features of the landscape, and if they do not all contain rivers today, they at least provide easy routes for the construction of canals. The present-day rivers make use of a section of one of these valleys before taking a transverse course to the next. This tends to give a somewhat rectilinear pattern to the drainage of the plain (Fig. 139). The drainage system that thus developed had two features of great significance. The rivers were oriented in a northwesterly direction. Silesia and Saxony were thus put in direct connection by river with the North Sea rather than with the Baltic. Bremen (385,500)[1] and Hamburg (1,403,500), lying, respectively, near the mouths of the Weser and Elbe, became the great commercial ports of Germany, rather than Lübeck (223,000), Rostock (115,000), and Stettin (Szczecin) on the Baltic coast. A second consequence lay in the provision of abandoned river valleys, linking one major river system with another and forming potential avenues of communication.

The development of the north German Plain has depended mainly upon the nature of the glacial deposits. Broadly speaking, there are three distinct types of region: (1) plain covered with boulder clay and terminal moraine and dotted with lakes and often forested, (2) infertile areas of sand and gravel, and (3) areas of alluvial deposits lying along the rivers and around the coast. To these should be added the loess region, outside the limits of the former ice sheet but covered with dustlike deposits of high natural fertility, probably blown outward

[1] The population is given only of cities of more than 100,000 inhabitants. All cities of this size are mentioned by name in the text.

by winds from the clay-covered plain to the north. The only city of large size in the western part of the plain is Oldenburg (107,500), a market center west of Bremen.

The glaciated plain of Holstein and Mecklenburg is contained within the arc of a great terminal moraine, which extends from Denmark to Russia. The moraines themselves are conspicuous features of the landscape, forming belts of hummocky country, which in the Baltic Heights, in what is now northern Poland, reach to more than 1,000 feet above sea level. The plain which these moraines enclose is covered by an uneven spread of boulder clay. The drainage pattern is indefinite. Many of the hollows have filled with water or even peat. The lakes themselves form long chains of narrow, irregularly shaped, and sometimes interconnected patches of water. The land is damp and ill drained. The soils vary greatly in quality. Some are heavy; others strewn with masses of rock worn from the hills and valleys of Scandinavia. Much of the higher ground is made up of sandy deposits, and its light, infertile soils are covered with conifers or with heath. Few parts are fit for crop production, though the heavier lands make good meadows for dairy cattle.

The region as a whole is sparsely populated, and there are few towns. The area was formerly distinguished by its large estates and its poor peasantry, only a few generations away from serfdom. Villages are small, and isolated or scattered settlements are common. The poor material culture of the region reflects its natural poverty and the difficulty of agricultural development.

The waters escaping from the ice sheets spread large sheets of sand and gravel over the area outside the moraines. These have in turn been cut up by rivers into numerous patches of sand or gravel, known as *geest*, each surrounded by the marshy plain of a former river valley or by the flood plain of a present stream. The most significant of these geest areas is the Lüneburg Heath, lying between the Weser and the Elbe Rivers, but patches of similar sand and gravel stretch westward into the Netherlands and southeastward into Saxony and Poland.

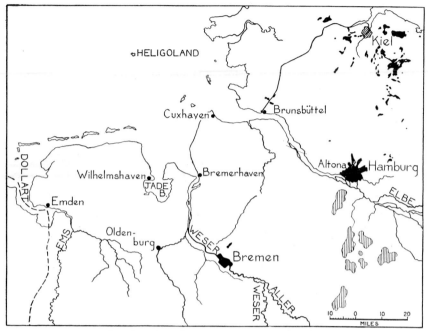

Fig. 140. The German ports of the North Sea.

In low-lying areas the sandy deposits become waterlogged. Peat forms in the hollows, and low bog, or *moor*, is produced. Moor is very extensive in northwestern Germany. In parts it has been drained and reclaimed for agriculture, and the black peaty soil is often very fertile. The more elevated areas, such as the Lüneburg Heath, are covered with a low growth of heath plants which can stand the dry and acid soil. The soil is thin and leached. Attempts have been made with an intensive use of fertilizers to break in some of the heath for cultivation. Some success has attended these efforts, but the most profitable form of land use appears to be afforestation. Very large areas have been planted with conifers. Population is very sparse on the heath, and the people live mostly, as is so often the case in areas of low agricultural value, in small and scattered settlements.

The ancient and present-day river valleys form a pattern which encloses many of the small areas of geest. The line of the river Weser is continued in the valley of the upper Elbe, while the direction of the lower Elbe is continued southeastward by the Havel and Spree, on which Berlin lies, and then by the upper Oder. These valleys are filled with alluvium. Some are marshy; all provide meadowland. They are more richly productive and more densely peopled than either of the regions of the northern plain already considered, the clay plain and the geest. At the mouths of the rivers are the leading commercial ports of Germany, Hamburg, Bremen, and Emden, and along their courses are numerous small market towns.

Berlin lies in one of the ancient river valleys. Its nucleus was an island in the river Spree, where was established in the Middle Ages one of Germany's eastern frontier posts. Near here the Electors of Brandenburg established their residence, and, with their rise to preeminence in Germany, the city of their choice grew in size and importance, if not also in beauty, and became an industrial city of very great importance. At this point the geest approaches close to the river on both north and south. There were thus a dry approach to the river (compare the sites of London and Paris) and a dry terrain over which the city expanded, while the rivers provided both routeways and cheap transportation. The present population is about 3,313,000, about a million less than in 1939. To the west is Potsdam (113,500), former seat of the Hohenzollern kings. The city is at present divided into four sectors, occupied, respectively, by the forces of the United States, Great Britain, France, and Russia. Its location, deep within the

Netherlands. In fact, new land is building forward from the coast all the way from the Dutch frontier to the Danish, broken only by the estuaries of the north German rivers, the Ems, Weser, and Elbe.

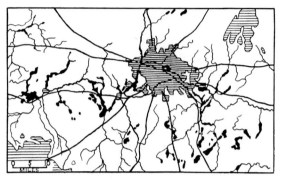

FIG. 141. The situation of Berlin. The map should be compared with those of the situations of London and Paris. Note the many small rivers and numerous lakes.

Bremen: the city hall (*Rathaus*) and cathedral. These buildings, with others in their vicinity, illustrate in the richness of their architecture the former wealth of this great city of the Hanseatic League. (*German Tourist Information Bureau, London.*)

Soviet Zone of Germany, renders it difficult for the Western nations to provision and maintain their sectors of the city.

The Danish peninsula divides the north German coast into two contrasting parts. To the west is a low, flat coast, where recent accretion and reclamation have extended the land at the expense of the sea. To the east the coast has been submerged in recent geological times and the valleys drowned by the rise in sea level. West of Denmark, a low, flat coast is fringed by equally low and inconspicuous islands. Between these Frisian Islands and the coast are stretches of shallow water, known as *Watten*, difficult to navigate but capable of reclamation as agricultural land, similar to the polders of the

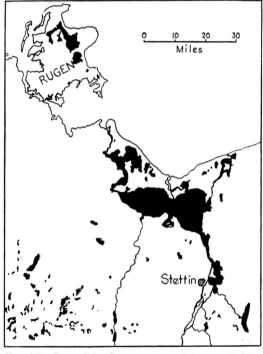

FIG. 142. Part of the German coast of the west Baltic.

The coastline of the Baltic Sea is more irregular than that fronting on the North Sea. The east coast of Schleswig is deeply indented by drowned valleys, on one of which lies the city of Flensburg (101,500), and farther east are many

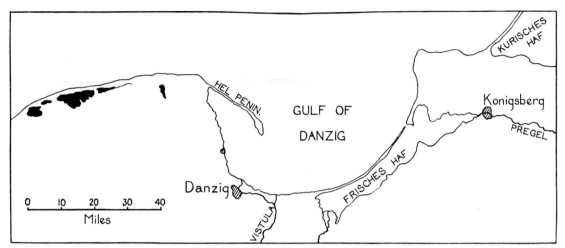

FIG. 143. Part of the German coast of the east Baltic. The west Baltic coast is a coastline of submergence, but in the east, the irregularities thus produced have been smoothed out by the alongshore drifting of material eroded by the sea from the glacial deposits.

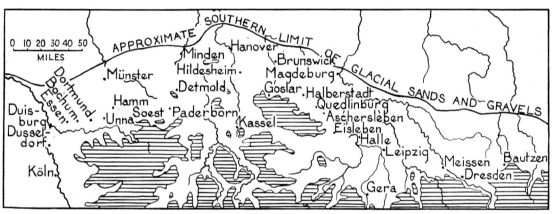

FIG. 144. Cities of the Börde. These form a belt between the hills of central Germany and the glaciated plain of the north.

irregularly shaped islands. The irregularities of the coastal forms, due to the postglacial submergence of this coast, have in part been smoothed away by the alongshore drifting of material derived from the erosion of the moraines. Long, narrow spits, or *Nehrungen*, have been drawn across the entrances to bays and estuaries, and on them high sand dunes have been piled by the wind. Lakes have been formed along the coast. Islands have been joined together, and in this way the estuary of the Oder has been almost cut off from the sea.

The ports of this coast were once of great importance in the trade of Germany. From Lübeck the ships of the Hanseatic League of the Middle Ages traded with the Baltic countries and Russia. In modern times trade with remote parts of the world has become more important than the Baltic trade, and with this change the North Sea ports have grown in importance as those of the Baltic Sea have declined. Many of the smaller ports of this coast have been closed by silting, but a few, including Lübeck and Stettin, now in Poland, retain some of their commercial importance. Kiel (214,500), at the eastern end of the canal that has been cut across the base of the Danish peninsula, has developed shipbuilding industries.

The Börde is a belt of country of irregular width, which stretches all the way from the Low

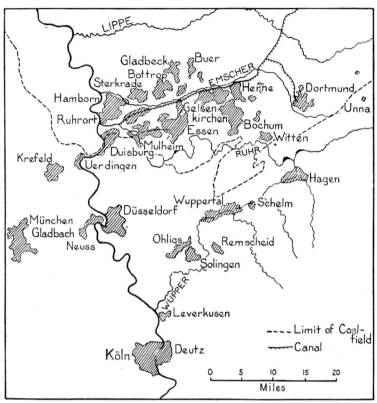

Fig. 145. The Ruhr.

Countries to Russia. It is a region of low relief, though generally rather higher than the glaciated plain, which borders it on the north. On the south it passes into the highlands of central Germany. This region has been covered with an uneven and in places irregular cover of fine, dustlike loess, swept outward by the winds which blew from the glaciated plain to the north. It gives a porous and dry soil, and it is fertile and supports an intensive agriculture. From early historical times it was at most but slightly wooded. Movement along it was easy, and clearing the land for cultivation offered few difficulties in former ages. It is one of the oldest regions of agriculture in Germany, as well as being one of the richest. It is a region of large, compact villages, most of them still surrounded by their open fields with intermixed strips. The cities of this region are mostly medieval in origin.

The loess-covered plain stretches southward in the neighborhood of the river Rhine as a sort

of "bay" between hills which are part of the hilly region of central Germany. The Rhine has laid down beds of gravel, which now form terraces over which the modern towns have been enabled to spread. Beneath the loess, gravel, and other deposits are coal measures. The loess belt has been since early times a routeway from west to east. Trading cities grew up here at an early date, and some, especially those at the crossings of rivers, attained great size and importance. Most important of these was Cologne (Köln), a city of Roman origin lying on the west bank of the Rhine. Cologne grew during the Middle Ages to be one of the greatest commercial cities of western Europe. It lay where the navigable Rhine crossed the west-to-east loess belt. Its location at a sort of commercial crossroads has enabled the city to continue to grow in modern times and to become the center of a very varied range of industries, which include the processing of food and the manufacture of steel. The city was one of great beauty and historical interest. Though very heavily damaged during the Second World War, some of its ancient buildings have survived, and it is slowly being rebuilt and is again an industrial and commercial center. In 1946 its population was 491,500; seven years earlier

The Ruhr landscape. In the foreground is the canalized river Emscher, crossed by a gas pipe line from one of the cokeries. In the distance are a coal mine and cokery (marked out by the plume of steam). Power is generated with coal and distributed by cable.

it had been 768,426. This is evidence of the immense destruction in the city during the intervening years.

West of the Rhine is the small coal field and industrial center of Aachen (Aix-la-Chapelle), an ancient home of the iron and brass industries. Aachen (110,500) was a favorite residence and became the burial place of the Emperor Charlemagne. The city has many remains from its brilliant past, though its frontier situation has detracted from its political importance in modern times. The Aachen coal field produced in 1949 only 5,077,000 tons of coal and is dwarfed by its neighbor east of the Rhine.

The little river Ruhr drains part of the highlands of central Germany and joins the Rhine near Duisburg. North of the river Ruhr lies the largest coal field in western Europe. The Ruhr industrial area has grown up on the basis of this vast resource in coal and forms a distinct region, only 40 miles from west to east and a great deal less from north to south, containing a population of some 5 million persons. Its nucleus over a

century ago was in the Ruhr Valley, where the coal seams came to the surface. Since that time mining has extended farther northward. The coal seams increase in depth in this direction, and even deeper and more elaborate shafts have become necessary. At present exploratory work has proceeded as far north as the latitude of Münster, and the most northerly worked coal mines are in the Lippe Valley. The older coal field along the Ruhr is largely abandoned. Iron ore was obtained at first locally from the bogs and marshes of Westfalen and from bedded deposits contained within the coal measures. These sources have long since been abandoned, and the blast-furnace industry of the Ruhr is now supplied from Sweden, Lorraine, Spain, and other countries. The basic industries of the Ruhr are coal mining, the manufacture of coke, iron smelting, and steelmaking. At the time of writing the Ruhr's coal output is at the rate of about 100 million tons a year, and the coke output about 24 million tons. In 1950, the Ruhr produced about 12 million tons of steel; the highest production in the years before the war was some 16 million tons. The smelting operations within the Ruhr have tended to move toward the river Rhine or toward the canals that lower the cost of transporting ore to the

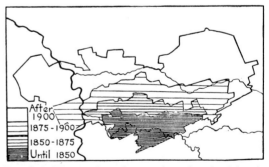

Fig. 146. The northward expansion of coal mining in the Ruhr area. The positions of Essen, Bochum, and Dortmund are indicated by dots. (*From P. Kukuk.*)

furnaces. The manufacture of steel is more widely scattered through the Ruhr area.

The manufactures of the Ruhr now include chemicals which may be regarded as a by-product of the coking industry. The chief centers of the metallurgical and chemical industries in the Ruhr are Essen (524,500), seat of the great Krupp concern, Bochum (246,500), Dortmund (436,500), Oberhausen (174,000), Gelsenkirchen (266,000), Mülheim (132,500), and Duisburg-Hamborn (356,500), which spans the mouth of the river Ruhr. To the north the

The docks at Ruhrort. These handle a greater volume of goods than any other inland port of the world. Barges in the foreground are unloading iron ore. Blast furnaces can be seen in the distance.

towns are smaller as well as newer, developing as the coal field expanded northward.

The Ruhr has the advantage not only of a highly developed railway network but also of a system of canals and of the best navigable highway in western Europe, the Rhine. At the end of the nineteenth century the canal from Dortmund to the river Ems was dug in order to put the Ruhr into closer communication with the North Sea ports. This canal has since been linked with the Rhine by the Rhine-Herne Canal and also by the Lippe Canal.

This region of metallurgical and chemical industries is merely the heart of a much larger region, which embraces the plain of Westfalen, the highlands of the Westerwald, and the Rhine Valley. The industrial development of these peripheral regions is in many respects older than that of the Ruhr region itself. Linen, once the chief industrial product of Westfalen, is still made in Bielefeld (132,500). To the south the ancient silk and woolen industry of Wuppertal (326,000) has continued, with the addition of cotton manufacture. Krefeld-Uerdingen (150,-500) and Aachen, west of the Rhine, are also ancient centers of the textile industry, and in München-Gladbach (110,500) the cotton, woolen, and silk industries continue to be of great importance.

Düsseldorf (421,000) lies on the Rhine a few miles to the south of the Ruhr area. From being the capital of one of the petty German principalities, it grew to be an industrial center without losing its character of a cultural and artistic center. It now acts as a business and administrative headquarters for many of the Ruhr industries.

The ancient centers of the metallurgical industries had been in the hilly country of the Sauerland, Westerwald, and Siegerland, where small forges had produced swords, armor, nails, wire, and cutlery. The fabrication of steel brought in from the Ruhr is still of importance. Remscheid, Solingen (133,000), Hagen (126,-500), and Altena, as well as a number of smaller places, remain important for the manufacture of finished-steel goods, especially cutlery and high-quality steel.

The great importance before the Second World War of the Ruhr as a producer of heavy steel goods has led France, Great Britain, and other countries to participate in schemes aimed at imposing some sort of international control on the region. During 1923 it was occupied by French troops, and after the Second World War an international authority was established to control Germany's use of the resources of this region. On the other hand, the Ruhr is part of the economy of western Europe. Most western European countries, except Great Britain, rely in greater or lesser measure on the coking coal of the Ruhr. Other countries, including Switzerland and the Netherlands, obtain crude steel from the Ruhr for their finishing industries.

East of the Rhine a long, narrow finger of hill country, known as the Teutoburgerwald, stretches northwestward into the plain. In some degree it presents a barrier to movement along the Börde and has forced railroads to take a course around its northern extremity, where the city of Osnabrück has become a route center and a city of considerable commercial impor-

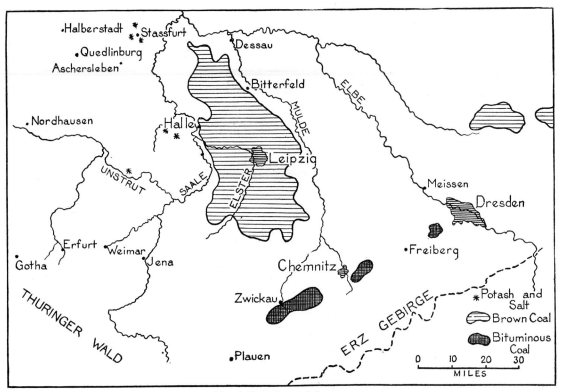

FIG. 147. Industrial Saxony.

tance. West of this ridge is Münster, focal point of the Westfalen Plain, market center, and now, with the development of the nearby Ruhr coal field, a city of growing industrial importance.

East of the Teutoburgerwald the Börde continues through Hannover (Hanover), a rich area of rolling, loess-covered farmland, with cities of such grace and beauty as Hildesheim, Hannover (355,000), Brunswick (Braunschweig, 181,500), and Goslar. Most of these suffered severely during the Second World War, and Hildesheim was practically obliterated as a city. Several of these cities, which owed their growth to the richness of the region in which they lay and to the trade which passed along the Börde, have attracted modern industries. Hannover has automobile and engineering industries, and in the neighborhood of Brunswick the local low-grade iron ores have been smelted with fuel brought from the Ruhr. These iron- and steelworks have now been dismantled.

Saxony (Sachsen), like Hannover, has the rich loess soil and is intensively cultivated. Along the margin of the Bohemian or Czech Massif are small, scattered coal fields. Farther to the north, between Halle (222,500) and Magdeburg (236,500), are extensive deposits of lignite. This fuel, which is obtained from vast strip mines, is of too low a quality to be worth transporting far but is used near the mines for power generation and as the basis of important chemical industries. Common salt and potash are also mined in Saxony and contribute yet further to the important chemical industries of Merseburg and other towns of Saxony. Saxony is an important industrial region. It lacks the immense resources in coking coal which make the Ruhr area important but has adequate fuel resources for a varied industrial development. Leipzig (607,500) and Dresden (468,000) are ancient cities of this region that have attracted modern industries. Chemnitz (250,000), Zwickau (123,-000), and Halle are now more specialized centers of the textile and chemical industries. This

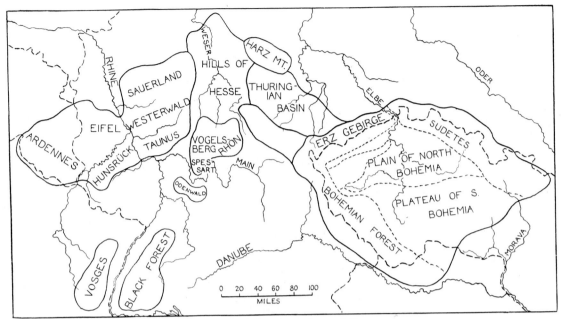

FIG. 148. Physical regions of central Germany.

region is drained by the Elbe and its tributaries, the Saale and the Mulde, and its chief commercial outlet is northwestward through Hamburg.

The northern plain is thus a region of gentle though varied topography. Despite the existence of limited areas of good soil, the region as a whole is one of low agricultural value. Large areas remain uncultivated, and it is doubtful whether the area under cultivation could be extended with any profit. The prosperity of the northern plain derives more from its mineral than from its agricultural wealth. The construction of means of communication, both railroads and canals, has been relatively easy, thus contributing to the development of industries. The most important single means of communication, however, is the river Rhine, along which a large part of the heavy merchandise passes between the Ruhr and the ocean ports of Rotterdam, Amsterdam, and Antwerp. The northern plain, particularly its southern edge, has become the most industrialized region of Germany.

Highlands of Central Germany. Reference has frequently been made to the belt of hilly country that stretches from west to east across the center of Germany. In the west it continues

through Belgium and into France under the name of the Ardennes, and in the east it is continued into eastern Czechoslovakia. The region is made up of many eroded hill masses, separated from one another by narrow belts of lowland. These hills rarely rise to sharp or rugged summits. Their upper surfaces are usually smooth or undulating, sometimes ill-drained and often thickly forested. The rivers that rise in or flow through this region occupy deep, narrow valleys, which furnish routes through the hills. In the west the valleys of the Rhine and Moselle (Mosel), farther east the Weser and Elbe provide such through routes.

Toward the west this region is commonly known as the Rhenish or Rhineland Highlands. A few miles below the city of Mainz (Mayence) the river Rhine enters the most familiar and the most spectacular part of its course. Between Bingen and Bonn it crosses the Rhineland Plateau in a deep gorge, around whose castled cliffs and terraced vineyards has gathered a host of legends of history and romance. The plateau itself is built of hard slates. It has a flat or undulating surface, broken by the deep valleys of the short streams that flow down to the Rhine or Moselle. The steep slopes are generally forested, and the plateau surface is in many places cleared for cultivation, but the climate is too harsh for agriculture to be really important. Iron ore was once mined in many parts of this region and was smelted with charcoal made in the forests. This industry has

The Rhine Gorge between Mainz and Koblenz. The river is incised in an almost level plateau. The valley sides are, wherever possible, terraced for vineyards (seen in the distance). The river is much used for navigation. In the Middle Ages castles were built above the river, such as the one seen in the distance, from which the German barons levied toll on the shipping. (*German Tourist Information Bureau, London.*)

now disappeared over most of the region, though a small iron-smelting and steelmaking industry survives near Siegen, the ancient center of ironworking in this region.

These highlands are divided by the river Rhine and its two tributaries, the Moselle and the Lahn, which both join the main river at or near Coblenz (Koblenz), into four quadrants. To the northwest is the Eifel, a continuation of the Ardennes of Belgium, noteworthy for its recent volcanic activity. To the southwest is the Hunsrück, and to the southeast, the Taunus.

The northeastern is the most dissected of these four areas. Its many small, swift streams once provided water power. Its narrow valleys formerly resounded with the beat of the water-driven forge hammers, which worked up the iron and steel made farther south in the Siegerland, the region around Siegen. These works are now silent, but many cities within these hills have inherited this ancient industry. Remscheid, Solingen, and Hagen are today important centers of the steel and metallurgical industries, and Wuppertal has become the seat of the textile industry, an inheritance from a period when the spinning machines and looms were worked with water power.

A scene in Lower Hesse. This illustrates the character of the hilly country of central Germany. The higher ground is in general forested. The lower and more gentle slopes are laid out in large "open fields" and are under cultivation. (*German Tourist Information Bureau, London.*)

Eastward from the Rhineland Highlands there stretches an area of very beautiful hill country, softer in its outlines and of a higher agricultural value than the Rhineland. The broader valley floors are well cultivated; they support large villages and are traversed by

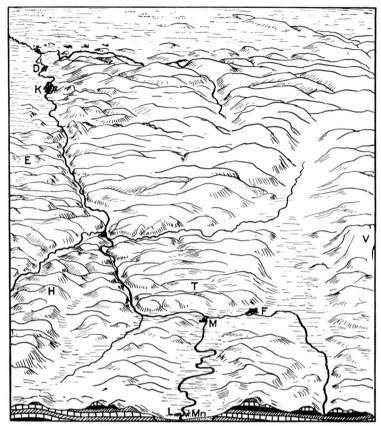

FIG. 149. Diagrammatic sketch of the Rhineland from Ludwigshafen-Mannheim (L-Mn) to Düsseldorf (D). The Eifel is marked E; the Hunsrück, H; the Taunus, T; F = Frankfurt; M = Mainz; V = The Vogelsberg.

important routes. There are small and ancient cities, such as Hameln, Göttingen, and Marburg, and one industrial city, Kassel (127,500), of great importance. In Thüringen (Thuringia) the area of low-lying agricultural land is greater and the prosperity of the area more marked. The loess, which gives the Börde its richness, is deposited over the Thüringen plain, and here a landscape somewhat like that of the Börde has been developed. There are many small medieval towns. In some of these, such as Erfurt (174,-500), the ancient craft industries have ripened into modern manufactures. Jena has thus become the seat of the Zeiss instrument works. Weimar was formerly a center of German thought and letters, the home of Goethe and of other great figures in German literature, and was for a time the seat of the German Parliament.

Thüringen is almost surrounded by hills,

some of which resemble the Rhenish Highlands in their composition and relief. On the north is the sharp-sided massif of the Harz Mountains, which in turn looks north over the Börde and the north German Plain. Its ancient rocks were richly mineralized, and lead, copper, and zinc have been mined here since the Middle Ages. Other similar massifs of old, hard rock lie to the south of Thüringen. In general they have a poor soil and are sparsely populated. Much of their area is forested. With the decline and gradual extinction of the mining and metalworking industries, these areas are left with few economic assets.

Southern Germany. South of the highland belt that has just been described is the plateau of south Germany, a region of undulating relief somewhat resembling eastern France. In the west is the Rhine Plain, with hills both to the west

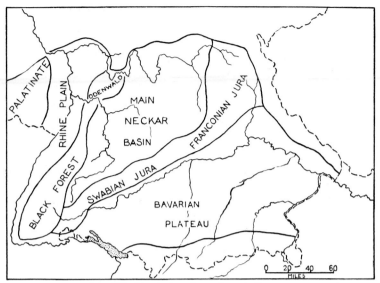

FIG. 150. Physical regions of south Germany.

FIG. 151. Diagrammatic sketch of South Germany. To the left are the faulted massifs of the Vosges and Black Forest; to the right the strongly folded Alps. N = Nürnberg; R = Regensburg; S = Stuttgart.

and to the east. On the eastern edge of the plain is the Black Forest, east of which are the Main Valley, the limestone uplands of southern Germany, and the Danube Valley. Rainfall is less than in the hills and plains of the north, and the climate is milder. Summers are hot, and in places the grape vine grows well.

The Rhine Plain resembles that of Alsace, which it faces across the river Rhine. Like Alsace, it is a region of light soil, of high agricultural fertility, and of early human settlement. The Rhine is here a broad, slow-flowing stream. A deep channel has been cut through its meanders, and the river is navigable up to the Swiss port of Basel. High enough above the level of the river to be free of the danger of floods are terraces, covered with the light loess soil and broader and more continuous here on the German side of the river than in Alsace. A line of towns has grown up along the river: Speyer, Mannheim (211,500), and Ludwigshafen (106,500), which face one another across the river, and Worms and Mainz. Another line of towns lies along the edge of the hills which border the plain on the east. This line includes the cities of Frankfurt (424,000), once the

A vineclad hill in the Swabian Jura, near Tübingen. This isolated hilltop is crowned by a small chapel of medieval origin. Such hills often have castles. The level plateau of the Swabian Jura can be seen in the distance. (*German Tourist Information Bureau, London.*)

greatest trading city of the upper Rhineland and now a center of engineering and other industries, Freiburg, Wiesbaden (188,500), and Karlsruhe (172,500).

West of the Rhine and north of the French province of Alsace are the hills of the Palatinate (Pfalz). In part they are built of infertile sandstones, in part of volcanic rocks. Most of the higher ground is forested, and cultivation is limited to the valleys. A depression extends through this area from the Rhine toward the Saar Valley and France. The city of Kaiserslautern lies in this gap, which has been of considerable strategic importance. It is today much used as a route from the Paris Basin eastward.

The small Saar territory has been detached from Germany and is closely associated with France, both politically and economically (page 144). The coal field has given rise to an important industrial development, and there are iron- and steelworks. In some degree the Saar area is complementary to the French iron-ore-producing area of Lorraine. The French have desired its coal resources and, as after the First World War, have succeeded in detaching it from

The village of Berneck in the Black Forest. Much of the area is forested and too high for the grape vine. Clearings are more often than not under grass. (*German Tourist Information Office, New York.*)

Germany. The area is nevertheless wholly German in speech.

Just as the Rhine Plain resembles the plain of Alsace, so the Black Forest is closely similar to the Vosges (page 144). Its western face is steep, its summits are rounded, and it drops gently eastward to the plateau of south Germany, as the Vosges sink westward to Lorraine. The Black Forest is thickly wooded and is a region of great natural beauty and a popular resort area. North of the Black Forest are the lower areas of the Spessart and Odenwald. Heidelberg (112,000) has grown up where the river Neckar cuts through these hills to reach the Rhine.

East of these hills is the plain of the rivers Main and Neckar. A sequence of beds of limestone and sandstone has produced a rolling country of moderate relief. Small towns, many of them, like Rothenburg and Würzburg,[1] places of great beauty, and large and compact villages are dotted about this area. The sandstone forms ridges that are generally infertile and are often forested. In some places they give rise to steep, westward-facing scarps; in others they are worn back, so that the sandstone scarcely shows up as a relief feature at all. Limestone and clay have given rise to lower and more productive land. Largest of the many cities of this area is Nuremberg (Nürnberg) (312,500), an ancient center of German arts and crafts, situated on the Regnitz, a tributary of the Main. Around it is a number of small industrial towns, such as Fürth and Erlangen. The city of Stuttgart (414,000) lies on the Neckar in an area of rich lowland. Like Nuremberg, it is an ancient city that has now become an important industrial center with, in particular, engineering industries.

The Swabian and Franconian Jura, which lie to the east of the Main and Neckar Valleys, is a high plateau of limestone, resembling closely the limestone hills of eastern France. It presents a steep edge to the west, where it rises to heights of well over 2,000 feet above sea level. The scarp is much dissected; many small isolated hills lie out in front of it as it runs in a curving line

[1] Würzburg was severely damaged during the Second World War.

from the Rhine near Schaffhausen to the valley of the upper Main. The surface of the plateau is dry, and its altitude gives it a severe climate. There are only a few small towns in this belt, and rural settlements are infrequent. Crop farming is much less important than animal rearing.

A small German town, Dinkelsbühl in Bayern. The student should note the town gate, the fountain, the cobbled streets, and the tall houses with steep roofs and shuttered windows. (*German Tourist Information Office, New York.*)

To the east and southeast the plateau sinks to the valley of the Danube. The river Danube, or Donau, rises on the eastern slopes of the Black Forest and reaches the Black Sea by a course of over 1,700 miles. Its romantic associations have made it perhaps the most familiar river in Europe, but it is not in general a beautiful or attractive stream. Nowhere are its waters as blue as they are reputed, and the river is more often brown with silt than otherwise. Nor is it, at least in its German tract, particularly important for navigation. Its course is very winding. In places it is deeply incised, and the water level varies a great deal with the seasons.

A small German town, Markgröningen in Württemberg. Here the houses are built mainly of a heavy wooden frame-work, with the interstices plastered. The traditional styles of building depend to some extent on the kinds of material available locally. (*German Tourist Information Office, New York.*)

Stuttgart. The city lies at the foot of the Swabian Jura, and its suburbs ascend the slopes. Note the considerable evidence of destruction as a result of bombing during the Second World War. (*German Tourist Information Office, New York.*)

The course followed by the Danube in south Germany is something of a compromise between a tendency to slip down the "dip" slope of the Swabian Jura and a tendency to be pushed northward by the discharge of the numerous silt-laden streams that flow northward from the Alps. In its upper course the Danube crosses the limestone hills of Swabia (Schwaben). At Ulm it receives the Iller, the first significant Alpine stream to join it. Then in quick succession follow the Lech, Isar, and Inn. There are few towns along the Danube besides Regensburg (Ratisbon, 108,500), a route center at its most northerly bend, and Passau, close to the Austrian border.

Between the Danube and the Alps is the plateau of Bavaria, a gently inclined platform that rises from the river Danube southward until the Alps rise steeply from it. Like the great northern plain, this region was greatly modified during the Ice Age by the large volume of material that was washed outward from the Alps. The area is strewn with boulder clay, morainic deposits, and gravel and sand laid down by the rivers. These deposits have served to even the relief. The present rivers have cut shallow valleys into them and have produced a series of land forms that resemble those of the northern plain. Toward the south, as the amount of end moraine increases, the terrain becomes more uneven. Hollows left by this uneven spread of deposits have been filled with water, and some have in turn accumulated peat and become marsh or moor. Around Munich (München) are extensive areas of such moor and also of sand and gravel, producing heath conditions like those found in North Germany. Locally loess has been spread over the surface, improving the soil and making it more suitable for agriculture.

The Bavarian Plateau is predominantly an agricultural region, though the soils are often poor and the winters severe. Munich (752,000) is the largest city not only of this area but also of all southern Germany. It lies on the river Isar, between the forested, lake-studded morainic region and extensive areas of marsh. No site could have been less propitious, but Munich

lay upon a routeway running from west to east. It also lay opposite the routes that followed the Engadine and the Brenner across into Italy. But accident played its part in the rise of Munich. It was no better placed for trade than many other cities in this area but was chosen as capital by the Bavarian dukes. On it they bestowed their care and wealth, and under their

The Schlossplatz, Stuttgart, typical of the spacious and beautiful planning of many of the larger cities of Germany. (*German Tourist Information Office, New York.*)

protection it grew to be a great city, railway center, and industrial town.

Augsburg (160,000), 40 miles to the northwest, was a Roman town at the crossing of the Lech and was at first of far greater importance than Munich. It suffered severely in the wars of the seventeenth century but had no fostering ducal hand to restore it to its former position of prosperity.

Toward the east the Alps and the hills of central Germany and Czechoslovakia draw together. The Bavarian Plateau narrows between them until in the end it disappears.

The Alps. Only a small extent of the Alpine

Mountains lie within Germany, whose southern frontier follows in part the most northerly of the mountain ranges. Only the foothills are German. These have a wild beauty that attracts tourists, and in their recesses are many small but widely known resorts. The chief resource of this region is its water power. Electric current is generated and transmitted by cable to many parts of south Germany. It has given rise to many small industries in this area, though the mountains are more noted for what is in reality their less important product, the wood carvings and similar articles produced by the artistry of the peasants.

BIBLIOGRAPHY

GENERAL

Ancel, J., "Manuel géographique de politique européenne," 2 vols, Paris, 1938–1945.

Dickinson, Robert E., The Economic Regions of Germany, G.R., XXVIII, 1938, 609–626.

——, "The German Lebensraum," London, 1942.

——, Mitteldeutschland: The Middle Elbe Basin as a Geographical Unit, G.J., CIII, 1944, 211–225.

——, The Morphology of the Medieval German Town, G.R., XXXV, 1945, 74–97.

——, "The Regions of Germany," London, 1945.

"Géographie universelle," Vol. IV, L'Europe centrale, 2 parts, Paris, 1930–1931.

"Germany's Contribution to European Economic Life," Council on Foreign Relations, Paris, 1949.

Lamartine Yates, P., "Food Production in Western Europe," London, 1940.

Mance, Sir Osborne, and J. E. Wheeler, "International River and Canal Transport," Oxford, 1944.

Sargent, A. J., "Seaports and Hinterlands," London, 1938.

SPECIALIZED PUBLICATIONS

Conzen, G., East Prussia, G., XXX, 1945, 1–10.

Harris, Chauncy D., The Ruhr Coal Mining District, G.R., XXXVI, 1946, 194–221.

Hartshorne, Richard, Geographic and Political Boundaries in Upper Silesia, A.A.A.G., XXIII, 1933, 195–224.

——, The Upper Silesian Industrial District, G.R., XXIV, 1934, 423–438.

Mutton, A. F. A., The Black Forest: Its Human Geography, E.G., XIV, 1938, 131–153.

Niehaus, Heinrich, Agricultural Conditions and Regions in Germany, G.R., XXIII, 1933, 23–47.

Partsch, J., "Central Europe" (English translation), London, 1903.

Pounds, N. J. G., Port and Outport in North-West Europe, G.J., CIX, 1947, 216–228.

——, "The Ruhr," Bloomington, Ind., 1952.

——, The Ruhr Area: A Problem in Definition, G., XXXVI, 1951, 167–178.

THE SAARLAND

Bauer, Hubert A., The Geographic Background of the Saar Problem, G.R., XXIV, 1934, 555–565.

Capot-Rey, R., The Industrial Region of the Saar, G.R., XXV, 1935, 137–141.

Cowan, Laing Gray, "France and the Saar, 1680–1948," New York, 1950.

"L'Economie de la Sarre," Institut national de la statistique et des études économiques, Paris, 1947.

Held, Colbert C., The New Saarland, G.R., XLI, 590–605.

Russell, Frank M., The Saar, Stanford, Calif., 1951.

THE RIVER RHINE, ITS REGIONAL SETTING AND SIGNIFICANCE FOR EUROPE

"Der Rhein," Duisburg, 1951. (This is a very thorough examination of the economic and technical problems of the Rhine and of its tributaries.)

"De Rijn als Europese rivier," Rotterdam, 1948. (This is a valuable collection of papers on the Rhine, presented to W. E. Boerman; all are in Dutch.)

Haelling, R., "Le Rhin," Paris, 1921.

Levainville, J., The Economic Function of the Rhine, G.R., XIV, 1924, 242–256.

Morgan, F. W., Rotterdam and the Waterway Approaches to the Rhine, E.G., XXIV, 1948, 1–18.

Demangeon, A., and L. Febvre, "Le Rhin," Paris, 1935.

"Le Rhin: Nil de l'occident," Les Ordres de chevalerie, Paris, 1946.

Periodicals concerned with the economic aspects of the Rhine are

La Navigation du Rhin, Strasbourg, and *Zeitschrift für Binnenschiffahrt*, Berlin.

There is a large literature on Germany's postwar problems. Most of the official United Nations and Organization for European Economic Cooperation publications have been listed on pages 52 to 54. To these should be added:

British Intelligence Objectives Sub-Committee Overall Reports, London, 1949–1951. (This is a series of some 25 reports on German industries; they are of high value as source material and embody the findings of the many small committees which examined German industries in 1945 and 1946.)

The Coal and Steel Industries of Western Europe, *Economic Bulletin for Europe*, Vol. II, No. 2, 1950.

"European Steel Trends," Geneva, 1949.

Regional Interdependence of Germany, *Economic Bulletin for Europe*, Vol. I, No. 3, 1949.

Report on Germany, Office of the U.S. High Commissioner for Germany, quarterly from December, 1949.

A well-documented study of Allied policy toward German industry is "Am Abend der Demontage," Bremen, 1951.

On urban and rural planning in Germany see two postwar publications, both for the British Zone: "Grundlagen der Landesplanung Nordrhein-Westfalen," *Landesplanungsbehörde*, Düsseldorf, 1947; "Ordnung und Planung in Ruhr-Raum," Institut für Raumforschung, Bonn, 1951.

There is a *Statistisches Jahrbuch*, published annually, and the *Länder* have each their own statistical publications. The German banks (now broken up into a number of local banks) also publish material of geographical value.

A series of provincial atlases has been published: "Rhein-Mainischer Atlas," 1929; "Elsass-Lothringischer Atlas," 1931; "Saar Atlas," 1934; "Atlas Niedersachsen," 1934; "Thüringen Atlas," 1939; "Bayern Atlas," 1949. An atlas of Nordrhein-Westfalen is being published as a series of separate sheets.

CHAPTER 19: *Poland*

Poland lies in the north European Plain between the mountains of the Alpine system and the Baltic Sea. To the west is Germany; to the east, Russia; and between, the land lies flat and uninterrupted. There are no physical barriers, except rivers, lakes, and forest, to the movement of men, whether in small groups or in armies. Germans moved east and settled in

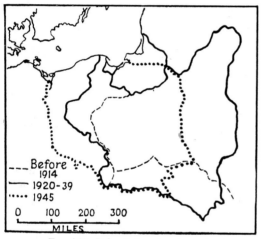

FIG. 152. Poland: frontier changes.

Poland, and Poles settled in Russia. This open nature of the Polish Plain has rendered the country particularly liable to invasion. Its existence in modern times has been precarious, at the mercy of its stronger neighbors to east and west, Russia and Germany.

The state of Poland grew up in the Middle Ages to the west of the river Vistula (Wisła). During the following centuries this early Polish state lost territory in the west to the Germans but itself expanded to the east. In the sixteenth century the Polish state was merged with the grand duchy of Lithuania. The joint state

reached eastward to beyond the river Dnieper. The political center of this enlarged state came to be the Polish city of Warsaw (Warszawa). Much of this great eastern territory was lost by Poland during the seventeenth century.

In the eighteenth century Poland was divided between her neighbors, made a short reappearance during the Napoleonic Wars, and reappeared again in 1918. At the same time the Lithuanians revolted successfully against the Russians and reestablished their independence. The western boundary of the new state was determined by the Allies and was made to conform as nearly as possible with the division between German and Polish peoples. The language frontier was far from clear. Germans and Poles dwelled intermixed with each other. The boundary that was ultimately demarcated was as fair as was possible but satisfied neither side. It split the industrial region of Upper Silesia and separated East Prussia from Germany by the so-called Polish Corridor. On Poland's eastern border, however, it was beyond the power of the Allies to enforce a settlement between Poland and Russia, though the British government did suggest to the Polish that the line which came to be known as the Curzon Line might be accepted as a boundary. Poland refused. She was successful in the campaign against Russia of 1920 and by the terms of her peace treaty with Russia secured much more extensive territories in the east. On the northeast she occupied Vilna (Vilnius, Wilno), which was claimed by the Lithuanians as their historic capital.

Poland had been promised an outlet to the sea. The "Corridor" ran down to the shore of the Baltic Sea between Germany and the

German province of East Prussia. Its population was predominantly Polish, but its port and chief city, Danzig, was German. Danzig (Gdansk) lies on one of the branches of the Vistula, a few miles from its entrance into the sea. It was the obvious outlet by sea for the new state, but its population was overwhelmingly German. To retain Danzig in Germany was to deny to the Poles the "free and secure access to the sea" which they had been promised. To deliver Danzig to the Poles was to violate the principle of self-determination, so dear to the peacemakers of 1919. The latter resorted to a compromise. Danzig became a free city under the control of the League of Nations. But the Poles, refusing to rely entirely for their seaborne commerce on the services of this German port, built the new city of Gdynia, about 10 miles to the northwest, on the bare, flat, sandy Baltic coast. Gdynia (111,000)[1] has grown to be a city and port of considerable size, equipped for handling the bulky cargoes, such as coal and timber, which enter into the foreign trade of Poland.

The settlement reached in 1919 barely lasted 20 years. In 1939, western Poland was overrun by the Germans, while the Russians occupied eastern Poland. With the defeat of Germany in 1945, the Polish state was reestablished. The centuries-old movement to the east was reversed, and a provisional western boundary of Poland was established along the rivers Oder and Neisse, with a sort of "bridgehead" west of the Oder in the city of Stettin (Szczecin, 159,000). At the same time the parts of eastern Poland occupied by the Russians in 1939 became a part of the U.S.S.R. The present eastern boundary of Poland approximates the Curzon Line which Poland had rejected 25 years earlier.

Since its reappearance in 1919 after a century of eclipse, Poland has been faced with heavy problems of internal organization and administration. The country was made up of three fragments, each of which had grown during the previous century into the economic life of Germany, Austria, and Russia, respectively.

[1] The population is given of all cities of over 100,000 inhabitants.

Railway gages differed. The transportation facilities of each were oriented toward Berlin or Vienna or Moscow. Currencies, tables of measurement, customs, and standards of living differed sharply. In the course of 20 years Poland went far to solve these problems, and when a new integration appeared to have been achieved, the country was again partitioned. The new Poland has lost to Russia about a third of its original area and has gained in the west a rather smaller area. The land lost was

Plowing on a farm in Poznań. The soil is heavy and of glacial origin. Such mechanized farms are still not common in Poland. (*Polish Photographic Agency.*)

poor, and its population relatively sparse and backward. The area gained in the west was superior in most respects. It was not one of high fertility, except in Silesia, but was better cultivated and had an air of greater prosperity than the former territories of eastern Poland.

It was assumed at the end of the Second World War that the German population living within the territorial limits of the new Poland would be driven westward into Germany by the Poles. Many have fled or have been driven out, but it seems certain that a considerable number have remained.

Comparative statistics of prewar and postwar Poland show that Poland has lost in territory and population. The cultivated area is smaller by 22 per cent, though the yield of the more important crops has not been proportionately diminished.

	1937–1938	1949–1950
Area in square miles....	149,960	121,131
Population...........	34,775,000	24,976,926
Cultivated area in square miles.............	71,647	55,458
Yield of wheat in metric tons..............	2,172,000	1,781,000
Yield of rye in metric tons..............	7,235,000	6,759,000
Yield of oats in metric tons..............	2,657,000	2,333,000
Yield of potatoes in metric tons........	34,558,000	30,901,000
Production of coal in metric tons........	36,218,000	82,000,000 (1951)
Production of steel in metric tons........	1,441,000	1,579,000 (1947)

The Regions of Poland. Poland lies almost wholly in the north European Plain and continues eastward the physical divisions that we have met with in northern Germany. The northern half of the country is covered with deposits laid down during the Ice Age. A heavy clay covers much of the land. Hollows in its surface have filled with water, and in parts of Prussia (Preussen) lakes make up a considerable part of the surface. The soil is often heavy, and much of it is forested. Morainic ridges extend eastward from Germany and in Pomerania (Pommern) reach heights of over 600 feet. They are also of low fertility and often forested. Much of this region was formerly divided into the great estates of the Prussian and Polish nobility and was cultivated by peasants whose ancestors only a century ago were serfs on the estates of their lords. Parts have now been divided into holdings cultivated by a free peasantry, but this has not removed the conditions of poverty and the lack of equipment which have hampered the inhabitants in the past.

The river Vistula takes a twisting course through the region, following depressions left by the glacial streams at the end of the Ice Age (see page 225). It is a broad, navigable river, though not greatly used except to float timber down to the sea. Danzig (169,675) lies close to the mouth of the Vistula, and a few miles to the west is Gdynia, a port established by the Poles in the 1920's to avoid having to depend upon Danzig. Cities are few in this region. Most serve as markets for the countryside, and, as this is one of no great productivity, the towns themselves are small and poor. Bydgoszcz (Bromberg, 156,000), Toruń (Thorn), and Poznań (Posen, 291,500) are engaged in timber and engineering industries. Warsaw lies on the Vistula near the southern margin of this

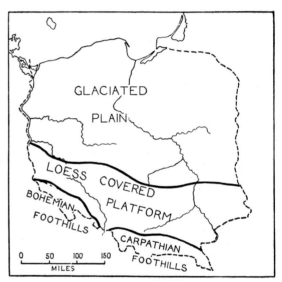

Fig. 153. Physical regions of the new Poland.

region. Before the Second World War, Warsaw was a city of about 1,300,000 people. It was attacked and partially destroyed in the fall of 1939. It was again the center of fighting as the Russians advanced westward in 1945. The city was then almost completely destroyed, and the heavy task of rebuilding has only recently been begun. Its present population is about 601,000.

South of this region of boulder clay and end moraine is one of gravels, which continues eastward from the heathlands of Germany. South again the land surface rises to a low platform; the glacial deposits become less extensive and then cease. Instead, a deposit of loess is spread over southern Poland. This region, so similar in relief to the north, is very much more fertile and productive. The peasantry is more

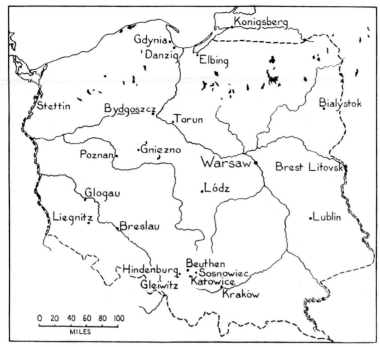

FIG. 154. The distribution of cities in Poland.

prosperous, and cities are larger and more numerous.

Toward the west is the province of Silesia (Schlesien), which Poland has recently acquired from Germany. It is drained by the Oder, part of whose lower course forms Poland's western frontier. On the Oder lies Breslau (Wrocław), formerly capital of Silesia and a large and impressive city of over a half a million people and many industries. Its population was reduced to a quarter of what it had been before the beginning of the war as the German population fled westward or was driven out by the Poles. The Germans are slowly being replaced by Poles. South and west of Breslau a number of small industrial cities lie along the foot of the Bohemian Mountains. Many carry on textile and metal industries, which were introduced centuries ago by German immigrants and depended originally on the water power which these hills provided. There is a small coal field in lower (or northern) Silesia. In Upper Silesia is, next to the Ruhr, the largest coal field in Europe.

The Upper Silesian industrial region is now united under Polish rule. The coal field was intensively developed earlier than that of the Ruhr. A number of mines were at work and the steam engine had been introduced for pumping by 1800. Iron smelting has been of importance

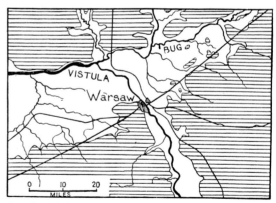

FIG. 155. The situation of Warsaw (Warszawa). The shaded area lies above 300 feet.

here since the eighteenth century, though it suffers today from the relatively poor quality of the local ores. The industrial region forms a compact and closely built area some 25 miles from west to east and 15 from north to south.

The chief urban centers are Gliwice (Gleiwitz, 113,500), Zabrze (Hindenburg, 128,000), and Bytom (Beuthen, 112,500) in the former German area of the coal field and Chorzow (131,000), Katowice (156,000), Sosnowiec, and Mysłowice in the Polish.

Polish Silesia. A general view of the coal mine, coking plant, and steel mill at Bobrek. (*Polish Photographic Agency.*)

A concealed coal field surrounds the area of exposed field and is worked toward the east, where the dip of the coal measures is less steep. The Upper Silesian region is an important exporter of coal. The German section of the field formerly supplied much of eastern Germany, and from her section Poland not only satisfied her domestic requirements but was able to export a considerable quantity through her Baltic Sea ports. Poland is now capable of producing about 75 million tons of coal a year and has a considerable surplus for export. The greatest demand lies in the Scandinavian countries and in western Europe; this is further

evidence that more extensive trade between eastern and western Europe would be greatly to the advantage of both. In addition to coal mining and steelworking, Upper Silesia has an important zinc-smelting industry, also based in origin on local supplies of ore. The steel production of Poland is today under 2 million tons annually.

Northward and eastward from the Upper Silesian industrial area the land rises to a limestone plateau, which forms a well-marked feature of the landscape. Northeast of this is the Lysogóry, a poor and forested region, where the older rocks come to the surface. It reaches little more than 2,000 feet in height but forms a sort of island rising above the rolling, loess-covered plateau of southern Poland.

North of the Lysogóry are a number of scattered industrial cities with varied manufactures. Łódź (592,000) is the largest and most important. It is a great center of the manufacture of

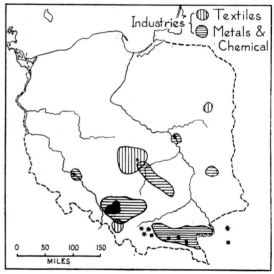

FIG. 156. Mineral resources and industrial regions of Poland.

cotton textiles, established here in the nineteenth century, when Łódź lay in Russia and the huge market of the empire of the Tsars seemed to be open for it. Other kinds of textiles are made at Częstochowa (115,000), which has also been developed as a center of the iron and

The Tatra Mountains, on the borders of Poland and Slovakia. The mountains have been deeply etched by ice and are characteristically alpine. (*Polish Photographic Agency.*)

steel industry. Częstochowa was formerly a famous place of Catholic pilgrimage.

East of the Lysogóry the valley of the upper Vistula and that of its tributary, the San, form a kind of triangle resting upon the Carpathian Mountains. At the southwestern corner is the city of Cracow (Kraków, 347,000), one of the oldest cities and once the capital of Poland. It lies to the east of a gap between the Lysogóry and the Carpathians. In some respects its situation resembles that of Vienna; it also served as a fortress guarding the approaches to western Europe from the east and on one occasion held out against the attack of the Turks. It has not grown into a great industrial city, and its present importance is rather as a business, commercial, artistic, and educational center, near but not in the industrial region.

At the southeastern corner is the city of Przemyśl. Along the south, close to the foothills of the Carpathians, are small reserves of petroleum, of some importance to Poland though of no significance for Europe as a whole. There are also immense reserves of common salt, which is mined at Wieliczka. Between the two wars the Poles had planned an industrialization of this region, but little progress had been made before the invasions of 1939. Mention should be made of the city of Lwów (Lvov, Lemberg) because, though at present outside the limits of the Polish state, it has played an important role in Polish history and is in most respects Polish. It lies in the open loess belt between the Carpathian Mountains to the south and the Pripyat marshes to the north. It was militarily an outpost to Cracow, though today it has fallen into the hands of the Russians. On the northern edge of the platform of southern Poland is the manufacturing city of Lublin (102,000).

Only a small fraction of Poland is mountainous—a narrow strip along the southern borders of the country. To the west, where Poland abuts against the Bohemian Massif, are the Sudetes. These mountains are broken up and can be crossed without difficulty, though they reach heights of over 5,000 feet in the Krkonoše hory (Riesengebirge or Giant Mountains). A number of towns are engaged in the textile industry, and there are sources of hydroelectric power as well as small coal deposits.

The continuity of the mountain border is broken by the so-called Moravian Gap (page 256), which separates Bohemia from the Carpathian Mountains. To the east, the Carpathians rise steeply from the plain. They are high and snow-capped, and in the Tatra, which lie on the borders of Poland and Slovakia, they are as grand and rugged as anywhere in the Alps. Poland obtains water power from these mountains, but life within them is rough and primitive, except at the few mountain resorts such as Zakopane.

Poland's Economic Development. Both Poland and eastern Germany had formerly been characterized by the great number of large estates, owned frequently by absentee landowners, managed by bailiffs, and cultivated by a poor tenantry. After the First World War many of these estates were broken up into small holdings and distributed to the cultivators, but the changes were insufficient to alter fundamentally the basic pattern of land tenure. The new Poland has carried this movement very much further, and the Communist regime showed no reluctance to expropriate the possessions of the former aristocracy and of the wealthier peasants. Probably by now the estates and larger farm holdings have been entirely broken up and distributed among the landless peasants and those who possessed only minute holdings. It does not appear that collective farms of the kind which have become common in Russia are yet at all numerous in Poland. The Poles are at present preoccupied with rebuilding their devastated country and do not appear to be willing to attempt experiments in collectivization that might arouse the hostility of conservative and Catholic peasantry. Polish agriculture has, however, been extensively mechanized in recent years. The number of farm tractors increased tenfold between 1938 and 1949, and there are now about 27,000 in use. Poland has also been faced with the task of recolonizing the newly acquired lands in the west. It appears that the German population has been largely, if not wholly, driven out and

their vacant lands colonized by the dispossessed Polish peasantry from the lost eastern provinces, but there is an over-all shortage of labor.

Rye and potatoes have long been the principal crops of Poland, and they are grown abundantly in the newly acquired German lands. Wheat and oats are important only in the south, where wheat does well in the light loess soils of the southern platform of Poland. Oats as well as rye are grown in the mountainous areas of the south. Sugar beet is grown in Silesia, Poznań, and Pomerania. Hemp and flax are commercial crops in parts of the northern plain.

The possession of a large number of farm animals is usually an indication of a high level of human welfare. Farm stock was not abundant in the old Poland, and the Polish government is today planning to increase its number very greatly. Cattle were relatively numerous in Poznań and Pomerania, areas that were German before 1919, and on some of the better lands of southern Poland. Pigs were numerous in the western provinces, where they were part of a dairy-cattle economy. Sheep were relatively abundant in the east.

At present about 22 per cent of the area of Poland is under forest, and the lumber industry is of great importance. Much of the forest is broad-leaved deciduous trees, but there are large areas of coniferous forest in the Carpathian Mountains in the extreme south and over the morainic country in the northern part of Poland. Much of the coniferous woodland has been planted in recent years, and the greater part of Poland's lumber production is softwood.

Rural settlement in general resembles that of eastern Germany. Compact, nucleated villages are met with most frequently in the southern area of fertile, rolling, open country. But over much of northern Poland the street or forest village (see Fig. 130) is the most common. A scattered settlement pattern, however, is found in the lake-studded regions of heavy boulder-clay soil in the former territory of East Prussia and neighboring areas of Poland.

The population of Poland in 1950 was 24,-976,926. On the eve of the Second World War it was over 34,500,000. Many Poles now live under direct Russian rule in the ceded territories east of the new boundary. Large numbers, including a high proportion of the Jewish population, were eliminated during the war. Before the war the birth rate of the Poles was high. The population rose from about 27,193,000 in 1921 to 34,534,000 in 1938, the sharpest rise of any European country. But at present Poland has a labor shortage, which hinders industrial development and probably contributes to the collectivization of Polish farms.

Before the Second World War about 10 per cent of the population of Poland had been Jews. Poland had then contained a large part of the "Pale," the area within which the Jewish population of Russia had been compelled to live. Here they dwelled in the ghetto quarters of the cities, often in overcrowded and unsanitary conditions and limited by custom or law to only a narrow range of occupations. The cities of Łódź, Warsaw, Lwów, and Vilna contained the largest Jewish settlements, but in some smaller towns of eastern Poland the Jews amounted to a far greater proportion of the population. In Pinsk, for example, they made up about 75 per cent of the city's total population. A large part of this Jewish population perished during the years 1939 to 1945, and a part of those who have survived have migrated from Poland.

The shift in the geographical boundaries of Poland has excluded from the new state most if not all the Ukrainian people of the southeast, the Lithuanians of the northeast, and the White Russians of the Pripyat (Pripet) region. Some of these peoples had before 1939 constituted difficult and sometimes irreconcilable minorities within the Polish state. But these eastern territories included also the cities of Lwów (Lemberg) and Vilna (Wilno). They had been predominantly Polish and Jewish in population, though the surrounding countryside had been Ukrainian and Lithuanian, respectively. They were both important in the national consciousness of the Poles, being regarded as bastions of their Western civilization against peoples and cultures of the East.

Despite the very large proportion of the population that is engaged in agriculture and living in rural areas—it was about 75 per cent before the Second World War—Poland has now a considerable number of large cities. Warsaw was before the war a city of over a million people, and there are in all 16 cities of over 100,000, with together a population of $3\frac{1}{2}$ million. This should be compared with Czechoslovakia, which has only 5 cities of this size. Most of Poland's industries are gathered into a group of large cities; much of Czechoslovakia's are scattered over a large number of cities of small or medium size.

Most important of the cities in the newly occupied German provinces are Stettin (Szczecin), Głogów (Glogau), and Breslau (Wrocław). The first, lying on the left bank of the lower Oder, was formerly one of the most important ports of the German Baltic coast. Breslau, capital of Silesia, is now the fourth largest city in Poland, an important commercial city, with engineering and textile industries.

Poland is today, potentially at least, a well-balanced though still only partially developed country. Its coal production is second only to that of Great Britain and Germany among European countries. In the Carpathian foothills are small reserves of petroleum, though production is less than one million tons. Lead and zinc have been worked in Silesia; iron ore in the provinces of Łódź and Kielce; salt at Wieliczka. There are considerable reserves of lignite, and large quantities of timber are found in most parts of Poland.

Poland is again faced with the problem of welding into a single political unit different territories with differing histories and traditions: the provinces of eastern Germany and the central and western parts of prewar Poland. Though her resources are now somewhat greater, the task is more difficult than in 1919, because Poland was devastated to a far greater degree during the Second World War than she was during the First. Some cities, including the capital, have been largely destroyed, and large areas were left almost unpopulated. Furthermore, Poland is today dominated by the military strength of Russia, which in 1919 was weak and torn by civil war. Owing to this dependence on Russia, Poland cannot borrow capital from the Western Powers and from the United States, the only countries capable of making advances and supplying equipment on a large scale for Poland's recovery and development. Poland is prevented from accepting the aid which America offered in the Marshall program. Furthermore, political barriers are raised to Poland's trade with the West, which under present conditions is her most natural and obvious trading partner.

BIBLIOGRAPHY

"Agrarian Problems from the Baltic to the Aegean," Royal Institute of International Affairs, London, 1945.

Baginski, H., "Poland and the Baltic," London, 1942.

Boyd, Louise A., The Marshes of Pinsk, G.R., XXVI, 1936, 376–395.

———, "Polish Countrysides," American Geographical Society, New York, 1937.

Cahnman, Werner J., Frontiers between East and West in Europe, G.R., XXXIX, 1949, 605–624.

"Conference on Rural Life: Poland," League of Nations, Geneva, 1939.

Conzen, G., East Prussia, G., XXX, 1945, 1–10.

Edwards, K. C., N. V. Scarfe, and A. E. Moodie, The Novy Targ Basin of the Polish Tatra: Its Human Geography, with Special Reference to the Bukowina District, S.G.M., LI, 1935, 215–227.

Frankel, H., "Poland," London, 1946.

Garnett, Alice, The Nowy Targ Basin: The Morphological Background to Its Human Geography, S.G.M., LI, 1935, 151–161.

Gorecki, R., "Poland and Her Economic Development," London, 1935.

Hartshorne, R., "The Upper Silesian Industrial District," G.R., XXIV, 1934, 423–438.

Kish, George, "Rural Problems of Central and Southeastern Europe," G.R., XXXV, 1945, 286–290.

Konovalov, Serge (ed.), "Russo-Polish Relations," London, 1945.

Machray, R., "The Problem of Upper Silesia," London, 1945.

Moore, Wilbert E., "The Economic Demography of Eastern and Southern Europe," League of Nations, Geneva, 1945.

Morant, G. M., "The Races of Central Europe," London, 1939.

Morrow, I. F. D., "The Peace Settlement in the German-Polish Borderland," Oxford, 1936.

Rose, W. J., "Poland," New York, 1939.

Russell, Sir John, Reconstruction and Development in Eastern Poland, G.J., XCVIII, 1941, 273–290.

Schmidt, Bernadotte E., "Poland," United Nations Series, San Francisco, 1945.

Steers, Mrs. J. A., The Artisan Element in the Slav Countries, G.J., CIII, 1944, 101–119.

Van Cleef, Eugene, Danzig and Gdynia, G.R., XXIII, 1933, 101–107.

———, East Baltic Ports and Boundaries, G.R., XXXV, 1945, 257–272.

Wanklyn, H. G., "The Eastern Marchlands of Europe," London, 1941.

———, "Geographical Aspects of Jewish Settlement, East of Germany," G.J., XCV, 1940, 175–190.

Postwar material on Poland is very scanty. The country is covered by the reports of the Economic Commission for Europe and statistics of population and production are given in the United Nations publications (see pages 52 to 54), but Poland was not in receipt of Marshall Aid and the voluminous reports of the Organization for European Economic Cooperation make no contribution to the geography of the country. Valuable material is given on the newly acquired territory in the west in:

"Agriculture and Forestry in East Oderland," Hannover, 1947. (This book is accompanied by a very beautifully printed agricultural atlas.)

"Atlas ziem odzyskanych" (Atlas, of the recovered territories of Poland), 2d ed., Warsaw, 1947.

These may be regarded as supplements to "Rzeczpospolita Polska, Atlas statystyczny" (Statistical Atlas of the Polish Republic), Warsaw, 1930.

A bibliography of geographical writings on Poland is Bruno Plaetschke, Das geographische Schriftum über Polen, 1929–1936, Geographisches Jahrbuch, LI, 1936, 313–357.

CHAPTER 20: *Czechoslovakia*

The state of Czechoslovakia first made its appearance on the map of Europe in 1918. Its territory embraced, as its name indicates, the lands of two small but distinctive peoples, the Czechs and Slovaks. Subsequently the Ruthene people living in the central Carpathians were added. The boundaries of the new state in the west were, in the main, those of the "historic kingdom" of Bohemia (Čechy). This involved the inclusion of about 3,123,500 Germans, who lived chiefly in the hilly area around the western margin of Czechoslovakia. The boundaries as ultimately delimited included also small numbers of Poles and Magyars. Unlike Poland, Czechoslovakia has been, territorially at least, comparatively stable. If wartime changes of frontier are excluded, Czechoslovakia is today very much the same as she was 30 years ago. Only the small Ruthene territory has been lost to the U.S.S.R.

Czechoslovakia is built of three distinct physical units. In the west is the diamond-shaped mass of Bohemia, consisting of ancient, hard rocks, with a ring of mountains and an interior depression drained by the Elbe. To the east is the plain of Moravia (Morava), and east of this again are the Carpathian Mountains which compose Slovakia (Slovensko).

Bohemia. Bohemia is a region only about 212 miles from west to east and 175 from north to south. On most sides the mountains which form its rim rise steeply from the plain or plateau of the interior. In places they attain considerable heights and include some of the highest mountains north of the Alps. The surrounding hills are least conspicuous on the southeast, where the plateau of southern Bohemia rises only to a rounded upland area, nowhere mountainous and in all parts easy to cross. On other sides, however, the mountains present serious barriers to movement. They are highest and most difficult to cross on the southwest, where the Šumava and Český les (Bohemian Forest, Bohmerwald) separate the Czech lands from southern Germany.

On the northwest is the Krušné hory (Erz Gebirge or Ore Mountains). These mountains rise gently on the German side from the plains

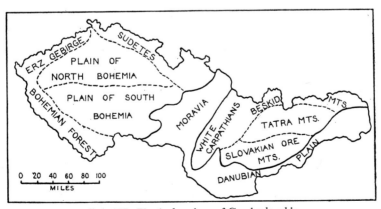

FIG. 157. Physical regions of Czechoslovakia.

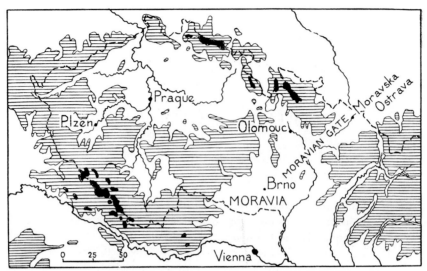

FIG. 158. Bohemia and Moravia.

of Saxony and present their steep face toward the interior of Bohemia. The Ore Mountains derive their name and also their former importance from their wealth of minerals. Ores, particularly of the nonferrous metals, have been found here in quantity. Mining is no longer of great importance today, though the region contains one of the very few occurrences in Europe of the mineral uranium. This is said now to be intensively worked.

In the north of Bohemia the river Elbe, which, with its tributaries, drains the whole of the country, breaks through the Ore Mountains by a defile below the town of Ústí (Aussig, 56,500)[1] and enters Germany. Along the northeast the separate ranges of the Sudetes Mountains form the border with Poland (page 249). The mountains are here less continuous than on other sides. The highest range is the Krkonoše hory (Riesengebirge or Giant Mountains). They contain many small, partially enclosed basins. Some of these contain deposits of coal, either black or brown (lignite), and most can offer the attraction of water power. Many industries, especially the manufacture of glass and textiles, have been established. Liberec (Reichenberg, 53,000) and Jablonec (Gablonz) are the largest of the many small cities of this region.

[1] The population is given of all cities of more than 50,000 inhabitants.

Most of this mountain rim of Bohemia was colonized during and after the Middle Ages by Germans, who established here their industrial and mining activities. The German settlers were in origin craftsmen rather than agriculturalists, settling among and doubtless exploiting a more primitive and agrarian Czech people. Considerable areas were wholly Germanized, and leadership in industrial matters formerly went naturally to the Germans. Until 1919 Bohemia, along with other parts of the Czechoslovak state, was part of the Austro-Hungarian Empire. The Germans of Bohemia, or Sudeten Germans as they were called from the Sudetes Mountains, were thus German subjects of an Austrian emperor. In 1919 they became members of a predominantly Slav state. It was said that the new state was willing to accept the 3,123,500 Germans in order to obtain the strategic advantage of the mountain frontier. President Masaryk, the first president of the new republic, believed that, given a long enough period of time—he asked for 40 years—the Germans could be assimilated and made into loyal subjects. He had not reckoned with the early rise of aggressive nationalism in Germany. In 1938, at the Munich Settlement, Germany annexed the areas in which most of the Sudeten Germans were settled but took at the same time about a million Czechs. The land in 1945 re-

Fig. 159. Diagrammatic sketch of Bohemia. D, Dresden; L, Leipzig; P, Prague; V, Vienna.

turned to Czechoslovakia, and a large proportion of the Germans was driven out and forced to migrate to Germany. The German penetration of Bohemia had been deepest on the northwest and northeast, where the mountains were at the same time more accessible and their resources greater.

The Bohemian Plain, which lies within the barrier of hills, is far from being a level or uniform region. The northern part, drained by the Elbe (Labe) and the Ohře, is a plain broken by many ridges and isolated hills. In the northwest, lying parallel with the Krušné hory, is a ridge of hills, partly volcanic in origin, where hot springs occur. These have earned a wide reputation for their medicinal qualities and have given rise to spas and health resorts such as Karlovy Vary (Karlsbad), Jáchymov (Sankt Joachimsthal), and Mariánské Lázně (Marienbad). There are several industrial towns engaged in engineering, textile manufacture, woodworking, and ceramic industries.

The plain is in reality a region of low rolling hills and broad fertile valleys. In places a dusting of loess adds to the fertility. The rougher land is wooded, but much of the area is fertile and well cultivated.

The climate is one of cold winters, with an average temperature in January of under 30°; summers are warm and bright, though rainfall is adequate for all agricultural purposes. The valley of the Elbe is the most valuable agricultural land in Bohemia. Wheat and sugar beet are important crops. Fruit is grown, and hops are raised to flavor the beer for which Pilsen is famous.

A particular resource of this region is lignite, here obtained from vast open workings. Some of it is compressed into briquettes and distributed over Bohemia, some is burned to generate electric power, and much of it is used as a basis for the manufacture of synthetic oil.

Southern Bohemia lies appreciably higher, and the rivers are incised in valleys that are often deep and narrow. The rise in level makes a considerable difference in the climate, which is here colder in winter and cooler in summer. Rye rather than wheat is grown; potatoes and pastoralism are more important than on the lower ground.

Prague (Praha, Prag, 922,500) lies close to the junction of these two regions of Bohemia, on both banks of the Vltava (Moldau), a tributary of the Elbe. High above the east bank of the river stands the ancient fortress, the Hradčany, and the cathedral of Saint Vitus. The old city lies on the slope below, and the newer but still essentially medieval city over the lower land on both banks of the river. Prague was in the Middle Ages a focus of routes which radiated over Bohemia and reached to Germany and Poland. Its central position gave it an advantage as capital of the Czech state; it has developed varied industries and is particularly occupied in engineering and in the manufacture of clothing and other consumers' goods.

A few miles west of Prague is the small coal field of Kladno, where an iron and steel indus-

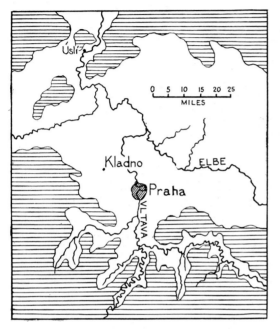

FIG. 160. The situation of Prague (Praha).

try has been developed. Plzeň (Pilsen, 118,000), southwest of Prague, is the site of the Skoda works, which manufactures steel and armaments. This industry was based originally on iron ore from the nearby Brdy Hills and the

local beds of coal. The former is no longer worked, and the coal field is almost exhausted, but the industry, one of the most important producers of high-quality steel in Europe, continues to operate on the basis of imported materials.

In the Elbe Valley to the east of Prague are a number of small industrial towns, which have increased greatly in importance in recent years. Many new industries have been located here. Largest of these cities is Hradec Králové (Königgrätz, 51,500).

Moravia. Moravia is very largely the basin of the Morava, tributary of the Danube. It is an area of low or undulating country which joins the plains of Silesia with those of the Danube. On the west, the land slopes gently to the hills of Bohemia; to the east the rugged Carpathians rise more sharply. The region narrows toward the northeast and on this side is only a few miles wide. The Moravian "Gate" provides one of the easiest and most important routeways between the north European Plain and the Danube Valley and is of great commercial and strategic importance.

The lower parts of Moravia form good, rich farmland, similar to the plain of northern Bohemia. There are many market and industrial towns, including Olomouc (Olmütz, 58,500) and Brno (Brünn, 273,000), where textiles are made and industries associated with the surrounding agricultural land are carried on. At Zlin the Bat'a boot and shoe factory was established to produce cheap and serviceable

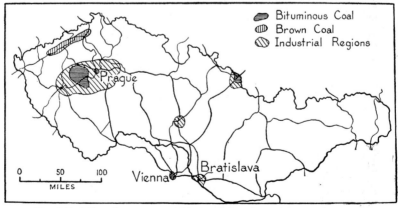

FIG. 161. Mineral resources and industrial regions of Czechoslovakia.

Rural landscape in Slovakia. The fields consist of many strips in "open" fields of immense size. The village consists of timber houses with steep-pitched roofs of wooden shingles. (*Courtesy of Ewing Galloway.*)

footwear for the millions of peasants of the Danubian lands.

In the extreme north of Moravia is a coal field, associated with though geologically distinct from the coal basin of Upper Silesia. On it have grown up the industrial cities of Moravská Ostrava (Märisch Ostrau, 181,000) and Vítkovice, with their blast furnaces and steelworks. Czechoslovakia's total production of coal was, in 1950, about 18 million tons. Steel production was about 3 million tons.

Slovakia. The Carpathian Mountains are a continuation of the Alps. Fingers of hill reach northeast from the Alps of Austria, are interrupted by the Danube, and then continue as the Little Carpathians (Malé Karpaty), getting higher and broader as they stretch northeastward. Like the Alps, the Carpathians consist of a series of west-to-east ranges, separated from one another by wide valleys. On the north are the Beskids (Bezkydy), which continue into Poland. These consist of short, dissected ridges, around which movement is not difficult. To the south are the High Tatra Mountains, the highest in the whole range and the only area within which truly alpine land forms have been produced. The Low Tatra lies to the south of the High, separated from it by the basin of Liptov. Both the Low Tatra and the Slovakian Ore Mountains, which lie yet further to the south, resemble the gentler topography of the Beskids but are nonetheless sparsely populated. They were formerly important for the minerals that were obtained here, and a number of Germans settled here and in the nearby Spiš (Zips) area. These mountains are today an important source of timber.

The valleys of the Carpathians support a sparse population of poor peasants. Life is hard. Winters are long and severe and greatly restrict crop farming. Hardy crops of oats and rye are grown, but pastoral farming is the most important. Settlements consist of small clusters of rude wooden houses. The gardens, the brightly colored walls, and the touches of artistry that characterize the villages in the prosperous Czech lands are absent from the Carpathians. The whole region is remote from

Bratislava. The city lies on the northern bank of the Danube and is overlooked by the ruins of a former Hungarian royal palace. The Danube is much used by barges. (*Courtesy of Ewing Galloway.*)

the main stream of the state's economic life and development.

The Carpathians are drained by the Váh, Hron, Hernad, and other streams which flow southward toward the Hungarian Plain. As the valleys widen toward the plain, the basis of economic life changes. The quality of the soil improves, the climate is less inclement, crop husbandry becomes more important, and the Slovak peasant gives way to the Magyar or Hungarian. The Magyar is, in general, an inhabitant of the plain as the Slovak is of the hills, though there are Slovak communities also in the plain. The former is in the main an agriculturalist; the latter, a pastoralist or lumberman who practices only subsidiary agriculture. The two are complementary, and they exchange their produce in the many small market towns that lie along the edge of the plain. A town lies opposite the opening of all except the smallest of the valleys; Nitra (Neutra) and Košice (Kassa, 58,000) are among the largest. The state of Czechoslovakia incorporated the margin of the Hungarian Plain partly to

secure possession of these market centers on which was focused the life of the mountain regions, partly to incorporate the Slovak communities in the new state, and partly to establish a defensible boundary along the rivers Danube and Ipel. This involved, however, the inclusion in the new state of over half a million Magyars. The Magyar-settled territory was occupied by Hungary in 1938 but returned to Czechoslovakia in 1945.

The only city of significance in this region is Bratislava (Pressburg, Pozsony, 172,500), lying upon the northern bank of the Danube about 40 miles downstream from Vienna. Its situation is a strong one. It lies on a spur of the Little Carpathians and served as a fortress for the defense of the upper Danube Valley from invaders from the east. It is a river port of some importance, an industrial center engaged in working up the produce of its agricultural hinterland, and it is the capital of Slovakia.

The Political Problem of Czechoslovakia. The most serious internal problem of the state of Czechoslovakia has been created by the variety of peoples within it. Greatest of these in number and in political importance have been the Czechs, who inhabit Bohemia and Moravia. It was around the Czech people that the new state was built, and the Czechs provided much of the political leadership. By contrast the Slovaks are, in the main, mountain dwellers of the Carpathians. In language and culture they resemble the Czechs, but they are to a greater degree a rural people. They lack the political experience and maturity of the Czechs, and they have tended to resent the latters' stronger position in administration and public service. It was not, however, until 1938 that the Slovak autonomous movement made much headway. At present there are about 8,000,000 Czechs and 2,800,000 Slovaks in Czechoslovakia.[1]

In addition to these two peoples, the Czech state formerly included about 3,250,000 Sudeten Germans, who inhabited the borders of Bohemia. They were on the whole somewhat more urbanized and industrialized than the Czechs, controlling much of the textile, glass, and chemical industries. Their expulsion is a serious loss to the internal economy of Czechoslovakia and has resulted in a lack of skilled labor. Only a small number, estimated at about 300,000 Germans, have been allowed to remain.

The Ruthenes formed only a small group of about half a million, inhabiting the mountains to the east of Slovakia. They were less mature than the Slovaks and are said to have been more than 50 per cent illiterate in 1921, as against 15 per cent in Slovakia. They were incorporated into Hungary in 1939 and after 1945 were added to Russia. They are closely related to the people of the Ukraine. The Hungarian or Magyar minority, however, remains. These people live, along with Slovak groups, in the plain of southern Slovakia. Plans to remove them to Hungary in exchange for the yet smaller group of Slovaks in Hungary have not been implemented. The Polish minority is least in number and smallest in political importance. It is found in the industrial region of northern Moravia, close to the Polish boundary.

[1] These figures are only approximate; there has been no postwar census.

The fundamental difference is that between the Czechs and Slovaks. These two related peoples differ in ways that have just been mentioned and did not always work harmoniously together in the new state. The growth of a Slovak independence movement was encouraged by Germany, which sought in this way to weaken the Czechoslovak state. In 1938 it secured a limited autonomy for Slovakia, and in the next year, under German patronage, a Slovak state came into existence. Slovakia is no longer independent, but the rift that separates Slovak from Czech is not completely healed, though both peoples fully realize the need for a single Czechoslovak state.

Economic Development. Czechoslovakia has a more balanced economic development than its neighbors to the north and south. Approximately 38 per cent of the employed population is engaged in agriculture, and 37 per cent in manufacturing industries. The German-speaking population had had a greater proportion of their number engaged in manufacturing than the Czechs themselves. The latter were much more agricultural in their pursuits. The expulsion of the Germans has had the effect of lowering the total of these engaged in manufacturing and of bringing about some transfer of the Czechs from agriculture to industry.

Agriculture in Czechoslovakia is on the basis of small peasant holdings. In the land reform which followed the First World War the large estates were broken up and the arable acreage of holdings was restricted to 250 hectares (about 625 acres). In 1948, the limit was reduced to 50 hectares (125 acres), but most farm holdings are a good deal smaller than this.

Standards of agriculture decline from west to east. In the plain of Bohemia and Moravia the villages have an air of prosperity and well-being. The open fields with cultivation strips are such as can be met with in Saxony or Silesia. This appearance of prosperity is not so conspicuous in the mountain fringe of Bohemia, and in Slovakia it is even less noticeable. Agriculture is also more primitive in the east than in the west. Fragmentation of holdings is greater, farm equipment and the use of fertilizers are less, and the range of crops grown is more restricted. This impoverishment of agriculture toward the east is only in part to be attributed to the harsher physical environment of the Carpathian Mountains. It derives also from the lower cultural level and former social structure, with large estates and absentee landlords, of these regions.

The range of crops grown is broadly similar to that in central and south Germany. Mixed farming is general. Three regions where crop farming stands out as of exceptional importance are the Elbe Valley in Bohemia, the "Golden Belt" as it is called; the Moravian Plain; and the borders of the Hungarian Plain. Elsewhere crop husbandry is relatively less important and animals more so. In Slovakia the altitude and greater severity of the climate restrict the range of crops, and much of the agriculture is on a subsistence basis. Rye is here the most important cereal crop, oats and potatoes are grown, and sheep rearing is carried on on a large scale. Much of Slovakia is forested, the area of agricultural land is restricted, and crop yields are small.

Before the First World War the Czech lands developed as the foremost center of manufacturing industries within the Austro-Hungarian Empire. For this they had peculiar advantages. Bohemia and Moravia had small but important coal fields, and the occurrence of minerals had given an early impetus to the smelting industries. The large population of the Austro-Hungarian Empire offered a wide market. In 1919, the independent republic of Czechoslovakia found its industries cut off from markets which they had grown up to serve. Czechoslovakia adjusted itself to these new conditions by exporting considerable quantities of cotton textiles, light metal goods, paper, pottery, and glass, especially to western Europe. After the German occupation of the Czech lands in 1939, the Germans located certain strategic industries in Czechoslovakia, whose position in central Europe offered it some protection from air attack. Czechoslovakia's industrial capacity is today considerably above that of 1938.

Czechoslovakia is a country of small towns.

There is no extensive and closely built industrial region, and manufacturing industries are carried on in small and scattered units of production (see page 251). Industries are located mainly in the hills of northwestern and northeastern Bohemia, in Prague and the region to the west of it, and in the Moravian Plain. Great dependence is placed upon brown coal, which is obtained from vast open cuts in northern Bohemia. This not only is compressed into briquettes and sold as fuel but is also the basis of the electric-power industry. A number of small centers, including Karlovy Vary, Chomutov, Most, Teplice, and Ústí, carry on a variety of industries, of which the manufacture of textiles, of chinaware and glass, and of machinery is the most important. East of the Elbe Valley, Liberec and Jablonec, in valleys of the Giant Mountains, make cotton cloth and glassware.

Between Prague and Pilsen is a small region of heavy industries. The local resources in iron ore and coal are now inadequate to supply the industries to which they have given rise, and ore and metallurgical coke are imported into the area. Czechoslovakia is now heavily dependent on Swedish iron ore. Pilsen and Kladno are centers of the iron-smelting and steel-manufacturing industries. Prague is also important for its engineering industries and adds to these the manufacture of textiles, clothing, chinaware, and chemicals. In southern Bohemia there are few towns and manufacturing industries are rare.

Moravia contains the largest and most important coal field in Czechoslovakia, which is in reality a part of the coal basin of Upper Silesia. This region produces the greater part of Czechoslovakia's output of coal but is nevertheless much smaller than its Silesian counterpart. The Czechoslovak industries are concentrated in and around Moravská Ostrava and Karvinná. The iron-smelting industry is carried on at Vítkovice (Witkovitz) and Třinec. Brno has more varied industries, which include textile manufacture as well as mechanical engineering.

The volume of steel production approximates closely that of Luxembourg, about 3,011,000 tons annually. Total bituminous coal production is about 17,750,000 tons, and lignite about 23,500,000 tons.

The problem of transportation has been a serious one in Czechoslovakia. In the days of the Austro-Hungarian Empire, the territory was served by railway systems which radiated from the Danubian towns of Bratislava and Budapest. It was the task of the Czechoslovak government to transform these separate sections of line into an integrated system. The topography was not helpful, and although the Czech lands of the west developed adequate rail communications, movement remained difficult in Slovakia, where improved transportation was most necessary in order to weld it into the new state.

Czechoslovakia faced more serious internal problems than most other states of central or eastern Europe. To these must be added the fact that from its birth until 1945 the Czech state was partially enclosed by German territory. The state's economic well-being and even its existence were at the mercy of the greater military strength of Germany. In spite of these difficulties, Czechoslovakia became by far the most successful of the democratic countries of central Europe and had gone far to solve its internal problems when the country was disrupted by Germany in 1938 and 1939. Today, Russia has replaced Germany, holding Czechoslovakia in a grip quite as strong as that exercised by the Germans. Czechoslovakia lies between east and west in Europe.

Czechoslovakia's population is too small and her resources inadequate to be sure of maintaining her independence. She relied upon a European balance of power. Associating herself with Romania and Yugoslavia (the Little Entente) and with France, she tried to offset the great strength of Germany. She was also a steadfast supporter of the League of Nations. The balance of power in central Europe is now gravely upset. The military strength of Russia is at present dominant, and the development of an alliance of Western Powers aimed at restoring the political balance and at mutual protection against Russia came too late to save Czechoslovakia from Russian domination and control.

BIBLIOGRAPHY

Ancel, J., "Manuel géographique de politique européenne," Vol. I, Paris, 1936.

"Atlas Republiky československé" (Atlas of the Czechoslovak Republic), Prague, 1935.

Basch, Antonín, "The Danube Basin and the German Economic Sphere," London, 1944.

Bielogurskas, O., and D. L. Glickman, Reconstruction in Czechoslovakia, *Economic Review of Food and Agriculture*, Food and Agriculture Organization of the United Nations, I, 1948, 12–36.

Macartney, C. A., "Hungary and Her Successors," Oxford, 1937.

Morant, G. M., "The Races of Central Europe," London, 1939.

Moscheles, Julie, The Demographic, Social and Economic Regions of Greater Prague, *G.R.*, XXVII, 1937, 414–429.

———, Natural Regions of Czechoslovakia, *G.R.*, XIV, 1924, 561–575.

Partsch, J., "Central Europe," London, 1903.

Setson-Watson, R. W., "A History of the Czechs and Slovaks," London, 1943.

Shute, John, Czechoslovakia's Territorial and Population Changes, *E.G.*, XXIV, 1948, 35–44.

Steed, Henry Wickham, "The Hapsburg Monarchy," London, 1913.

Steers, J. A., The Middle People: Resettlement in Czechoslovakia, *G.J.*, CXII, 1949, 28–42.

Thompson, S. Harrison, "Czechoslovakia in European History," Princeton, N.J., 1943.

Wanklyn, H. G. (Mrs. J. A. Steers), "The Eastern Marchlands of Europe," London, 1941.

———, "Czechoslovakia. A Geographical and Historical Study," London, 1952.

Wiskemann, E., "Czechs and Germans," Oxford, 1938.

Young, E. P., "Czechoslovakia," London, 1938.

An excellent short bibliography of books on Czechoslovakia, "What to Read about Czechoslovakia," was compiled by Janko Suhaj and published in London, 1943. Current United Nations publications contain statistical and other data, but detailed reports, such as have been prepared on West European countries, have not been made on Czechoslovakia.

A bibliography of geographical works on Czechoslovakia is Hermann, Mikula, Tschechoslowakei, 1912–1927, *Geographisches Jahrbuch*, XLIII, 1928, 111–134.

CHAPTER 21: *Austria*

Austria grew up in the Middle Ages as a province of Germany. It was an easterly outpost, the *Ostmark* or eastern March, whose purpose it was to protect Germany and western Europe from invasion by way of the Danube Valley. For many centuries Austria as a whole and its capital Vienna (Wien) in particular were the bastions of Western civilization. We cannot say that in this their role has yet been terminated. The Turks, who from the fourteenth century onward spread over southeastern Europe, on more than one occasion reached and besieged the city of Vienna. After their final repulse in 1683, the Austrian forces followed them in their retreat across the Hungarian Plain. In this way the Austrians built up an empire which stretched down the Danube Valley and embraced not only Hungary but parts of present-day Romania and Yugoslavia. In the sixteenth century the Hapsburgs, dukes of Austria, became kings of Bohemia and subsequently made the Bohemian Crown hereditary in their family. Bohemia was thus absorbed into the Austrian lands. Austrian

occupation of Hungary brought with it control over the Slovak people of the Carpathians. Even parts of southern Poland were added to the Austrian Empire in the eighteenth century.

This great empire broke up in 1918, and from its fragments the so-called "Succession States" were formed. Austria was itself reduced to a small territory about the size of Maine. Most of its area is mountainous and of little agricultural value. Its area of 32,375 square miles now contains about 7 million inhabitants. The former empire of Austria-Hungary had contained at the time of its dissolution about 54 million.

Austria extends from the eastern border of Switzerland to the Hungarian Plain, a distance of 400 miles. At most the country is 160 miles from north to south. Its most westerly province, Vorarlberg, lies in the drainage basin of the Rhine. The Danube flows through northern Austria, and all parts except the extreme west of the country are drained by the Danube or its tributaries. Much of the southern boundary of

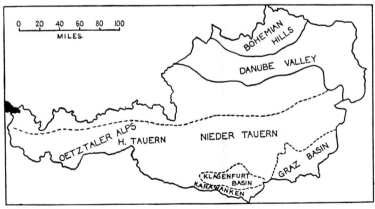

Fig. 162. Physical regions of Austria.

262

Alpine meadows in the Austrian Alps near Salzburg. (*Austrian State Tourist Bureau.*)

Austria follows the divide between the north-ward-flowing drainage of the Rhine and the Danube and the drainage of the Italian Po.

Austria is now inhabited almost entirely by people of German speech, the only exception being the small group of Slovenes, one of the Yugoslav peoples, who inhabit the southernmost part of the province of Carinthia (Kärnten). Austria is essentially a rural and agricultural country, despite the fact that almost a third of its present population lives in the capital city of Vienna.

Vienna grew to be a city of over a million and a half when it was the capital city, the business and commercial center, and the focus of transport for the large Danubian empire of Austria. The breakup of this empire left Vienna with the outward manifestations of a great capital but without its functions. The problem of Vienna, of the "big head on little shoulders," has been one of the most serious in Austria since 1918. A partial solution might have been the absorption of Austria into Germany, but this was forbidden by the terms of the Treaty of

Saint-Germain of 1920 between Austria and the Allied Powers. An attempt to bring about a customs union of Austria with Germany failed when it was held that this violated the Geneva Protocol of 1922, which required the maintenance of Austrian economic independence. It was not until 1938 that the German government of Hitler annexed Austria. Austria was again separated from Germany in 1945 and has since, like Germany, been divided into four zones and occupied by the forces of the Allies of the Second World War. The city of Vienna is, like Berlin, divided into four sectors and administered jointly by the four powers.

Austria consists of four contrasted physical regions. In the north is a small part of the Bohemian hills. South of this is the narrow valley of the Danube. The Alps compose the greater part of the country, but on the east these end abruptly, and on this side Austria embraces a small strip of the Hungarian Plain.

The Bohemian Region. This small region is built of ancient crystalline rocks, similar to those which compose the highlands of Bohemia itself. The region is very hilly. Much rises in parts to over 3,000 feet above sea level and is known to the Austrians as the *Waldviertel* (the wooded quarter). Agriculture is here devoted to the production of rye and potatoes. To the east the relief becomes more gentle, the altitude

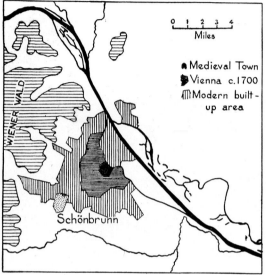

FIG. 163. The situation of Vienna. Note the old meanders of the river Danube and the straightened present course.

lower, and the ancient rocks sink beneath younger, softer, and more fertile deposits. This is the *Weinviertel* (the wine-producing quarter), where are large and prosperous villages. Wheat and the grape vine replace the hardy crops of the sour Waldviertel soil.

The Danube Valley. The Danube Valley is shut in on the north and south by hills. In parts its banks rise steeply from the river, rather in the manner of the gorge of the Rhine. Navigation is far from easy in the swirling waters of the river, and with the exception of Linz (181,500) there are no cities of large size and importance on its banks in this section of the valley. Below Krems the valley widens and the hills draw back on each side.

Despite the difficulties which the Danube presents to navigation, this region has been an avenue of human movement throughout history. It is divisible into the valley above and the valley below Krems. The many hills and the narrow valleys above Krems have hindered

but never stopped transportation. This region is mantled with young and soft deposits. Agriculture is profitable, and this is one of the more densely peopled areas of Austria. There are many small towns and large villages, which together give an appearance of rural prosperity and well-being.

Below Krems the valley of the Danube widens to a plain bordered on all sides by low and rounded hills, often cultivated to their summits. Its young and soft rocks have been dusted with loess, and the area is well settled and well cultivated. This is the most valuable agricultural region of Austria. To the northeast the plain is continuous with the plain of Moravia (see page 256), and it extends southward to the Wiener Neustadt, where the mountains begin to rise. On the east it is bordered by a hilly ridge known as the Little Carpathians, east of which lies the Hungarian Plain.

This plain of Lower Austria may be described as the crossroads of Europe, and here, at the crossing of routes, lies the city of Vienna (1,731,500). From the south the easiest crossings of the Alps converge on the city, by which the products of Italian trade were formerly carried northward to Germany. North of the city lies an easy routeway through what is often called the Moravian Gate (see Fig. 159). This gap separates Bohemia from the hills of Slovakia and offers a low, level route from the Danube Valley to Silesia and Poland. Proposals to cut a canal through this route have not matured, but the gap is much used by road and rail transportation. East and west of Vienna is the routeway that follows the Danube Valley from Germany to Hungary and the Balkan peninsula.

In this part of Europe cities have retained their fortress character longer than in less disturbed regions to the west. In this Vienna is the fortress par excellence. Founded in the Middle Ages as the capital of a "Mark," or frontier state, it has for many centuries fulfilled its function of protecting south Germany from invasion. Vienna was built on a terrace above the river Danube. To the east, its exposed side, it was protected by the marshes of the river. The early dukes of Austria made the city their capital. It outgrew its medieval walls, which were taken down and replaced by the Ringstrasse, a boulevard in horseshoe plan, along which were built many of the most splendid buildings of Vienna. Much of this building was done in the eighteenth century in the ornate style known as "baroque." Vienna and Prague are the chief European homes of this style, which reflects so completely the grace, the refinement, and the artificiality of pre-Revolutionary Europe. The Vienna of romance belongs to the nineteenth century, when the Austrian emperors held their court at the Schönbrunn and the city was the prosperous capital of a large and expanding empire. Vienna is now the largest—almost the only—industrial city of Austria.

The industries of Vienna are chiefly those which call for much skill and finesse and relatively little raw material. Its former role of an imperial capital encouraged the production of luxury goods. Mechanical engineering, the production of fine metalwork, woodworking, electrical engineering, and the textile and clothing industries are the most important. Vienna is also a university city and an important center of European art and culture. South of Vienna are a number of small industrial towns, which carry on engineering, textile, and woodworking industries. Largest of these is Wiener Neustadt.

The Alps. The Alps occupy two-thirds of Austria. They continue eastward the main features of the Alps of Switzerland, but in Austria the mountain mass broadens and becomes lower in altitude. Toward the east the sharp glacial forms disappear and the rounded hills sink toward the Hungarian Plain. The highest and most inaccessible area of the Austrian Alps is the Hohe Tauern, which continues the high mountains of the Engadine district of Switzerland. The Hohe Tauern consists of hard crystalline rocks that have been eroded by ice into sharp and striking forms. There are no breaks in the continuity of the range. Its crestline is almost continuous, rarely dropping below 8,000 feet. The Brenner Pass at 4,494 feet is the lowest crossing. The Hohe Tauern is continued eastward as the Nieder Tauern. This is lower, but its barrier nature is

scarcely less conspicuous. Much of this region is inaccessible to the ordinary tourist, and it has not in general been commercialized like the Swiss Alps. Towns and hotels are small and infrequent. Rural life is primitive. Many of the remote valleys are almost self-sufficing and have little contact with the outside world.

This central core of the Austrian Alps is limited on north and south by clearly marked

A wayside church in Zillertal, Austrian Alps. Note the poor quality of the road, suited only to the movement of animals and farm carts. (*Austrian State Tourist Bureau.*)

depressions, eroded by rivers along lines of geological weakness. To the north the rivers Inn, Salzach, and Enns occupy differing parts of such a depression, which is in fact continuous from Switzerland to near Vienna, with only a low pass to separate the tract occupied by one river from that occupied by the next. Two of these passes are the Arlberg and the Semmering. On the south the river Drava (Drau) occupies a similar depression.

In the extreme west of Austria is the small province of Vorarlberg. It lies in the Rhine

Valley, and its communications with the rest of Austria are only by the Arlberg Pass and rail tunnel. This is the least populous of the Austrian provinces. Its bonds of sentiment and loyalty to the Austrian state are loose, and after the First World War its population appealed for admission to the Swiss Confederation.

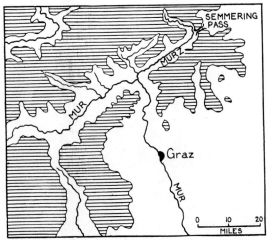

FIG. 164. The situation of Graz.

On the borders of Vorarlberg is the little principality of Liechtenstein, a small and independent state of only 62 square miles and a population of 13,000.

To the east, where the Alps give way to high but rounded hills, the land is at once more accessible and more valuable. The rivers Mur and Mürz provide routes through the region. Much of this area is forested, and agriculture is of some importance in the valleys, which are here wider as well as lower than farther to the west. This area was once famous for its iron industry. The ancient manufacture of steel has died out, but the iron ore of Eisenerz is still worked, and in recent years the Germans established a modern steel industry near Graz. Graz (220,000), like Vienna, was a frontier city, lying where the eastern Alps drop down to the Hungarian Plain. But Graz has never rivaled Vienna in size or importance. The city lies where the river Mur leaves the mountains. Like Vienna it was a fortress city. It grew up round a steep-sided and castle-crowned rock, which

rises beside the river and once guarded the approaches to the eastern Alps.

Between the Hohe Tauern and the Danube Valley is a series of short ranges, separated from one another by transverse valleys or easy passes. The region is picturesque, and its openness and accessibility have caused it to be more frequented than the forbidding Hohe Tauern. It contains such resorts as Innsbruck (97,000) and Salzburg (105,500). These are the only cities of considerable size in the area. They grew up on medieval trade routes. Their ease of access, combined with the beauty of their buildings and of their surrounding countryside, has brought tourists, and this in turn has led to their development as cultural and artistic centers.

The valley of the Drava, which bounds the Hohe Tauern on the south, widens as it nears the Hungarian Plain. In the basin of Klagenfurt its agricultural potentialities increase. Cereals, fodder crops, and fruit are grown, and the rural population is found living in large and compact villages like those of the richer parts of Germany. Along the southern border of the Klagenfurt Basin lie the Karawanken Alps, a sharp, steep-sided range with snowy summits, which cut Austria off from Yugoslavia. A small number of Yugoslavs has settled here within the Klagenfurt Basin. But in general it has been the Germans who have crossed the mountains and settled to the south. South of the Brenner Pass, for example, Germans have settled the Italian province of Alto Adige, or South Tyrol. This district had been Austrian until it was lost in 1920 to Italy.

Eastern Austria. The last region of Austria is a very narrow strip of plain which lies along the eastern border of the country. Part of this region, which is known as the Burgenland, was gained in 1921 from the Hungarian kingdom, and Hungarian influences are still strong. It is a region of good agricultural land, and wheat, corn, and the grape vine are grown in the hot summers of the plain.

Economic Development. The large area of infertile and sparsely populated mountain territory greatly reduces the wealth of Austria. Agricultural conditions resemble those of Swit-

Salzburg. The city lies on the river Salzach near where it leaves the mountains. A castle on a steep, isolated hill formed the nucleus around which the city grew. Note the rich, baroque architecture of the churches, erected mainly during the eighteenth century. (*Austrian State Tourist Bureau.*)

zerland, but conditions are in general a little poorer in Austria. The severity of the winters in the Alps and the cool and often moist summers limit the crops to hardy cereals and fodder over much of the country. Even these are sometimes ripened or matured with difficulty. Cattle and sheep are kept in large numbers, and transhumance, the seasonal movement of animals up and down the mountainside, is practiced. The remoteness of much of the Austrian Alps and the general inadequacy of communications prevent the production of agricultural specialities, such as cheese, for export.

Crop farming is more important in the Danube Valley and on the margin of the Hungarian Plain, where the flat or rolling country, the lower rainfall, and greater sunshine are more suited to grain cultivation. The Danube Valley is more hilly. Forest is more extensive, and here animal husbandry is at least as important as crop. The grape vine is

grown along the border of the Hungarian Plain as well as in a few places near Vienna, though the climate of central Europe is in general too severe for viticulture.

Rural conditions of settlement and housing resemble those of south Germany and Switzerland. In the mountain valleys, the villages are often grouped on the terraces of the valley side, leaving the small areas of better land for agricultural use. In the hilly and less productive areas isolated settlements are common.

Austria is far from self-sufficing even in the agricultural products that the country is capable of producing. This is because of the requirements of its overgreat capital city. Before 1918, when Vienna served the needs of the whole Austro-Hungarian Empire, the grain fields of Hungary supplied the Viennese market; now Austria has to export its manufactures and its services to pay for the necessary imports. But manufacturing industries are not of great im-

Zell am See, a resort town on the northern edge of the Hohe Tauern, seen in the background. This region offers good climbing and scenery, but its agricultural resources are seen to be very slight. (*Austrian State Tourist Bureau.*)

portance. Austria has some lignite but no large deposits of coal, and she is not well placed to import fuel from Germany. The extension and enlargement of Germany's canal system might facilitate the import of coal, but this is not likely to be realized in the near future. In recent years petroleum has been worked at Zistersdorf, in the Danubian Plain below Vienna, but has not hitherto benefited greatly the industries of Austria. Meanwhile Austria has developed her resources in hydroelectric power. With the exception of the Danube, all the Austrian rivers are small. Generating stations are numerous, but their size is restricted by the smallness of the streams on which they depend. The river Mur and some of the tributaries of the Danube are used intensively, but the river Danube itself, which has the greatest potentialities, has hitherto been developed least. At the present time, however, generating stations are being established here also. Electric power is now widely used in the factories and on the railways of

Austria, encouraging here, as in Switzerland, the development of small and scattered units of production.

The mining of iron ore has been important for a very long time in Styria (Steiermark). At Eisenerz is a vast open iron-ore quarry which is slowly being driven into the mountainside, producing today nearly 2 million tons a year. The large-scale smelting and steelmaking industry is a recent development and owes its origin to the strategic advantage of this relatively sheltered situation rather than to any other local advantages. It has yet to be seen whether the steel industry of Graz will survive the political conditions that brought it into being. The production of steel in 1950 was less than a million tons. Graz, Vienna, and Linz are all centers of the engineering industries and of the manufacture of electrical equipment.

The textile and clothing industry is carried on in many small centers in the mountains, but it is a survival of ancient domestic crafts and has little advantage here except the low wages demanded by the Austrian peasantry. In Vienna a clothing industry has grown up to supply the large local market.

Nearly 40 per cent of Austria is forested, and the timber-using industries are important.

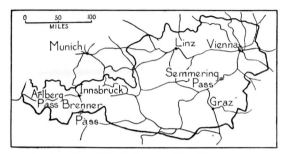

FIG. 165. Railroads of Austria.

These include not only the direct use of wood in the manufacture of furniture, especially in Vienna, but also its use in the preparation of pulp and paper, carvings, implements, and tools.

A large part of the total industrial activity of Austria is carried on in Vienna itself. Graz is next in size and importance, though its population is only about an eighth of that of Vienna. All other cities are relatively small, and their manufacturing activities are relatively insignifi-

cant. Only Linz and Salzburg, in addition to these two, have a population of over 100,000, and only Innsbruck and Klagenfurt have more than 50,000. Many of the smaller towns survive only by virtue of their attraction to tourists; some are little more than groups of hotels.

Communications present serious difficulties in a country as mountainous as Austria. Routes from west to east are able to follow the Danube and the longitudinal valleys of the Alps, but movement in a north-to-south direction is difficult. The main mountain range is crossed by rail at the Brenner Pass and also by a tunnel east of the Hohe Tauern. The Semmering Pass, by which the valleys of southern Austria communicate with Vienna, is fortunately a low and easy route, followed by both road and rail. All transport has necessarily to be by road in the higher mountains, and some of the roads are closed by snow during the winter months.

Vienna, on the other hand, is a focus of railway routes which radiate up and down the Danube Valley and northward into Czechoslovakia. The Danube is the only really navigable river of Austria. It was formerly a very difficult river for navigation, with a branching and island-studded channel below Vienna. Much effort has gone to regulate its course, but river transport is still of only small importance and

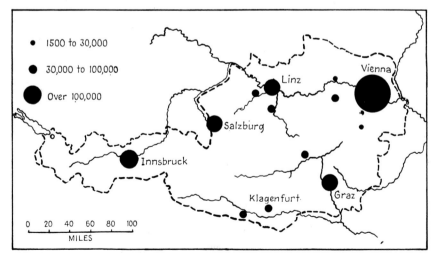

FIG. 166. The cities of Austria. Only one city, Vienna with 1,548,000 in 1947, has a population of over a quarter million. With the exception of the resorts of Innsbruck and Salzburg, almost all cities are in the valleys of the eastward-flowing rivers.

is fraught with dangers and difficulties in the form of shallows and shifting banks.

Austria is economically one of the weakest countries of Europe. Her liabilities in the shape of her overgrown capital and of the obligations that remain from her imperial past are offset by no commensurate potentialities. Her agricultural advantages are slight, and her agricultural equipment and methods are backward. Her manufacturing industries are relatively small, and their further extension is hindered by lack of resources. Exports are few, while the problem of provisioning Vienna alone necessitates a considerable import of foodstuffs. For this reason Austria encourages the tourist industry as much as she can; it is one of her very few assets.

BIBLIOGRAPHY

Bodo, Fritz, "Burgenland: ein deutsches Grenzland im Südosten," Vienna, 1941. (This is a provincial atlas similar to those published for some provinces of Germany.)

Buschbeck, Ernest H., "Austria," New York, 1949.

"Die Donau als Grossschiffahrtstrasse," Vienna, 1941.

"Géographie universelle," Vol. IV, L'Europe centrale, Part 2, Paris, 1931.

Hoffman, George W., The Survival of an Independent Austria, G.R., XLI, 1951, 606–621.

Kish, George, A TVA on the Danube, G.R., XXXVII, 1947, 274–302.

Krebs, N., "Die Ostalpen und das heutige Österreich," 2 vols., Stuttgart, 1928.

Lengyel, Emil, "The Danube," New York, 1939.

Mutton, A. F. A., The Glockner-Kaprun Hydroelectric Project, Hohe Tauern, G.R., XLI, 1951, 332–334.

Partsch, Joseph, "Central Europe," London, 1902.

Passant, E. J., "The Problem of Austria," Oxford, 1945.

Rothschild, K. W., "The Austrian Economy since 1945," Royal Institute of International Affairs, London, 1950.

Steed, Henry Wickham, "The Hapsburg Monarchy," London, 1913.

Straus, F. S., Austrian Agriculture, Foreign Agriculture, XI, 1947, 50–64.

Taylor, A. J. P., "The Hapsburg Monarchy," London, 1941.

Turner, R. M. A. E., Report on Economic and Commercial Conditions in Austria, Department of Overseas Trade, London, 1938.

Much information can be obtained from the Reports of the United States High Commissioner in Austria and from the Economic Cooperation Administration and Organization for European Economic Cooperation documents and reports listed on pages 52 to 54. Austria has been receiving Marshall Aid, and her recovery has thus been well documented. Current economic statistics appear in *Gesamtschau der österreichischen Wirtschaft*, published by the Osterreichisches Institut fur Wirtschaftsforschung, Vienna, and details of current developments in *Austrian Information*, also published in Vienna.

The tourist guidebooks, especially Baedeker's guide to Austria, are useful supplementary sources.

CHAPTER 22: *Danubian and Balkan Lands*

From its source in the Black Forest of south-western Germany the Danube flows eastward for 1,725 miles to its mouth in the Black Sea. It flows through or past the territory of no less than seven separate states. Its source is on the borders of western Europe, within 40 miles of the Rhine; its mouth is on Europe's eastern frontier. It flows between mountains for much of its course, and nowhere, except in Hungary, are they far distant from its banks. The Danube forms a kind of corridor by which people from southeastern Europe and the borders of Asia have sought to move northwestward. Within historical times Huns, Avars, Magyars, and Turks have come this way. Germanic peoples from the northwest have expanded down the Danube Valley, forming settlements and creating empires. Vienna is the focal point in the upper Danube Basin; for a thousand years now it has stood firm in defense of the West.

The Danube does not today constitute a high-way of commerce as important as its location and history might suggest. Its upper course, above Vienna, is too swift and too winding to be easily navigable. Below Vienna it is more navigable though not well used; the countries that border it are not enough developed to have a large commerce. If the Danube were con-nected by canal with the Rhine, it is probable that commerce might be stimulated by the exchange of goods between Germany and eastern Europe. Navigational facilities on the Danube have in the past been controlled by an international commission. Though still inter-national in name, this Danube Commission is now in effect a Russian agency, and the hostility of West and East limits yet more the traffic of the river.

At the Slovak town of Bratislava the Danube flows across the low ridge which joins the Carpathian Mountains with the Alps. A few miles downstream the Danube enters Hungary. The hills draw back on each side, and the river flows for about 130 miles across an almost treeless plain. This is the Little Alföld. Another hilly ridge, the Bakony Forest, stretches north-eastward from the Alps to join the Slovakian Mountains. The Danube cuts across these hills between Esztergom and Budapest. The hills again retreat, and the Danube enters the Great Hungarian Plain. This is the Great Alföld, broader, flatter, and drier than the Little Alföld, which was crossed between Bratislava and the Bakony Forest. It is the only large area of steppeland in Europe west of the Ukraine, and here, some 15 centuries ago, nomadic peoples from the Russian steppes found a temporary home suited to their pastoral way of life. They have disappeared, leaving only their name in that of Hungary. They were followed by later invaders from the steppes, the Avars and the Magyars, the last of whom have settled in this region. Magyar blood flows in the veins of the Hungarians, and their language is basically Magyar.

From the north the Danube receives the Tisza (Theiss), which drains the Carpathians. The Drava (Drau) enters from Austria. The Sava, rising in the Slovene lands of northern Yugoslavia, collects a number of tributaries from the Dinaric Hills before reaching the Danube at Belgrade (Beograd). A few miles below Belgrade the Danube is joined by the Serbian Morava, whose valley provides a corridor southward into the former kingdom of Serbia and thence by way of the Vardar Valley to the Aegean Sea.

Fifty miles to the east of Belgrade the Hungarian Plain is bounded by the mountains of Romania. The Tatra Mountains of Slovakia are continued eastward and then southeastward in the Carpathians. The line of these mountains then turns abruptly to the west and continues as the Transylvanian Alps, curves to the south,

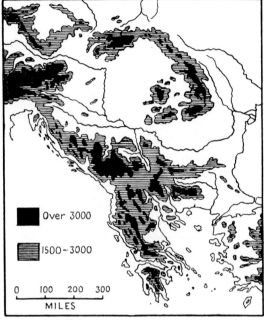

Fig. 167. Relief of the Danubian and Balkan region.

crosses the Danube, and again assumes a west to east direction as the Balkan Mountains (Stara Planina). The section of this range which lies between the Transylvanian Alps and the Balkan Mountains is lower than the rest, and here the Danube breaks through the barrier in a deeply incised valley, almost 80 miles in length. At its deepest and narrowest this is known as the "Iron Gate."

Below this barrier the Danube again enters a plain reaching from the mountains to the Black Sea: on the north of the river, the plain of Walachia, rising to the Transylvanian Alps; on the south, a narrow belt of lowland between the river and the Balkan Mountains. On the south of the latter and reached by passes from the valley of the Morava as well as from the Danube Valley is the plain of the Mariça (Maritsa), the heart of Bulgaria. South of the Mariça Plain are the Rhodope Mountains,

separating Bulgaria from the plains of Macedonia and Thrace.

Some 300 miles below the gorge of the Iron Gate the Danube curves to the north and then resumes its eastward course toward its delta. Within this bend of the lower Danube is the Dobrogea, a low chalk plateau. North of the lower Danube, following the curve of the Carpathian Mountains, is the hilly province of Moldavia, which becomes more level and more open as it passes eastward into the steppes of Russia.

Peoples and Languages. The Danubian and Balkan countries have a greater variety and confusion of language than any other area of Europe. The basic language may be regarded as Slavonic, with a Romance survival in the mountains of Romania. Ural-Altaic languages, brought into this area by invaders from Asia, have given rise to Hungarian, and have strongly influenced Bulgar. German, brought by invaders from the west, was carried down the

Fig. 168. Political boundaries of the Danubian and Balkan area.

Danube Valley and was spoken by isolated groups until recently. The Slavonic language was in reality a group of many dialects. The northern group, Polish, Czech, and Slovak, are not spoken in the area now under consideration. They were separated by the German of Austria and the Magyar of Hungary from the southern Slavonic languages. The latter are Slovene, spoken in the upper valley of the Sava; Serbo-Croat, the language of the Yugoslav mountains; Bulgar, a Slavonic language which has absorbed some words of Asiatic origin; and Macedonian, a language which is basically Slavonic with an admixture of Greek and Turkish.

The present pattern of peoples and languages was established by the sixteenth century, when the Turks invaded Europe and conquered most of the area considered in this chapter. The Turks reached Vienna in 1683. They submerged the Hungarian Plain, invaded Walachia and Moldavia and even southern Poland. The mountains of Serbia, Bosnia, Montenegro, and Albania offered a natural obstacle to the Turkish invaders. Though the Turkish overlordship was admitted, the more remote and inaccessible areas were, in practice, free of Turkish interference. The Turks were not numerous enough to settle their vast Balkan empire. Scarcely could they garrison and govern it. They made up for their numerical weakness by the harshness and arbitrariness of their rule. They relied upon fear rather than upon good government in order to maintain order and peace. The oppressive and corrupt rule of the Turks, lasting in Bulgaria, Macedonia, and parts of Yugoslavia for over 500 years, is one reason for the backwardness of this region today.

The Turks were expelled first from the Danube Valley, then from the Balkans. The Hungarian Plain was conquered by the Austrians. The Serbs revolted at the beginning of the nineteenth century. The Austrians occupied the more northerly Slav provinces of Slovenia and Croatia. The Romanian principalities of Walachia and Moldavia established their independence in the nineteenth century and united to make the kingdom of Romania. The Bulgars revolted in the 1870's and, with the help of Russia, created an independent principality of Bulgaria, which a few years later extended its frontiers southward. Until 1912 the Turks continued to hold a large area in the southern Balkans, including Albania and much of what is now southern Yugoslavia and northern Greece. In the first Balkan War of 1912 they were driven from this territory and were left with only the small foothold of Turkey-in-Europe.

The expulsion of the Turks prepared the way for the fierce feuds between the peoples of the Balkans. The limits of each cultural group were far from precise. Each cherished claims, based upon the medieval extent of its territories, to the lands of its neighbors. Each could offer good economic reasons for the annexation of some city or some piece of territory, and at least until the First World War, Germany and Russia each used the Balkan states as pawns in the larger game of politics. Since 1918 the rival nationalisms of the Balkans have become more intense. The alliances between France and Yugoslavia, Czechoslovakia and Romania, the Italian and, later, German alliance with Hungary and partiality for Bulgaria deepened the rift and contributed very materially to the war of 1939 to 1945. Today the mantle of Russia is spread over all these lands, with the exception of Yugoslavia, and their nationalisms are subsidiary to the ambitions of the U.S.S.R. Yugoslavia has rejected the Russian discipline, and it is questionable how long it may be before Slav nationalism opposes more vigorously and more openly the spread of the new Russian imperialism.

The Danubian countries have a common heritage from the long period of Turkish domination and misrule—their poverty and backwardness. The wars which accompanied the rise of the peoples of southeastern Europe to form nation-states caused further destruction. None of these countries is naturally well endowed, and the mountainous terrain makes transport and communications difficult. Many areas have of necessity to live in semi-isolation from the outer world, self-sufficing and self-contained, at a very low level of existence. The extent of good agricultural land is small, there is little coal, and the petroleum of Romania is the most valuable mineral asset. Reserves of metal are small, and only bauxite, the ore of aluminum, in Hungary is of really large extent.

Yet the poverty of the region does not spring wholly from its lack of natural endowment. The Scandinavian countries are no better off materially but have evolved a very much higher standard of life. The region lacks capital. The incentive to save is reduced by recurring wars

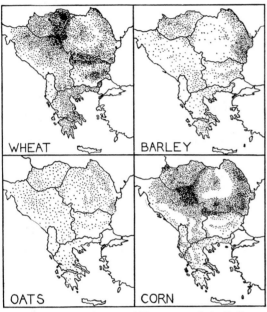

Fig. 169. The chief crops of Hungary and the Balkans.

which destroy savings, and even the ability to accumulate capital is reduced by the ineffectiveness of human labor.

The four countries considered in this chapter have together a population of 48 million. About 75 per cent of this is engaged in agriculture; only 12 per cent in manufacturing. By countries these figures are as follows:

	Population	Per cent in agriculture	Per cent in industry
Hungary.......	9,317,000 (1941)	53	24
Yugoslavia.....	15,772,000 (1948)	78	11
Romania.......	15,873,000 (1948)	79	7
Bulgaria.......	7,022,000 (1946)	80	8

The corresponding population figures for Czechoslovakia and Greece, which are both

adjacent to the countries considered here, are as follows:

	Population	Per cent in agriculture	Per cent in industry
Czechoslovakia..	12,409,000 (1948)	40	38
Greece........	8,070,000 (1950)	54	29

The following statistics give some measure of the effectiveness of agriculture in these countries:

ANNUAL YIELD PER ACRE IN HUNDREDWEIGHT[*]

	Wheat	Rye	Potatoes
Czechoslovakia........	14.8	12.9	103.3
Hungary..............	10.9	8.9	56.2
Yugoslavia...........	8.9	6.6	48.9
Romania.............	7.3	7.4	63.7
Bulgaria.............	10.7	8.5	53.0
Greece..............	7.7	6.4	43.9

[*] After "Agrarian Problems from the Baltic to the Aegean," p. 53, Royal Institute of International Affairs, London, 1944.

Whatever measure be adopted, whether child-mortality rates, the number of automobiles and radios, participation in peasant cooperatives, or the adequacy of human diet, the living standards of the Danubian countries, with Greece and Albania, appear far below Czechoslovakia and Germany. Greece and Albania could be treated in this chapter, as they have so much in common with the Danubian countries. They are, however, organized in the next section of this book, that on southern Europe.

It is clear that poverty such as exists in these countries does not allow the peasant to invest and accumulate capital, and he is too poor a risk for anyone to lend to him except the village moneylender and that at an exorbitant rate of interest. The land is grossly overcrowded, and the pressure on the land is greatest in the poorest countries. The following table gives an estimate of the agrarian population before the Second World War per 100 acres of farmland:

In those countries where the greatest dependence is placed on agriculture, agriculture is least productive and most backward and the rural overcrowding is the most serious.

The whole of this is a run-down region. It requires a heavy investment of capital in transport and communications, in irrigation, in the improvement of seeds and stock, in the provision of fertilizer, and in the improvement of the level of rural education. Were such developments to be put into effect, they would leave a large surplus of labor. Alternative employment, perhaps in manufacturing, would need to be provided or else some opportunity for emigration.

The German solution for the problem of this region lay in taking its farm surplus and supplying it with factory goods. Applied wisely, such a policy could have led at least to an amelioration of conditions here. The Germans, however, exploited the region, taking its surplus production of foodstuffs and minerals and supplying it with goods which could not be of much value in the development of the region.

Many have spoken of a "TVA for the Danube," meaning the reconstruction of this region by international effort and with capital subscribed internationally. The problems raised by such a project in administration and control are great but by no means insuperable,[1] but they pale before that of securing agreement between the countries of eastern and western Europe. At present the Danubian lands are, with the exception of Yugoslavia, controlled by Russia, which of all the great powers is perhaps the least able and the least willing to invest capital outside its frontiers, the income from which will be chiefly in the betterment of life in this region. In the long run, of course, better standards in the Danube Basin would result in a greater market for an endless variety

[1] Finer, Hermann, "The T.V.A., Lessons for International Application," International Labor Office, Montreal, 1944.

of products of the industry of other countries, but a great deal of investment would be necessary before such returns became apparent. The Danubian countries are a suitable area for the implementation of a policy such as that referred to as Truman's "Fourth Point" policy.

A far greater degree of collaboration is needed between the nation states of the Balkans. They have in the past shown little disposition to agree among themselves, and it will be necessary for each to forget a great deal of its past and to work with its neighbors for the common good.

The analogy between the Danube Basin and the Tennessee Valley must not be pressed too far. It is not the Danube River itself that presents the problem, but rather the underdevelopment of the countries that border it. In places, as across the Hungarian Plain and through the Iron Gate, where it crosses the line of the Carpathians, the river has to be regulated and controlled. But in general it is adequately maintained for the traffic it bears. The small degree of international collaboration necessary for this has not been achieved easily, and there have been incessant quarrels among the members of the Danubian Commission. The development of the upper Rhine as a source of power has occasioned such disputes between France and Germany that little progress was made. No greater achievement can be expected of the Danubian countries unless they are brought to heel by the strong hand of an outside power.

In the past the old Austro-Hungarian Empire gave the required degree of unity to this region. This broke up in 1918. Since then Germany and now Russia have spread their military and political control over the Danubian area. But neither was benevolent or enlighted. They exploited rather than developed, and though both in differing ways controlled the whole region, neither achieved any constructive results.

HUNGARY

Until 1918 the kingdom of Hungary was a unit in the dual monarchy of Austria-Hungary. Its defeat in the First World War was followed by its separation from Austria and the loss of territory. Hungary became a plain state, with no more hill country than is contained in the Bakony Forest and in its continuation northeast of the Danube. In the course of the dismemberment of Czechoslovakia in 1938–1939 Hungary acquired parts of Slovakia and Ruthenia and

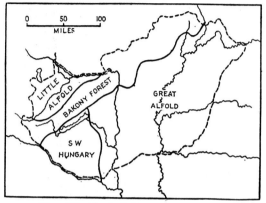

Fig. 170. Physical divisions of Hungary.

later northern Transylvania from Romania. These gains were, however, lost after the end of the Second World War.

The Hungary of today falls naturally into four physical regions: the Little Alföld, the Bakony Forest and its northeastern continuation, the rolling country between the Bakony Forest and the Danube, and the great plain east of the Danube.

Little Alföld. The land is not completely flat. Its low, swelling hills are covered with a dusting of loess. Most of the region is drained by the Raba (Raab) and its tributaries, which have left gravel terraces along the gentle slopes of their valleys. Low-lying land is marshy, but most of the region is dry and fertile. It attracted German settlers from the west, and though Magyar in speech, it is a region of very complex racial origins. Summers are hot, and winters very cold. Rainfall shows a summer maximum. Wheat, maize, and sugar beet are grown, and vineyards are planted on the sunny slopes. The region is one of compact and rather prosperous villages, often very German in their appearance. The small towns, such as Györ (56,000), Sopron, and Szombathely, serve as markets for the grain and fruit.

Bakony Forest. This limestone ridge bounds the Little Alföld on the southeast. Its highest peaks do not greatly exceed 1,500 feet. It is well wooded and contains the most extensive areas of forest in Hungary. Population is relatively sparse, and settlements few. Toward the southwest the hill ridge drops in height toward the valley of the Drava. Toward the northeast it is crossed by the Danube. Beyond the deep valley of the river the line of the Bakony uplift is continued in the broken hill masses of Matra, Bükk, and Hegyalya, all wooded and somewhat difficult of access despite their generally low altitude. A number of market towns lie along

Budapest. A mosque remaining in the city, a survival of the period of Turkish conquest in the sixteenth century. (*Legation of the Hungarian People's Republic, Washington, D.C.*)

the southern margin of these hills at their junction with the Great Hungarian Plain. Gyöngyös, Eger, Miskolc (109,500),[1] and Tokay

[1] In this chapter the population is given only of cities of over 50,000. All cities of this size are named in the text, but in certain instances, especially Hungary, the censuses on which the figures are based are rather old.

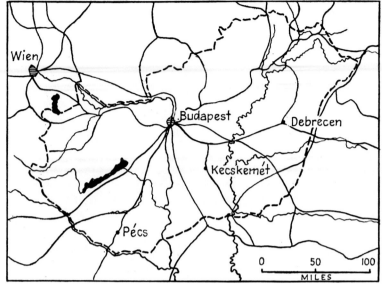

Fig. 171. Hungary: cities and communications.

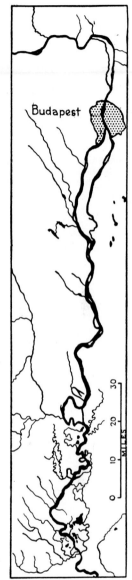

Fig. 172. The Danube below Budapest. The river here breaks into a number of channels, and changes in its course are frequent. Note that the river flows from north to south.

(Tokaj) are the largest. The lower slopes of the hills which partially surround these towns are clothed with vineyards, for which the hot summers and the southerly aspect are particularly suitable. Here are made the tokay wines.

Largest and most important of these towns which lie at the junction of hill and plain is Budapest (1,058,000) itself. The fortress and palace of Buda were built high up on the right bank of the Danube, where spurs of the Bakony Forest reach out to the river and command the approaches to the gap through the hills. Below Budapest the Danube breaks up into many channels with low, marshy banks, across which movement is difficult. On the low, flat land opposite developed the commercial city of Pest. Budapest was formed by the merging of the military and administrative town on the hill with the commercial city on the plain.

The Great Alföld. The Great Hungarian Plain, or the Puszta, as it is called, has a monotony which is absent from the Little Alföld. Its surface is in general level and covered with loess. In places, particularly between the Danube and the Tisza, are areas of wind-blown sand dunes. The drifting sands block the drainage, and the land is dotted with small lakes. To the east and north beds of gravel have been laid

down by torrents as they issue from the encircling ranges of mountain. The Danube and Tisza flow sluggishly across this flat region in valleys that are sunk but little below the level of the plain. The Danube breaks up into many channels, separated one from the other by marshy

The town and fortress of Sümeg in Hungary. The ruins of a castle remain on the summit of an isolated hill. The town has grown up around it. Note the ventilators in the roofs of the houses; food and grain are often stored in the attics. (*Legation of the Hungarian People's Republic, Washington, D.C.*)

Great Hungarian Plain. Much of this area is under cultivation for wheat. (*Legation of the Hungarian People's Republic, Washington, D.C.*)

islands. All the rivers are liable to flood violently, and along their banks are broad belts of damp land, too wet to cultivate, avoided by settlements, and difficult to cross.

The climate is one of cold winters, when ice floes drift down the Danube and navigation is brought to a halt, and very hot summers, when the shimmering mirage beguiles the traveler. Most of the rain falls in the summer, when thunder and hailstorms occur. The natural vegetation of this region must have been grass, like that of the Russian steppe, with trees and bushes along the watercourses. Areas of grassland remain today, in the sandy region which lies to the east of the Tisza, grazed by herds of dun-colored long-horned cattle. This region is known as the Hortobágy. Much of the plain, however, is under cultivation. Wheat, maize, and rye are the commonest cereals, and sugar beet is grown. Vineyards are planted over many of the sandy hillocks. In recent years agriculture has been extended into less favorable areas, and here hamlets and even isolated farmsteads have appeared. But the rural settlement of the Hungarian Plain is for the greater part in large villages, which in size and population resemble towns. This springs from the insecurity which has characterized the plain and from the danger to which isolated settlements or even small groups of settlements have been exposed. The Hungarian farmstead is typically a low, white building roofed with thatch or with wooden shingles, with a dwelling house, stable, and barn under one roof. Close by is the long counterpoise of the well, upon which the farmstead depends for water.

The towns of the plain are relatively large, but most of their inhabitants are engaged on the land. They combine the functions of agricultural village and market town. Kecskemét (83,500) between the two rivers, Szeged (137,-000) on the Tisza, Debrecen (126,000) in the Hortobágy, and Bekescsaba (50,000) and Hodmezövasárhely (61,500) in the rich grain land of eastern Hungary are the largest.

Southwestern Hungary. This region, between the Bakony Forest and the Danube, is a rolling or even hilly country. Its forest cover has largely been cleared, and much of it is now under cultivation. The region was exposed, like the Alföld, to the attacks of the Turks. The same nucleation of settlement is apparent, though villages are smaller than on the Great Alföld. The type of agriculture resembles that practiced in other parts of Hungary, and the towns are merely overgrown villages. Only Pécs (70,500) has the aspect and functions of a town in the

The Danube above Budapest. In this part of its course the river cuts across the hilly ridge of the Bakony Forest. (*Legation of the Hungarian People's Republic, Washington, D.C.*)

Western acceptance of the term, and here are located some of the few industries of Hungary.

Economic Development. Hungary has today a population of just over 9,300,000. About 53 per cent of the employed population is engaged in agriculture, and only about 24 per cent in manufacturing and mining industries.

Hungary was formerly noteworthy for the existence of great estates, worked by landless laborers. After the First World War some of these were broken up, and it appears that this process has been completed since the end of the Second World War. Before the Second World War many of the holdings were uneconomically

The Danube at Győr. The river is here flowing across the level plain of the Little Alföld. (*Legation of the Hungarian People's Republic, Washington, D.C.*)

small and much divided, and rural indebtedness, especially among the cultivators of the smaller holdings, was high. On the other hand, the crop yields were higher for most crops than in other Balkan countries, and the products of Hungarian agriculture constituted over half the total exports of Hungary.

Hungary has few resources for the development of industry. There is a very small coal field near Pécs producing only about a million tons of coal a year. Lignite, about 9,400,000 tons, is also mined, and there are reserves of bauxite, the output from which in 1950 was only 350,000 tons. The Hungarian rivers flow too sluggishly to be used for power generation. In terms of the value of goods turned out, the food-processing industries predominate, followed by the metallurgical and textile. These last are small and very far from satisfying the requirements of Hungary. The trade of Hungary consists largely in the export of foodstuffs and the import of manufactured goods. Hungary, in the Russian sphere of influence, is associated with countries which are not short of foodstuffs and have few manufactured goods for export.

ROMANIA

The relief and structure of Romania are very much more complex than those of Hungary. The Carpathian and Transylvanian Mountains form a kind of axis in their curving course from the Russian border to the Iron Gate. Within the curve which they form lie the upland basin of Transylvania and, forming the center of the circle of which the mountains are an arc, the Bihor (Bihorului) Mountains. Outside the sweep of the mountains are the plains and plateaus of Walachia, Moldavia, and Dobrogea.

Carpathian and Transylvanian Mountains. The Carpathian Mountains narrow around the headwaters of the Tisza, but southeastward they expand again into the massive range of

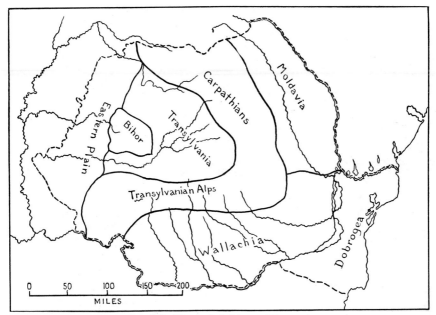

FIG. 173. Physical divisions of Romania.

northern Romania, in many parts over 6,000 feet. The relief is strong, the peaks are fretted, and the valleys deepened by ice action. The climate is severe in winter, and snowfall is heavy. Summers are cool, and the growing period for plants in some of the Carpathian valleys is less than 150 days in the year. Much of the region is thickly wooded, chiefly with conifers. The region is drained by the tributaries of the Tisza, the Someşul and the Mureşul, and by the Siret, which joins the Danube. The range becomes lower toward the south, where there are a number of easy routes across the mountains. The Carpathians are densely wooded. Population is sparse and settlements rare in the more rugged northern part of the range. Population is greater toward the south, where the valleys are wider and agriculture more easily practiced. The Carpathians served during the Middle Ages as a region of refuge for the Romanian people, and the area is still difficult of access. Roads are few, and the peoples live to themselves.

The Transylvanian Alps, which lie in an east-west direction, are higher and even more rugged than the Carpathians. The mountains are built of sedimentary rocks with a core of hard igneous rocks, which give rise to the strongest relief. The

Alps are breached in several places by transverse valleys. Near the center of the range the river Oltul, which rises within the Transylvanian Basin, breaks through the mountains by a deep, narrow valley to reach the Danube. This valley is followed by a railway. In the east is the straight, serrated ridge of the Făgăraş Mountains, and in the center, the Vulcan and Sebeş Massifs, the highest and most "alpine" of the Transylvanian Alps. In the east are the lower hills of the Banat province.

The southern face of the Transylvanian Alps is abrupt and straight. The mountains give way suddenly to the plain. On the north their margin is less distinct. They drop through foothills to the undulating plateau of Transylvania. The population of the Transylvanian Alps is sparse and settled mainly in villages in the larger valleys and in the many small basins which occur within the range. Here, too, an Alpine pattern of transhumance is practiced.

Bihor Mountains. The crystalline massif of Bihor lies within the sweep of the Carpathian and Transylvanian Mountains. Its borders rise steeply from the surrounding lowlands. It is dissected by deep, narrow, and rocky valleys, and much of its surface is thickly wooded.

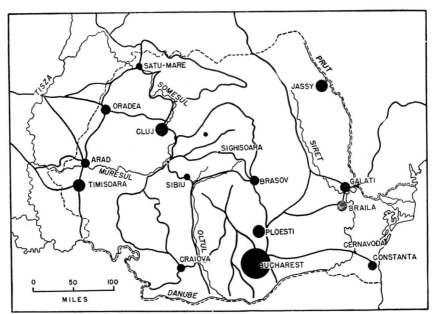

FIG. 174. Romania: cities and communications. The size of the circles is proportionate to the cities' populations (see text).

Valley settlements are few and small, and at higher levels forest clearings provide summer grazing for the animals. Northern Bihor is a wild and forbidding region, but toward the south, the austerity of the region is somewhat moderated. The population is greater, and agriculture more important.

Transylvania. Between the arc of the Carpathian and Transylvanian Mountains and the Bihor Massif is the rolling upland of Transylvania. The region is one of low hills, carved from young, soft rocks, with higher hills, built of lava and other volcanic rocks, toward the east. The region is drained by the Someşul and Mureşul, which flow westward toward the Tisza, and by the Oltul, which breaks through the barrier of the Transylvanian Alps to reach the Danube. The plateau of Transylvania is well settled and well cultivated. The higher land is often wooded. The valley sides and areas of gentle slope are cleared and cultivated. There are large, compact villages. The houses are built of wood, single-storied, with steep roofs of straw or wooden shingles, each house with its small courtyard and stables.

The severity of winter is intensified by the altitude of Transylvania and by the settlement here of cold air masses in winter from the surrounding mountains. Snow may lie for 4 months or even longer. Summers are hot, and rainfall, except in thunderstorms, is slight. Despite this far from favorable climate the region has been settled from an early date, and its population today is descended from numerous immigrant groups. Most is Romanian, and it was in the mountains bordering Transylvania that the Romanian people probably preserved their identity and maintained their independence during the Dark Ages of barbarian invasion. Hungarians, or Szeklers, were then settled in the valleys of eastern Transylvania, where they served as guardians of the passes across the Carpathians from Moldavia. Germans came down the Danube Valley and across the Hungarian Plain, and in Transylvania they founded the "seven towns" of Siebenbürgen. Southern Transylvania became almost a German colony. Brasov (85,000), Sibiu (63,500), and Sighisoara were in the main German towns. The city of Cluj (Klausenburg, Kolozsvar, 111,000), the largest in Transylvania, was established in the Middle Ages as a German city. "There are long and straggling villages of a single street, a street that is a churned-up sea of mud, while the houses, which are large and separate like farmhouses, are built sideways with their end toward the road. These are not the characteristic villages of Romania where each house, however small, is a microcosm of present life, with individual granary and barn and wooden dwelling house rich in carving; these are Saxon villages with many characteristics of medieval German villages, only necessarily altered after eight hundred years of emigration."[1]

Borders of the Hungarian Plain. A broad belt of the Hungarian Plain, from Oradea in the north southward to the Danube, was acquired by Romania in 1920 and has been retained through all the changes that have since taken place. The transition from hill to plain is abrupt, except in the valley of the Mureşul. Two contrasted environments and two different ways of life are brought close together: the lumbering, mining, and pastoral activities of the hills and the crop farming of the plains. The towns of the plain, Satu-Mare (52,000), Oradea (93,000), Arad (83,000), and Timişoara (Temesvar), serve chiefly as market towns where are exchanged the products of east and west, of hill and plain. The plain itself is a rich farming land (page 277) where heavy crops of wheat and maize are gathered and horses, cattle, and sheep are bred. It is also the meeting place of Romanian and Magyar, with, in the towns, large settlements of Jews, who pursue their traditional occupation of petty trading.

Walachia. Between the Transylvanian Alps and the river Danube is Walachia. The land rises gently from the Danube, here a broad stream with low, marshy banks on the Romanian side, toward the Transylvanian Alps. It is crossed by innumerable rivers which rise in the mountains and flow to join the Danube through valleys incised in the dry and dusty plain. East of Bucharest (Bucureşti) the land becomes flatter and toward the Danube passes into the level, treeless Bărăgan steppe. These plains of eastern Romania mark the transition from the still moist and wooded lands of central Europe

to the grasslands of Russia. Much of Walachia bears a thin covering of loess, which increases both the fertility and the dryness of the soil. There is little woodland, only patches on the hilltops. The land lies open and unfenced, stretching to the skyline in gentle rounded hills and shallow valleys, without fence or limit. The villages are large and compact, usually sheltering in some hollow of the ground. Their agriculture is mainly crop farming—wheat and maize predominate—though sheep and cattle are reared in large numbers on the dry steppe.

There are numerous small towns along the course of the Danube. Some handle the grain trade of Walachia or the timber brought down from the mountains; some lie at crossings of the river. All are small, and most are only locally important. Brăila (97,500) is the largest, a modern, rectangularly planned town, which handles a large part of the sea-borne trade of Romania. Galaţi (93,000), a few miles downstream, lies where the Danube turns to the east to enter its delta. Like Brăila it handles part of the grain trade of Romania.

Bucharest grew up at a crossing of the marshy valley of the Dâmboviţa. It has some 985,000 inhabitants and is a spacious town with wide streets and good shops, a business and administrative town rather than an industrial center.

The oil-producing district lies on the borders of the Walachian Plain to the north of Bucharest. Oil has been obtained for more than a century, but it was not until the later years of the last century that its development became significant. Romania is now the only important oil-producing state in Europe except the U.S.S.R., though its output before the last war was about 6,500,000 metric tons, only 2.4 per cent of the world production. The volume of output in 1950 is not known with any degree of certainty but is much less than in 1939. The town of Ploeşti (105,000) lies at the center of the Romanian oil field and is its largest and most important refining center. The only other city of significance in Walachia is the industrial town of Craiova (75,000), about 120 miles west of Bucharest.

Moldavia. Between the Carpathian Moun-

[1] Sitwell, Sacheverell, "Romanian Journey," p. 8, London, 1938.

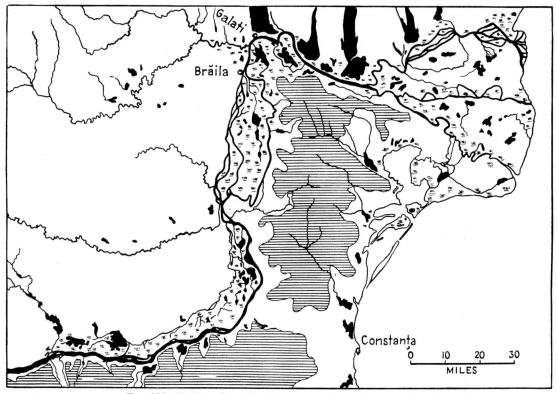

FIG. 175. The Danube delta. Shaded area lies at above 600 feet.

tains and the river Prut is the province of Moldavia. Its surface becomes lower toward the east, broken by a number of high and sometimes severely eroded hills. The region has a climate of extremes, with severe winters and hot, dry summers. The higher land is wooded, but much of Moldavia is mantled with loess and is under cultivation. Cereal crops are the most important. Standards of cultivation are low, transportation undeveloped, and the marketing of agricultural surpluses difficult in the extreme. The relatively high degree of self-sufficiency among the peasants of Moldavia is reflected in the comparative lack of towns. Jassy (Iaşi, 109,000) is the largest, a poor, sprawling town in which a majority of the population is Jewish.

Dobrogea. Between the lower Danube and the Black Sea is a low, chalk plateau. The natural dryness of the chalk surface is accentuated by the loess cover. The population is sparse, and the agriculture of the region is more pastoral than crop. On its eastern coast is the town and

port of Constanţa (79,500), which is linked with Bucharest by a railway that crosses the Danube by a great modern bridge at Cernavodă. North of Constanţa the coast is flat and fringed with lagoons and then passes into the marshy delta of the Danube. The Danube has three major distributaries. The most southerly, the St. Gheorghe Channel, is of diminishing importance. The center channel, the Sulina, is now the most important, carries the greatest part of the discharge of the Danube, and is most used by shipping. The delta is building forward comparatively rapidly and is now, excluding the Volga, the largest delta on the coast of Europe. Fishing is carried on, and the sturgeon is hunted, in part on account of the extravagant delicacy, caviare, which is made from it.

Economic Development. Romania is overwhelmingly an agricultural country. About 79 per cent of its population are peasants, engaged in working their small holdings by traditional methods. Romania, like all other countries of the "frontier" of Europe, was formerly characterized by the large estates of its great landowners. The measures of agrarian reform which were carried through in the years following the First World War greatly reduced their number, and it is doubtful if any at all remain now. Peasant holdings consist frequently of intermixed strips, which are often planted only with grain crops. The most productive lands are on the border of the Hungarian Plain and in Walachia. Here corn and wheat are the dominant crops. In Transylvania maize, favored by the summer heat, and rye are of greatest importance, and in the mountains and in parts of Moldavia and Dobrogea rye is the chief crop. Crop yields are low by European standards, and in the past the government of Romania has done little to improve standards of agriculture or of rural well-being. The cultivation of vineyards and orchards is carried on where the climate permits: on the south-facing slopes of the Walachian Plain and on the western and southern edges of the Bihor Mountains. Cattle are reared in most parts, both for their milk and meat and as draught animals. Sheep are numerous on the dry steppe of eastern Romania. The forested and sparsely populated mountain areas possess large timber resources. Conifers predominate at the higher levels, beech at the lower, and lumbering is an industry of some significance.

Manufacturing industries are new, and their development hitherto has been slight. Ancient craft industries are carried on in every town: spinning, weaving, tanning, leatherworking. In addition simple metallurgical and engineering processes have been developed. Romania has a large number of small mineral deposits but, except the natural oil of Walachia, none that are large enough to afford the basis of modern industry. There are a number of minute coal fields in the west, and lignite is worked in the Carpathian and Transylvanian Mountains. The total output is only about 2.5 million tons a year. Such factory industries as have developed are related to the agricultural wealth of the country: flour milling, sugar refining, brewing, sawmilling.

Means of communication are less developed in Romania than in any other European country. The railway network is poor, and only a very short mileage has been double-tracked. The condition of the roads is very unsatisfactory. Few are fitted for motorized transport, and even fewer have ever been surfaced. However, the river Danube, flowing along the margin of the

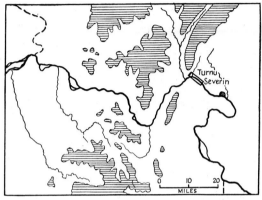

Fig. 176. The Danube at the borders of Romania and Yugoslavia. The river here flows between the Transylvanian Alps and the Balkan Mountains. The small area enclosed by a rectangle is shown in detail in Fig. 177.

most populous and most developed parts of the country, offers a highway of great importance. The large number of river ports shows the use made of the Danube. The Iron Gate, formerly an obstacle to shipping between the lower and middle stretches of the river, has now been improved. A navigable channel has been constructed, and though the speed of the current remains high, the channel is at least deep enough for navigation.

The foreign trade of Romania, like that of the other Balkan States, consists of the export of primary produce and the import of manufactured goods. Wheat and maize predominate in the export trade, followed by petroleum, animals, and timber. Imports consist very largely of textiles, metal goods, and other manufactured articles. The direction of trade before the Second World War was predominantly with the countries of central and western Europe. Germany assumed a dominant position in both the export and import trade of Romania. The German conception of the role of Romania

The Danube at the Iron Gate. The water is here extremely rough, and the tugs and barges cannot in places make headway against it without help from traction on the bank. (*Yugoslav Information Service.*)

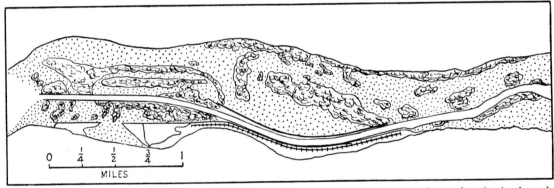

Fig. 177. The Iron Gate. The river here flows swiftly through a narrow gorge in the mountains, and navigation is made difficult. Upstream traffic has to be pulled by locomotives on the bank.

and of her neighbors was that of a producer of foodstuffs and a market for Germany's manufactured goods. The defeat of Germany in 1945 and the absorption of Romania into a Russian sphere have severed this earlier relationship. Romania is now the ally of a country whose economy, whatever may be said of the industrialization of recent years, is basically like her own, agricultural.

BULGARIA

The state of Bulgaria came into existence in 1878 after the defeat and withdrawal of the Turks from the territory immediately to the south of the Danube. At first it consisted only of approximately the northern half of its present territory. Much of the rest was added in 1885, while the southernmost part was gained as recently as 1912. Bulgaria had enjoyed an independent existence during the Middle Ages, when it extended over a considerable though ill-defined area. The memory of the former empire has aroused unfortunate ambitions in modern Bulgaria.

The Bulgar people derive their name and also part of their language from a Turanian

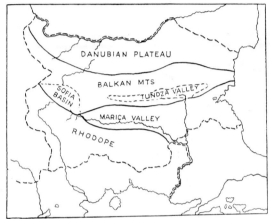

Fig. 178. Physical divisions of Bulgaria.

people who invaded Europe from Asia during the Dark Ages. They have been, however, strongly Slavonized, and their language is now basically Slavonic. Bulgaria's losses of territory in 1913 and again in 1920 left her with few linguistic minorities. The small number of Greeks were removed to Greece, and there are few Turks and Romanians.

A northern plain borders the Danube and rises to the Balkan Mountains. South of the latter is a depression drained mainly by the Mariça. The Rhodope Mountains shut in Bulgaria on the south.

Danubian Plateau. The Bulgarian Plateau to the south of the Danube resembles the Romanian province of Walachia. It is a low plateau built mainly of chalk. The rivers which cross the region from the mountains to the Danube have cut deep valleys. The plateau surface is dry, and much is covered with a deposit of loess. Villages—there are no scattered settlements—lie in the valleys, where water is more plentiful. The plateau itself is rolling and treeless. In parts it is too dry for regular cultivation, and its aspect is like that of the steppe of eastern

Romania. Wheat and maize are grown, and in places sheltered from the bitter winds which blow in winter from the Russian plains, the grape is harvested. Winters are severe; summers very hot, suited to the cultivation of maize and sunflower, which is grown as a source of vegetable oil. Towns of the region are little more than large, untidy villages, in which is sold the produce of the fields. The largest of these is Rusčuk (Ruse, 53,000), a port on the Danube.

Toward the south the surface of the plateau becomes more hilly and woodland more extensive. Among these hills is Trnovo, a former Bulgarian capital, situated in one of the larger valleys. Toward the east the plateau rises to the Deli Orman Hills, of no great height and

A scene in the arid lands of southeastern Bulgaria. Plowing is with a primitive wooden plow, and a peasant is seen breaking clods with a mattock. (*Courtesy of Ewing Galloway.*)

sparsely peopled, partly on account of the low rainfall and the extreme dryness of the chalk soil. North of the Deli Orman a plateau of diminishing height stretches into Romania.

Stara Planina. The range of folded mountains which crosses the Danube at the Iron Gate

Sofia, the capital of Bulgaria. The mosque with its minaret not only is a survival of the period of Turkish domination but also serves to show that Moslems are still an appreciable part of the population. (*Courtesy of Ewing Galloway.*)

swings to the east and extends, diminishing in height and breadth, to the Black Sea. It is composed mainly of limestone and sandstone, with crystalline rocks composing the core of the range and forming the higher peaks. The range is neither particularly high nor difficult to cross. The river Isker, on whose banks lies Sofia (Sofija), rises to the south and flows across the Stara Planina toward the Danube, and there are a number of passes of no great difficulty. The mountains have a severe climate, a heavy rainfall in parts, and are sparsely peopled. Immediately to the south of the crystalline central ridge is a narrow depression carved from younger sedimentary rocks and enclosed on the south by the Srĕdna Gora and Sărnena Gora, smaller and less continuous ranges than the Stara Planina, which are nevertheless also composed in part of crystalline rocks. The intervening depression is drained for almost half its length by the river Tundza. It has a milder climate than that of the Danubian Plateau and is protected from the winds, cold in winter and hot in summer, from

the Russian plains. The valley is divided into a number of separate basins in most of which the soil is good and light. An intensive agriculture is practiced. The warm hill slopes are planted with the vine and fields of roses, whose petals yield the attar of roses, important in the manufacture of perfume. The towns of Sliven, Kazanlik, and Karlovo lie in this depression. They are market towns, and Kazanlik is furthermore the manufacturing center for attar of roses. Toward the west, in a basin drained by the upper course of the Isker, is Sofia.

Sofia (435,000) is one of the smallest of European capitals. It has nevertheless developed a number of manufacturing industries, most of which are concerned with the processing of agricultural produce. Northwest is the Dragoman Pass between the Sofia Basin and the Morava Valley. It is used by the railway from northwestern Europe to Constantinople which passes through Sofia.

Marica Valley. The valley of the Marica is a triangular area of lowland developed largely on

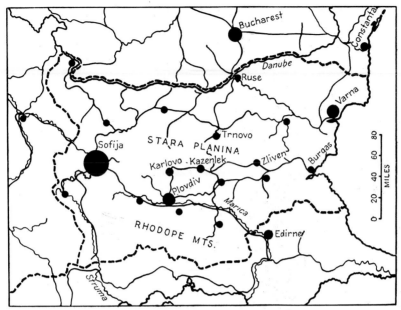

FIG. 179. The cities and communications of Bulgaria. Sofija has a population of just over 400,000, but the only other cities exceeding 50,000 are Plovdiv and Varna. Note the relative absence of through railroad lines. A number of lines run parallel to the frontier, and others run up to the frontier and then stop. The existence of these lines cannot always be explained by the economic potentialities of the regions in which they lie. Most have a strategic purpose.

young soft rocks. On its southern edge the Rhodope Mountains rise steeply from the plain. In the east are the forested and sparsely peopled Istranca Mountains through which runs the Turkish frontier. Toward the northeast the plain narrows between the Istranca and the Stara Planina, becomes less regular where there are volcanic intrusions, and reaches the Black Sea. The climate of the Mariça Plain is milder even than that of the depression of the upper Tundza Valley, and winters are shorter and less severe. Rainfall, however, is small, and there are areas of steppe. Irrigation is practiced where there is sufficient water, and rice is grown along the rivers. Wheat, maize, tobacco, tomatoes, and sunflower are grown and also the grape vine and southern fruits, such as the peach and apricot.

There are few towns. Plovdiv (Philippopolis, 125,500) in the west, is the largest. It lies on both railway and river, was an ancient focus of trade, and has now grown to be the second largest city of Bulgaria. Other towns are mostly market centers on the edge of the plain, at the meeting place of highland and lowland, where are exchanged the products of each.

The town and port of Burgas (43,500) lies where this plain reaches the Black Sea. It is connected by rail with the interior and tends to replace Varna (78,000), renamed Stalin, some 50 miles to the north, as the chief port of Bulgaria.

Rhodope. The Rhodope is a high and rugged massif of crystalline rock which presents a very serious barrier to communications. It has no transverse valleys and few passes to assist travelers. It contains the highest mountains in the whole Balkans. South of Sofia is the Rila Planina, a stretch of land of over 6,000 feet in height, which rises in Musala to 9,600 feet. A little to the south is the Pirin Planina, whose greatest heights are only a few hundred feet lower. Similar altitudes extend eastward for over 100 miles before the land drops to the Mariça Valley. The Rhodope Mountains are drained southward by the Struma and Mesta Rivers, which cross northern Greece to the Aegean Sea. There are a number of small, fertile basins in the western part of the Rhodope; agriculture is practiced, but the range as a whole is unproductive and inhospitable. Snow lies for much of the year on the higher ground. Its summits have been fretted by ice action. Much of the lower slopes are forested, and only the lumberjack and the transhumant shepherd find employment.

Economic Development. A higher proportion of the people of Bulgaria is engaged in agriculture than of any other European country, and nowhere, except in Albania, have manufacturing industries been less developed. The former large estates have generally been broken up into small holdings, which are generally very small by western European standards. The conditions of cultivation, as in other Balkan countries, are very poor, and an overgreat concentration on cereal crops does not give the soil an opportunity to recover. It was estimated after the Second World War that nearly a quarter of the farms had no draught animals and nearly a fifth, no plow. Animal husbandry is important, as so large an area is suited only to rough grazing. In particular there are very large flocks of sheep. The wool is used in the domestic cloth industry. Industrial crops, such as cotton and hemp, are grown but are not important and have not given rise to any important manufacturing industries.

Mineral resources are little explored, but there are no indications of any great wealth in this respect. There are a number of deposits of brown coal, and production in 1949 was about 5 million tons. The manufacturing industries are almost wholly related to the domestic agricultural production: flour milling, sugar refining, and tanning.

Exports have consisted in recent years very largely of goods of agricultural origin. Tobacco predominates; live animals and animal products, such as skins and wool, and cereals and fruit make up most of the remainder. The imports are mainly textiles, metal goods, and machinery. The volume of trade has always been small, and the amount of trade per head of population was before the last war less than in any other European country. Its direction was very largely toward the industrial countries of central and western Europe, and a restoration of this trade must be considered urgent for the prosperity of Bulgaria.

YUGOSLAVIA

The "Land of the Southern Slavs" first gained political independence in 1918. This new state, however, was built around the nucleus of the older kingdom of Serbia, which had achieved its independence of the Turks early in the nineteenth century. Modern Serbia, however, took its rise in the forested hills which lie south of the Sava and the Danube in the province of Šumadija. From this area the Serb state expanded southward during the first century of its existence and in 1912 absorbed the upper valley of the Vardar. West of Serbia and close to the coast of the Adriatic Sea lay the barbaric little kingdom of Montenegro, which at the end of the First World War threw in its lot with Serbia in the new Yugoslav state.

More than half of the territory of the new state consisted of land which had been under Austrian or Hungarian domination. Yugoslavia was faced with the claims of Italy and Hungary for the restoration of some part of this territory, but apart from the Italian seizure of Fiume, these claims were not pressed.

Yugoslavia is a state put together in modern times. It is a polyglot state, still far from having a national tradition. Its human complexities are matched by its varied and irregular physique.

Yugoslavia consists of a region of plains and low hills in the north drained by the Danube, a mass of tangled hill country which forms the center of the country, and the Dinaric Mountains which fringe the Adriatic coast.

Sava Valley and Danubian Plain. The northern region of Yugoslavia resembles closely the adjoining areas of Hungary. Soft recent deposits cover an ancient mass of crystalline rock, which shows through its mantle of later deposits in a few places and forms the forested hills of Psunj, Papuk, and the Fruška Gora. The region is drained primarily by the Drava and Sava, right-bank tributaries of the Danube, and by the Danube and the Tisza. Along the rivers

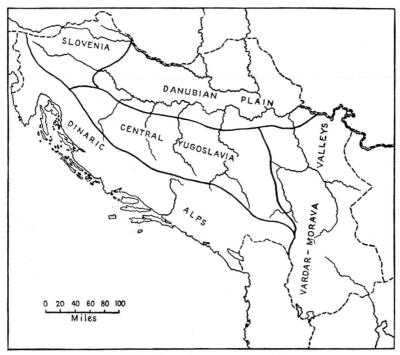

FIG. 180. Physical divisions of Yugoslavia.

is a belt of low land, marshy and liable to flooding. Away from the streams is a dry loess-covered plain. This is fertile agricultural land and supports a dense population. The hilly lands of western Slavonia are the most densely populated. The more productive flatter regions to the east, known collectively as the Voivodina, were exposed to the fury of the Turkish wars, and their economic development inhibited. Though hamlets and isolated dwellings are now beginning to appear, most of the peasants live in large, nucleated villages, like those of Hungary (p. 279), designed to give protection to their inhabitants. The fields often lie at great distances from the villages to which they belong. But the region is well cultivated, especially toward the east. Wheat and maize are grown, and rye in the hills. The grape vine is widely distributed, and orchards, chiefly plum, are numerous.

Zagreb (Agram, 290,500) is the chief town in the west of the region. It stands back from the northern bank of the Sava, ringed by the mountains. It is a natural center for the fertile

and populous plain of the upper Sava and has agricultural industries which serve the surrounding area. Belgrade (Beograd, 389,000) lies to the west, at the junction of the Sava with Danube and on the boundary of the central hilly region. The city crowns a limestone cliff above the Danube on a site which the Romans had utilized for a fortress. Its position at the junction of the two rivers has brought it trade. Belgrade lies on the railway from Vienna to Constantinople and also to Thessalonike, and its position on the edge of the Voivodina has encouraged the growth of agricultural industries.

The town of Subotica (112,500) is the largest of the market centers of the fertile Voivodina. Novi Sad (77,500), a bridge town on the Danube, is a similar center for the more southerly plains.

Slovenia. Slovenia is a small, mountainous unit contained between branches of the Alpine chain. On the north, forming for much of its length the frontier between Yugoslavia and Austria, are the Karawanken Alps, a steep and narrow range, whose snow-capped and serrated

Zagreb in Croatia. This is one of the most Western cities of Yugoslavia. Its broad streets, parks, and handsome buildings are reminiscent of Austria, and the area at one time formed part of the Austrian Empire. (*Yugoslav Information Service.*)

ridge appears to separate the two countries as if by a knife. On the west are the Julian Alps. These extend and broaden southward into the limestone plateau of the Julian Karst, a region so distinctive that it is considered separately. Slovenia is of great strategic importance because here the headwaters of the Danubian rivers approach the coast of the Adriatic. The karst which separates them is low and, in general, not difficult to cross, and Adriatic ports have developed to serve a Danubian hinterland. The railway from Vienna to Trieste and Fiume passes through Maribor (67,000), where it crosses the Drava, and Ljubljana (Laibach, 121,000), the capital of Slovenia.

The region is one of great scenic beauty. Agriculture is practiced wherever the land is sufficiently level. Maize and wheat are grown, and vineyards cover the sunny slopes. Villages are compact, without the uniformity and great size of those of the region last considered. They are more tasteful in their style, and their appearance more German than Slavonic. Lju-

bljana, a small and attractive town with baroque architecture of the eighteenth century, belongs, as far as its appearance is concerned, to western Europe rather than eastern.

Karst and the Dinaric Mountains. The limestone hills which formed the western limit of Slovenia broaden as they continue southeastward into the Dinaric Mountains. These are characterized by the great extension of their limestone deposits. Limestone forms much of the surface of an area of from 50 to 100 miles in breadth and no less than 350 miles in length from Italy to Albania. Within this area surface drainage is rare. Only the Neretva, deeply sunk in a gorgelike valley, flows across this region. A few streams, including the Una, a tributary of the Sava, rise within the limestone, but most of the drainage is underground. The surface of the limestone is broken by solution hollows, known as *poljes*, and by vertical pipes, known as *dolines*, formed by the solution of the limestone. Most inland settlements are situated in *poljes*, where a residual clay, left after the solution of the limestone, provides soil and retains moisture. All around is the rolling plateau, part with a soil and grass, part with a thin cover of scrub forest dwarfed by lack of moisture, part showing the bare dry limestone, without soil or plant.

The mountains form ridges which lie from northeast to southwest. Between are valleys,

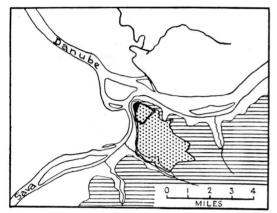

Fig. 181. The situation of Belgrade (Beograd). The original fortress and city, enclosed by a thick line, lay on a steep bluff overlooking the Sava and Danube.

sometimes with sparse settlements but often devoid of flowing water. The coastal ranges drop steeply to the shores of the Adriatic Sea, and off the coast long, narrow, and rocky islands are all that remain of other limestone ranges, now in large measure destroyed by the sea. Along the coast are narrow and disconnected areas of flat land, each backed by the steep, limestone front of the Dinaric Mountains. The contrast between the eastern and western borders of the region is very marked. The east belongs to central Europe. Its summers are hot and winters cold; snow may lie for several months on the higher ground. The west is Mediterranean in climate. Its summers may be only a little less hot than those of the interior, but its winters are mild. Rain falls in winter. The hillsides are terraced for the vine, and near the sea the olive grows.

Houses and villages are not attractive in the mountains of the interior. They are roughly built of stone or wood, the house serving often to shelter both man and beast. Near the coast, however, the Italian influence is dominant, as is the German in Slovenia, and in the coastal

towns the predominating architectural style is that of the Italian Renaissance. As a result of recent changes of frontier, Yugoslavia has acquired the towns of Fiume and Pola, though Trieste still lies outside its borders. Fiume (Rieka, 73,000) is a port of some importance and is linked by rail with the Danubian Plain. Zadar (Zara), Šibenik (Sebenico), Split (Spalato, 50,000), Dubrovnik (Ragusa), and a num-

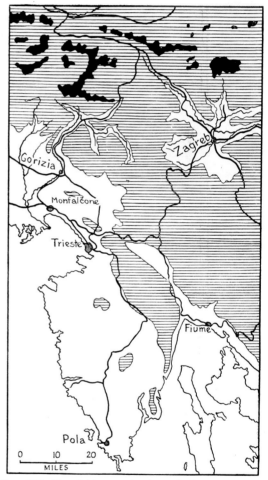

Fig. 182. The Istrian peninsula and the situation of Trieste.

ber of lesser towns are all "Venetian" in their appearance, and many were established by Venice in the days of its commercial greatness. Their present importance, however, is small; they are cut off from the rest of Yugoslavia by the karst, across which transportation is diffi-

Dubrovnik. The city lies on the warm and sunny shore of the Adriatic Sea. Italian influences are very strong in the architecture of the city and the ways of the people. (*Yugoslav Information Service.*)

cult. Though Šibenik, Split, and Dubrovnik are linked by rail with the Danubian Plain, the railroads are inadequate for modern requirements. They cannot expect to develop as great ports. They have small fishing industries, entertain tourists, and live, like other Mediterranean cities which have no dominant industries, by every variety of petty trafficking.

The Istrian peninsula, newly acquired by Yugoslavia, is a dry and sterile limestone tableland, of little height above sea level and dotted with deep and rocky solution cavities. The Quarnero Gulf, between Istria and the Jugoslav coast, is dotted with islands, like the fiord coast of Norway. The Velebit Mountains rise abruptly from the coast and interpose a serious barrier to all movement between the coast and the interior. A gap between the Velebit and Dinaric Mountains is followed by a railway, and south of the latter range is the Neretva Valley, used by the railway from Dubrovnik to Sarajevo. Southeast of the Neretva Valley are the hills of Herzegovina (Hercegovina) and Monte-

negro (Crnagora), wild and difficult of access, in which groups of Serbs maintained their freedom from Turkish rule. On the coast is the deep, rocky inlet of Kotor (Cattaro), formerly used by the Austrians as a naval base.

Central Yugoslavia. Between the limestone plateau of the Dinaric Mountains and the fertile valley of the Sava are the mountains of central Yugoslavia, a rugged area traversed by numerous rivers whose deep valleys make communication difficult. High, forested, and inhospitable masses of harder rocks alternate with *poljes*, dissolved from the limestone, in which settlement is thicker and agriculture more intensive. The region is broadly triangular in shape, narrowing westward between the Dinaric highlands and the Sava Valley. Four major rivers rise on the southern borders of the region and cross it in deep, winding valleys to reach the Sava. In the west is the Una, followed in part by the railway to Split. Next is the Vrbas, which drains the wild mountains of central Bosnia and emerges onto the Sava Plain near

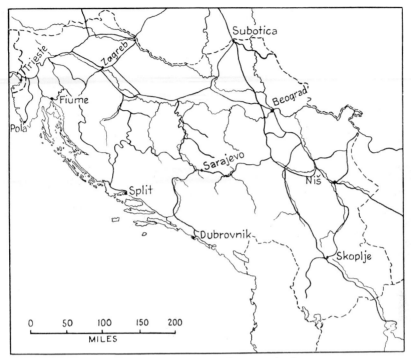

FIG. 183. Yugoslavia: cities and communications.

the town of Banjaluka. The Bosna rises in the same hills. For most of its course northward it is cutting across the high mountain ranges of Bosnia, but near Sarajevo its valley widens to a fertile plain. This is the heart of the province of Bosnia, the most densely peopled area within the Yugoslav highlands. Sarajevo (119,000) is its largest town, an industrial and business center for the whole region and one of the largest towns of Yugoslavia. The Drina, the largest and most easterly of the four rivers, takes its rise in the yet wilder mountains of Crnagora, where the princes of Montenegro once maintained a rude independence in their little capital of Cetinje, renamed Titograd. Except in the north, the valley is steep and rugged, more suited for rough grazing than for agriculture. The river formerly constituted the frontier between independent Serbia and Turkish-held Bosnia, a fact which militated yet further against settlement and development.

Along their northern margin the mountains drop through the hills of Krajina and Posavina to the Sava Plain. The area under agriculture

increases, and population becomes more dense. A line of small towns lies here, as so often in such circumstances, along the border of hill and plain. These are sprawling, insanitary, and sometimes ugly but nevertheless are Western in their architecture, plan, and function. Within the mountains, where the imprint of the years of Turkish occupation went deeper, the small towns belong to the East. Their low houses are of bricks of sun-dried mud. The roofs, flat or with only a slight slope, and the mosque, with dome and minaret, even if the muezzin no longer calls the faithful to prayer from its high platform, show that a cultural divide has been passed.

Vardar-Morava Valleys. Eastern Yugoslavia differs from central in the isolation of its mountain masses, in the number of natural routeways through them, and in the development of more numerous and larger plains and basins. It is drained northward to the Danube by the Serbian Morava and southward to the Aegean Sea by the Vardar. The valleys of these two rivers are continuous in a north-to-south direc-

Skoplje in Yugoslav Macedonia. The city grew up around a fortress on a steep crag above the river Vardar. The surrounding country is mountainous and forbidding, and the city lacks the grace and dignity of those of more Westernized parts of Yugoslavia. (*Yugoslav Information Service.*)

tion, their watershed presents no sharp divide, and together they form one of the most important routeways in the Balkans. In its northern part, from Belgrade to Niš, it is followed by the Orient Express route. West of the Morava-Vardar route and parallel with it is that which follows the Ibar Valley, through the Kossovo Basin, to join the Vardar Valley at Skoplje (Üsküb).

The region is divided into a number of separate mountain masses. In the north, between the Morava and the Danube, is the region known as the Šumadija, an area of hills of limestone and schist, in which harder rocks give rise to higher and more rugged topography. It has a severe climate, cold in winter with heavy snow and hot in summer. Until modern times it was thickly forested with oak and elm and provided a refuge for the Serbs in their revolt against the Turkish rule. In recent times, however, the Šumadija has been in part cleared of its woodland cover and, wherever possible, brought under cultivation. The lower and more open valleys are now well settled and cultivated. Urban settlements are found exclusively in the surrounding lowlands, where they depend upon both long-distance commerce and the trade between mountain and plain.

South of the Šumadija and west of the Ibar is the mountainous district of the Raška, and east of the Ibar, the similar Kapaonik Mountains. Settlements are limited to loosely agglomerated villages of wooden houses, each standing in its small garden patch. The economy is more pastoral than arable. Sheep and goats are kept on the rough grazing of the hills, and transhumance is practiced. Between the two areas of hill is the Ibar Valley, deep and narrow in part but widening south of Mitrovica into a broad, upland basin, the Kossovo *Polje*. This is a small area of some natural wealth and during the Middle Ages was the nucleus of the earliest kingdom of Serbia. It was practically deserted, except for the transhumant shepherds who wintered here, during the disturbed period of the Turkish occupation, and the present settlement and development of the basin are comparatively recent. The towns of Mitrovica and Priština, which lie on its margin, are still quite small market towns, in which Turkish influence remains strong.

Between the Kossovo *Polje* and the Albanian frontier is a similar but larger basin, the Metohija *Polje*, drained by the White Drin, which flows westward through Albania to the Adriatic. Despite the relatively favorable conditions, the Metohija Basin is still not well populated. In Roman times it was a corridor from the Adriatic to the Morava and Danube Valleys, and in modern times Serbia looked upon it as a potential outlet toward the sea. It was, in fact, the conflict between Serbia and other powers for the possession of this routeway that contributed in 1912 to the creation of the state of Albania. There are a number of towns around the margin of the basin. Peć and Prizren are now the chief towns of the area.

South of the Metohija Basin lies the basin of Tetovo, containing Skoplje (91,500) and Kumanovo. This is larger than the Metohija but, like it, has urban centers which derive from the period of Roman occupation. It is also an old lake basin, possessing soils of high natural fertility. Its development has, however, been inhibited by centuries of unrest. The towns are large, but oriental both in appearance and function. Life centers in the bazaar, where are innumerable craftsmen in wood, leather, and metal. There are no factory industries.

In southwestern Yugoslavia, close to both the Albanian and the Greek frontiers, is the Bitolj (Monastir) Basin, which is not unlike the basins lying to the north. West of it are the smaller basins which contain Lakes Ohrid and Prespa, only part of which lies in Yugoslavia. The climate becomes drier toward the south, but the extremes of temperature are moderated only little. The mountains are forested or covered only with rough grass. The basins are steppe-like. Pastoral activities are important throughout the region, and transhumance is still practiced, though of diminishing importance as the lowland winter grazing comes to be used for crop farming.

The Morava, which takes its source quite close to the Skoplje Basin, widens northward into a broad valley which continues to the Danube. This region is relatively populous, and there are a number of towns: Leskovac, with its cotton textile industries; Niš (50,500), a commercial and route center, where the Sofia railroad branches from that to Thessalonike; Kruševac and Kragujevac, each with chemical and food industries.

The Vardar Valley broadens southward into Macedonia. It crosses in turn a number of east-west hill barriers which divide the area into a series of small plains, broadly resembling the "compartments" of the lower Rhône Valley. As the Aegean Sea is approached, the climate becomes progressively more Mediterranean. The extreme temperatures of winter are moderated, and rainfall shows increasingly a concentration in the winter months. Its total is generally small, and much of the lower land is covered with a steppe over which graze large flocks of sheep. Macedonia is a byword for racial intermixture and for the political unrest which is in part a consequence of it. Even today the groups of Turks, Gypsies, and nomadic Vlachs add to the complexities of the area, to which the Bulgars cherish long-standing claims.

East of the valleys of the Morava and Vardar are the borders of the Balkan and Rhodope Mountains. Their sparsely populated wildernesses serve to divide Bulgaria from Yugoslavia, though within their fastnesses dwell peoples whose allegiance to one side or the other is far from clearly defined and whose wanderings across the frontier have in the past occasioned friction between the two countries. The southern bank of the Danube at the Iron Gate lies within Yugoslavia, and east of the Iron Gate, where the river emerges again onto the plain, is a small region of Yugoslavia, formed by the Timok Valley, which is cut off by mountains from the rest of the country. Its frontier position and difficulty of access have hindered its economic development.

Economic Development. Yugoslavia is one of the newer countries of Europe, like Czechoslovakia, with which there are certain similarities. Both are composed of more than one linguistic group, both are predominantly Slav, and both have a tradition of resistance to the Germans. Neither, lastly, has effected a real integration of its several groups into a single nation. The Yugoslavs consist predominantly—about 57 per cent—of the Serbs, the most numerous, the least developed economically, but the politically dominant group; the Croats, about 24 per cent, more cultured and more Germanized; and lastly, the Slovenes, about 9 per cent, the smallest group but economically the most advanced. To these should be added the Macedonians, the Italians who have remained in the Dinaric coastal belt, the Albanians of the Raška, the Bulgars of Macedonia, the Hungarians and Romanians of the northern plain, together with the seminomadic Vlachs and residual Turkish groups.

The total population on the eve of the Second World War was over 15,800,000. The birth rate is high, and this total may be expected to increase. The bulk of the population is rural in its habitat and agricultural in its pursuits. There are many market towns, but most are very small. Belgrade, the capital, has about 389,000 inhabitants, and altogether there are only five cities with a population over 100,000. Most towns lie in the Danube and Sava Valleys in northern Yugoslavia and on the Vardar-Morava routeway. Over three-quarters of the employed persons are engaged in agriculture, and the distribution of population is largely determined by that of cultivable land. Agricultural population is dense on the small areas of agricultural land in the Dinaric Mountains, and very high densities are recorded in Herzegovina and along the Dinaric coast.

Farm holdings are in general small. Before the Second World War there was a very large number of small and dwarf holdings, and large holdings which existed then seem since to have been broken up.

Yugoslavia may be divided into three agricultural regions which accord closely with the physical divisions. The northern plains are good agricultural land and well cultivated. The hilly region of central Yugoslavia has more grazing and rough pasture than the north, and here a more primitive agriculture is practiced. Wheat is less important, rye and oats more so than in the plains. The coastal region of the Adriatic is Mediterranean in its climate and agriculture. The grape and the olive predominate, and animal husbandry is of only trifling importance.

Yugoslavia has a considerable mineral wealth. Coal, much of it brown coal, is mined in Slovenia, Bosnia, and the Morava and Timok Valleys. Altogether there is an annual output of about 12 million tons of coal of all kinds. There are a number of copper, lead, zinc, and chrome mines, and the production of lead ore has in recent years been one of the largest in Europe. Most of the industrial development is in the northern plain, where the means of communication are better developed and the market larger. It is concerned principally with working up the agricultural produce of the country. Metallurgical, engineering, and textile industries are relatively undeveloped and unimportant.

Railway development is uneven. In the northern plain it is adequate but in the mountains which cover the greater part of Yugoslavia is confined to a few trunk lines and a number of narrow-gage lines. Of the ports only Fiume has an adequate railway connection with the interior. Under normal political conditions the Danube is an important commercial highway in northern Yugoslavia. The Sava is used to a smaller degree, but other rivers are of only slight value.

The foreign trade of Yugoslavia formerly resembled that of its Balkan neighbors. It was an exporter of agricultural produce and minerals and an importer of metal wares, textiles and textile materials, chemicals, and other manufactured goods. It appears that a trading pattern not unlike that of the 1930's is gradually being restored.

Yugoslavia belongs in part to southern Europe. Its Mediterranean coast, 400 miles from the Istrian peninsula to the border of Albania, is backed by high mountains difficult to cross in most places. There are few railroad crossings, but this region does serve to link Yugoslavia with the countries of the west. Yugoslavia thus faces both east and west. This is reflected in Yugoslav politics. Before 1914, there was a strong pro-Austrian faction opposing the nationalistic Serbs, who generally depended upon Russia. Between the two wars a not dissimilar situation existed. Today Yugoslavia, profiting from her geographical position and from the relative ease with which she can obtain material support from her western allies, has broken with Russia. All the Slav nations of central Europe are in varying degrees hostile to Russian domination, but only Yugoslavia has hitherto escaped from the Russian fold.

In other respects Yugoslavia resembles her Danubian neighbors. She is poor and backward, like the rest, but has plans of agricultural and industrial development which are being implemented. She is able, as other Danubian states are not, to obtain capital equipment from the west, either by loan or by purchase, for her development. Alone of the Danubian states, Yugoslavia is reviving what may be regarded as the normal pattern of trade, an exchange of the agricultural and mineral produce of the east for the factory products of the west.

BIBLIOGRAPHY

GENERAL

"Agrarian Problems from the Baltic to the Aegean," Royal Institute of Internal Affairs, London, 1944.

Ancel, J., "Manuel géographique de politique européenne," Vol. I, L'Europe centrale, Paris, 1938.

Basch, A., "The Danube Basin and the German Economic Sphere," London, 1944.

Beaver, S. H., Railways in the Balkan Peninsula, *G.J.*, XCVIII, 273–294.

Chamberlain, J. P., "The Regime of the International Rivers, Danube and Rhine," New York, 1923.

Cvijić, J., "La Péninsule balkanique: Géographie humaine," Paris, 1918.

"Economic Development in S. E. Europe," Political and Economic Planning, London, 1945.

"Géographie universelle," Vol. IV, Part II, Suisse Autriche, Hongrie, Tchecoslovaquie, Pologne, Roumanie; Vol. VII, La Méditerranée et les péninsules mediterranéennes, Part II, Italie, Péninsule des Balkans, Paris, 1934.

Kish, George, Rural Problems of Central and Southeastern Europe: A Review, *G.R.*, XXXV, 1945, 286–290.

———, A TVA on the Danube, *G.R.*, XXXVII, 1947, 274–302.

Kolarz, Walter, "Myths and Realities in Eastern Europe," London, 1946.

Macartney C. A., "The Danubian Basin," Oxford, 1939.

———, "Problems of the Danube Basin," Cambridge, 1942.

Moore, Wilbert E., "Economic Demography of Eastern and Southern Europe," League of Nations, Geneva, 1945.

Morgan, O. S. (ed.), "Agricultural Systems of Middle Europe," New York, 1932.

Popper, Otto, The International Regime of the Danube, *G.J.*, CII 1943, 240–253.

Seton-Watson, H., "Eastern Europe between the Wars," Cambridge, 1945.

Seton-Watson, R. W., "Danubian Clues to European Peace," London, 1935.

Steers, Mrs. J. A., The Artisan Element in the Slav Countries, *G.J.*, CIII, 1944, 101–119.

Wanklyn, H. G., "The Eastern Marchlands of Europe," London, 1941.

Warriner, Doreen, "Economics of Peasant Framing," Oxford, 1939.

HUNGARY

Beynon, Erdmann D., Budapest: An Ecological Study, *G.R.*, XXXIII, 1943, 256–275.

———, Migrations of Hungarian Peasants, *G.R.*, XXVII, 1937, 214–228.

"Conference on Rural Life: Hungary," League of Nations, Geneva, 1939.

Macartney, C. A., "Hungary and Her Successors," Oxford, 1937.

Ormsby, H., The Danube as a Waterway, *S.G.M.*, XXXIX, 1923, 103–112.

Teleki, Count Paul, "The Evolution of Hungary and Its Place in European History," New York, 1923.

Wanklyn, Harriet, The Role of Peasant Hungary in Europe, *G.J.*, XCVII, 1941, 18–35.

A bibliography of geographical works on Hungary is J. V. Cholnoky, Ungarn, 1910–1928, *Geog. Jahrb.*, XLIII, 1928, 181–192.

ROMANIA

"Atlas de l'agriculture en Roumanie," Bucharest, 1929.

Beynon, Erdmann D., The Eastern Outposts of the Magyars, *G.R.*, XXXI, 1941, 63–78.

De Martonne, E., The Carpathians, *G.R.*, III, 1916, 417–437.

Fleure, H. J., and R. A. Pelham (ed.), "Roumania: Eastern Carpathian Studies," Le Play Society, London, 1936.

Fleure, H. J., and E. Estyn Evans, "Roumania: South Carpathian Studies," Le Play Society, London, 1939.

Kormos, C., "Rumania," British Survey Handbooks, Cambridge, 1944.

Roberts, M. Catherine, Rumania Today, *E.G.*, IX, 1933, 230–255.

Roberts, Henry L., "Rumania: Political Problems of an Agrarian State," New Haven, 1951.

Roucek, Joseph S., Economic Geography of Roumania, *E.G.*, VII, 1931, 390–399.

Seton-Watson, R. W., "A History of the Roumanians from Roman Times to the Completion of Unity," Cambridge, 1934.

Bibliographies of Works on Romania

Conover, Helen F., "The Balkans. IV, Rumania: A Selected List of References," Library of Congress, Division of Bibliography, Washington, D.C., 1943.

Wachner, Heinrich, Rumänien, 1929–1937, *Geographisches Jahrbuch*, LIII, 1938, 631–686.

Bulgaria

Ancel, J., "La Macédoine," Paris, 1929.

Batakliev, Ivan, Viticulture in Bulgaria, G., XXIV, 1938, 85–94.

Beshkov, Anastas, Tobacco in Bulgaria, *E.G.*, XVI, 1940, 188–194.

———, The Upper Thracian Plain in Bulgarian Agriculture, *E.G.*, XV, 1939, 179–184.

Bruman, Henry J., The Bulgarian Rose Industry, *E.G.*, XII, 1936, 273–278.

"Conference on Rural Life: Bulgaria," League of Nations, Geneva, 1939.

Doukas, Kimon A., Bulgaria's Modes of Transport, *E.G.*, XIX, 1943, 337–346.

Gellert, J. H., "Mittelbulgarien," Berlin, 1937.

Logio, G. C., "Bulgaria Past and Present," Manchester, England, 1936.

Roucek, Joseph S., Economic Geography of Bulgaria, *E.G.*, XI, 1935, 307–323.

Wilhelmy, H., "Hochbulgarien," 2 vols., Kiel, 1935–1936.

Bibliographies of Works on Bulgaria

Wilhelmy, Herbert, Bulgarien, 1910–1932, *Geographisches Jahrbuch*, XLVIII, 1933, 51–100.

Conover, Helen F., "The Balkans. III, Bulgaria: A Selected List of References," Library of Congress, Division of Bibliography, Washington D.C., 1943.

Yugoslavia

Bicanic, Rudolf, The Effects of War on Rural Yugoslavia, *G.J.*, CIII, 1944, 30–49.

"Conference on Rural Life: Yugoslavia," League of Nations, Geneva, 1939.

Cornish, V., Bosnia, the Borderland of Serb and Croat, *G.*, XX, 1935, 260–270.

Kerner, R. (ed.) "Yugoslavia," United Nations Series, Berkeley, 1949.

Kostanick, H. Louis, Post-war Yugoslavia (a bibliographical note), *G.R.*, XLI, 1951, 494–497.

Lebon, J. H. G., The Jezera, A Mountain Community in Southwest Yugoslavia, *G.*, XX, 1935, 271–282.

Lodge, O., "Peasant Life in Yugoslavia," London, 1941.

———, Villages and Houses in Yugoslavia, *G.*, XXI, 1936, 94–106. (This is also contained in O. Lodge, "Peasant Life in Yugoslavia.")

Moodie, A. E., "The Italo-Yugoslav Boundary," London, 1945.

Newbigin, M. I., "Geographic Aspects of the Balkan Problem," New York, 1915.

Roucek, Joseph S., Resources of Yugoslavia, *E.G.*, IX, 1933, 413–425.

Shackleton, M. R., Economic Resources and Problems of Yugoslavia, *S.G.M.*, XLI, 1925, 346–365.

Stamp, L. Dudley, (ed.), "Slovene Studies," Le Play Society, London, 1933.

West, Rebecca, "Black Lamb and Gray Falcon," New York, 1941.

Wilkinson, H. R., "Maps and Politics: A Review of the Ethnic Cartography of Macedonia," Liverpool, 1951.

Bibliographies of Geographical Works on Yugoslavia

Conover, Helen F. "The Balkans. V, Yugoslavia: A Selected List of References," Library of Congress, Division of Bibliography, Washington, D.C., 1943.

Vujević, P., Südslawien, 1913–1928, *Geographisches Jahrbuch*, XLV, 1929, 252–288.

Official publications are very scanty for the four countries considered in this chapter. Their recovery and development are reported on in the statistical and other publications of the Economic Commission for Europe. But, with the exception of Yugoslavia, they have been under Soviet domination since the close of the Second World War, and detailed commercial and other reports are not available.

Only a relatively small amount of geographical work has been done in these countries. The study of geography is progressing in Yugoslavia (see Chauncy D. Harris, Present Status of Geography in Yugoslavia, *G.R.*, XLII, 1952, 314), and there was formerly a Royal Geographical Society in Bucharest (Romania) whose bulletin contained geographical articles.

CHAPTER 23: *The Mediterranean Region*

The Mediterranean region is the most distinctive of all the major regions dealt with in this book. All other titles—western, northern, central—are in some degree vague, but Mediterranean Europe has a precise meaning. This degree of definition is due to the similarity of climate over the region, which contrasts strikingly to other European climates. The Mediterranean, we have seen in Chap. 2, has a climate distinguished by mild winters, when the rainfall mostly occurs, and by hot dry summers. The greatest heat, occurring during the season of drought, limits the natural vegetation to a sparse covering of dry, aromatic scrub or thin forests of drought-resisting trees. The climate and vegetation of the Mediterranean are considered more fully in Chap. 2.

The climatic character of the region restricts its agriculture. Grass dries up during the summer, and then there is little food for stock. Pastoral husbandry is limited to those animals —chiefly sheep and goats—which can live on this poor growth. Cattle are few. Crops grow during the winter and spring and are harvested in the early summer. Fruit crops are relatively very important. The olive, which requires freedom from frost and can stand hot and dry conditions, is the typical tree crop. So representative is the olive of the Mediterranean region that its climate has been described as coextensive with the olive. The grape vine is also grown widely, and wine is one of the commonest drinks. The grain crop most extensively grown is wheat; other cereals, especially barley, are of secondary importance. Beans and vegetables are grown, but the staple foods of the Mediterranean are bread and wine, and olive oil supplies the fat required in the human diet.

The Mediterranean region is further distinguished by its hilly or even mountainous terrain. For about three-quarters of its circumference, the Mediterranean Sea is bordered by mountain ranges. In general these drop steeply to the water. In places there are small coastal plains. Only along the southeastern shore is there a large and continuous area of low-lying and flat coast. The region under consideration encloses the Mediterranean Sea; nowhere does it stretch far from the water. Only in central Spain, northern Italy, and the interior of Turkey are conditions met with that cannot be described as marine.

The Mediterranean Sea is highly irregular in outline. Many peninsulas stretch into the water and are continued in chains of islands. This means that marine conditions are carried far into the land while at the same time no part of the sea is far from some island or headland. This assisted early man to become a sailor, allowing him to "hop" from one island to another until he had mastered the craft of navigation.

The sea is divided itself into a western and an eastern basin, cut off from each other by the narrows between Sicily and Tunisia. In the western basin is the Balearic Island group, as well as the large islands of Corsica and Sardinia. Opening off the eastern basin is the deep, narrow Adriatic Sea and the smaller, island-studded Aegean. Navigation conditions are generally good, especially during the summer months. The atmosphere is clear, and visibility excellent. The sea is almost tideless, the rise and fall of the water being scarcely perceptible in most places. The weather is more predictable than in the stormy northwest. In ancient times the summer was the season for navigation; danger was to be expected if the frail craft sailed too late in the year, as did the boat on which Saint Paul set sail for Rome. The shores of the Mediterranean have a wealth of good natural harbors, many of them naturally free from silting. However, the Mediterranean Sea has never been rich in fish. Its fisheries—the sardine, anchovy, and tunny are the most important species—are of only small and local importance.

Hills and the sea combine with the fair, warm climate to give the Mediterranean its individuality and charm. It has always attracted peoples from the colder, damper, and more cloudy lands of the north. The "barbarian" invader of the Dark Ages, the medieval pilgrim, and the modern tourist all witness to the attractions of the region. Its beauties have been the subject of endless writings, and a very fair "geography" could be put together from the poets and travelers of the past. Shelley, Byron, and Browning among the English poets; Goethe among the German; and Henry James among American writers have all succumbed to its charms.

But the individuality of the Mediterranean does not spring only from the beauty of its natural landscape and the delights of its climate. The Mediterranean region is the home of Western civilization. Close to its shores, in the Nile Valley and in the riverine lands of the Middle East, fundamental steps in early human progress were taken. Man learned to plant and irrigate his crops, to improve the wild plant species, to carry out engineering works to supply his fields with water, to build towns and live in them, and to practice the arts and crafts. Material civilization spread to the Mediterranean shores and was carried to Cyprus and Crete, the "forerunner," as it has been called, of Western civilization, and thence over the islands and peninsulas of Greece to Sicily, Italy, and the rest of the Mediterranean region.

The debt of Greek civilization to that of Crete and of Cretan to Egyptian civilization is difficult to evaluate, but the debt of Western civilization to ancient Greece is great and obvious. Greek civilization grew up around the Aegean Sea, where numerous "city-states" each occupied a small plain between the mountains and the sea. Civilization was urban. The Greek was an agriculturalist, but the refinements of city life—good buildings, the theater, the conversation of the market place—attracted him. Material needs are less here than in the north of Europe and more easily satisfied, and there was leisure for philosophy and poetry at a time when the inhabitants of northwestern Europe were fully employed in an unrewarding agriculture.

Greek civilization spread around the shores of the Greek peninsula and extended to Sicily and Italy, to Libya in North Africa, to the shores of Asia Minor, even to the southern coast of France. It did not permeate the whole Mediterranean, but the civilization of Rome became truly Mediterranean in extent. The Roman Empire expanded outward from the city of Rome (Roma) in central Italy from the fifth century B.C. onward. From Italy it spread to Sicily in the third century B.C., then to Spain, Greece, North Africa, and the Middle East. By the beginning of the Christian era it enclosed the Mediterranean Sea.

Greek civilization had been spread by the foundation of colonies from the mother cities in Greece. The Roman Empire, by contrast, spread by settlement but also by the conquest and assimilation of Mediterranean peoples. Saint Paul, a Jew from Tarsus in Asia Minor, was a Roman citizen; so also was the African, Saint Augustine of Hippo (Bône) in Algeria. The Roman Empire was essentially "thalassic," based upon an internal sea which served as a bond of union between its parts. Commerce moved freely over the Mediterranean; Rome was provisioned with grain from Egypt and North Africa. All roads led to Rome. The Mediterranean was a functional and administrative unit.

This unity was threatened by the invasion of the so-called "barbarians" in the fifth and sixth centuries and was brought to an end when the Arabs occupied the coastlands of the Middle East and North Africa and spread into Spain. This became a frontier. The cities on the coast of southern Europe, which had formerly been centers of commerce, now became fortresses. The coasts were even raided by pirates or corsairs, and the Barbary pirates from the African coast were a danger down to the early years of the nineteenth century. Attempts were made by the states of Europe to reestablish their control over the shores opposite. The Crusades, springing from a mixture of religious and commercial motives, led to a temporary occupation of Egypt and the Holy Land. At this time trading cities, especially the Italian cities of Venice (Venezia) and Genoa (Genova), profited from the revival of trade with the Middle East.

But it was not until the nineteenth century that a degree of unity was restored to the Mediterranean region. The French and the British interested themselves in Egypt. Beginning in 1830, the French conquered Algeria and later extended their control to Tunisia. The British occupied Egypt, and early in the present century, Libya was conquered by the Italians. The southern shores of the sea thus came, as in the period of the Roman Empire, to be controlled by European powers.

This renewed interest in the Mediterranean Sea was in part due to its revival as a highway of commerce. In the nineteenth century the ports of southern Russia, particularly Odessa, began to pour grain into the European market. This came through the Turkish "Straits" into the Mediterranean and thence to the ports of western Europe. In 1869 the Suez Canal was opened. At once ships began to abandon the long and hazardous route around the Cape of Good Hope and to take the shorter route through the Red and Mediterranean Seas. Commercial nations, of which Great Britain was the most important, became interested in protecting this new route. Cyprus was taken by Great Britain in 1878, and Egypt occupied in 1881. Gibraltar at the western entrance of the Mediterranean and the island of Malta in its midst were already in British hands.

During this modern period, which was ushered in 150 years ago, when Napoleon tried to conquer Egypt, no single power has succeeded in controlling the sea. Great Britain, occupying several strategic bases, has come nearest, but it has been Italy, self-constituted heir to the Roman Empire, which has voiced most loudly its claim to control "our sea."

Though not politically united or woven into an economic whole, as in the time of the Roman Empire, the Mediterranean Sea has again a kind of unity. This it derives from the common interest in it of Great Britain, France, Italy, and Russia. Each is interested in the control of some island base or coastal fortress or airfield, and in their deliberations they cannot help considering the sea as a whole. Of the greatest strategic importance are the outlets from the sea:

1. The Straits of Gibraltar are dominated by the rock fortress of the same name. All neighboring areas are kept under international control, like Tangier, or are in the possession of the weak power Spain.

2. The Bosporus and Dardanelles, the "Straits" (see page 303), are in the hands of Turkey, which has power to fortify their banks and thus can prevent the movement of ships between the Black Sea and the Mediterranean. Turkey is under treaty obligation to permit the free movement of peaceful commerce, but Russia takes exception to the fact that Turkey can, if she will, close the Straits.

3. The Suez Canal was dug with private capital and opened in 1869. The shareholders in the canal company are today mainly British and French, though by the terms of the original charter the canal reverts to Egyptian possession in 1968. Since 1881 British troops have been stationed in Egypt, and they now garrison the Suez Canal. Other powers, among them Italy before the Second World War, objected to this British control, and it has further roused the opposition of Egyptian nationalists.

Political control of certain islands and bases within the Mediterranean is scarcely less important than that of the entrances to the sea. The strait between Tunisia and Sicily is dominated by the French naval base of Bizerte (Bizerta). To the east is the British naval, air, and military base of Malta. Under Mussolini, the Italians attempted to control the central Mediterranean by building naval and air bases in southern

Italy, Libya, and the "Dodecanese" Islands, which they then controlled. Political control of the Mediterranean is the result of an unsatisfactory balance between the major European powers.

So far we have considered the similarities which give the Mediterranean region a degree of unity. Only part of the northern shore is European; the rest is Asiatic and African. The Asiatic and African parts of the Mediterranean region were invaded from the seventh century onward by Moslem peoples. The racial composition of these regions may not have been greatly changed, but in religion and culture they became Islamic. Important economic and social consequences sprang from this, a fatalism and an unwillingness to invent or to experiment. These lands slipped back in their material culture in comparison with the European shore. They became oriental, unchanging, and hostile to the Christian and in general more progressive West.

Today these regions are scenes of the utmost poverty. Overcrowding, lack of capital and of education, and rotten and corrupt governmental institutions are characteristic to a far greater degree than in the Danubian and Balkan countries that have just been considered. In recent years material progress has been made in Turkey, where a breach has taken place between the state and Islam. In Israel, immigrants from the West have created a cultural oasis in this region, and the French in Algeria and Tunisia have achieved some progress. But in Egypt, Syria, and parts of North Africa living conditions are extremely low.

It must not be assumed that the European part of this region is in all respects better off. The Spanish, Italian, and Greek peninsulas have been raided or invaded by Islamic peoples for over 1,000 years. They have been continually troubled by war and the material destruction that war brings with it. The southern parts of all three peninsulas have been reconquered by Europeans from Islamic peoples, and the lands divided in large estates, or *latifundia*, among the conquerors. These large estates, owned by absentee landlords and cultivated by a poor, uneducated, and ill-equipped peasantry, continue to characterize southern Spain and southern Italy. The problem is not that these regions cannot accumulate the material wealth necessary for a better life or, except in Italy, that the population is too large but rather that the wealth passes, through the hands of the landowners, into unproductive channels. We shall touch again on this agrarian problem in the next three chapters.

Despite the precocity of the Mediterranean region in the growth of civilization, it is not naturally rich or well-endowed. It has little good soil. Most of its area is mountainous, and much is heavily eroded. The climate precludes animal husbandry on a large scale, with a consequent loss both of manure for the land and of fat and meat for human consumption. There are very few mineral resources and almost no coal. The topography is suited for the generation of hydroelectric power, but little use can be made of streams that run dry in summer.

This section of the book begins with Greece and Albania, countries which belong climatically to the Mediterranean but which could equally fittingly have been included with the Balkans, of which historically they are also a part, in the previous chapter. It seemed illogical to the author to accept too literally the traditional division of the land surface world into continents. Such a division would have permitted him to consider Turkey-in-Europe without reference to the main body of Turkey. It would have excluded Algeria, which is an integral part of France; it would have considered Gibraltar without Tangier. The solution appeared to be to embrace the whole Mediterranean, including Turkey and French North Africa. This raises the question of Egypt, Israel, and Syria. It was decided to include these countries, though not to consider them in so great a detail as would be the case in books devoted to Africa and Asia, respectively.

BIBLIOGRAPHY

Boveri, M., "Mediterranean Cross-Currents," London, 1938.

Cary, M., "The Geographic Background of Greek and Roman History," Oxford, 1949.

East, W. Gordon, "Mediterranean Problems," London, 1940.

———, The Mediterranean Problem, *G.R.*, XXVIII, 1938, 83–101. (This is, in effect, a review of geographical literature, chiefly political geography, on the Mediterranean sphere.)

Monroe, Elizabeth, "The Mediterranean in Politics," Oxford, 1938.

Newbigin, M. I., "Frequented Ways," New York, 1924.

———, "Southern Europe," New York, 1949.

Parain, Charles, "La Méditerranée: les hommes et leurs travaux," Paris, 1936.

Petrie, Sir Charles, "Lords of the Inland Sea," London, 1937.

Pirenne, H., "Medieval Cities," Princeton, N.J., 1925.

Pounds, N. J. G., "Historical and Political Geography of Europe," New York, 1947.

Philippson, A., "Das Mittelmeergebiet," Leipzig, 1922.

Semple, E. C., "The Geography of the Mediterranean Region: Its Relation to Ancient History," New York, 1931.

Siegfried, André, "The Mediterranean," New York, 1947.

CHAPTER 24: *Greece and Albania*

Greece, the third of the three Mediterranean peninsulas of Europe, differs markedly from the other two. It has neither extensive coastal plains, like Italy, nor a wide interior plateau, like Spain. The Greek peninsula is built of rugged mountain ranges, with steep and narrow valleys, few basins or plains, and only a narrow and discontinuous strip of lowland around the

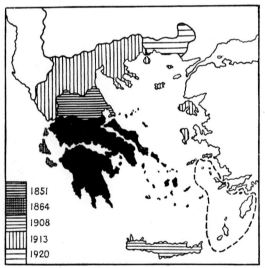

1851
1864
1908
1913
1920

Fig. 184. The territorial expansion of Greece in the nineteenth and twentieth centuries.

coast. It is, as Plato described it in the "Critias" more than 2,000 years ago, like "the skeleton of an emaciated body; the good productive earth has disappeared."

The Greece of today is a peninsula, together with its continental base and certain island groups lying to the east. The Greece of classical times consisted of the periphery of the Aegean Sea, and the sphere of ancient Greek culture embraced areas which now form part of Turkey.

The whole of modern Greece lay, at the beginning of the nineteenth century, within the limits of the Turkish empire. Much of the peninsula achieved its independence by a revolt from the Turks. The Ionian Islands were acquired in 1863. Thessaly was added in 1881; the northern territories of Greek Epirus, Macedonia, and western Thrace, together with Crete and the larger Aegean islands, in 1913; and eastern Thrace in 1923. Albania appeared on the political map in 1912, having been created out of the Turkish Empire.

GREECE

The Greek Peninsula. The center of the Greek peninsula is occupied by a range of folded mountains of extreme geological complexity, great ruggedness, and sparse population. They extend southward from the Prizren Basin on the Yugoslav-Albanian border to the shores of the Gulf of Corinth. There is no name for the range as a whole. In the north it is broken into a number of separate mountain blocks, between and around which movement is possible. Between these formerly ran the Roman road from the Albanian coast to Macedonia and Thrace, and the gaps have been important in modern times rather for their potential than actual value for commerce. In such gaps in the range lie Lakes Ohrid and Prespa, through which runs the frontier of Yugoslavia and Albania. South of the Greek frontier the range becomes more continuous and its barrier nature is accentuated. In the north of this section it is known as the Grammos Mountains and farther south as the Pindus.

There are no towns and few large villages in central Greece. In the north the population is

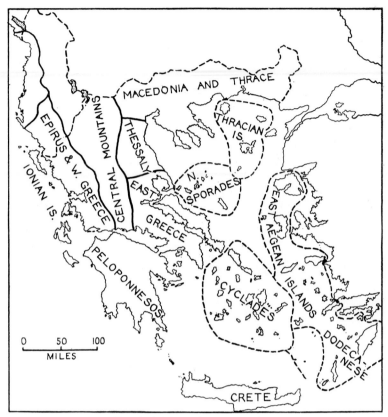

Fig. 185. Physical regions of Greece.

partly made up of Vlach herdsmen, who move seasonally up and down the mountain sides with their animals. Little agriculture is practicable in these desolate mountains. The region was once well forested, but destruction of timber for commerce and in the course of wars has greatly reduced the woodland cover, though it remains one of the best wooded areas of Greece. Rainfall is heavy and increases in volume and in duration northward. Summer temperatures are moderated by the altitude. Winters are often severe, and deep snow may accumulate and lie well into the summer.

The topography of Epirus and western Greece is lower than the central mountains, but the difficulties which it presents to movement are nevertheless great. The region consists of a series of ranges lying parallel to the coast and built of folded sedimentary rocks. It is more productive and more densely peopled than the mountains of the center, and around the deep,

shallow Gulf of Amvrakia is the most extensive of the few areas of lowland formed by the plain of Arta. This was formerly marshy and ill drained, but much of it now makes highly productive land. The climate is milder than in the interior, and rainfall, quite heavy except in the sheltered valleys of the interior, occurs largely in winter. Rivers are merely short torrents which in winter and spring cascade from the mountains to the sea and in summer dry away in their boulder-strewn beds. Despite the better physical conditions, agriculture is backward. Wheat, the vine, and the olive, the three staples of Mediterranean agriculture, are grown, with tobacco and maize. The agriculture is largely subsistence, and the holdings small. Neither fertilizers nor crop rotation are regularly used, and the productivity is low.

Eastern Greece is historically the most famous and important part of Greece, as it contains Athens and Attica (Atticé), the shrine of Delphi

A village on the slopes of Mount Parnassus, north of the Gulf of Corinth. Note the arid appearance of the country and the cultivation terraces in the distance. Note the similarity between this and villages in Italy and Spain (see pp. 326 and 341). (*Hellenic Department of Information.*)

(Delphoi), and the ancient cities of Thebes (Thébai), Megara, and Eleusis (Elevsis). Topographically it is very broken. A series of short ranges extend eastward or east-southeastward from the central mountain mass. Between are small, alluvial plains. Of these the plain of the Kifissos, the classical Boeotia, is the largest. The shallow Lake Kopaïs (Copais), which formerly occupied the center of this plain, was drained in the later years of the nineteenth century, and its site is now agricultural land. The more famous plain of Attica is smaller and broken up by isolated hills, on one of which lies the citadel, or Acropolis, of Athens (Athénai, 481,000). The city grew up during the first millennium B.C. on the steep-sided hill which gave protection to its early inhabitants. The settlement spread over the surrounding lowland. Even in classical times, Athens was linked with its port of Piraeus (Peiraievs) on the Gulf of Salamis by the "Long Walls." Now Athens and Piraeus are merged into one city, which

embraces both the governmental and business offices of the modern capital and, on the Acropolis, the remains of ancient Athens.

Winters are mild, summers hot, and rainfall is slight and limited to winter. Athens has a January average of 48°, a July average of 80°. Agriculture is better practiced than in the regions just considered, though irrigation is required in most parts at some time of the year. Grain crops and fruit are grown, and on these eastern plains tobacco and cotton are produced for export. Beyond the narrow Atalante Channel, the classical Negropont, is the island of Euboea (Evvoia), a long, narrow, and hilly island, in many respects similar to the mainland.

East of the mountainous central area are a number of lower ranges of hills. These are broken up by rivers into short segments and enclose and surround areas of lower and flatter ground. In the north the broad plain of Thessaly stretches from the coastal mountain range to

The Port of Volos, Thessaly. Not a great deal of traffic is handled. In the distance is snow-capped Mount Pelion. (*Hellenic Department of Information.*)

the foothills of the Pindus Mountains. This area is covered with alluvial soil and has from classical times been noted for its fertility, but it is marshy in parts, liable to flooding, and malarial. Much of the lower land is cultivated, though in winter it is visited by the flocks of sheep and goats, often owned by seminomadic Vlach herdsmen, which spend their summers on the high pastures of the Pindus. There are a few small towns in the plain of Thessaly, some of them fortresses built in the course of the centuries of conflict between Greeks and Turks, all of them small, squalid market towns. Rainfall is slight, though many of the rivers are liable to flood in winter. In summer irrigation is necessary in most places if agriculture is to be carried on.

The eastern mountain range is broken by transverse valleys into a number of short segments, in which lie the mountains, famous in Greek mythology, of Olympus, Ossa, and Pelion. The most southerly extension of this range partially encloses the landlocked gulf on which lies the town of Volos. This was an area famous in the history of Greek navigation. Here was fitted out the legendary *Argos*, and many a ship was built of the timbers of nearby Pelion.

Peloponnesos. The most southerly region of Greece is separated from the mainland by the deep, narrow Gulf of Corinth and the Gulf of Aegina, between which is the Corinth Canal. The Peloponnesos continues the Pindus Mountains, but they are broader here and are split up into a number of separate mountain chains. Within the mountains are a number of enclosed basins, whose rivers break through the encircling mountains to the sea. From northwest to southeast across the region is a structural trench, drained by the rivers Alpheios and Evrotas. Along the northern and western margins is a belt of lowland, and smaller plains lie at the heads of the gulfs on the southern and eastern coast.

The climate is even milder here than in western Greece. The summers are hot, and rainfall almost wholly confined to the winter months. Much of the land has been deforested

Macedonia. Much of Macedonia is a dry, rolling, treeless plain. In parts it is naturally very productive, but centuries of war have made it one of the poorest regions of eastern Europe. (*Hellenic Department of Information.*)

and is now covered with only *maquis.* Stands of pine survive on the higher and less accessible lands, but large areas have been practically denuded of soil by erosion and the persistent nibbling of the goats, for which this wild region provides sustenance. Agriculture is no less primitive than farther north, and here, too, wheat, the vine, and the olive are the staples. Small black grapes are dried and exported as currants. The small port of Patrai (Patras, 79,500), on the shore of the Corinthian Gulf, handles most of the currant export. Towns are few and small and situated generally on hilltops. The classical cities of Argos and Sparta (Spartē) are no more than villages, and Corinth (Korinthos) is only a small town of 10,000.

Macedonia and Thrace. This northeasterly region of Greece embraces physical regions which are extensions of areas already met with in the Balkans. The region is one of rolling plains and low hills which increase in height northward until they merge into the Rhodope Mountains. It is of higher agricultural value than much of Greece. In places it is well settled and cultivated, but the political insecurity which has characterized this region for centuries and is even today far from eliminated has seriously hindered its economic development. Here was settled a large proportion of the Greeks evacuated from Asia Minor at the conclusion of the Greek-Turkish war in 1923.

Stretching northward from Macedonia is the Vardar Valley, providing a routeway to the mid-Danubian region. The Yugoslavs have come to look upon the Vardar Valley as one of their outlets to the sea, and this in part has led them in the past to raise claims to the possession of territory in Macedonia and to the use of the port of Thessalonike. At present the Yugoslavs have a small "free zone" in the port.

The plains of Macedonia and Thrace are rather dry but, as elsewhere in eastern Greece, are liable to flooding in winter and spring. Parts of the low-lying land remain marshy and malarial throughout the year, but summers are generally dry, and agriculture is difficult without irrigation. The winters are not free from frost. The olive is, in consequence, rare,

The island of Ithaca, Ionian Islands. This lies off the west coast of Greece and has a higher rainfall and richer vegetation than in eastern Greece. Much of the land is terraced for cultivation. (*Hellenic Department of Information.*)

though the grape vine and other fruits are grown. Tobacco has become important in recent years.

The coast is flat and in many parts fringed with saline marshes. Settlements avoid the coast, and there are only two ports of importance: Thessalonike (Salonika) and Kavalla. The latter is small and has a population of only 50,000, but Thessalonike (226,000), at the head of the Gulf of Thermaikos a few miles east of the mouth of the Vardar, is a port not only for northern Greece but also for Yugoslavia.

The Greek Islands. The "Isles of Greece" have cast their romantic spell over poets and travelers for many generations. They are places of rare beauty. Most of the islands are high and rugged, lifting their crown of brown and olive green from the blue waters of the Aegean and bearing above their steep crags the small white villages of flat-roofed houses. The islands are of small agricultural value. Some are uninhabited; others are visited by goatherds with their animals in summer. At best they produce grapes, olives, and a little grain, the trio upon which Mediterranean life is based.

There is little in the Greek islands today to indicate their great importance in classical times. These islands which were once in the forefront of civilization are now backward and sparsely peopled. Delos (Dhílos), once the center of the great Athenian League of the fifth century B.C., is now merely grazed by goats. It is common to explain this present degeneration at least in part in terms of the Turkish conquest. The long night of Turkish rule was deadening, but it is doubtful whether this alone brought the Greek islands to their present condition.

The Ionian Islands lie to the west of the Greek peninsula. They differ from the islands of the Aegean in their higher rainfall, milder climate, and very much denser population, but culturally they belong with the rest. The Greek hero Odysseus came from the island of Ithaca (Ithakē), one of their number. There are seven in the group. All are mountainous. The olive groves provide the chief employment in the islands, though the vine is grown and its fruit is dried for export.

The Thracian Islands, in the northern Aegean, lie close to the shores of Thrace and Turkey. Thasos and Samothrace are mountainous, forested, and sparsely populated. Lemnos, farther to the south, is less mountainous than the others, and agriculture is of rather greater importance. On Lemnos is the sheltered harbor

Mykonos. This is a small Aegean island. The climate is dry, as is shown by the flat roofs of the houses and the lack of vegetation. The town occupies a steep-sided hill for protection from sea-borne raiders. Much use is still made in the Aegean of windmills as a source of power for grinding grain and other operations.

of Moudros (Mudros), now little used but of some military significance. To the south lie the Sporades, a group of small and rocky islets.

The "Circle of Islands," or Cyclades (Kyklades), is a group of over 20 small islands, some of them low but most mountainous. Sheep and goats are reared, sometimes in considerable numbers, but crop husbandry is not important. Holdings are small, and the peasantry poor. Naxos is the largest and most populous island, though even here the population amounts only to about 20,000.

Close to the coast of Asia Minor, or Turkey,

are the large islands of Mytilene (Lesbos), Khios, and Samos. To the south is a group of smaller islands, scarcely distinguishable from the Cyclades, which they adjoin, known as the Dodecanese. These were occupied by the Italians from 1912 until 1945, when they went to Greece. Rhodes, with a population of 55,000 in its city, also called Rhodes, is the largest and historically the most important, though Leros has in recent years acquired an importance as an Italian naval base. The islands are hilly, but their mild climate and moderate rainfall allow considerable areas to be cultivated. Olives, for which the climate is very well suited, are on some islands the most important crop.

Crete is the largest of the Greek islands but is less than 160 miles from west to east and up to 36 miles from north to south. The island is mountainous, though its mountain ridge is broken into three distinct masses. The mountains drop steeply to the sea on the south. On the north is a narrow coastal plain. The climate is mild; the small rainfall occurs mainly in winter. The vegetation is *maquis*. The once rich forests have now very largely been destroyed. Much of the lowland is under cultivation, though water is often short. The olive, as on so many other Greek islands, is the most important single crop and is followed by wheat and the grape vine. Olive oil and dried grapes are exported. Settlements are most numerous on the flatter northern coastal plain, and here are the few small towns.

Economic Development. Greece, like the Balkan countries in general, is primarily agricultural. Little more than 16 per cent of the working population is engaged in industry and mining. The total population is about 8,025,000. The number was greatly increased after 1923 by the settlement of 800,000 Greeks from Asia Minor, part of the exchange of population between Greece and Turkey. The assimilation of so large a group presented very serious difficulties. The majority were settled in Macedonia and Thrace, where low land, capable of agricultural development, was relatively abundant. Here they developed the cultivation of tobacco, which they had grown in Asia.

Agriculture, however, is primitive. Holdings are generally small, rotation of crops rarely practiced, manure little used, and farm equipment is rudimentary in the extreme. Wheat is grown on the lower and flatter land, but the only other crops of importance are tobacco, the olive, and the vine. Dried grapes, wine, and olive oil are among the more important exports of Greece. The soil is poor except on the alluvial coastal plains, and agricultural returns small. Agricultural production has remained lower than before the war but is being improved with the help of American skill and equipment.

There are in Greece almost as many industrial concerns as there are men engaged in industry. Most are occupied in working up the local produce: wool, hair, tobacco, leather, skins, and hides. Greece has no fuel reserves, except very small quantities of lignite, and there has been little development of hydroelectric power. Mineral resources are of little importance, though small quantities of lead, magnesite, emery, and bauxite are obtained. Only in the few large towns like Athens and Thessalonike are there industrial units which may be called factories, and even here they are small and inefficient.

Transportation routes consist over much of the country of nothing better than rough tracks through the mountains. The only significant railway runs from Thessalonike along the east coast to Athens and then continues to Patrai. There is a line running eastward into Thrace, and certain lines in the Peloponnesos, but most of Greece is untouched by railway development.

The statistics given on page 274 show that Greece is as poor and, in relation to its small extent of agricultural land, as crowded as any country in southeastern Europe. Reference has already been made to the contrast between its present poverty and the glory that once belonged to it. Many a European liberal, aiding the Greeks in their struggle against the Turks in the nineteenth century, discovered with a shock how much the nation of Pericles had degenerated in 2,000 years. The problem of Greece today hinges in part on its political instability, in part on the nature of its economy.

Democratic forms of government have not worked well. The nation's resources have been frittered away in political squabbles or squandered through political corruption.

Climate and terrain combine to restrict the agricultural output of Greece. Self-sufficiency in foodstuffs is unattainable, and Greece has lived by exporting specialities, such as currants, tobacco, and olive oil. Given the facilities to export these and to import grain and other

Fig. 186. Cities and railroad development of Greece.

foods, the Greeks can live and, by Balkan standards, live well. When, as during the period of German occupation between 1941 and 1945, these opportunities were denied, the Greeks starved, for their own products scarcely made up a balanced diet.

The destitution of the peasant, with sometimes a condition of near-starvation, makes him desperate. It encourages banditry and opens up the danger of Communist infiltration or attack. In this has lain the danger of recent years, and the United States has invested heavily in the restoration of the Greek economy. Greece has been the scene in the last few years of a desperate struggle between Communism and Western democracy. So far the West has won, though its advantage is precarious in such conditions as prevail in Greece. Greece belongs to the West. The Western political tradition derives in part from the practice and precept of the Greeks of classical times. Greece's markets are in the West; her merchant fleet, in which, like Norway, Greece employs some of her surplus manpower, carries coal and cotton and iron ore from the nations of western Europe.

ALBANIA

Albania is made up of an alluvial plain, backed by high, rugged mountains, with the high Albanian Alps shutting it in on the north and the mountains of Epirus on the south. The country is thus an enclave on the borders of Greece and Yugoslavia. The population, probably little more than a million, is economically backward and politically unsettled. The majority are Moslem, and they are further distinguished from their Greek and Slavonic neighbors by their language, which is older than and different from those of most of Europe. A number of Albanians live in Greek Epirus and in southern Yugoslavia. Albania has laid claim to these territories but has hitherto lacked the political and military power to enforce its claims. At the present time Russia is in a position to encourage the territorial ambitions of Albania against both her neighbors.

Albania appeared on the political map of Europe as late as 1912, very largely as a result of the strategic importance of this small area. Through Albania lie routeways of potentially great importance, linking Macedonia and the Morava and Vardar Valleys on the one hand with the Adriatic on the other. The rivalry of the Balkan and central European powers for the possession of this area was settled only by the creation of the kingdom of Albania. During the interwar years an attempt was made by King Zog of Albania, with the help of Italian capital, to develop the country. A small oil field was opened up, but despite this Albania remains an overwhelmingly agricultural country, more primitive in its methods even than Greece. Tirana (Tiranë, 31,000), the capital, and Durazzo (Durrës), the chief port, have the air of modern towns. This is the work of the Italians after 1926, but behind this façade is a self-sufficing and almost oriental people, among whom the blood feud still continues in remote parts and advanced agricultural methods are unknown.

In the spring of 1939 Italian armies occupied Albania. The country had been for many years under Italian economic control, and this occupation made little difference to the country as a whole, though it did result in Albania's trade being oriented more directly toward Italy. It did, however, allow the Italians to prepare their invasion of Greece. The defeat of Italy in the Second World War was followed by the restoration of the independence of Albania and the establishment of the Communist regime which still controls the country. Albania has little economic significance, but strategically its location, opposite the "heel" of Italy, is an important one. It could serve as a base for attack on Yugoslavia or Greece and could be developed as a Mediterranean submarine base. It is of no less significance to the Western Powers now than in 1912, when it was established.

BIBLIOGRAPHY

"Agrarian Problems from the Baltic to the Aegean," Royal Institute of International Affairs, London, 1944.

Almagia, Roberto, Modern Albania: A Review, *G.R.*, XXII, 1932, 464–473.

Ancel, J., "La Macédoine," Paris, 1930.

"Economic Development in Southeastern Europe," Political and Economic Planning, London, 1945.

"Géographie universelle," Vol. VII, Part II, Italie, Péninsule des Balkans, Paris, 1934.

Gomme, A. W., "Greece," Oxford, 1945.

Mavrogordato, J., "Modern Greece, 1800–1931," London, 1931.

Moore, Wilbert E., "Economic Demography of Eastern and Southern Europe," League of Nations, Geneva, 1945.

Myres, J. L., The Position of Greece in the East Mediterranean, *G.*, XXVI, 1941, 101–109.

Newbigin, M. I., "Southern Europe," London, 1950.

Nowack, Ernest, A Contribution to the Geography of Albania, *G.R.*, XI, 1921, 503–540.

Ogilvie, A. G., Physiography and Settlements in Southern Macedonia, *G.R.*, XI, 1921, 172–197.

———, Population Density in Greece, *G.J.*, CI, 1943,
251–260.

Roucek, Joseph S., Economic Conditions in Albania,
E.G., IX, 1933, 256–264.

Zavalani, T., Resources of Albania, *G.*, XXIX, 1944,
80–85.

Greece figures prominently in the official publications of the United Nations, Economic Commission for Europe, and Organization for European Economic Cooperation (see pages 52 to 54). Two important reports of the Food and Agriculture Organization of the United Nations are: Report of the F.A.O. Mission to Greece, Washington, D.C., 1947, and Nutrition Work in Greece, May, 1951. These official reports can be supplemented by the valuable surveys of Greece's economy, published annually by the Bank of Greece, Athens.

CHAPTER 25: *Italy*

Italy, like Greece, is an almost wholly Mediterranean country. It is a peninsula reaching nearly 600 miles southeastward from the continent of Europe. On the north it is bounded by the high and snow-capped Alps. Much of Italy is hilly or mountainous. The Alps of the

Fig. 187. Physical regions of Italy.

north and northeast are continued as the Apennines into the peninsula, where they form a sort of backbone and extend to the extreme south of Italy. The areas of coastal plain are small, and despite modern reclamation, parts are still malarial. Off the southern extremity of Italy is the island of Sicily, and 150 miles offshore to the west of the peninsula is Sardinia. In the north is the only large area of low-lying plain, the valley of the Po.

In the Po Valley summers are hot and rice grows well, while in winter the rivers are often locked in frost. The Italian peninsula is cut off by the Apennines from the Po Valley. The cold of the northern winter sometimes reaches Rome, and snow flurries may on rare occasions be seen among the orange groves of Naples, but southern Italy in general is warm and sunny.

The northern plain is today the most densely peopled, the most highly developed industrially, and in many respects the most progressive part of Italy. The central parts of this peninsula, from Rome or even Naples northward to Florence, were the chief center of the cultural developments of the Italian Renaissance of the fifteenth and sixteenth centuries, when the cities came to be graced by cathedrals, galleries, and palaces. In contrast, the southernmost part of Italy and the island of Sicily are poor and backward. Like southern Spain, these areas lie on the frontier of Europe. They have been exposed to attack and to some extent invaded and settled by peoples from North Africa.

Italian unity was not achieved until the middle years of the nineteenth century. From the end of the period of the Roman Empire until 1860, the peninsula was divided into a number of small political units, not unlike those into which Germany had been divided. Those of the north were closely linked with Austria and had been fought over by the armies of Germany. Those of the south had been preyed upon by raiders from over the sea and settled by groups of invaders, varying from Arabs to Norsemen. Central Italy was the least disturbed. This region could not easily focus the aspirations of the Italians to become a single nation, politically united, because it was itself dominated by the papacy. Here from the closing years of the Roman Empire onward, the popes grew to wealth and temporal importance. Until 1860 the popes ruled a large area in Central Italy. The pope continued to control Rome until 1870 and in 1928 became again the ruler of a small state, the Vatican City. In 1860 the greater part of modern Italy was united by a popular movement associated with the names of Garibaldi and Cavour. In the north, the province of Venice (Venezia) was not taken from Austria until 1866, and Rome was not occupied and made the capital of a united Italy until 1870. *Italia Irredenta*, consisting of the South Tyrol and the extreme northeast of Italy, remained outside the new state, and these territories were the reward for Italy's entry into the First World War.

In 1919 the Italian frontier was extended to the Brenner Pass in the north and the Julian Karst in the northeast, but this fell short of the ambitions of Italy, who had hoped to gain Fiume and the eastern shore of the Adriatic, where many Italians had settled (see page 293). In 1919 a band of Italian nationalists seized the free city of Fiume, and a few years later it was incorporated into Italy.

As a result of the Second World War, Italy has lost possession of Fiume, now the Yugoslav city of Rieka, of the Istrian peninsula, and of the city of Trieste, now administered internationally as the free city of Trieste. Italy has retained the South Tyrol, however, despite its considerable German-speaking population.

Northern Italy. The Alps rise steeply from the Lombardy Plain. Their unbroken line runs around the horizon of the plain, to all appearances an impenetrable barrier, yet these "splendid traitors" have let in more invaders than they have ever served to deter. The Italian Alps are divided into a number of compact mountain masses by valleys and passes which afford easy ingress.

South of the latitude of Turin (Torino) the Maritime and Cottian Alps constitute a sharp crest, difficult to cross though generally under 9,000 feet in height, which continues eastward into the Ligurian Alps and Apennines. The region is a sparsely populated area of crystalline rock, with no through railway routes and few roads. But rivers which water the Lombardy Plain flow from them and in their swift descent generate power for the factories of Turin.

The valley of the Dora Riparia, at the head of which are the Mont Cenis Pass and Tunnel, separates the Cottian from the Graian Alps. The valley is wide, and its flat floor is well cultivated. The small town of Susa, the most important in the valley, lies at the meeting place of the route over the Mont Cenis Pass and those over a number of lesser passes.

The Franco-Italian frontier between Menton and Ventimiglia on the coast of the Mediterranean. The frontier here follows a deeply incised watercourse. The French frontier post is to the left, the Italian to the right of the bridge (note the flags), which here joins the two countries.

Between the Dora Riparia and the Dora Baltea, another tributary of the Po, are the Graian Alps, a compact and rugged area which contains the beautiful Gran Paradiso Massif, more intensely glaciated than the mountains farther south. The Dora Baltea is also broad and well cultivated between its steep, forested sides and rises upstream to the Little and Great Saint Bernard Passes. Aosta, the highest town in the valley, is, like Susa, a road center and a station on what has been for centuries one of the most used of the Alpine roads.

To the east Italy includes the southern slopes of the Pennine Alps (see page 204), Lake Como, and most of Lake Maggiore. The beauty of the Italian Alps has hitherto been rather hidden by the remoteness of the mountains and the difficulty of access to them. Here they show their

Lake Como and the town of Bellagio. Como is a moraine-dammed lake in the Italian Alps. The area has a mild, sunny climate and is famous as a resort. Many of the buildings seen in this picture are hotels. (*Italian State Tourist Office, New York.*)

full magnificence on the edge of the Italian Plain. The steep mountains are mirrored in the blue lakes. Around the shores are small villages and hotels and the slopes behind are terraced for vines. Winters, with a January average of about 37°, are milder than in Switzerland and a little warmer even than in the low Lombardy Plain. Summers are hot, rainfall is heavy, but sunshine is abundant.

East of Lake Como is a mass of hills and mountains. In the south are the Bergamasque and Brescian Alps, with gentle, rounded land forms and broad valleys, which pass northward into the lofty, snow-covered Bernina, Adamello, and Ortles (Ortler) Alps.

From the Adige Valley the Brenner Pass, lowest and easiest of the major Alpine routes, crosses the Alpine divide to Austria. South of the Brenner is the South, or Italian, Tyrol, an area where German peoples migrating southward over the passes have settled in the upper valley of the Adige. Both language and cultural traits are Germanic, and the region has now been given a measure of autonomy within the Italian state.

East of the Adige Valley are the Dolomites (Dolomiti) and Venetian Alps, built in part of limestone, which have been eroded into fantastic shapes. The region offers the spectacle of steep precipices, isolated stacks, and serrated ridges; it is further well dissected by the Brenta, Piave, and their tributaries, which have opened it up to the tourist traffic.

In the northeast the Carnic and Julian Alps shut in the Lombardy Plain and cut it off from Yugoslavia. These are lower than the Dolomites. The Tagliamento and Isonzo Rivers have opened up routeways into these hills and through them into Austria. They consist for the greater part of high, bare limestone plateaus, in which percolating water has formed huge solution cavities.

The south-facing Alpine slopes have a bright and mild climate. Southern fruits, with the exception of the olive, grow well, and the vegetation is made up of the dry, aromatic plants of the south, but the rainfall is not concentrated in the winter months as it is in the true Mediterranean area, and winters are colder. The Italian Alps are neither industrialized nor urbanized, but throughout their length hydroelectric stations are numerous and supply the industrial towns of the plain.

The plain of the river Po extends almost 250 miles from the Alps in the west to the Adriatic Sea. Its width varies from 50 miles near Turin to about 130 miles on the coast. An arm of this lowland plain, about 30 miles wide, extends northeast to the Julian Alps. The plain has been for many centuries building forward into the Adriatic Sea. The Po has a complex delta, with lagoons and silted harbors, evidence of the aggradation of the coastline within historical times.

The Lombardy Plain, as this region of lowland is called, is built up almost wholly of young soft sediments laid down by the Po and its tributaries. Around the margins of the plain is a belt, varying in width from 4 to 40 miles, of old alluvium and outwash. This material forms gravel terraces, generally permeable and dry, above the level of the center of the plain. The Alpine and Apennine rivers cross these terraces in valleys, which are incised sufficiently to make irrigation difficult. The lower terraces are built of finer deposits above which springs issue. These make up the *fontanili*, or spring line. Many of the small streams which flow to join the Po originate in this way below the line of terraces.

The center of the plain is composed of alluvium. The region is flat. Drainage is sluggish and often difficult, and the rivers sometimes flow between dikes and are above the level of the plain for much of the year. The towns and villages stand away from the rivers for greater safety in time of flood, and the rivers are of very slight importance for navigation. The northern tributaries of the Po are torrents in spring and early summer, when they are fed by the melting Alpine snows, and from late summer onward their wide, shallow, stony beds are almost empty. The southern rivers have a high level in winter and spring; all are low in late summer and fall.

The coast is also building forward at the mouths of the Brenta, Piave, Tagliamento, Isonzo, and Reno. In classical times Adria and Ravenna were ports. They silted, and their place was taken by Venice (Venezia, 321,000),[1] growing up on sand flats in the coastal lagoons. Venice in turn is silting and losing ground before Trieste. Much of the coast is fringed by dunes, behind which are brackish lagoons,

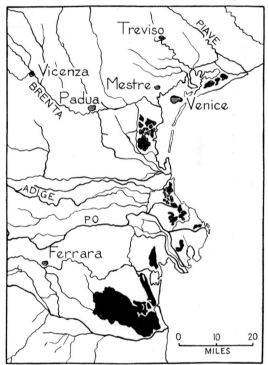

FIG. 188. The Po delta and the situation of Venice (Venezia).

marshes, and damp salt pastures, slowly undergoing reclamation and conversion to agricultural uses.

The alluvial plain (see Fig. 187) itself is rich and fertile. Its soils have to be drained in many parts by ditches cut between the fields. Roads run straight across this flat land, bordered by the tall, dark, slender Lombardy poplars. A very high proportion of the land is cultivated. Holdings are small, and the population dense. Meadow is abundant, owing to the high moisture content of the soil, particularly in the

[1] The population is given only of cities of over 100,000 inhabitants. All cities of this size are named in the text.

The Dolomites near Bolzano in the Italian Tyrol. Erosion of the horizontally bedded rocks has produced bizarre land forms, which are a great attraction to tourists. (*Italian State Tourist Office, New York.*)

central part of the plain. Here cattle are raised in large numbers, cheese for which Italy is famous is made, and pig rearing is a subsidiary occupation. Wheat and maize are grown where the soil permits, and rice is planted in flooded fields of the Po delta and also in the plain west of Pavia, where irrigation water is readily available from the rivers which converge from the surrounding hills.

Towns are few in this central area of the plain. They have never had the advantage of good river communication, and movement by land over the flat and marshy Po Plain has not been easy. Pavia, Piacenza, Mantua (Mantova), and Ferrara (138,000) all lie in the plain, but only Pavia can be described as on a river. The others are better described as out of its reach.

Largest of the towns of this region is Venice, built on a low island in the lagoons to the north of the Po mouth and cut off from the sea by a dune-covered bar, known as the Lido. Venice was founded on this unpropitious site in the fifth century by refugees driven from the town of Aquileia which was destroyed by the Huns. Venice abundantly illustrates the thesis that the "stimulus of a harsh environment" can sometimes produce greatness. These fugitives on their sandbanks developed a local trade, which, during the later Middle Ages, they extended to all parts of the Mediterranean. Venetian galleys sailed in the fifteenth century to the ports of northwestern Europe, and with the wealth which they earned the Venetians made their city one of the most beautiful in Europe. It would be difficult to find anywhere a group of buildings more impressive in their beauty and magnificence than those around the *Piazza* of San Marco in Venice. The republic of Venice continued in independence until the end of the eighteenth century; it then passed to Austria and later was incorporated into the kingdom of Italy. Its greatness waned when the trade from the East ceased to pass overland from Mediterranean ports. Its harbor is shallow, and though a small port has been made on the mainland nearby at Mestre, Venice remains today a glorious fossil.

Meadow is less important on the gravel terraces which surround the central plain; wheat and maize are grown in the drier soil.

Venice, the Doge's Palace. This building of white and pink stone and brick symbolizes the wealth and greatness of medieval Venice. In the foreground are the black gondolas, used more or less as cabs to get about the city. (*Italian State Tourist Office, New York.*)

The mulberry is grown, and its leaves used to feed silkworms. The grape vine is also important, especially on the gentle, south-facing slopes. The plain is interrupted by a number of isolated areas of hill. West of Padua (Padova, 169,500), two small, isolated areas of volcanic hills, the Monti Berici and Monti Euganei, also support a large area of vineyards. On the west of the plain are the Monferrato Hills, in reality a low spur of the Apennines. These, too, are suited climatically to viticulture and are one of the most important wine-producing areas in Italy.

Over much of the Po Plain the characteristic rural settlement is the *corti* village, a development probably of the villa of classical times, in which the houses, barns, and animal sheds are gathered round a rectangular courtyard. Toward the east, however, where the land is but recently reclaimed, settlements tend to be linear in pattern and to consist of lines of houses built along a road or embankment. The pattern resembles closely that which has grown up in northern Europe under similar geographical conditions. The Italian farmstead is often white, with a roof of red tile or of thatch. Around it are a few trees for shade, a garden patch, and some vines; beyond are the cultivated strips, the ever-present poplars which give shade and yet take up little room, the narrow, dusty roads, and the clumsy wooden farm carts and plows, drawn by teams of long-horned, soft-eyed Lombardy oxen.

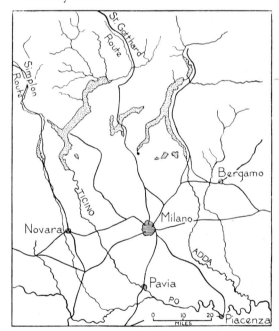

FIG. 189. The situation of Milan (Milano).

The towns of the Lombardy Plain lie for the greater part around its margins, where the land is drier and movement easier. They lie in two distinct lines across the plain from west to east. The more northerly and on the whole the older of the two is close to the Alps. The towns of which it is composed grew up at the approaches to the Alpine valleys. Many of them have been important route centers since ancient times; all of them have been fortresses. Some have attracted modern industries, particularly cotton, woolen, and silk, because of the availability of

The grape harvest in central Italy. Note the similarity between this scene and that of the same operation in France (see p. 147). The vine covers the gentle slopes; the olive tree, the steeper. (*Courtesy of Hamilton Wright, New York.*)

hydroelectric power. Como lies at the end of the routeway which follows the Valtellina to Austria, Bergamo (107,000) and Brescia (152,000) lie at the very foot of the mountains; Verona (198,000) controls the approaches to the more important Brenner route, and Udine those to the passes of the Carnic Alps.

To the south lies a second line of towns, close to or a little above the fontanili line. It includes Turin (Torino), Vercelli, Novara, Busto Arsizio, Legnano, Milan (Milano), Monza, Padua (Padova), and Treviso. On the whole these towns are larger; Turin and Milan are the two most important industrial centers of Italy. At this distance from the mountains transport is less impeded by spurs from the Alps. Turin (730,500) lies at the convergence of several valley routeways of the western Alps. In recent times the availability of hydroelectric power has assisted the development of the metallurgical and automobile industries for which Turin is famous.

Milan (1,289,500) also lies at the convergence of Alpine routes. It grew to be a wealthy manufacturing and commercial city during the Middle Ages, and it has not since ceased to be a center of manufacture and trade. Its industries are metallurgical, chemical, and textile. Around it are a great number of small towns and large villages engaged in the manufacture of textiles which are marketed in Milan. It is now the most important center of communications in the north Italian Plain.

A third line of towns has developed along the southern margin of the plain, in the province known as Emilia. Most of these lie along a Roman road, the *Via Emilia*, from the coast at Rimini to the crossing of the Po at Piacenza. Along this line are Forli, Bologna (346,000), Modena (117,000), Reggio (105,000), and Parma (123,500). To the west, on a tributary of the Po, is Alessandria. These towns are far from small, but they have failed to attract the industries which are a feature of the more northerly towns, perhaps because their water supply is small and irregular and the generation of hydroelectric power inadequate to attract industries. Most, however, lie at the mouths of Apennine valleys, and some, like Bologna, Parma, and Alessandria, control important crossings of the range. Bologna is the largest of these towns and lies where the ancient road from central to northeastern Italy crossed the Emilian Way.

Peninsular Italy. The Italian peninsula is shut off from the plain of the Po by the northern Apennines. These mountains are the dominant geographical feature of Italy. Beginning in the Maritime Alps, they first trend eastward as the Ligurian Apennines. Their breadth and height increase in the Etruscan Apennines as they swing over to the east coast of the peninsula, then back again to the west, becoming yet wider and higher, until in southern Italy they break up into detached masses of which the last overlooks the Strait of Messina. Within the broad curve of the central Apennines are Tuscany and Umbria, hilly regions with small areas of flat land along the coast or in the valleys. South of Rome (Roma) and around Capua this coastal plain widens only to disappear as the Apennines again approach the west coast. On the east the coastal plain is narrow except in the south, where the mountains lie toward the west.

Both the Apennines and the Tuscan and Umbrian Hills are built of young rocks. Limestones, clays, and marls predominate in the south; sandstones are more common in the north. All these beds are soft and easily eroded, and the disturbance of the natural vegetation cover in ancient and medieval times has exposed the steeper hillsides to serious soil erosion. West of the Apennines there has been recent volcanic activity, and the hills north and south of Rome are of volcanic origin. In the vicinity of Naples (Napoli) the vulcanism is still active and the land is composed mainly of volcanic rocks. In Calabria, the "toe" of Italy, are two ancient crystalline massifs which, in the hardness of their rocks and their human development, contrast strongly to the softer rocks of the Apennines.

The climate of peninsular Italy is Mediterranean but changes quite markedly between the north and the south. Southern Italy has very hot summers and mild winters, but in the northern Apennines winters are sometimes quite severe. January temperatures are below freezing point, and the snowfall is heavy. Even on the coast, in Rome, and as far south as Naples, sharp frosts and snow are not infrequent in the winter months. The distribution of rainfall also varies. In the north the summers are far from rainless, but toward the south the summer drought begins to show itself, and in southern Italy the summer months are quite dry.

The high temperatures bring about the rapid decomposition of humus, and the characteristic soil is the *terra rossa*, a red clay soil, deficient in lime. The limestone areas are often bare of soil.

There are considerable areas of alluvial and volcanic soils which, owing to their chemical composition, are often very fertile. Peasants in the south often brush up the volcanic dust from the roads after an eruption of Vesuvius in order to use it on their fields as a fertilizer.

The northern Apennines consist of a number of short ranges trending generally from northwest to southeast. The rocks are soft and easily eroded, valleys are deep and narrow, and landslides common. The Ligurian Apennines are

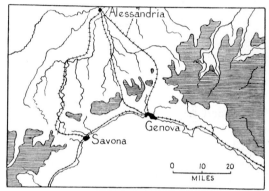

Fig. 190. The situation of Genoa (Genova). Land above 2,000 feet shaded.

narrower and lower than the rest of the range. They lie close to the sea and enclose the Gulf of Genoa (Genova) like a wall. The coastal plain is here only a very narrow strip of land, scarcely wide enough for a town. The climate is mild. Genoa (676,000) is warmer than Rome and little different from Naples, but the rainfall is heavy, and the cloudiness greater. Along the coast are a number of winter resorts from Ventimiglia to Spezia (124,500), each occupying a small patch of flat land between the mountains and the sea. Genoa is the largest city. It stretches for almost 10 miles from west to east between the hills and the sea. The site is unsuited for the development here of a great port. There is no natural harbor on this bare and exposed coast, and much labor has gone to making the present port safe for shipping. Yet Genoa grew up as one of the few great ports of the Middle Ages, handling, like Venice, the produce of the East, which it sold in the cities of the West. Its advantage lay in the passes

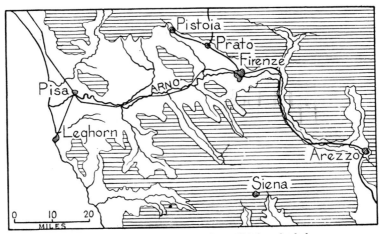

FIG. 191. Tuscany. Land above 600 feet shaded.

across the Apennines to the north of the city, which put Genoa into communication with Turin and Alessandria from which routes radiated over the plain. Genoa is now the chief port for the north Italian industrial area.

The Ligurian Apennines pass eastward into the Tuscan Apennines, which are broader and higher but in general not difficult to cross. They rise steeply on the southwest, dropping more gently toward the northern plain. The highest points are rather more than 5,000 feet above sea level. The mountains were never glaciated. Their summits are flat or rounded, and their valleys lack the distinctive land forms of a glaciated landscape. The valleys are cultivated, and the lower slopes terraced for the vine, but much of the higher ground is forested or covered with scrub. The Spanish chestnut, mulberry, and beech are the commonest trees, but nevertheless centuries of unrestricted felling have destroyed much of the former forest cover and left only a scrub that is often too light to bind the soil and check erosion.

In the Apuan hills, west of the main range, are older rocks among which limestone predominates and is quarried as white Carrara marble.

The central Apennines form a tangled mass of hills carved in beds of limestone and clay. The limestone produces in some places extensive dry plateaus, in others, areas of rugged topography with sharp precipices and isolated peaks. The clay lands are more undulating but exposed to serious soil erosion. The range contains a number of small basins, some of them produced by faulting. Some of these are damp and ill-drained, but most are well cultivated. A number of small towns lie in these basins and are focal points for the activities of the surrounding agricultural areas.

East of Aquila a high limestone plateau culminates in the Gran Sasso Range, whose highest peak, Corno Grande, reaches 9,500 feet. Here in the Abruzzi, the mountains present a formidable barrier to communications between the east and west coasts. To the southeast are the similar plateau areas of Matese and Molise.

Throughout this central Apennine region the rainfall is light in the sheltered basins and for agricultural purposes has to be supplemented by irrigation. Agriculture is practiced by methods that can have changed but little since the Romans conquered these mountains from the Latin tribes. Villages are compact and usually on hills in order to lift them above the damp ground of the valleys and to give them some protection. A subsistence agriculture is practiced. The low-growing scrub which has replaced the forests is grazed by the sheep driven to these upland regions from the coastal pastures during the summer months.[1]

[1] See the novels of Ignazio Silone, "Fontamara" and "Bread and Wine," for a vivid description of the life in the villages and small towns of Marsica and the Fucino Basin.

Within the curve of the Apennines are four more low-lying regions which present a sharp contrast to the rugged and poverty-stricken mountains which they border. The first of these is the basin of the river Arno, or Tuscany. The Arno rises in the northern Apennines and makes its way by a circuitous course to the Tyrrhenian Sea. Near Florence (Firenze) it leaves the mountains and enters the plain of Tuscany. This is itself broken by hill ridges which the river crosses by narrow gaps. The intervening plains are flat and, now that they have been drained, are well cultivated. The central parts are still under grass, and dairy cattle are raised, but elsewhere wheat and maize are grown for local consumption, and everywhere there are vineyards, olive groves, and mulberry trees. To the south, low, rolling hills extend to the limits of the region. It is dotted with the brightly colored villages of the rural population, its elevations often crowned with the ruins of a castle of the Middle Ages. The slopes are covered with vineyards, and the whole "lighted with the dark green candleflames of the cypress trees." Toward the east the grapes of the Chianti Hills provide the wine of the same name.

Florence (385,000) is in every respect the capital of Tuscany. It is a large city with a distinguished history and noble buildings. It lies on the northern bank of the Arno where the river enters the plain, at the meeting place of trans-Apennine routes and roads southward to Rome. Above all, Florence became the seat of the greatest of the princely house of medieval Italy, the Medici, who lavished their wealth on its beautification.

Within the Florence basin are the old but small towns of Prato and Pistoia, lying where Apennine routes open on to the plain. The Arno has never been easily navigable. Pisa, some 8 miles from the sea, was the medieval port through which passed the commerce of Florence. In the later Middle Ages Pisa silted, and its decline was further assisted by the actions of its rivals in choking its harbor mouth. Pisa was replaced by Leghorn (Livorno, 147,000) about 12 miles to the south and safe from the silt brought down by the rivers. Small rural towns

are scattered about the plain behind. One of these, Lucca, lies in the center of an olive-growing area—olives are grown here only near the coast owing to the danger of frost—and is a well-known market for the oil.

Siena lies in the center of the hill country of Tuscany in a valley which extends from the Arno Valley to the upper valley of the Tiber

Florence. The buildings reflect the former wealth and greatness of the city. Giotto's tower is seen behind the Baptistry, both built in the fifteenth century. On the right is one of the massively built houses of the wealthy class of earlier centuries, with ornate entrance, grilled windows, and a broad overhang of the roof to give shade. (*Italian State Tourist Office, New York.*)

(Tevere) and provides a routeway of considerable importance. Siena, a typical central Italian town, lies upon a low hill, with its houses gathered close around its *piazza*, or square, and cathedral.

Umbria, lying to the south, resembles Tuscany. It is a country of rolling hills, of poorly cultivated or scrub-covered upland, of well-cultivated valleys, of villages and small towns perched on the hilltops for defence against both invaders and the mosquito. The plains and

San Gimignano, Tuscany. This is a small central Italian hilltop town of the Middle Ages. The towers, many of them attached to castlelike houses, are survivals from an age of feud and civil war. They were formerly not uncommon, and others survive in Bologna and Florence. (*Courtesy of Hamilton Wright, New York.*)

basins were once the sites of lakes, and much of the region is drained by the upper Tiber. They are now highly productive but in parts still marshy. The Val di Chiana, in which lies Lake Trasimene, all that is left of a once large lake, is one of the largest of such basins. At its northern end is Arezzo. To the east is the lake basin of Perugia, commanded from the heights of the surrounding hills by Perugia, Assisi, and Spoleto. They have strong natural defenses, and today they exist to serve the needs of the agricultural region in which they lie. Assisi has further become a religious center owing to the life and burial here of Saint Francis of Assisi, and great wealth and care have been lavished on its adornment.

Lying between the Tiber (Tevere) Valley and the sea is a region of recent volcanic activity. There are numerous peaks and craters which together produce a topography very much more rugged than the smooth hills of Tuscany. Monte Amiata reaches a height of 5,690 feet. The region has more forest than most in the Italian peninsula, and considerable areas are covered with *macchia*[1] scrub. The volcanic tuff of which the surface is composed is easily gullied and eroded. The towns, such as Orvieto, are often perched upon the summits of steep volcanic plugs. Volcanic craters are numerous, though none are active. Some, like Bolsena and Bracciano, are filled with water, others form marshy depressions, and a few are cultivated. The volcanic hills reach to within a few miles of Rome and south of the Tiber Valley are continued in the Albano and Lepini Hills. These are not high but look impressive as they rise from the level plain of the Roman Campagna. The soils are more fertile. The higher ground is wooded, but much is terraced for the vines and field crops, and large villages cling to the steep slopes.

Between the volcanic hills and the sea is a

[1] This is the Italian equivalent of the French *maquis*, the Spanish *matorral*, and American *chaparral*.

coastal plain of varying width, built up of deposits brought down from the hills. The coast is straight and is fringed by dunes blown up by the west winds. Small islands which once lay offshore have been joined to the shore by loops of sand. The mouths of rivers have been choked, and the plain, known as the Maremma, rendered marshy and of little value. In recent years progress has been made in improving or reclaiming these coastal marshes, which once served only to graze animals.

The confusing terms *Campagna* and *Campania* are given to the coastal plain of Italy from the Tiber Valley southward to Naples (Napoli). The Campagna is the valley of the lower Tiber, a fertile region of low, rolling hills, built of alluvium and volcanic tuff. It has always been comparatively free of marshes except close to the river and thus has escaped malaria, the scourge of the low-lying land of southern Italy. The valley routes open from the Campagna northward toward Tuscany and eastward to the Apennines. Here on a group of low hills on the southern bank of the Tiber the city of Rome (1,665,500) grew up in early classical times. The "Seven Hills" gave the Romans the advantages of altitude above the plain. The Tiber Valley gave them easy communications with the sea and their early port of Ostia and with the central Italian hinterland. Rome became the center of the Roman Empire, and after its collapse Rome retained the respect of much of western Europe. With the end of the emperors, the bishops of Rome, the popes, inherited many of the attributes of the secular rulers. From the early Middle Ages until 1870 Rome was part of the secular possessions of the papacy, and only at the latter date did it become the capital of the kingdom of Italy. Alongside the ruins of the civilization of the ancient Roman Empire—the Forum, the Coliseum, and the triumphal arches of Titus and Constantine— the Church built its basilicas and churches, of which the largest and most impressive is St. Peter's itself. These, along with the Vatican, or papal residence, chapels, and secular buildings, were embellished by the artists of the Renaissance, so that Rome became a place of artistic

no less than of spiritual pilgrimage. During the last 80 years Rome has developed the duties of a secular capital. It is a focus of communications, but its industrial development is small. Since 1929 the papacy has again possessed a secular state in the form of the small Vatican City, across the Tiber from Rome.

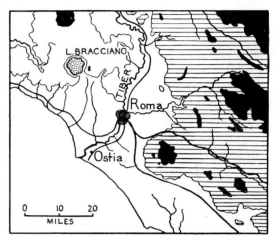

FIG. 192. The situation of Rome. Contours shown at 1,000 and 6,000 feet. Note the two crater lakes to the north of Rome.

To the south of Rome for 60 miles is a broad belt of coastal lowland, up to 20 miles wide. The coast is fringed with dunes. Behind these are salt lagoons, and between these and the hills a level plain, which, at least since the later years of the Roman Empire, has been marshy and ill drained, a barrier to movement and source of illness and disease. Several attempts to reclaim this region had failed before, in 1926, the Italian government took the work in hand. The Mussolini Canal was dug to carry the drainage from the limestone Lepini Hills to the sea. The Pontine Marshes were crisscrossed by canals, and pumps were installed to lift the water from the fields and to drive it toward the sea. A number of agricultural settlements was established, beginning with Littoria in 1932, and the plain has been divided into holdings of from 20 to 60 acres and leased to peasants on a sharecropping basis.

Spurs from the coastal ranges reach out to the sea between Terracina and Gaeta, but south

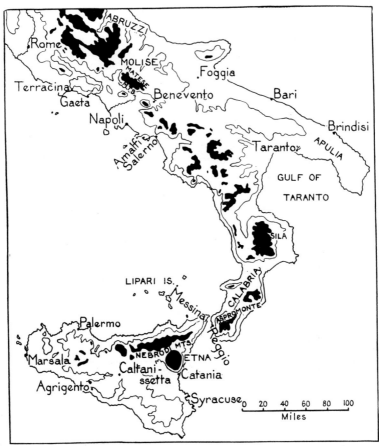

FIG. 193. Southern Italy and Sicily; 600 and 3,000 feet contours are shown.

of the Liri River a similar area of lowland, the Campania, extends south to the Sorrento peninsula. The plain has been the scene of violent volcanic activity which is still far from extinct. In the north is an extinct cone. At the opposite end of the plain is Vesuvius, an almost perfect cone which rises 3,891 feet from the shores of the Bay of Naples. It is often in a state of mild activity. "From the cone of Vesuvius across the bay rose thick columns, densely spiralling, of purple smoke shot with a fierce flush or melting glow of pink. High into the tall and clouded sky they rose in oily whorls, until the upper wind caught and bent them suddenly, and sent them flying over the sea in a flat brown canopy from which descended the close volcanic dust. Oozing from the crater's lip and trickling down the upper slope of the mountain came scarlet rivulets, thick and slow,

of molten lava. Below them, under clouds of evil smoke, the glaciers of iron-dark cinders crawled down hill, filling the hollows, shirking heights and promontories, and crushing houses, tumbling pines and chestnut trees in their sluggish flow. . . . At night the molten lava, creeping slowly in blunt-headed streams, shone like wet silver, and the dark air smelt more strongly of sulphur."[1]

Between lie the Campi Flegrei, a small area where survives the wreck of a former volcanic cone, with a number of small craters and hot, sulfurous springs. Solfatarra, close to the sea at Pozzuoli, is the largest crater, and here it is possible to walk over the warm, hollow-sounding crust of lava that has congealed on its floor and through which the lava spurts at intervals in

[1] Linklater, E., "Private Angelo," pp. 105–108, London, 1946. The description is of the eruption of 1943.

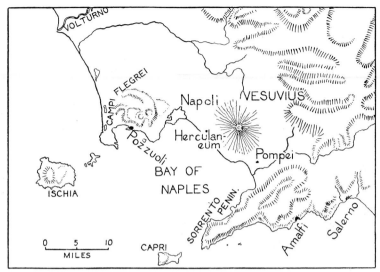

FIG. 194. The situation of Naples (Napoli) and Mount Vesuvius.

small holes which it forms. Former eruptions of Vesuvius have left a trail of destruction. To the south are the excavated remains of Pompei (Pompeii), a Roman town overwhelmed during the eruption of A.D. 79 by mud which washed down the sides of the cone. Herculaneum (Ercolano), on the shore of the bay, was buried by hot ash.

The Campania is crossed by the Garigliano and Volturno Rivers, and the valleys of these form inland extensions of the Campanian plain. The alluvium of which the plain is built has been worn from the surrounding volcanic hills, and over the region in times of eruption there settles the fine fertile dust. The region is one of the highest fertility. Its agricultural population is very dense, and holdings small and intensively cultivated. Wheat, maize, and vegetables are grown. The vines and olive, lemon, and orange trees have vegetables planted between them, so valuable is the land. Cultivation climbs high on the slopes of Vesuvius and intrudes into the steaming, sulfurous craters of the Campi Flegrei. Despite the fertility of the soil and the intensity of its cultivation the region is one of great poverty. Villages are mean collections of shacks, grouped like those of the northern plain around a central courtyard.

The poverty of the Campania culminates in Naples (Napoli), a city of about 1,030,000 inhabitants. Its situation at the foot of Vesuvius and on the shores of the Bay of Naples has become a byword for beauty. The town itself is untidy and sprawling. Its buildings are decaying, and its huge population underemployed. It collects the surplus of the overpopulated south, but its engineering and textile industries are insufficient to employ it fully. It is, however, a commercial port and has road and rail communications with its central Italian hinterland.

South of Vesuvius the steep-sided, craggy peninsula of Sorrento projects some 12 miles into the Tyrrhenian Sea. Its rugged beauty and the splendor of its little coastal towns, such as Amalfi and Sorrento, which begin at the water's edge and climb the almost precipitous mountain with their steep, narrow streets built tier above tier, have made it a tourist center. Off the extremity of the peninsula is the island of Capri, which has no less a reputation. Stretching south from the Sorrento peninsula is the Salerno Plain, an alluvial but still only partially drained area, where crops are grown intensively on the drier ground and cattle raised on the wetter.

Inland from Naples the Volturno, with its tributary, the Calore, has eroded a valley which reaches far into the Apennines and gives an easy communication with the east coast. The southern Apennines consist of a number of tabular limestone masses, separated from one another by upland basins in which lake deposits have accumulated. Rainfall is small in volume and irregular. Agriculture is heavily dependent upon irrigation, but the region is too poor to be able to afford the engineering works that are

The Isle of Capri. Capri lies off the extremity of the Sorrento peninsula near Naples, and its beauty has made it a famous resort. (*Courtesy of Hamilton Wright, New York.*)

necessary. The lowlands are malarial. The hill slopes are steep, severely gullied, and liable to landslides. The villages and small towns are commonly built on the limestone, which forms the highest ground, in order to avoid these dangers. A third affliction of southern Italy is its liability to earthquakes, which have on many occasions destroyed whole towns. The region has been exposed to pirates and sea-borne invaders. Settlement has in consequence tended to be highly nucleated. Most of the population, though working in the fields, lives in large, compact villages, often many miles from the fields.

Wheat, maize, and vegetables are grown in the valleys. Tree crops are important, though

agriculture is largely subsistence. Much of the land is divided into large estates, which in many respects resemble those of southern Spain. The poverty of southern Italy is extreme. For so many centuries it has seen its best efforts frustrated by some human or natural cause that an attitude of despair and hopelessness has settled upon the region. The Italian government has in modern times carried through reforms and improvements in the center and north, but the attitude of the south is expressed in the phrase "Christ stopped at Eboli,"[1] a small town on the edge of the Salerno Plain and thus at the gateway to the south.

In the so-called "toe" of Italy, or Calabria, rocks older and harder than those which comprise the Apennines make their appearance. The massifs of Sila and Aspromonte consist of crystalline rocks, which yield only thin, poor soil. These hill masses are separated from the southern Apennines by the plain of the river Crati, a dry area, but liable to sudden floods, where the land is largely devoted to grazing. The mountains are themselves forested or scrub-covered. The population is small, and agriculture unimportant. The coastal plain is very narrow but contains most of the population of Calabria. Its soil is generally fertile, but the streams which flow as winter torrents from the mountains change their courses frequently and may spread gravel and sand over the fields.

Between the hills and the sea is one of the most important areas in Italy for the cultivation of oranges, lemons, and other citrus fruits. Vines and olives are also grown, figs are dried for export, and mulberry trees feed the silk-worms. Settlement here also is in large villages, which stand away from the coast and often on rising land for protection. The region once knew a greater prosperity than it enjoys today. Along its eastern coast were city-states founded by the Greeks. Some of these once flourishing towns are now no more than villages, and once great Sybaris and Croton have disappeared. This decline is probably to be attributed to a com-

---

[1] This is the title of a brilliant novel by Carlo Levi, which presents a vivid picture of geographical and economic conditions in Lucania.

bination of war and piracy, of deforestation and soil erosion and a bad system of land tenure.

The Apennines leave but a narrow coastal plain on the east, at most 20 miles wide and often less. It is built of young clays and marls, which have been eroded into a series of ridges and shallow valleys. Rainfall is small, though adequate for the cultivation of wheat, the most important crop of this region, and the rural population is relatively dense. Toward the north the pattern of settlement is more scattered, perhaps because the peculiar dangers of the south are here less serious, but southward, toward Apulia and the Mediterranean Sea, the compact pattern becomes more common. The coast from the peninsula of Monte Gargano northward to the beginnings of the Lombardy Plain is straight and unbroken. Only the headland of Monte Conero gives some protection to a small bay where has grown up the only port, Ancona.

Monte Gargano is an isolated limestone mass which projects into the Adriatic Sea. Between it and the Apennines is the plain of Tavoliere. East of this is another limestone tableland, which diminishes in height eastward into the "heel" of Italy. Rainfall is low, and few places have more than 20 inches in the year, almost all in the winter months. The short streams are torrents at this time, and for the rest of the year their boulder-strewn beds of gravel and sand lie hot and dry under the sun. Water is inadequate even for human use, and streams from the west of the peninsula are brought by tunnel and aqueduct to the Tavoliere. The limestone areas are waterless; there are large areas of bare rock and yet more where the only vegetation is *macchia* scrub. The difficulties of irrigation are so great that tree crops, particularly the olive, are most often grown.

There are no villages. The population, the majority of which is engaged in agriculture, lives in towns of considerable size. Apulia, which was more exposed to piratical attack than any other part of Italy, developed this protective settlement pattern to a higher degree. Bari (272,000), on the east coast, and Taranto, at the head of the Gulf of Taranto, are both

industrial centers. Taranto (195,000) has developed on the shores of a large harbor, which has provided a valuable naval base. Brindisi is a commercial port and important as a port of call for passenger vessels sailing through the Mediterranean.

Agrigento, Sicily. There are many evidences of the classical civilization of Greece in Sicily and southern Italy, and the ruins of an ancient temple are seen in the foreground. Note the rather arid appearance of the landscape and the scattered olive trees. (*Italian State Tourist Office, New York.*)

Sicily. This island is separated from the mainland of Italy only by the narrow Strait of Messina which, at its narrowest, is only 2 miles wide. Sicily continues the land forms of southern Italy, which it very closely resembles. The island is triangular in shape. In the northeast the Peloritani Mountains are a continuation beyond the Strait of the Aspromonte of Calabria. They consist of crystalline rocks and are rugged and forbidding. Their direction is continued westward in the Nebrodi and Madonie Ranges and the tangled hills of western Sicily. The hills are built, like the Apennines, of limestone and sandstone which often produce a very strong relief. They rise to over 6,000 feet and drop steeply to the Tyrrhenian Sea on the north. The coastal plain is very narrow but is well watered and densely settled.

Toward the south this line of hills drops more gently to an undulating plateau developed in beds of clay. The land here is heavily eroded and liable to landslides. In wet weather it is marshy and badly drained; in summer, parched and hard. Much of it has the appearance of a barren and treeless wilderness, but large quantities of wheat are grown, and Sicily has been, from classical times onward, a considerable exporter of grain.

South of the Nebrodi Mountains is Etna, an active volcano of much greater size than Vesuvius. It rises to a height of 10,741 feet above the nearby coast. It is a symmetrical ash and lava cone of great beauty. For much of the year its summit is streaked with snow. Below are scrub and forest. Cultivation has pressed far up its fertile sides, and its lower slopes are covered with lemon and orange groves and vineyards. The volcanic ash has added to the fertility of the surrounding plains, which are densely populated. South of Etna is the plain of Catania, the largest area of lowland in Sicily, but much of it is too dry for cultivation. Along the southern coast, where the climate is somewhat moister, cotton and flax are grown and there are orange, lemon, and almond groves.

The population of Sicily is almost wholly gathered into large centers which are urban in size but rural in occupation. Some of these were planned and founded in the sixteenth and seventeenth centuries to accommodate the rapidly increasing population. Small villages and scattered settlements are rare. Most of the larger coastal plains have each a large, partly urban, partly rural settlement. Palermo, with a population of 497,000, is the largest and has a number of industries related to its agricultural hinterland. Catania, with 295,000 inhabitants, lies on the edge of the Catanian plain. Messina, Syracuse (Siracusa), Agrigento, and Marsala are smaller but similar agricultural settlements.

Marsala is the focus of the wine industry of western Sicily.

The mineral resources of Sicily are not unimportant. Gypsum occurs in the clay beds of the center. Rock salt is mined near Agrigento as well as being dried in pans along the coast. Sulfur is mined around Caltanissetta and Enna and refined by primitive methods, which destroy much of the sulfur as well as the vegetation of the surrounding countryside.

The Lipari Islands are a group of seven islands lying in the Tyrrhenian Sea off the Sicilian coast. All are volcanic in origin, though volcanic activity has long since ceased on most. Vulcano, however, the nearest island to Sicily, is still the scene of hot, sulfurous springs, and Stromboli is almost continuously active. The population of the island group is small. Agriculture and fishing are the main pursuits, and the islands are an important source of pumice, a fine volcanic tufa which is used as an abrasive.

Sardinia. This is a large compact island which had long been a possession of the royal House of Savoy before it became part of the kingdom of Italy. The island is very largely built of hard crystalline rocks, which give it an irregular relief and produce a rugged coastline. The eastern half of Sardinia consists of a granitic mass, which forms an undulating plateau and rises in the Gennargentu Mountains to heights of almost 6,000 feet. Deep valleys have been cut by the short rivers, and in these, in more favored hollows in the plateau, and over the granitic plateau are the few settlements and areas of cultivation. Over the granitic plateau as a whole pastoral activities predominate, and large flocks of sheep and goats are kept on the *macchia*.

West of this plateau is a more broken region of recent volcanic rocks, its scrubby vegetation given over to pastoralism.

Areas of low-lying and productive land are small. In the northwest is the small plain of Sassari, a well-cultivated region where wheat, vine, and olive predominate. The plain of Campidano lies diagonally across Sardinia from the middle of the western hills. This plain is potentially an area of considerable productivity, but it lacks water in spite of attempts to irrigate it from the hills on each side. In summer it is parched; in winter, damp and malarial. Near the coast is Cagliari (138,000), the capital and port, a small town with a good harbor from which small boats sail to the mainland. For

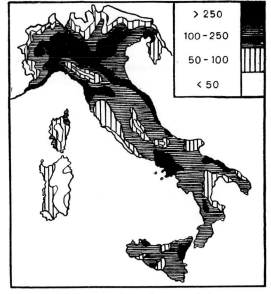

FIG. 195. Distribution of population in Italy per square mile.

the rest, the coast is deserted; coastal settlements have always been unsafe unless strongly protected.

Economic Development. Despite the recent development of manufacturing industries, Italy remains primarily an agricultural country; 48 per cent of the employed population is on the land, as against 23 per cent in industry. As in so many countries where agriculture is the dominant occupation, it is carried on by ancient and primitive methods. Yields are low, and the rural population poor. Nor is the land particularly well suited to intensive agriculture. Soils are good only in a few areas, such as the Campania and the northern plain. Rainfall is seasonal over much of the country and in some parts inadequate. Far more irrigation works are needed than have hitherto been constructed. Furthermore the peninsula is hilly, and its soft rocks are easily eroded when the vegetation cover is disturbed.

The system of land tenure in Italy shows evils similar to those which we shall find in Spain. Farm holdings, especially in the highly productive areas, are too small for economic and efficient farming. Only in Tuscany, Umbria, and the Campagna are there holdings which might fairly be described as adequate in size. A majority of farm holdings, most of them very small, are owned by the families which work them, but a large proportion of the total area is in the form of large estates, particularly in the south and Sicily. Attempts are being made to break up these estates and to distribute them among the peasants. Such a step might well be good for the morale of the peasants, but it is doubtful whether it would do much to improve the low standards of living. At the present time

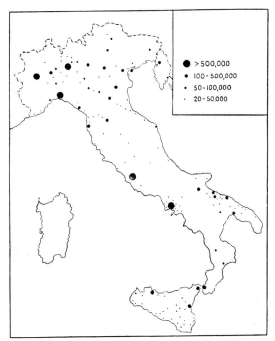

FIG. 196. Distribution of the larger cities of Italy. The relatively considerable number of large cities in southern Italy and Sicily should be noted.

the popular demand for the division of the estates appears to be growing.

The rural population is too large, and there has been for very many years a migration of peasants from the land, especially in the south. In the past, much of this surplus population emigrated to the United States. Some has gone to North Africa, and some has merely been swallowed by the vast squalid towns such as Naples and Bari, where it lives in indolence, hunger, and disease. The outlet which migration formerly supplied has now in large measure

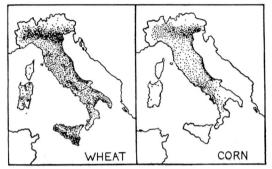

Fig. 197. Distribution of cereal cultivation in Italy.

been closed, and under the Fascist rule attempts were made to increase the area of agricultural land within Italy. These took the form of the drainage and reclamation of lowland marsh areas and the improvement and reafforestation of areas of hill. Most noteworthy of these achievements has been the reclamation of the Pontine Marshes, but similar work has been done in the Maremma, in the Campania, and in the Po Valley.

Over much of Italy the rainfall is seasonal and irrigation of considerable importance. The northern plain, however, where there is sometimes a large rainfall in the summer months, is also extensively irrigated. Here the water from the Alpine rivers and from the springs of the *fontanili* line are fed southward by canal to the meadows and crops, which despite the rainfall become very dry in the heat of summer. Irrigation is less practiced in the center and south of Italy, where it is actually more needed. There are few sources which may be tapped, and these require engineering works that are generally beyond the means of the region. Conditions are best in the northern plain and worst in the south and Sicily. Mention has also been made in various places of the distribution of crops. This information is summarized in the maps, which show the distribution in Italy of grain and fruit crops.

Animals are widely distributed in Italy but are generally poor in quality, and in few areas is attention paid to scientific breeding. Cattle are most numerous in the plain of the river Po, where are large areas of permanent grassland. They are found throughout the peninsula, and many serve both as dairy cattle and as draft animals. Pigs are similarly widespread except in the dry areas of the south. In a few places, as in Lombardy, they are kept in association with cattle, but in general they are regarded as scavengers. Sheep and goats are able to live in the poor, dry *macchia*. In the past transhumance was extensively practiced, as it was in Spain. *Tratturi*, or sheep walks, linked the winter grazing of the Maremma and other lowland areas with the summer pastures of the Abruzzi, but reclamation and improvement of the lowland areas have greatly restricted this practice.

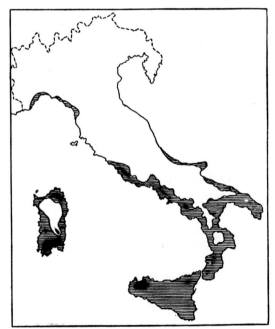

Fig. 198. Distribution of the cultivation of citrus fruit in Italy.

Goats are most common in the south, Sicily, and Sardinia, where they replace cattle as a source of milk. They are easily fed on the dry plant growth, but their destruction of the vegetation cover has been an important cause of soil erosion.

The resources of Italy are not well adapted to industrial development. Reserves of coal are very small, and output is considerably below 1 million tons a year. Most of the total Italian consumption of coal has to be imported. Deposits of petroleum and associated natural gas are also small and are practically confined to a small field on the southern edge of the Lombardy Plain. Most of Italy's requirements have to be imported. Nor is Italy much better endowed with metalliferous minerals. She has large reserves of mercury, chiefly in Monte Amiata in Tuscany, and in 1948 produced about a third of the world's production. Bauxite for aluminum is mined in the southern Apennines but amounted to only about 2 per cent of the world production. Iron-ore output, chiefly from Elba and the coastal range of Tuscany, is also small. Certain other minerals, such as gypsum, sulfur, common salt, building stones, and the materials for the manufacture of cement, are obtained on a large scale, and there is some export of these materials.

Industrial power is heavily dependent upon the streams of the Alps and Apennines. The total production of electric power is today over 22,700 million kilowatt-hours, of which 90 per cent is hydroelectric. The generation of electric power from steam was only a tenth of this. Most of the electric current was used in factories and in transportation. The chief sources are in the Italian Alps and northern Apennines. The regimes of the rivers of these two regions are strongly contrasted. The Alpine rivers discharge most abundantly in summer; the Apennine rivers in winter and spring. Their current generation is thus complementary, and by linking the two areas the deficiencies of each can in some degree be made good. The greater production by far is from the Alpine streams. Power generation in the south is small, partly owing to the less favorable river regime, partly owing to the poverty and lack of economic development in this region.

The textile industry is the most important of Italy's manufacturing industries. One of the oldest branches is the manufacture of silk cloth. The silkworm was introduced early in the

Middle Ages, and Italy is now the most important European country for the production of silk. The worms are reared and tended by the peasants, an unpleasant and laborious process. The monetary reward is small, and the practice is continued only in areas where the peasantry is very poor. The cocoons are reeled and the silk scoured in numerous small mills in the silk-producing areas. The weaving of silk fabrics

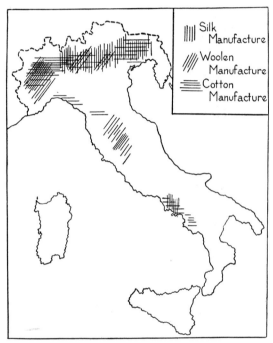

FIG. 199. Distribution of the manufacture of textiles in Italy.

is more concentrated. Como is its chief center, but silk weaving is also carried on in numerous small towns and villages of the Alpine foothills.

The woolen industry is more widely distributed. Much of the wool is imported, though originally the sheep of the Alpine foothills and of the Apennines supplied most of the wool used. This early source of materials, together with the availability here of water power, has determined the location in these areas of most of the Italian woolen industry. The small towns of Piedmont predominate in the spinning and weaving of wool, and Biella is to the woolen industry what Como is to the silk. Woolen mills are, however, found throughout the foothills belt from Turin to Udine as well as in many small towns of central Italy.

Cotton manufacture was practiced in Italy before the nineteenth century, but it was not until after 1800 that it was established on a large scale. From the first Lombardy was the center of the Italian cotton industry. The earliest mills were on the edge of the hills to the north of Milan, and still the most important manu-

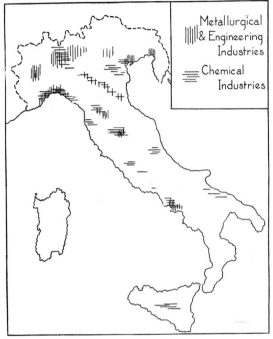

FIG. 200. Distribution of metallurgical and chemical industries.

facturing centers are Milan and its industrial satellites, Legnano, Gallarate, and Busto Arsizio.

The manufacture of synthetic fibers has been established close to the older centers of textile manufacture, partly on account of the availability here of power and water, partly because there is here also a labor force accustomed to the processes of textile manufacture. Most of the factories are in small towns near Turin and Milan. Lesser textile industries, such as the manufacture of lace and of flax, hempen, and jute fabrics, are distributed throughout Italy and carried on mainly in very small mills.

The iron and steel industry is limited by the relative absence of coal and ore. Little smelting is carried, on and in 1949 only about 2,300,000 tons of steel were made. The steel industry is based on imported pig iron and local scrap. The steel produced is used in the automobile industry of Turin and Milan and the shipbuilding industry of Genoa. The dependence on electric power has encouraged the development of electrical engineering. A wide range of light steel goods is produced, and in the large towns of the northern plain agricultural machinery is made.

The metallurgical and engineering industries are heavily concentrated in and around Turin and Milan, though a number of smaller towns, such as Brescia, Vicenza, and Bologna, are also important. The coastal towns of Savona, Genoa, Spezia, Naples, Taranto, and Venice are centers of heavy industries, not only shipbuilding but industries greatly dependent upon imported materials.

There is a close railway network in the northern plain, but peninsular Italy is ill served. Main lines follow the eastern and western coasts, but in the southern half of the peninsula trains are infrequent and the volume of transport small. Owing to the industrial development, the northern lines are well used.

Despite the high reputation of the ancient Romans as road builders, the network of roads is today neither extensive nor good. In its geographical pattern it is broadly similar to that of the railways, most developed in the northern plain, least south of Rome.

Despite the extent of industrial development, Italy is not a great commercial nation. Her foreign trade is smaller in relation to her total population than is that of most west European states. Textiles predominate in the export trade. Metal goods are of smaller importance and are exceeded by the export of fruit and wines. Imports have been of greater value than exports, and the balance of payments has in part been adjusted by the monetary remittances sent home by the Italian emigrants. The most important single import is fuel, chiefly coal and coke. This is followed in importance by the raw materials of the textile and metallurgical industries. The import of foodstuffs, other than such crops of tropical origin as coffee, is small.

The basic problem of Italy today is one of acute overpopulation. Her population, about 46,121,000, is increasing rapidly and has far outstripped the capacity of the country to support it. The remedy in the nineteenth century was migration. The Italian population of the United States was in 1940 about 4,600,000, and there are considerable Italian colonies also in South America and Australia. When, in the twentieth century, this outlet began to close, the Italians turned to colonization within their own empire and to the intensification of agriculture at home. Neither succeeded. The Italian empire was not suited for mass migration (see Chap. 28), and the settlement of each family required so much equipment as to be too expensive for so poor a country. At home Mussolini waged the "battle of the grain," urging his followers to work harder in the fields and to reclaim marsh and waste. But the hard-working Italian peasant already cultivates as much land as is possible without greater capital.

Manufacturing industries take off part of the surplus population, but they have few advantages and few domestic sources of raw material. They rely on imports which must be paid for by export of finished goods. Economically the Italian situation is a precarious one. Italy is the most industrialized of the countries of southern Europe. It is wealthier than Greece or Spain, but nevertheless very poor by the standards of northwestern Europe. Its workers are organized and thus more susceptible to political propaganda than agricultural workers. It is not surprising that socialism and communism have a strong following in the cities of the north. It is more unexpected to find the oppressed and poverty-stricken south conservative and Catholic. In the plebiscite on the monarchy, the south was in the main royalist. But this is the conservatism that springs from ignorance and superstition. When their eyes are opened, the peasants of the south may well turn to the opposite political faith. Already there have been outbreaks of violence and the seizure of large estates. It would take little to bring revolution to this region. Desperate people do not shrink from violence, and the condition of the south is desperate.

How often are we faced in Europe with this spectacle of poverty, ignorance, and distress in regions which once led the world's civilization. The half-starved Italian sitting by the ruins of the Greek temples of Paestum symbolizes the past glory and present decadence.

Further industrialization is possible. No one who knows them doubts that the Italians are an able and hard-working people. If they were not, they would not keep alive in some parts of Italy. But the extension of manufacturing depends upon capital which the country could not raise and on markets overseas which are far from assured. So many countries look to industrialization as a remedy for their economic ills that not all can possibly be satisfied with markets. As long as poverty continues, there is likely to be political unrest and discontent. Karl Marx considered Italy ripe for communism. He may yet be proved to have been right.

BIBLIOGRAPHY

Ahlmann, Hans W., The Geographical Study of Settlements, *G.R.*, XVIII, 1928, 93–128.

Almagia, Roberto, The Repopulation of the Roman Campagna, *G.R.*, XIX, 1929, 529–555.

Blanchard, W. O., The Status of Sericulture in Italy, *A.A.A.G.*, XIX, 1929, 14–20.

———, White Coal in Italian Industry, *G.R.*, XVIII, 1928, 261–273.

Buxton, L. H. Dudley, Malta: An Anthropogeographica Study, *G.R.*, XIV, 1924, 75–87.

Copp, P. J., Italy's Food in War and Peace, *Foreign Commerce Weekly*, Vol. XII, No. 9, 1943.

Dietrich, B. F. A., The Italian Harbors on the Adriatic Sea, *E.G.*, VII, 1931, 202–209.

Fleure, H. J., Cities of the Po Basin, *G.R.*, XIV, 1924, 345–346.

Frost, Ruth S., The Reclamation of the Pontine Marshes, *G.R.*, XXIV, 1934, 584–595.

"Géographie universelle," Vol. VII, La Méditerranée et les péninsules mediterranéennes, Part II, Italie, Péninsule des Balkans, Paris, 1934.

Gibb, R. W., Alpine Valleys and Italian Plains, *G.*, XXV, 1940, 25–28.

Hazen, N. W., Italian Agriculture under Fascism and War, *Foreign Agriculture*, 1940, 627–702.

Jenness, Diamond, The Recovery Program in Sicily, *G.R.*, 1950, 355–363.

Kish, George, Italian Boundary Problems, *G.R.*, XXXVII, 1947, 136–141.

Langobardi, C., Land Reclamation in Italy, London, 1936.

Levi, Doro, Sardinia: Isle of Antitheses, *G.R.*, XXXIII, 1943, 630–654.

Macartney, M. H. H., "The Rebuilding of Italy," Cambridge, 1945.

Medici, Giuseppe, "Italian Agriculture and Its Problems, Bartlett Foundation, Champaign, Ill., 1945.

Newbigin, M. I., "Southern Europe," New York, 1950.

Pantanelli, Enrico, "Problemi agronomici del mezzogiorno," Bologna, 1950.

Reclamation of the Pontine Marshes, *Nature* (London), CXXXV, 1935, 980–984.

Robertson, C. J., Agricultural Regions of the North Italian Plain, *G.R.*, XXVIII, 1938, 573–596.

———, The Italian Beet-sugar Industry, *E.G.*, XIV, 1938, 1–15.

———, Italian Rice Production in Its Regional Setting, *G.*, XX, 1935, 13–27.

Sullam, Victor E., Fundamentals of Italian Agriculture, *Foreign Agriculture*, VII (12), 1943.

———, Recent Developments in Italian Agriculture, *Foreign Agriculture*, IX, 1945, 66–74.

Toniolo, A. R., Studies of Depopulation in the Mountains of Italy, *G.R.*, XXVII, 1937, 473–477.

Toschi, Umberto, The Vatican City State: From the Standpoint of Political Geography, *G.R.*, XXI, 1931, 529–538.

Unger, Leonard, The Economy of the Free Territory of Trieste, *G.R.*, XXXVII, 1947, 583–608.

Van Valkenburg, S., Structure of Italian Agriculture, *E.G.*, XVIII, 1942, 109–124.

Vinelli, Marcello, Water Conservation in Sardinia, *G.R.*, XVI, 1926, 395–402.

Weigend, Guido G., Effects of Boundary Changes in the South Tyrol, *G.R.*, XL, 1950, 364–375.

The official publications of the United Nations, Economic Commission for Europe, and Organization for European Economic Cooperation contain a great deal of material on Italy (see pages 52 to 54).

REPORTS SPECIFICALLY ON ITALY

Economic Effects of an Investment Program in Southern Italy, Svirnez, Rome, 1951.

Survey of Italy's Economy, United Nations Relief and Rehabilitation Administration, Rome, 1947.

The periodic reports of the Italian banks are more lavish and more valuable than those of any other European country.

BANK PUBLICATIONS

Italian Economic Survey, Association of Italian Joint-stock Companies, Rome, published every 2 months.

Italian Economy, Banco di Napoli Ufficio Studi, Naples, published monthly.

Quarterly Review, Banco Nazionale del Lavoro, Rome.

Review of the Economic Conditions in Italy, Banco di Roma, Rome, published every 2 months.

There are a number of geographical periodicals published in Italy, which contain articles on the geography of the country. Foremost among them is *Rivista geografica italiana*, published by the Società di Studi Geografici, Florence.

BIBLIOGRAPHIES ON ITALY

Hellman, Florence S., "Sicily and Sardinia," Library of Congress, Division of Bibliography, Washington, D.C., 1942.

Almagià. R., Italien, *Geographisches Jahrbuch*, XLVI, 1931, 137–202.

Bibliografia geografica della regione italiana, published periodically by the Reale Società Géografica Italiana, Rome.

CHAPTER 26: *The Iberian Peninsula*

SPAIN

The Iberian peninsula is cut off from the rest of Europe by the mountain chain of the Pyrenees and is less open to continental influences than any of the Mediterranean peninsulas. So distinct is it from Europe that it has been said that "Africa begins at the Pyrenees." The topography of Spain and Portugal has hindered the growth of communications; the climate has reduced large areas to a semidesert waste. Military campaigns in the Iberian peninsula have been fraught with great hard-

ship. It is a land in which large armies are said to starve and small armies get lost. It is furthermore an area in which a regional or local spirit survives more strongly than in any other country of western Europe.

The Meseta. The Iberian peninsula consists essentially of a tableland, the Meseta, built of hard rocks, much folded and eroded, but generally lying at a height of between 2,000 and 3,000 feet above the sea. Across the surface of this plateau run hill ridges, roughly from west to east. These ranges of hills are in places high, and

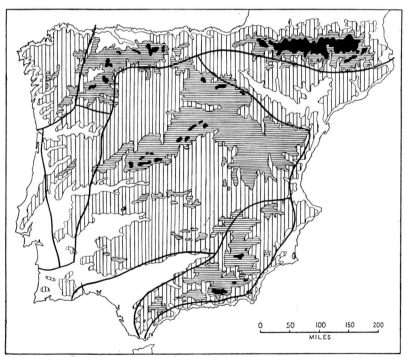

FIG. 201. Physical regions of the Iberian peninsula. The regions grouped around the Meseta are, in the northwest, Galicia; along the north, the Cantabrian Mountains and the Pyrenees; in the northeast and east, the Ebro valley and Mediterranean coastal region; in the southeast, the Beltic Mountains; in the south, the Guadalquivir Valley, and, in the west, the Portuguese coastal plain and the hilly region along the Portuguese margin of the Meseta.

339

in winter the more northerly passes are closed by snow. Across the plains between these ridges flow rivers whose deep valleys form yet further obstacles to movement. Mountains, forming part of the Alpine system, have been folded against the northern and southern edges of the Meseta. Around the margin of the land are narrow, disconnected strips of low-lying land, the most densely populated and most productive in the peninsula. On parts of the Meseta shallow deposits of clay and sand have been laid down and remain today as a level plain.

Most of the peninsula is drained westward to the Atlantic. The Douro (Duero), Tagus (Tajo), Guadiana, and Guadalquivir are long and important rivers, each draining one of the basins between the mountain ranges of the Meseta. The divide lies toward the east; of the rivers which discharge to the Mediterranean, only the Ebro is of considerable size. Others are short torrents in the rainy season and dry river beds at other times. Only the rivers of the north show a regular flow, though even here in summer the discharge is much reduced. Over the rest of the peninsula the summers have little rainfall. The torrent beds run dry, and the larger rivers are reduced to pools of sluggish water, slowly drying up in the heat of the summer sun.

The dominant physical region of the Iberian peninsula is the Meseta. It contains the present capital of Spain, Madrid, and most of the peninsula was united by being annexed to the province of Castile (Castilla), which is very broadly coterminous with the plateau. Around it are mountain ranges and the marginal plains. In some of the latter, especially in Catalonia (Cataluña), Valencia, and Andalusia (Andalucia), there is an intense local patriotism which shows itself in hostility to Madrid and the Meseta.

The central tableland of Spain is divided by the central Sierras into a northern and a southern part. Both are composed of ancient rocks, covered in parts with a deep deposit of young clays, sandstones, and limestones. These beds tend to form monotonous, level plains. Where the surface rock is limestone or sand-stone, the soil is often dry and infertile, vegetation is sparse, and agriculture little practiced. Rivers have deepened their courses below the plateau level. Harder beds of limestone sometimes form a resistant cap, protecting the steep-sided, isolated hills that are a feature of the Meseta; sometimes the softer clays on the valley sides have been scoured and eroded and a "bad-land" topography produced.

In the northern basin there is a low rainfall. The poorer soil is grass-covered, and wheat is grown over the plains of Tierra de Campos and Tierra del Pan. The northern part of the Meseta is drained by the river Douro, which rises in the hills to the east. Villages are few and widely spaced; most are nucleated and built of mud or local stone. There are few towns. Valladolid lies near the center of the basin, a short distance to the north of the Douro, and is a road, rail, and market center. To the northeast is Burgos (72,500); to the northwest León (54,500).[1] Both lie close to the mountains and constituted bases from which the little Christian states of the northern mountains advanced southward to reconquer the peninsula from the Moslems. Palencia, Zamora, and Salamanca (87,500) are small market towns and route centers and form, with the towns already mentioned, a broad network of widely spaced urban centers.

The central Sierras are a series of short mountain ranges, reaching heights of considerably over 6,000 feet, trending obliquely across the Meseta from southwest to northeast. Between each section of the chain are routeways which present no serious difficulty to the traveler except in winter. The mountains are highest and least easily crossed in the Sierra de Guadarrama, to the north of Madrid, but on both the northeast and the southwest are defiles which separate the Sierra de Guadarrama from the more westerly Sierras. These depressions are used by railways, and the small town of Avila commands the approaches from the north. To the west, short, detached Sierras stretch into Portugal. Toward the east the central Sierras

---

[1] Population is given only of cities of over 50,000. Not all cities of this size, of which there were 51 in 1950, are named in the text (see Fig. 209).

The city of Teruel, set in the barren Montes Universales of the eastern Iberian peninsula. It occupies a hilltop, commands a routeway from the Meseta to the east coast, and is dominated by its castle. Note the close spacing of the houses, the gently sloping roofs covered with pantiles, and the open attics in which food and other goods are stored. (*Spanish Tourist Office, London.*)

merge into the ranges which constitute the eastern margin of the Meseta.

The Sierras are built of granite and schist. They have not been fretted, like the Pyrenees, by the action of glaciers. Their summits are flat or rounded, and they lie along the skyline of the Meseta like a wall, without any appearance of gateway or opening. Many ranges of far greater altitude are more penetrable than the high Sierras of Spain. The slopes are in part forested with cork oak and conifers, but the forest cover has been destroyed over very large areas, and the land has only a thin cover of grass, shrubs, and stunted trees.

To the south of the central Sierras the plateau of the Meseta expands to an area almost twice as large as the northern basin. Toward the east it is covered, as in the north, by the level plains of young, soft clays and sandstones. In these the Tagus and Guadiana have incised their deep valleys. The plains of La Mancha, lying at about 2,000 feet above the sea, are dry, bare, and almost level. In winter the cold is severe; in summer the scanty vegetation is dried up and the land parched and burned to a deep red. The vegetation over large areas is only sparse esparto grass which provides a winter feed for flocks of sheep. The rest is covered with *matorral*, a low scrub of drought-resisting plants.

In the western part of the plains the cover of young rocks thins away and the underlying foundation of ancient rocks is exposed. The surface is more broken. A number of hill ridges appear, conforming with the general direction of the central Sierras. These include the Sierra de Toledo and Sierra de Guadelupe. Lower ranges are prolonged westward into the lowland plains of Portugal. These more southerly Sierras are very much lower than the central, and they are so interrupted by gaps that they scarcely constitute a physical barrier to movement. The southern Meseta is drier than the northern, its summers hotter, and its winters less severe. Natural vegetation becomes increasingly sparse.

Forests of Mediterranean evergreens occur in the mountains, but elsewhere the vegetative cover is a thin *matorral* scrub which in La Mancha degenerates into steppe. The region provides winter feed for animals but in summer is parched and barren.

Madrid, a main street of the city. The center of Madrid is a well-built and attractive modern city. (*Spanish Tourist Office, London.*)

Much of the southern Meseta is sparsely populated. Villages and towns are less frequent than on the plains north of the central Sierras. They are smaller and poorer, and such picturesqueness as they possess they owe to their striking situations. Many lie on the summits of isolated hills, on the edges of the small plateaus or *paramos*, or perched high upon the banks of the deep and gorgelike valleys. The rivers are valueless for navigation and are a barrier to movement.

The city of Toledo lies on the northern bank of the Tagus within a sharp bend of the river, protected by the swift current as well as by the steep crags above which it lies. The town is of pre-Roman origin. In the Middle Ages it became a fortress to protect the Christian state of Castile from the Moors. The ruins of its fortress, the Alcazar, destroyed during the Civil War, together with the great Gothic cathedral, still dominate the little town.

Madrid (1,511,500) lies some 30 miles to the north of the Tagus. It is, for Spain, a modern town. The settlement is old, but the capital was not located here until the sixteenth century, after the political unification of the peninsula. The site for the new capital was chosen because of its central position in Spain. About 20 miles to the northwest is the Escorial, the place of the Spanish kings. The city has failed, however, to focus the loyalties of all Spaniards, who tend to look rather to their local or regional capitals. Madrid has become the center of road and rail communications. It is a center of banking and commerce, but manufacturing activities are limited to the manufacture of a narrow range of consumer goods.

The valley of the Guadiana is less populous and has fewer towns than the Tagus Valley. Ciudad Real is the center of the basin of La Mancha. Badajoz (88,000), a town of some strategic and historical importance, lies on the Guadiana close to the Portuguese frontier, where the ranges of the Meseta draw together and leave only a narrow passageway between the lowlands of Portugal and the plateau of the southern Meseta.

On the south the Meseta is bounded by the Sierra Morena. This range rises gradually from the plains of Estremadura (Extremadura) and La Mancha and drops steeply to the low-lying plains of the Guadalquivir. The tributaries of this river have cut back into this southern wall of the Meseta, producing a rugged scarp. The valleys of these rivers are followed by the few roads and railways that cross the Sierra Morena. The Sierra Morena extends, west of the lower Guadiana, into southern Portugal and terminates in the cliffs of Cape Saint Vincent. The Sierra Morena is more highly mineralized than other parts of the Meseta. Toward the west are the famous copper mines of Rio Tinto, which have been worked since classical times.

Almadén, on the northern slopes of the range, has been important for its mercury, and Linares for silver and lead.

The mountains which bound the Meseta on the east resemble the Sierra Morena. They rise very gradually from the plains of both Old, or

Toledo. The city lies on a steep cliff on the northern bank of the Tagus. It was a Christian outpost against the Moors and is dominated by its Gothic cathedral (seen behind the tree) and the castle, or Alcazar. (*Spanish Tourist Office, London.*)

northern, and New, or southern, Castile and drop more steeply to the valley of the Ebro or to the Mediterranean. The name Iberian Mountains is often given to these hills. The Henares, a tributary of the Tagus, and the Jalón, which flows to join the Ebro, have together cut a broad depression which divides the range into a northwestern and a southeastern part and have created the most important transverse routeway. To the northwest of this depression the mountains reach heights of 7,000 feet. To the southeast the Montes Universales and Sierra de Gúdar are only a little lower.

The eastern ranges of the Meseta have formed a far more serious barrier to movement than have those which enclose the Meseta on the south. The distinctiveness of Castile on the one hand and of Aragon and Catalonia on the other is in part a consequence of this physical barrier. Only two naturally marked routeways cross the mountains: the one already mentioned, which follows the Jalón and Henares Valleys, and the one which reaches southward from the Jalon Valley through Teruel to the Mediterranean shore at Valencia.

Not only does the northern Meseta differ from the southern in climate and to some degree in relief; the history and current problems of the two portions of the Meseta are distinct. The Moors, who invaded Spain in the eighth century, occupied the northern Meseta for only a short period of time. Its climate was unsuitable to them, and they yielded ground to the Spanish people without much resistance. But the southern Meseta was held for a very much longer period of time. Its dry steppe was less tempting to Christian settlers from the north, and it was reconquered from the Moors by a great effort on the part of the Christian leaders.

Olive trees on the Meseta of southern Spain. Olive oil is one of the most important products. The trees are widely spaced owing to the lack of moisture.

This episode in the history of the peninsula is reflected in the land tenure and social structure of the two regions. The north is characterized by medium-sized holdings and by a peasantry which, though poor, is not depressed. The south is a land of great estates, carved out by

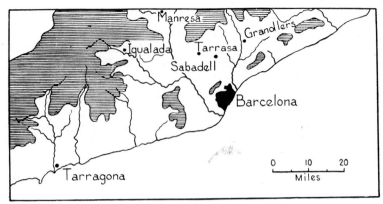

Fig. 202. The situation of Barcelona. Areas above 1,000 feet are shaded.

the conquerors in the late Middle Ages. The abject poverty of the peasant, working on the great estates, contrasts to the wealth of the absentee "grandee." The problem of the great estates of southern Spain is similar to that of southern Italy, except that, in southern Spain, extreme political beliefs have already spread among the people. The landless peasantry is ripe for revolution and has already, after the abdication of Alfonso XIII in 1931 and during the Civil War, tasted the fruits of bloody revolution. The problem of agriculture in the southern Meseta is not that it is impossible but that it requires a greater capital in irrigation and other works than has ever been made available, at least since the withdrawal of the Moors, and that the land is best under tree crops, such as citrus fruits. This form of agriculture represents a long-term investment and necessitates the mechanism of exchange. Southern Spain is too primitive for this.

Eastern Spain. Between the Meseta and the shore of the Mediterranean are areas of low-lying land. The largest is in the Ebro Valley; the smallest consists merely of a few fields between the mountains and the sea. They lie on the dry side of Spain, cut off from rain-bearing winds by the Meseta. Winters may be cool in the Ebro Valley, but in general this is an area of very hot, dry summers and mild winters with a rainfall too small in many parts for agriculture. This coast, however, fronting the Mediterranean as it does, has been open to civilizing influences from Greece and Italy. Many of its cities derive from ancient times, founded by the Carthaginians or Romans. They took part in medieval trade and even rivaled Venice and Genoa. This part of Spain is oldest in civilization. Higher cultures entered through its ports and spread slowly through the peninsula, until at last they reached the wild and, in early times, savage northwest. Today eastern Spain is foremost in industrial and commercial development. Barcelona is a modern, forward-looking city in contrast to those of the Meseta, which are still in many respects medieval.

The Ebro Valley northeast of the Meseta stretches for 250 miles from the point where the river Ebro leaves the Cantabrian Mountains to its delta in the Mediterranean. The plain varies in width from 50 to 100 miles. It is cut off from the sea by the low, narrow range of the Catalonian Mountains, across which it flows in a narrow valley a short distance above its delta. The plain is almost completely surrounded by mountains which cut it off from rain-bearing winds. The annual rainfall in the center is less than 15 inches a year, and a large area, known as Los Monegros, is covered by a thin steppe vegetation similar to that found in La Mancha. The relief of the plain is far from level. The soft beds have been eroded to form a great number of isolated, flat-topped hills. Water supply is a serious problem, and settlement is sparse. Irrigation is practiced in the valleys of some of the northern tributaries of the Ebro, and the Gallego and lower Segre Valleys are both well cultivated with the help of water brought down

Alicante. This is a typical large city of the Mediterranean coast of Spain. It occupies a narrow plain between the mountains and the sea. (*Spanish Tourist Office, London.*)

by the Pyrenean tributaries of the Ebro. Most of the few towns in the Ebro Valley lie on the river. Zaragoza (271,500) lies at an ancient crossing of the river near the northern opening of the Jalón Valley.

The Catalonian Mountains rise to heights of over 4,000 feet but are broken by the water gap of the Ebro and, to the northeast, by the narrow, rocky valley of the Llobregat. The climate is wetter than that of the plains which they shelter, and the vegetative cover is thicker, with conifers and broad-leaved evergreens, such as the cork oak. But inland, *matorral*—low, evergreen, aromatic shrubs—takes over and passes gradually into the steppe of the interior, except where irrigation has made agriculture possible.

Between the mountains and the coast is a narrow plain separated from the sea by a low, narrow limestone ridge, which forms a picturesque and rocky coast. The lowlands and the coastal hills are well cultivated, and grain crops, including rice on the irrigated lands, and southern fruits are grown. Tarragona, on the coast, is a center of the wine trade but in most respects has been eclipsed by Barcelona. Barcelona (1,286,000) is a city of Carthaginian origin. An isolated hill, Montjuich, provided a defensive site, beneath whose shelter and protection the modern city has grown up. It was of commercial importance in the Middle Ages, suffered somewhat with the annexation of Catalonia to Castile, but in modern times has developed as the most important industrial and commercial city of Spain. Inland from Barcelona are many small towns, some with textile industries, which use water power from the surrounding hills.

The people of Catalonia are distinct from those of the rest of Spain. They speak the Catalan language, which resembles the now extinct *langue d'oc* of southern France. They are a vigorous and enterprising people; they have engaged in commerce since the Middle Ages and have never experienced the religious fanaticism and intolerance of the people of the Meseta, occupied for many centuries in their

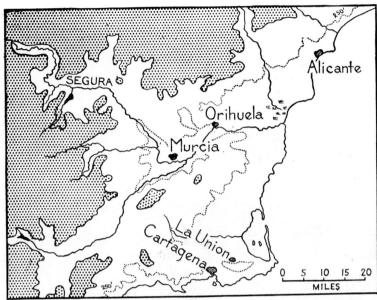

Fig. 203. The plain of Murcia; 500 and 1,000 feet contours are shown.

struggle with the Moors. Religious crusading does not lie within their capacities. Nor are they favorable to Spanish or Castilian nationalism. They dislike the Castilian and distrust everything that emenates from Madrid. Local autonomy is their object, and this they attained under the short-lived Spanish republic, only to lose it with the victory of Franco.

South of the Ebro Valley the mountains of southern and eastern Spain come close to the coast of the Mediterranean, and spurs from the mountain chains form projecting headlands. Between the latter, however, are a number of separate coastal plains. Many of these are made up of the alluvium laid down by the short rivers and are fertile, needing only a regular supply of water to become highly productive. Rainfall, however, is low, almost everywhere less than 20 inches and in places under 15 inches. This is quite inadequate for the intensive cultivation that the quality of the soil warrants, and agriculture is heavily dependent upon irrigation. Water is stored in innumerable reservoirs in the mountains and released to water the small coastal plains. These are flat and furrowed with a network of irrigation channels. The use of the water is strictly controlled, and it is rationed between the cultivators. The agricultural population is dense, and holdings small. The *huertas*, literally "gardens," are intensively cultivated, and two or three crops are taken from them in each year. The *vegas* are larger and less well irrigated and cultivated. Rice, maize, wheat, vegetables, and fruit are grown. The olive and grape vine are common, oranges are important, and the banana and date palms here make their only serious appearance in Europe. The plains of the Mediterranean shore are in effect oases, shut in on the landward side by a waste of *matorral* scrub and steppe.

Between Gibraltar and Cape de Gata the areas of irrigated lowland are small and separated by stretches of coast where the mountains drop steeply to the sea. The plains of Málaga, Vélez Málaga, Motril, and Almería are the largest, the plain of Málaga being a plain of almost 20 miles from west to east and 10 from north to south. North of Cape de Gata the plains are larger. The lowlands of Cuevas de Vera, Cartagena (120,000), Murcia (220,500), Alicante (107,500), Valencia (535,000), and Castellón de la Plana (56,000) are each extensive. Along the coast are lagoons, swamps, and sand dunes. North of Alicante the coastal ranges reach out to the rocky Cape Nao, which separates the plain of Murcia from that of Valencia.

The latter is a semicircular sweep of plain, at most 15 to 20 miles wide. Along the coast are also lagoons and sand dunes, and behind them the rich *huertas* reach up to the edge of the mountains. Valencia lies as nearly as possible in the middle of this plain, its market and business center.

Fig. 204. A *huerta* of southeastern Spain. Note the irrigation canals from the mountainous interior.

The antipathy which exists between the Catalan and the Castillian exists also between the inhabitants of Valencia and of other "gardens" of the Mediterranean coast and the Meseta. But these areas are individually too small to resist domination from the interior. Valencian home rule is a dream that is yet far from realization.

Southern Spain. On the south the Meseta drops steeply to the plain of the Guadalquivir. South of this again a range of high mountains, the Betic Mountains, named from Baetica, the Roman name for this region, interposes between the plain and the Mediterranean Sea. All the problems of southern Spain are accentuated here. Moorish occupation was longer, and its effects have gone deeper. The climate, hot with a small winter rainfall, necessitates more capital, not less, in an area where people are even poorer and more overcrowded. A hopelessness has settled on the south of Spain, as on the south of Italy, relieved only by the prospect of a revolution at some future date.

The Guadalquivir Valley broadens westward to the Atlantic. Unlike the Ebro Valley, which

in certain other respects it resembles, the Guadalquivir Valley is exposed to oceanic influences as the Ebro plain is not. Rainfall is higher, winters warmer, and the summers very hot. Much of the plain is flat, and west of Seville, (Sevilla, 391,000) stretches a low flat plain, known as Las Marismas, across whose salty pastures and wastes the Guadalquivir and its distributaries meander toward the sea. Along the coast the Atlantic winds have piled up a belt of sand dunes. Above Seville the Guadalquivir keeps close to the edge of the Sierra Morena. The greater rainfall and the relative abundance of water for the purpose of irrigation have given to the Guadalquivir Valley a far greater agricultural importance than has the Ebro Plain. Wheat and vegetables are grown in the valley bottoms, vines grow on many of the lower hill slopes, and olive groves cover large areas.

Seville lies on the Guadalquivir near the junction of the alluvial plain of Las Marismas with the more undulating land in the center of the region. It lies 60 miles from the sea and has been a city and port at least since Roman times.

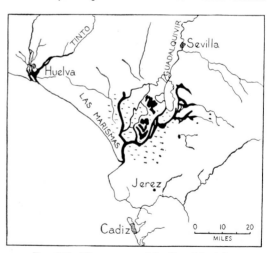

Fig. 205. The estuary of the Guadalquivir.

It is now a modern industrial town with engineering and food-processing industries. Córdoba (164,500) lies some 80 miles further upstream and, like Seville, was a Roman town. It became one of the most important cities of the Moslem world and is now famous for its Moorish architecture. The cathedral of Córdoba was formerly a mosque. Cádiz (100,000) lies at the end of a narrow peninsula which partially closes the Bay of Cádiz. It was a port of great importance during the period of Spanish imperialism from the sixteenth to the eighteenth centuries. Its site

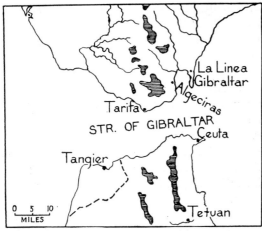

FIG. 206. Straits of Gibraltar.

is restricted, and the resources of its hinterland limited. It now exports the wine of southern Spain, olives, and cork. The town of Jerez de la Frontera (107,000), from which the name "sherry" is derived, lies only about 12 miles from Cádiz. On the northern edge of the Guadalquivir Plain and close to the mouth of the Tinto River is the small port of Huelva, which handles copper export from the Minas de Ríotinto. It was from Palos de la Frontera, across the Tinto, that Columbus sailed in 1492.

The mountains that shut in the Guadalquivir Valley on the south are made of rocks very much younger than those of the Meseta itself, and their summits attain heights very much greater than those of the central Sierras. The Betic Range is really divided into two parallel belts of hill separated from each other by a long and narrow depression. The more southerly of these attains the greatest altitudes and presents the most rugged appearance. Beginning near Gibraltar, it extends northeastward to Cape Nao, a distance of 350 miles. It is broken by several transverse valleys into short segments of hill, of which the highest is the Sierra Nevada,

upon which the snow lies throughout the year. Their highest point, the Mulhacén, reaches a height of 11,240 feet. In this small area truly alpine landforms are found.

The Sierras to east and west are lower but would still present a serious barrier to movement if gaps had not been opened between them by rivers. These are followed by roads and railways into the central depression and through the whole mountain mass to the Guadalquivir Valley. The northern range of hills is lower and yet more broken. A number of small towns lie along the northern foothills where the rivers spread out over the plain of the Guadalquivir.

The depression between the two ranges expands at intervals into fertile, irrigated basins, in which are small market towns. In one of these depressions "the road twisted down from the mountains, and suddenly beneath its heights Granada spread, bosomed in its wide, high plain, climbing over its three hills, towered and valleyed, delicately shadowed in the evening light, guarded by the cold lilac peaks of the Sierra Nevada."[1] In the midst lies the Alhambra, the Moorish palace and castle, crowning its steep, wooded hill, the greatest and the loveliest relic of the long period of Moorish domination and proof of the high civilization to which these people attained.

The Balearic Islands are a continuation eastward from Cape Nao of the Betic Mountains. The group consists of three islands, Minorca, Majorca, and Ibiza, together with a few rocky islets. All are hilly, with a mild climate and sufficient rainfall for agriculture. The population lives in small villages and is chiefly engaged in agriculture. The Balearic Islands display a characteristic of Mediterranean islands—the absence of coastal settlement due to the danger of pirates in earlier times.

At the opposite extremity of the Betic chain is the Rock of Gibraltar, occupied by Great Britain since 1704 because of its command of the Straits. Other places, such as Tangier and Tarifa, are even better suited in this respect but are less easily defended. The Rock contains a

[1] Macaulay, Rose, "Fabled Shore," p. 125, London, 1949.

The town of Estello in Navarra. This is a typical small town of northern Spain. It has much in common with Teruel (see p. 341) but has a more prosperous air. Note the slight differences in architecture, dictated mainly by climatic reasons. (*Spanish Tourist Office, London.*)

considerable British garrison and an even larger British and Spanish civilian population, whose primary purpose it is to minister to the wants of the military.

Northern Spain. Northern Spain is made up of a chain of mountains which rise from the northern limits of the Meseta. They lie far enough north to be exposed to westerly winds at all seasons of the year. It is in general a region of cool winters and warm summers, with rain at all times. The natural vegetation is deciduous woodland. Man has made clearings and cultivated temperate crops.

These hills were never really conquered by the Moors. Instead they formed a bastion from which the Christian peoples moved southward to reconquer the peninsula. The north is a region of peasant proprietors, more progressive and independent than the natives of other parts of Spain except Catalonia. They have developed manufacturing industries in Asturias and the Basque country. Like the Catalans, they show

no love for the Castilian and have many times demanded some degree of home rule. They were promised the fulfillment of their wishes by the Republican government (1931 to 1936), but the Civil War came before they could be satisfied.

Northern Spain is made up of the Pyrenees, lying to the east of the Cantabrian Mountains, which continue westward the line of the Pyrenees, and of the hilly country of Galicia in the northwest. The Pyrenees of Spain repeat the features found on the French side of the range. A core of crystalline rocks forms the central backbone and gives rise to the greatest heights and most rugged scenery. The French frontier follows in general the watershed of the Pyrenees, but the Pic d'Aneto, the highest peak, lies wholly in Spain. The Pyrenees are bordered by limestone rocks of younger geological age. These have been eroded into a series of east-to-west ridges, between which flow the Pyrenean rivers. Between these lower hills and the main

Pyrenean range is a depression, not wholly continuous throughout the length of the range, in which agriculture is practiced and a few small towns, such as Pamplona (75,500) and Jaca, have grown up. A similar line of small market towns lies along the southern edge of the limestone hills at their junction with the Ebro Plain. The slope of the Pyrenees on the Spanish side of the range is, on the whole, a great deal more gentle than on the French, but the broad features of the human geography are similar on each side of the range.

On the Spanish, as on the French, side the Pyrenean ridges present a barrier to movement, and the transverse valleys are narrow, difficult, and easily defended. The upper valleys of the Pyrenean rivers not only were held successfully against the Moorish invaders of Spain but have since retained a strong feeling of local independence. The nominally independent republic of Andorra still occupies the upper valley of the Segre River, a small, remote area of only 191 square miles and a population of only 5,230. Toward the western end of the Pyrenees the Basque province of Navarre, with its capital of Pamplona, was for a long while a Pyrenean rather than a Spanish state and retains today a powerful urge toward local independence.

East of the pass of Roncevaux the crystalline core of the Pyrenean Range disappears from view, and for a distance of considerably over 100 miles there are east-west limestone ridges. These are nowhere high, almost the whole area lying below 4,000 feet, but it has been dissected by the many short rivers and is rugged and forested. This is the Basque country. The most northerly of the limestone ridges lies close to the coast; its spurs reach out into the sea to form steep headlands, between which the sea runs up the valleys to form the *rias*, such as those of Bilbao, Santoña, and Santander. The defiles of the Basque province lead to the most westerly crossing of the Pyrenees at Irún.

The Basque language is still spoken to a small extent in this hilly region. It was once widespread over Navarre (Navarra) and the Pyrenees and stretched far into the French province of Gascony. The Basque province is now dis-

tinguished as much by its industrialization and its vigorous, commercial outlook as by its Basque speech. Iron ore occurs in the hills of the coastal range, and although reserves are small, much is exported to other European countries and there is an iron-smelting industry at Bilbao. Bilbao (235,500) lies at the head of the long narrow ria of the river Nervion. San Sebastian (116,500) is a resort on the beautiful coast to the east, and Santander (107,000), a small, industrial town, lies on a ria to the west.

The Cantabrian Mountains, which lie west of Santander, resemble the Pyrenees. They have a core of ancient crystalline rocks, which come to the surface toward the west and give rise to rugged alpine scenery. They are, however, lower than the Pyrenees. The highest peaks are only little more than 8,500 feet, but the range as a whole is continuous and unbroken and offers an obstacle to movement. The greatest heights are attained toward the east in a group of peaks known as the Peñas de Europa. In about 150 miles only one railroad, that between the Meseta and the town of Oviedo, crosses it at a height of over 4,200 feet. Toward the west the Cantabrian Mountains curve toward the southwest and then the south. Here branches from the Cantabrian Range enclose the level, fertile basin of the river Sil, known as El Bierzo. On the east mountains cut it off from the Meseta, on the west and south from the mild and humid region of Galicia. The Sil Basin is transitional from the maritime region of northwestern Spain to the Meseta.

Between the Cantabrian Mountains and the sea is a narrow coastal range, but the rocks which compose it are softer, soils richer, and agriculture of considerable importance. In this depression also is found the only significant coal field of Spain, that of Oviedo. Oviedo (107,000) handles the coal and iron ore of the region and has developed metallurgical industries.

Rainfall is heavy in the higher mountains but quickly diminishes on the edges of the Ebro Basin and the Meseta. At lower levels the climate is mild, but as in all areas of strong relief, conditions of temperature, cloudiness, and humidity differ sharply within quite short distances. Much of the region is forested and lies within the limits of northwest European coniferous and broad-leaved trees. Oak and beech grow on the lower ground, and northern conifers and birch on the higher. But southern trees, however, begin to appear; the evergreen

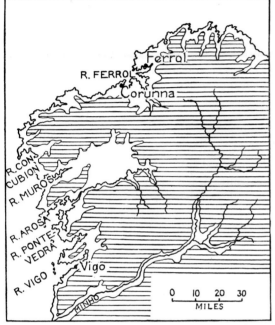

FIG. 207. Galicia. Shaded area lies above 1,000 feet.

oak and Spanish chestnut are found, particularly in the Pyrenees.

In the extreme northwest is a plateau formed in old, hard rocks like the Cantabrians. It slopes toward the sea, and its general height increases from less than 2,000 feet in the north to nearly 4,000 feet near the Portuguese border. It has been deeply eroded by rivers and now presents the aspect of smooth, rounded hills separated by broad valleys, which reach down to the coast and terminate in long, branching rias. The rias of the Galician coast are very much larger and more beautiful than those of the Basque country, reaching 20 miles inland and providing deep and sheltered anchorages. Fishing ports have grown up along their shores but no large cities except Vigo (139,000). Their rugged hinterland prevents their development as significant ports for the Spanish peninsula.

Galicia has a mild, moist climate. Rainfall is heavy, a great deal more than 40 inches in most parts, and cloud considerable, but frost and snow are rare except on higher ground. Vegetation is rich and of the kind which in France is known as *bocage*. The landscape is one of small fields and thick hedges, of meadow, grassland, small patches of woodland, and small and scattered villages. Towns are few and small, but Santiago (58,000), despite its situation in the extreme northwest of Spain and its difficult communications with the rest of Europe, became during the Middle Ages an important center of pilgrimage, where the shrine of Saint James of Compostella attracted the faithful from all parts of Christian Europe.

The Development of Modern Spain. Since 1640 the Iberian peninsula has been divided into two political units, Spain and Portugal. For 60 years previously both had been united under the Spanish throne. The history of the Middle Ages is one of the gradual expulsion of the Moors by the Christian powers and of the unification of the latter. The states of the Meseta, León and Castile, were first joined; to

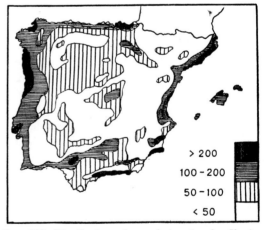

FIG. 208. Distribution of population in the Iberian peninsula, in density per square mile.

these was added the kingdom of Aragon in the later years of the fifteenth century. In 1492, Granada, the last Moorish stronghold in Spain, was captured by the Spaniards, and with the exception of Portugal, the whole peninsula united under a single rule. Portugal was itself occupied from 1580 to 1640 by the forces of Spain.

This political unification has failed to bring with it any strong sense of nationalism. Feeling in Spain is local rather than national, and in recent years there have been a number of movements to establish some measure of local autonomy in Catalonia, the Basque territory, Valencia, and Andalusia. There is little reason, other than the accident of history and the patronage of Great Britain, why Portugal should now be independent and Catalonia a part of Spain rather than the reverse. The peninsula has a common history; the settlement pattern and agricultural and industrial development of both Spain and Portugal are broadly similar.

The population of Spain is at present about 28 million. Its density of about 120 to the square mile is one of the lowest in Europe. Portugal, by comparison, has about 180 to the square mile. This does not, however, indicate any great difference between the two countries; the population of Portugal accords closely with that of the coastal regions of Spain.

The population is peripheral. Almost the whole of the Meseta and its bounding ranges has a density of less than 100 and at least a half of it of less than 50 to the square mile. The capital of Spain, Madrid, in order to be geographically central, is in the midst of the least populated area and far from all areas of dense population. This peripheral distribution of population serves further to deepen the intensity of local patriotism in the regions which are geographically marginal.

The population of both countries is predominantly rural and agricultural. Fifty-two per cent of the employed population of Spain and 49 per cent of that of Portugal are engaged in farming activities. Geographical conditions, and with them the practice and methods of agriculture, differ widely over the peninsula. The style of dwelling and the distribution of settlements are in part a reflection of these conditions. In the moist and mountainous region of the north the pattern of settlement is in the main a scattered one. The farmsteads stand among their fields; there are hamlets but few large villages. In the more arid regions of both the Ebro Valley and of the Meseta the pattern becomes one of large and widely spaced nucleated villages, amounting in size sometimes to small towns. The nucleation may be due in certain instances to the nature of the water supply, but it appears that the predominant reason lies in the need for security and defense against the Moors during the period of the Christian reconquest. The standard of housing is low. The villages of the Meseta are frequently made up of low, single-floored mud or stone-built dwellings, with a low-pitched roof of tile or thatch. In parts of Castile are villages of troglodytic dwellings carved in the hillsides. Conditions are better in the north and also in the irrigated lands of the southeast. An interesting feature is the change in the pitch of the roof from the steep roofs of the wet north to the almost or quite flat roofs of the dry southeast.

The most striking characteristic of the rural population of the whole of the Iberian peninsula is its poverty. Conditions are worst over the southern part of the Meseta and in Andalusia, but indications of rural well-being are hard to find in any part of the area. To some extent this is due to the semifeudal conditions that have continued to prevail through modern times. The southern half of Spain is predominantly a region of large estates, often owned by absentee landlords and cultivated by a poor and landless peasantry. The breakup of the large estates has been heralded as a solution to the agrarian problem, and efforts were made in this direction during the 1930's. The problem goes deeper. To distribute the land among the cultivators is not to remedy their ignorance and their lack of equipment and capital. Nor will redistribution alone bring about a change in the demographic pattern, in which large villages and agricultural towns occur in areas least suited to support them. In the north the peasants usually cultivate their own fields, but these are often too small. In Galicia, famous for the minute size of its agricultural holdings and the relative density of its agricultural population, there is an acute pressure of population on the limited agricultural resources, with the result that land which should have been left under grass is plowed and sown to crops.

Only a small proportion of the total population lies in towns. Two towns, Madrid and Barcelona, have a population of over 1 million,

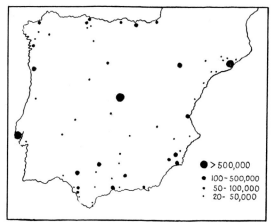

FIG. 209. Cities of Spain and Portugal. Note the coastal location of the majority.

and only Lisbon has over half a million. Many towns well known in the history and literature of Europe are very small. León and Toledo have each less than 60,000 inhabitants, and Segovia and Ávila less than 30,000. The distribution of the larger towns accords with that of the population as a whole. With the exception of Madrid, Zaragoza, and Córdoba, they are coastal or near the coast.

Though agriculture is by far the most important occupation in both Spain and Portugal, the produce of only two crops, the grape and the olive, enters largely into the export trade of the two countries. For the rest, agriculture is carried on on a subsistence basis. Crops are grown that yield the greatest volume of food under existing conditions of soil and climate and the present stage of technological development. Manures are very little used, and resort is commonly had to bare fallow to restore the fertility of the soil. Up to a third of the total agricultural land may at any one time be under bare fallow. Over half would be under cereal crops, chiefly wheat, which is grown in all parts except the humid north and northwest. Barley is a crop of the dry

south; rye of the damp northwest. Maize is grown in the wetter parts of the north and west, and rice is planted in the irrigated fields of the Ebro Valley and the southeast. The yields per acre of all these crops are low—very far below the average for western European countries. Olive groves cover large areas in Andalusia, the southern Meseta, and the Ebro Valley. They afford the most important source of vegetable oils, the only fat consumed by the greater part

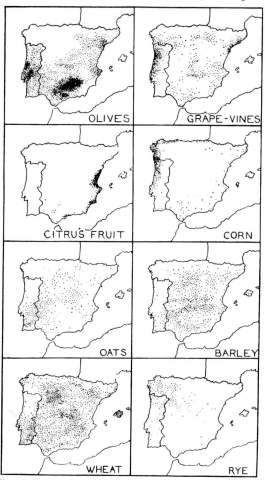

FIG. 210. Distribution of cultivated crops in Spain and Portugal.

of the population, and provide an important export. Grape vines are more widely distributed. Few parts of the peninsula produce no wine, but the most intensive production is in the Douro Valley of Portugal and along the coast of eastern Spain.

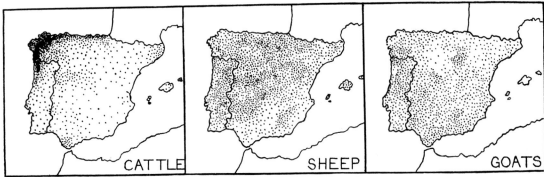

FIG. 211. Distribution of cattle, sheep, and goats.

Spain was formerly famous for its livestock husbandry. From the time of the Moorish retreat until the beginning of the last century large flocks of sheep made their twice-yearly journey from the winter grazings in Andalusia to their summer homes in the northern Meseta and back again. Wool was one of the most valuable products of Spain, and the merino sheep was originally Spanish. Sheep are now less important but remain the most numerous branch of livestock, particularly on the poor grasslands of the Meseta. Cattle are confined

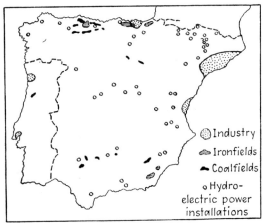

FIG. 212. Distribution of minerals and industrial regions.

almost wholly to the damp north, where grass grows throughout the year.

By contrast, manufacturing industry is a recent development, is highly localized, and employs only a small proportion of the total population. Spain itself is not without resources. In addition to the deposits, important but not

large, of nonferrous metals, there are deposits of iron ore in the Basque country and of coal in Asturias. Water-power resources in the Cantabrian Mountains and the Pyrenees are considerable and have been developed to some extent, but elsewhere in the peninsula the rainfall is too small and too irregular for power resources to be important. The textile industry of Spain is, like that of most western European countries, the oldest and still one of the most important. It is no longer widely distributed, however, and about 90 per cent of the productive capacity of Spain is located in Catalonia. Factories are small and located either in the suburbs of Barcelona or in the small towns of its hinterland. There is no geographical distinction between cotton- and wool-producing centers. Imported materials, such as raw cotton, are brought in through Barcelona, and the region depends in general upon hydroelectric power.

The metallurgical industry of Spain is more recent in origin, though this, too, has roots in the medieval ironworking for which Spain was famous. The modern smelting industry is located primarily in the Basque country, particularly in and around the town of Bilbao, where the ore is mined, but there are lesser centers at Barcelona and in and near Gijón in Asturias. The total steel production is only about 720,000 tons (1949) a year. The output of iron ore has diminished and in 1949 was only 1,811,000 tons. Other industries are developed to only a very modest degree. There is a small chemical industry, subsidiary to the metallurgical, and attempts have been made in recent years to develop further the manufacture of synthetic fertilizers, so much needed by Spanish agriculture.

Transportation facilities are also relatively undeveloped, and the network of roads and railways is thinner than in any other country of western Europe. The chief characteristic of both roads and railways is their concentration on Madrid. Cross-country travel is difficult in most parts of Spain. This gravely restricts the development of manufacturing industries owing to the obstacles in the way of the internal distribution of the produce and serves at the same time to increase the dependence of the provinces on Madrid.

The foreign trade of these countries is small, and the volume, per capita, of both exports and imports is among the lowest in western Europe. This high degree of self-sufficiency is a measure, not of the efficiency and productivity of Spain, but rather of its backwardness and of the lowness of its economic standards. The export trade of Spain is dominated by certain specialized agricultural products, of which fruit, both fresh and preserved, is by far the most important. These are followed in order of value by wines and vegetables. Minerals, especially iron ore, are among the more important exports. The exports of Portugal are similar: the most important are cork, wines, preserved sardines, and certain minerals, particularly pyrites. The imports of both countries consist mainly of manufactured goods, coal, petroleum, and the raw materials, such as cotton, of the limited manufacturing industries of the peninsula.

Spain thus demonstrates problems that are common to the whole of southern Europe—of poverty and overpopulation in regions that were once bright with promise, of lack of capital and initiative in lands that were once in the forefront of human progress. The initiative has passed to northwestern Europe, while civil war and unrest, which commonly accompany low living standards, lower yet further the level of human welfare. Within the last 20 years Spain has been the scene of one of the most bloodthirsty and destructive of all civil wars.

The last of the enfeebled Bourbons left the throne of Spain in 1931. The Republican government was faced with heavy economic problems. Its moderate progress outraged the extremists, while conservatives and nationalists opposed it on all counts. It fell between the extremes of the political Right and Left. It suppressed revolts of the latter until in 1936 it

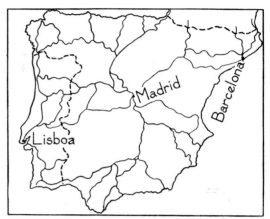

Fig. 213. Railroads of the Iberian peninsula. Madrid has become the focus of the railroads of the peninsula.

was faced with the rising of General Franco. The civil war that followed engulfed the whole of Spain, lasted 3 years, and did an immense amount of material damage. It did not, however, prevent the population from increasing by 4 million between 1930 and 1950. A population larger by a sixth now lives on resources diminished by the war.

Spain fits ill into the European community of nations. The fanaticism and conservatism of the Castilian, his pride and obstinacy, his clinging to the outworn modes of medievalism, which not even Cervantes laughed wholly out of existence, all have kept Spain aloof from other nations. Spain is proud and poor, and her poverty is in some degree the price of her pride.

PORTUGAL

Portugal is but the western fringe of the Spanish peninsula. For the greater part it lies off the Meseta and at a lower altitude, though the Sierras of Spain reach across it toward the sea. Nowhere is the country much over 100 miles from west to east, but it is over 300 miles from north to south. It thus lies open to the sea, and the sea has been even more important in Portuguese history than in that of England. Rain and cooling winds come in from the Atlantic. Portugal's position has brought it the friendship and patronage of Great Britain, and the nation is proud to call itself Britain's oldest ally. Spanish nationalism has conceived of the complete union of the whole peninsula. Cata-

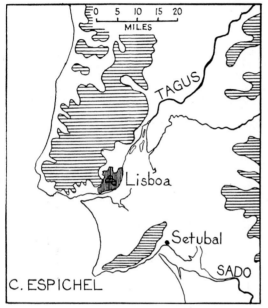

FIG. 214. The situation of Lisbon (Lisboa). Shaded area lies at above 300 feet.

lonia has been absorbed into Spain, but Portugal, except for the period 1580 to 1640, has maintained her independence. Franco, in the first flush of his victory, spoke of uniting the peninsula, but this is no longer mentioned.

Portuguese independence owes much to Britain's friendship and to British sea power. This alliance was based upon a fourteenth-century marriage and confirmed by the British liking for port wine. Its chief basis today lies in the port of Lisbon (Lisboa), the best harbor on the west coast of Europe and, in the hands of an enemy of Great Britain, a great threat to her sea-borne communications. Great Britain, for example, defended the approaches to the harbor of Lisbon during the Napoleonic Wars and held the port as a base.

Northern Portugal is a plateau made up of the hard rocks which compose the Meseta, less dissected than Galicia but more so than the plateau of Castile, which adjoins it to the east. Between the valleys, many of them deep and narrow, of the Douro (Duero) and its tributaries are bare ridges of granitic and other crystalline rocks. These ridges trend generally from northeast to southwest. On the south of this plateau region are the western continuations of the central Sierras of the Spanish Meseta, short, narrow ranges, which demonstrate the same northeast to southwest trend. The river Tagus (Tejo) flows close to the southern edge of these ranges. South of the Tejo the plateau of Extremadura diminishes in height in Portugal until it disappears in the Portuguese lowlands. In the extreme south, the hills of Algarve carry the line of the Sierra Morena out to the sea.

The climate changes gradually from north to south. On the Spanish frontier in the north rainfall is heavy and the climate mild. The rainfall diminishes southward, sunshine becomes greater, temperatures warmer, the rainy season more restricted, and the summers longer and drier. The vegetation changes with the climate. South of Galicia the northern trees disappear. Spanish chestnut and evergreen oak take over and pass southward into woods of cork oak or matorral scrub. The grape vine is cultivated in the Miño Valley and becomes more important in the Douro Valley, where it is the chief cultivated crop.

Portuguese Lowlands. These are separated from the plateaus of northern and eastern Portugal by a fault line, along the east of which the older rocks rise steeply. The plain is composed of young, soft rocks. Much of it is under cultivation. The plain begins to the north of the Douro and widens as it progresses southward. Near Coimbra it is some 30 miles wide. South of this point the plain narrows as a range of low limestone hills continues the direction of the Sierra da Estrella and forms the Lisbon (Lisboa, 709,000) peninsula. The coastal plain has a straight, harborless coast fringed with sand dunes, on which conifers have been planted. Shallow lagoons have been formed by the drifting sand. But behind this sandy area the land is intensively cultivated with cereals and fruit. Oporto (Pôrto, 262,000), on the Douro estuary, is the focus of the Portuguese wine trade; Coimbra, on the inner edge of the coastal plain, is a former capital of Portugal and an artistic and cultural center.

The Tagus widens into the harbor of Lisbon, which is one of Portugal's most valuable natural assets, a waterway almost 20 miles from north to south and from 4 to 8 miles wide. Its entrance is narrow, but its waters are deep enough for any modern craft. The town of Lisbon lies at the entrance to the harbor, on the southeastern extremity of the Lisbon peninsula. Lisbon is a settlement of ancient origin, but it was not until the mid-thirteenth century that it became the capital of Portugal. It was important in the Portuguese maritime enterprise of the sixteenth century and had grown to a considerable size before it was destroyed by an earthquake in 1755. Most of the present town has been built since this date. Lisbon now handles much of the trade of Portugal, is a commercial and business city, and has a number of light industries.

South of the Tagus the coast plain reaches to the hills of Algarve, broken by many low hills of dry, infertile limestone. The lower land, sometimes covered with a fertile alluvium, is well cultivated, but the hills are too dry for agriculture and are covered with either forests of cork oak or *matorral*. The Sado, which drains much of this plain, has a large estuary comparable in many ways to that of the Tagus but has always been excelled in importance by that of Lisbon. It is of little importance, except for fishing. The town of Setubal at the entrance is a center of the Portuguese sardine fishery.

Portugal is predominantly an agricultural country. Its resources are, in proportion to its size, greater than those of Spain, and it supports a denser population. Agricultural standards are in general not noticeably better than those of Spain, but Portugal has advantages denied to her neighbor. Proximity to the coast and greater ease of communications allow her to export more easily, and this has in turn encouraged the production of agricultural specialities, of which port wine is the most important.

The population of Portugal is estimated to be 8,271,000 (1947) and is increasing steadily. Attempts are being made to extend cultivation in areas hitherto uncultivated and to build up manufacturing industries. In this Portugal can expect to be more successful than Spain, because her relatively successful economy inspires confidence and she can borrow capital more easily. Portugal has a considerable foreign trade. In value the wine export is the most important, followed by cork, salted and canned fish, and minerals. The export of pyrites and wolfram brings in a small revenue. The cotton-textile industry has grown in recent years to be sufficiently large for cloth to be among the exports.

THE ATLANTIC ISLANDS

Both Spain and Portugal control certain island groups at no great distance from their

FIG. 215. The Atlantic islands.

shores. If the Cape Verde Islands are omitted as being too far south for consideration in this volume, we are left with three groups of Atlantic islands.

Azores (Açores). These islands have been Portuguese since the sixteenth century. The group of nine islands lies some 800 miles west-southwest of Lisbon. The population is almost half a million and is engaged very largely in a self-sufficing agriculture. The islands themselves are largely of volcanic origin. Their relief is

Las Palmas, Gran Canaria. The port receives large vessels and has a considerable export of fruit. It is more wealthy, as the buildings indicate, than many towns of mainland Spain. (*Spanish Tourist Office, London.*)

generally rugged, but soils are fertile and productive. Ponta Delgada on the island of São Miguel is the chief port and largest settlement and was once of importance for provisioning and watering ships. It still exports small quantities of fruit. With the development of airplane transport the Azores have begun to assume a very considerable importance in transatlantic communications because they offer the only possible landing field between the Bermuda group and the coast of Europe.

Madeira, also Portuguese, lies closer to the coast of Africa and is less than 600 miles southwest of Lisbon. It is a rugged volcanic island. Soils are fertile, but owing to the strong relief, only small areas around the coast are under cultivation. The population is less than a quarter million. Though lying close to the desert coast of Africa, the island is far from barren, and much is heavily forested. Irrigation has to be practiced for crop cultivation, but fruit is important, and the wine exported from the island is widely known. Funchal (54,000),

the capital, is the largest town and port and occupies almost the only area of low flat land.

Canary Islands. These lie even closer to the coast of Africa, and the nearest is only 70 miles from the mainland. Like the other groups, the Canary Islands are volcanic in origin and rugged in relief. There is little flat land, and much of the group is semiarid and scrub-covered. Tenerife, consisting of the crater of a still active volcano, is the largest island and has the biggest population. The islands are famous for their fruit and vegetable production, much of which is grown on the terraced hillsides of the volcanoes. Bananas, tomatoes, citrus fruits, and wine are exported from Santa Cruz de Tenerife (108,500) and Las Palmas (151,500), the chief ports and largest towns of the group.

Yet farther south is the Cape Verde group of islands, lying 320 miles off the desert coast of this part of Africa. The islands are Portuguese and are mountainous and of little commercial significance.

BIBLIOGRAPHY

GENERAL

"Géographie universelle," Vol. VII, La Méditerranée et les péninsules méditerranéennes, Pt. II, Généralités, Espagne, Portugal, Paris, 1934.

Newbigin, M. I., "Southern Europe," London, 1950.

Philippson, A., "Das Mittelmeergebiet," Leipzig, 1922.

Villar, Emile E. H., "Soils of Spain and Portugal," London, 1937.

SPAIN

Aitken, Routes of Transhumance on the Spanish Meseta, *G.J.*, CVI, 1945, 59–69.

Brennan, Gerald, "The Face of Spain," London, 1950.

———, "Spanish Labyrinth," Cambridge, 1943.

Bull, William E., The Olive Industry of Spain, *E.G.*, XII, 1936, 136–154.

Cereceda, J. D., The Natural Regions of Spain, *The Geographical Teacher*, XI, 1922, 333–345; XII, 1923, 19–27, 82–90.

———, "Regiones naturales de Espana," Madrid, 1942.

De Madariaga, Salvador, "Spain," London, 1942.

Dobby, E. H. G., Agrarian Problems in Spain, *G.R.*, XXVI, 1936, 177–189.

———, Catalonia: The Geographical Basis of Its Regionalism, *G.R.*, XXVIII, 1938, 224–249.

———, The Ebro Delta, *G.J.*, LXXXVII, 1936, 455–469.

———, Galicia: A Little Known Corner of Spain, *G.R.*, XXVI, 1936, 533–580.

———, Water Power and Economy of La Riba, Spain: An Outlier of Catalan Industry, *E.G.*, XIII, 1937, 413–424.

Fairhurst, H., Types of Settlement in Spain, *S.G.M.*, LI, 1935, 283–305.

Gaussen, Henri, A View from Canigou, *G.R.*, XXVI, 1936, 190–204.

Gilbert, E. W., The Human Geography of Mallorca, *S.G.M.*, L, 1934, 129–146.

Klein, Julius, "The Mesta," Cambridge, Mass., 1920.

Oliviera, A. Ramos, "Politics, Economics and Men of Modern Spain, 1808–1940," London, 1946. (Book III is entitled "The Economic Geography of Spain.")

"Overseas Economic Surveys: Spain," London, 1948.

Peattie, Roderick, Andorra: A Study in Mountain Geography, *G.R.*, XIX, 1929, 218–233.

Trend, J. B., "The Civilization of Spain," London, 1944.

Trueta, J., "The Spirit of Catalonia," Oxford, 1946.

Whittlesey, Derwent C., Transpyrenean Spain, the Val d'Aran, *S.G.M.*, IL, 1933, 217–228.

PORTUGAL

Dobby, E. H. G., Economic Geography of the Port Wine Region, *E.G.*, XII, 1936, 311–323.

Lautensach, H., Portugal auf Grund eigener Reisen und der Literatur, *Petermanns Mitteilungen, Ergänzungshefte*, 213, 230, Gotha, 1932.

Livermoore, H. V., "History of Portugal," Cambridge, 1947.

"Overseas Economic Surveys: Portugal," London, 1948.

ISLANDS

Jensen, Sören, Agricultural Methods in the Canaries, Fuerteventura and Lanzarote, *E.G.*, X, 1934, 99–108.

The current official publications of the United Nations and Economic Commission for Europe report generally very briefly on Spain. Spain is not a member of the United Nations and has not been receiving American aid. In consequence she has not been the subject of large-scale reports as have most other Mediterranean countries. Portugal, which is a member of the United Nations and was also one of the countries grouped to receive Marshall Aid, has been enjoying a high enough degree of prosperity since the war to make detailed surveys and reports less desirable than in several other countries. Both countries are adequately reported in the statistical works mentioned on pages 52 to 54.

CHAPTER 27: *French North Africa*

The subject matter of this and of the three chapters following is African and Asiatic rather than European. The countries considered differ in their history and their social and economic structure from the countries of Europe. Yet they are bound up with Europe closely enough to justify their inclusion here (see page 302). All these territories were formerly part of the Arab empire. This empire formerly extended into Spain in the west and the Balkans in the east. The Moors were deprived of their last stronghold in Spain in 1492, though the Turks, who succeeded the Arabs in the Middle East, still retain today a small Balkan foothold in the shape of Turkey-in-Europe.

The whole of the area from the Straits of Gibraltar to the Bosporus was settled by a population of mixed racial origins before it was invaded by the Arabs in the seventh century. The latter were far from numerous, but they brought with them the crusading faith of Islam. They made many converts and built up their armies from those whom they conquered and converted. At no time was there any real political unity through Moslem lands. Rather, the Moslem sphere broke up into semi-independent units. A new vigor was injected into Islam by the coming of the Turks, a distinct people of Asiatic origin and Ural-Altaic speech (page 35). Under Turkish leadership the Anatolian Plateau of present-day Turkey was conquered and Europe was invaded as far as the gates of Vienna.

The spiritual head of Islam, the Caliph, was the same person as the temporal ruler of the Turks, the Sultan. The whole of Islam thus

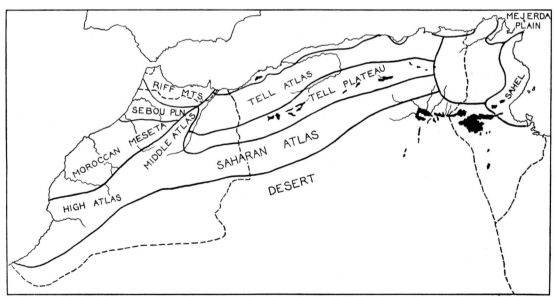

Fig. 216. Physical regions of French North Africa.

came to be in theory the empire of the Turks. The Sultan's authority was little respected, and the outlying parts of his empire achieved virtual independence of the government in Constantinople. During the nineteenth century one part after another of the Islamic empire was torn away from the Sultan, by either revolt or conquest by another power. The former empire has been reduced to the present republic of Turkey, and much of its former territory has been ruled by Spain, France, Italy and Great Britain, though all has now achieved political independence.

French North Africa consists of the Atlas Mountains and a belt of desert lying to the south. Politically it is made up of Algeria, which is considered an integral part of metropolitan France, and of the two French protectorates of Morocco and Tunisia. Forming part of this broad region, though politically distinct, are Spanish Morocco and the International Zone of Tangier, which form a small enclave of the Moroccan coast.

The Atlas Mountains. The region is dominated by the folded chains of the Atlas Mountains, built of young, soft limestones, sandstones, and clays. Older crystalline massifs, however, were caught up in the folding of the Atlas and are now exposed within the ranges.

Between the most northerly ranges of the Atlas and the coast of the Mediterranean is a narrow and discontinuous strip of lowland. It widens near Oran in a low but irregular region. To the east, however, the Dahra Massif reaches the coast in steep cliffs, separating the plain of Oran from that of Algiers (Alger, 315,000).[1] East of Algiers, also, the Djurdjura and Kabylia Mountains also run out to the coast. The Mitidja Plain at Algiers and the plain of Bône, farther to the east, are large and important. The coastal plain is rather wider in Tunisia but narrows and eventually disappears at Bizerte (Bizerta). Between Oran and Bône a depression lies between the coastal mountains and the Atlas Range which is situated farther to the

[1] The population is given of cities of over 50,000 inhabitants; most, though not quite all, cities of this size are mentioned in the text.

south. This is drained in its western part by the Chélif. It is a low though very far from level plain.

The climate of the whole coastal belt is Mediterranean. Rainfall is generally limited to winter. Summers are dry and very hot, though temperatures on the coast are moderated by the sea breezes. Winters are mild. The small difference in latitude between the coast of Morocco and western Algeria on the one hand and of eastern Algeria and Tunis on the other is responsible for a considerable difference in climate. Rainfall in the east is often over 30

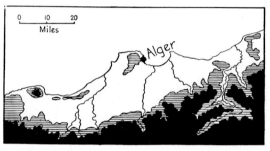

Fig. 217. The plain of Algiers (Alger). Shaded areas lie respectively above 500 and 1,500 feet.

inches in the year. This diminishes toward the west to less than 15. This transition is reflected in changes in the vegetation and agriculture. The forest cover, mainly of cork oak and other Mediterranean evergreens, is very extensive in the coastal mountains of eastern Algeria and Tunis. Wheat and barley are grown, and the cultivation of grape vines and olives is widespread and important. Toward the west, however, the natural forest thins away on the higher ground and gives place to scrub. In places the vegetation cover is restricted to a broken carpet of garrigue. The cultivation of fruits diminishes and then disappears from all areas where there is not an adequate supply of irrigation water. Cereal crops, particularly the drought-resisting barley, are the most widely grown.

Population is most dense and agriculture is carried on with the greatest intensity in the small coastal plains and in the east-to-west depression, a few miles inland. The Chélif and other smaller valleys, in each of which there is alluvial soil and water for irrigation, are the most developed. Towns are located generally on the small coastal plains.

Ceuta, in Spanish Morocco, lies on a small headland which stretches outward from the African coast directly south of Gibraltar. The position is of great strategic value, and the town was formerly of some international importance, though its functions have now very largely passed to Tangier, 15 miles to the west.

The French port of Oran, a town of about 256,000 inhabitants, over three-quarters of them Europeans, lies on one of the largest of the areas of low, agricultural land on the African coast. Its harbor is sheltered by a headland to the West. Immediately within the shelter of this point is the French naval base of Mers-el-Kebir. Oran is in large measure a product of the nineteenth-century French settlement. It is now the largest town and chief port of western Algeria. The situation of Algiers is similar to that of Oran, at the head of a shallow bay with a headland protecting it on the west and an extensive low-lying hinterland. It has a population of about 315,200, of whom about two-thirds are Europeans. Like most other ancient towns of North Africa, Algiers has grown around a fort, or Kasba. Around this is the old town, a maze of narrow and insanitary streets and low and overcrowded houses, in which ancient craft industries are carried on by the Arab or Berber people. A modern, well-laid-out, and handsomely built suburb has grown up during the period of French rule. A number of factories have been built, most of them engaged in preparing the raw materials and vegetable produce of Algeria. Algiers is the political capital of Algeria and is the most important center of commercial air lines in French North Africa. The small ports of Bougie, Philippeville (57,000), and Bône (103,-000), each on a small coastal plain protected by a headland to the west, handle some of the trade of eastern Algeria and prepare the tobacco, wine, and similar products of their hinterlands.

The Rif Mountains are largely in Spanish Morocco. They are an isolated and rugged massif, well wooded in the west, where they receive a fair rainfall, but increasingly dry toward the east, where the predominant vegetation is *maquis*. The valley floors are often fertile and cultivated, but the region as a whole is sparsely populated, and its inhabitants unruly tribesmen, who present a grave problem to the Spanish authorities.

The Tell Atlas is the name given to the series of rugged and broken ranges behind the coast of Algeria. Between them are elevated and fertile basins in which agriculture is important wherever sufficient water is available. In the west they are covered with only thin scrub, but toward the northeast, where rainfall is heavier, are forests of cork oak. Valley floors are generally cultivated, and the terraced lower slopes bear the vine and olive. Villages often occupy the summits of steep hills, high above their fields, but well placed for defense. It was in these mountains that the Berber tribesmen were able for a long time to defy the French. The massifs of Djurdjura and Kabylia, which lie close to the coast, are notorious for their wildness and inaccessibility and the resistance of their Berber inhabitants to the French. A number of small towns have grown up, generally in the larger basins or on the routes across the mountains. These include Tlemcen (69,500), Mascara, and Constantine (119,000), the last a natural fortress standing above the steep and narrow gorge of the river Rummel.

The high and rolling Tell Plateau, also known as the Plateau of the Chotts, from its great number of shallow saline lakes, or chotts, lies between the Tell Atlas and the southern or Saharan Atlas. The plateau has a small and irregular winter rainfall, and the region is covered with steppe, in places thin and saline. Though certain of the Mediterranean rivers rise on its northern edge, the Tell Plateau is largely a region of internal drainage. Agriculture is not of importance, and the region is chiefly used for grazing sheep and goats.

South of the Rif Mountains of Spanish Morocco is a broad alluvial plain drained by the Sebou River and lying mainly in French Morocco. It lies open to the Atlantic and receives a small winter rainfall, which with the assistance of irrigation is enough for agriculture. Dry limestone masses break the continuity of the plain, which is nevertheless the most productive and most densely peopled region of Morocco. To the east the Taza Gap, of great strategic importance, separates the Rif Mountains from the Middle Atlas and joins the Sebou Plain with the coastal region of Algeria.

Fez (Fès), the largest town of this region and former seat of the sultans of Morocco, has about 201,000 inhabitants. Meknès (160,000), Rabat (160,500), and Salé (57,000) are small, congested walled cities around which modern suburbs have grown up. Rabat is the administrative capital of French Morocco.

South of the Sebou Plain, between the Atlas Mountains and the Atlantic, is a rolling plain of considerably higher elevation than the Sebou Valley. Rainfall is small and diminishes toward the south to about 5 inches a year. The coast is fringed by sand dunes. Much of the land is dry and stony, with scattered shrubs which become thicker along the water courses. Agriculture depends upon irrigation. Water is obtained from wells and springs and from man-made tunnels, known as *foggaras*, driven into the hillsides to reach water-bearing rocks. Cereals, particularly wheat and barley, are grown in the few places where irrigation is possible. The date palm is a feature of most human settlements, and vegetables and fruits are grown in irrigated fields. The most important agricultural use of this region, however, is the grazing of vast flocks of sheep and goats.

Marrakech (238,000) is the largest town of southwestern Morocco. It lies in a broad, well-irrigated plain. Like most of the larger North African towns, it is made up of two distinct and contrasted sections: the old city, with its fortress, walls, congested houses, and narrow streets, and the new city, with broad, straight boulevards and modern shops and offices.

Casablanca (551,500) is the largest city and most important port of Morocco. It lies on a flat coast where projecting rocks, now reinforced by a mole, give some slight protection from the

sea. Mogador and Agadir are smaller ports situated on bays on the semidesert coast.

The Atlas Mountains consist in reality of a number of separate ranges in an echelon pattern. In the southwest is the Anti-Atlas range, north of it is the High or Great Atlas, then the Middle Atlas, which receives the greatest rainfall and gives rise to most of the rivers, and to the northeast, the Saharan Atlas. These ranges are bare

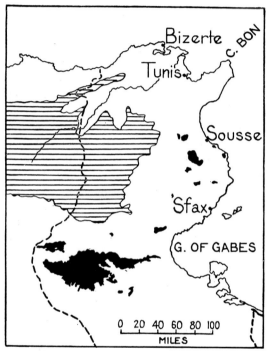

Fig. 218. Tunisia. Shaded area lies above 2,000 feet.

and rugged, deeply dissected by the winter torrents, and their summits etched by former glaciers. The greatest heights reach more than 12,000 feet and bear a permanent snow cover. Much of the higher land is bare of both soil and vegetation and is virtually uninhabited. Intermediate slopes bear Mediterranean forests of cork oak and pine, and the lower ground is covered with scrub which merges eastward into desert. The Saharan Atlas drops abruptly southward to the Saharan tableland. Both the Tell and the Saharan Atlas converge eastward in the mountains of eastern Algeria and Tunisia.

The hills of eastern Algeria and Tunisia are a rugged, mountainous region, better watered than the Atlas and having a richer woodland cover. Much of it is clothed with forests of cork oak and pine. Population is generally sparse, but villages occur in the valleys, where alluvium and irrigation combine to make agriculture possible. There is evidence that this region was once more fertile and productive than it is at present, and there are ruins of ancient settlements. It is likely that the apparent drying up of this area is in fact due only to the destruction of the ancient irrigation works.

The valley of the Medjerda River lies south of the eastern extremity of the Tell Atlas. In places it is marshy, and there are salty, infertile depressions, but most of it is floored with good, alluvial soil. It is fertile, and the inadequacy of water supply is the only serious obstacle to its development. Irrigation is practiced, but the streams which water the plain are small and seasonal in their flow. Much of the area is steppe, though grain crops, especially barley, and the vine are grown in the moister areas near the rivers and the coast.

The coastal area of the Medjerda Plain is one of the most densely populated and historically one of the most important in North Africa. Here, on the northern shore of the Gulf of Tunis, was the ancient Carthage, destroyed by the Romans in 146 B.C. The city of Tunis (364,500), founded by the Romans, gradually replaced it. Tunis lies on a lake protected from the open sea, though joined to it by a navigable canal. Tunis is the port and market town of the Medjerda Plain. Its situation opposite the constriction of the Mediterranean between the Sicilian and African coasts gives it a strategic importance which has, in fact, been transferred to Bizerte, 40 miles northwest. Tunis is the largest town of Tunisia and seat of the native ruler and of the French authority.

Between the mountains of central Tunis and the shore of the Mediterranean, which here penetrates to the Saharan hinterland, is a rolling steppe which becomes drier toward the south. Small rivers enter this region from the mountains and lose themselves in its wastes, failing ever to reach the sea. Here and there are oases, which provide water and crops for the seminomadic

Arabs. Settled agriculturists are few; most of the inhabitants graze their flocks over the poor grassland and occasionally pause to take a crop where the land is moist enough for crops to grow. Near the coast, however, olive groves have been planted and are very extensive and important behind the small ports of Sfax and Sousse. The vine is very much less important and is grown only in the north where the rainfall is greater.

The Desert. This extends southward from the foothills of the Atlas Ranges and reaches from the Atlantic to the Mediterranean. Only a small part of French Morocco falls within this region, but half of Tunisia and by far the larger part of Algeria lie within the desert. The region is one of gentler relief than that of the regions to the north but is nevertheless characterized by isolated hills and hill ridges. Only parts of the desert are actually composed of sand. Much is formed by bare rock or boulders from which the wind has swept the finer particles. Other areas again have a hard, shallow soil baked by the sun but yielding nevertheless a very sparse plant growth. Oases, where water is available and plants are grown, occur within the desert margin. Some are large areas of green amid the prevailing yellow and brown of the desert. Within them are self-contained and settled communities which grow wheat, barley, and vegetables; maintain groves of date palms; and even raise animals—sheep, goats, asses, and mules. Their houses are often mud-built and flat-roofed. They are placed within the shade of trees and maintain as far as possible an even temperature by having very few openings for windows and doors. In some oases, the blown sand of the desert encroaches on the cultivated areas and has to be laboriously collected and carried back to the desert whence it came. Low fences are sometimes erected to hold back the drifting sand.

A few rivers flow into the Sahara from the Atlas, only to die of suffocation among its sands. Toward the east these feed a group of low and saline depressions, or chotts, where shallow lakes form in the west season only to disappear in the dry, leaving a flat incrustation of salt.

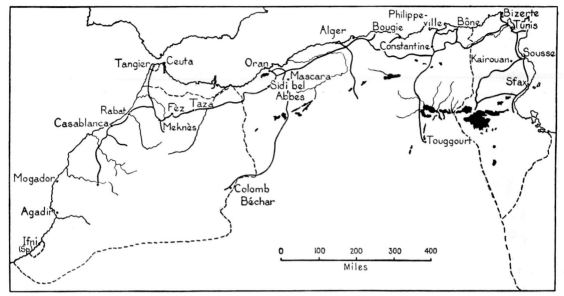

FIG. 219. Cities and communications in French North Africa.

Morocco. Morocco is a protectorate established by the French government in 1912. In 1912 the French asserted their right to "protect" the sultanate of Morocco, but not all the Sultan's possessions became the French Protectorate. They include also the Spanish Zone of Morocco and the International Zone of Tangier, but his authority here is very greatly restricted by the overriding powers of the European "protectors."

European settlement was never encouraged; instead the French administration strove to develop and improve native institutions and methods of land development. The population of Morocco is settled mainly in the coastal plain from Fez southwest to Casablanca. It is of mixed Berber and Arab origin and is Moslem in religion. It is estimated to number about 8,540,000, of which only about 3 per cent is of European origin. A vigorous nationalist movement, though probably not great in numbers, has developed in recent years and seeks to terminate the French protectorate. Most of the population is engaged in agriculture, though no more than about 10 per cent of the total area is fit for crop farming. The soils are fairly good, and the rainfall in some parts is adequate, but the amount and reliability diminish toward the south. More irrigation projects are needed in most parts of Morocco. There is a contrast between the few European-owned farms, generally large, efficient, modern, and located usually on the better soil, and the primitive native agriculture, which seems to have undergone neither change nor improvement since ancient times.

Barley is the most important crop. Hard wheat is grown but requires rather more moisture than is often available. Olives are grown on the dry soils of the plain; vines and cotton on the wetter. Sheep and goats are grazed over the poor pasture, and cork is cut from the forests of the hills.

Manufacturing industries are undeveloped. Native crafts in leather, metal, wood, and cloth are pursued, but factories are very few and confined to the larger towns. The mining of phosphates and manganese is the largest extractive industry. The phosphates occur abundantly in the plateau to the south of Casablanca and constitute one of the major exports of French Morocco.

Spanish Zone of Morocco. The Spanish Zone consists of a coastal strip no more than 50 miles wide, embracing the Rif Mountains and the coastal plain. It was occupied by Spanish forces in 1904, but the area is mountainous and poor, and the native Berber tribes warlike and unruly. Little has been done by the Spanish authorities to develop the country. The largest city is Tetuan (93,500). The area of the zone is about 18,000 square miles, and its population about a million.

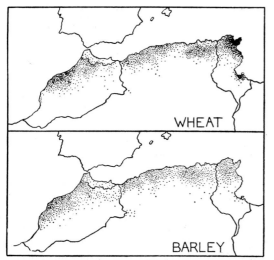

FIG. 220. The cultivation of wheat and barley in French North Africa.

Tangier. The town and bay of Tangier were considered to be of the greatest strategic importance, and competition between European powers for this corner of Africa led in 1912 to its internationalization. It is now under the joint administration of Britain, France, Spain, and Belgium. The International Zone consists of the town and its immediate hinterland. It is not of any great economic importance but is an international money market. The town is a free port. The area of the zone is 225 square miles, and its population, about 100,000.

Algeria. The French began to occupy Algeria in 1830 during a period in their history when they were looking for some foreign achievement to offset the sense of frustration which existed at home. Their policy was one of *refoulement*, of driving back the native Berbers into the mountains and of occupying their former lands with white people. In this process the French aroused the deep hostility of the native peoples. Official policy came, especially after 1870, to recognize Algeria as an integral part of France and to

settle there groups of French peasants who would lead the same sort of life and grow the same kind of crops as their ancestors had done in France. But France, as we have already seen, has little manpower to spare, and no more than some 200,000 Europeans took up land in Algeria. A number of Spanish settlers came in, especially in the western province of Oran, and of Italians in the eastern province, and these now form groups whose loyalty to France is not unquestioned. A dual agricultural and social system developed, that of the Berber, who, it was reported, "will not change his methods in the slightest, and he will not allow others to change them for him,"[1] and that of the French peasant. The latter introduced the grape vine and, when the vineyards of France were decimated by the phylloxera disease, were able to develop a large export in wine. The standard of Berber farming has been improved in recent years, chiefly through the efforts of the French themselves but also with the aid of technical and material assistance provided by the United States.

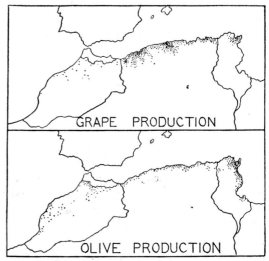

FIG. 221. The cultivation of the grape vine and olive in French North Africa.

The area of Algeria is about 847,500 square miles. The total population is about 8,876,000, of whom no more than a million are Europeans. Most are engaged in agriculture. Barley and

[1] Roberts, S. H. "History of French Colonial Policy," Vol. 1, p. 244, London, 1929.

wheat are almost universal crops, with barley more important on the drier land and wheat on the more moist. The development of speedy communications with France, coupled with the warmth of the North African winters, has encouraged the growth of fruits and vegetables which can be sold in the European market before the European crops mature. Citrus fruits from the coastal region and dates from the desert margin are also sent to Europe, though the roughness of the native methods of handling the produce detracts considerably from their value.

Native crafts are practiced in most towns and villages, but factory industries are limited to the processing of the local crops: cotton, tobacco, olives, grapes, and cereals. Of the minerals of Algeria only phosphates, iron ore, and coal are important. The first occur close to the Tunisian frontier, and iron ore in the Tell Atlas near the coast. Export of iron ore on the eve of the Second World War was at the rate of about 3 million tons a year.

Algeria is an integral part of France. Northern Algeria is constituted as three *départements* of the Republic, but owing to the sparse population and the unsettled conditions, the huge interior of Algeria is subject to a special military administration. Its trade is overwhelmingly with European France, which takes four-fifths of Algeria's exports and supplies three-quarters of its imports.

Tunisia. Like Morocco, Tunisia is a protectorate. France assumed control in 1881. Even before this date economic penetration has been considerable. French settlement, however, has always been very small, and the French were formerly less numerous than the Italians. Large numbers of the latter left Tunisia during the Second World War, and the French now constitute a majority of the European population. Tunisia is not an integral part of France as is Algeria, and Tunisian imports into France, like Moroccan, are subject to duty. Tunisia has developed more smoothly than either of the other North African territories under French control. It may be that French control has been more enlightened than that in Algeria, but it has none the less met with strong resistance, and Tunisia has a vigorous nationalist movement.

The country is predominantly agricultural, and as in the other territories, industry is almost limited to the domestic crafts of the native peoples. Phosphates are mined close to the Algerian border and are exported. Other minerals are of slight importance, though small quantities of iron and of lead are obtained and exported to Europe. Its population of about 3,143,500 is mainly Arab; only 8 per cent is made up of Europeans.

BIBLIOGRAPHY

Ackerman, Edward A., An Algerian Oasis Community, *E.G.*, XII, 1936, 250–258.

Brodrick, Alan, "North Africa," Oxford, 1942.

Fitzgerald, W., "Africa," London, 1943.

Gautier, E. F., "Sahara, the Great Desert," New York, 1935.

"Géographie universelle," Vol. XI, Part I, Afrique septentrionale et occidentale, Paris, 1937.

Kimble, G. T. H., The Berbers of Eastern Algeria, *G.J.*, XCVII, 1941, 337–348.

Pounds, N. J. G., The Political Geography of the Straits of Gibraltar, *J.G.*, LI, 1952, 165–170.

"Review of Economic Conditions in Africa," supplement to World Economic Report, 1949–50, United Nations, New York, 1951.

Roberts, S. H., "History of French Colonial Policy," London, 1929.

Stuart, Graham H., "The International City of Tangier," Stanford, Calif., 1931.

CHAPTER 28: *Egypt and Libya*

From Arabia westward to the Atlantic Ocean is the most extensive area of desert in the world. Between the borders of Israel and of the French protectorate of Tunis this desert reaches the shores of the Mediterranean. Egypt and Libya are made up very largely of desert, broken, in the case of Egypt, by the narrow strip of irrigated and cultivated land along the Nile Valley and, in Libya, by the highlands of Cirenaica. Rainfall is slight and unreliable along the coast. On the Egyptian coast it averages in most places less than 5 inches a year; in Cairo it is about 2 inches. Rainfall is higher in the more hilly country of Cirenaica, where it reaches 20 inches. On the coast of Tripolitania the rainfall diminishes to less than 5 inches. Within a few miles of the Mediterranean coast the rainfall drops sharply, and the Sahara Desert is, for practical purposes, rainless. The climate of Egypt and Libya is one of very hot summers, when the sun shines day after day from a cloudless sky, a heat haze shimmers on the horizon, and the mirage deludes the hopes of the traveler. But even in summer the night temperatures drop sharply. Winters are warm and pleasant, with temperatures not unlike those of southern California.

The Desert. This northeastern part of the continent of Africa is made up of a platform of ancient rocks, over which have been laid down horizontal beds of more recent limestone and sandstone, resulting in a rolling surface from which rise low, flat-topped hills, produced by the denudation of the almost level beds. Between the Nile Valley and the Red Sea the underlying platform of ancient rocks is ridged up to form a range of mountains which diminish in height northward and eventually disappear about the latitude of Cairo. West of the Nile mouth the younger beds form the Barca Plateau of Cirenaica. Along the southern border of Libya are little-known mountains, the Ahaggar and Tibesti Mountains. Parts of the desert surface bear a scanty vegetation of drought-resisting plants: tough, low-growing bushes, "mat" plants, and coarse grass. Large surfaces are bare

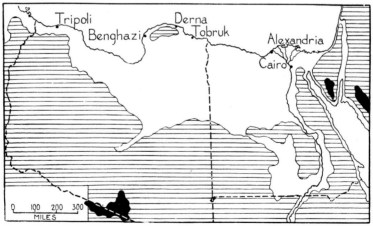

Fig. 222. Relief of Egypt and Libya. Shaded area lies above 1,000 feet; black, above 3,000 feet.

368

of soil, exposing the rock to the heat of the sun and to the erosive power of the wind. The surface is rough and though traveling is difficult, the rock desert, or *hamada*, is usually preferred to the *reg* and the *erg*. The *reg* is a surface of stones and boulders loosened from the bedrock and always in process of comminution. The *erg* is the sandy desert, regarded by many as the typical desert environment. Sand covers a very large area of the Libyan Desert, where it is called the "great sand sea." The dunes consist of the small rock particles produced by the shattering of the surface rocks and swept by the winds into heaps, which are continually being moved and their shapes changed by the wind. The dunes are a serious obstacle to movement, soft and yielding to the feet of men and animals and easily traversed only by track-laying vehicles.

Generally the sand just drifts along, but at intervals a stronger and more persistent wind drives the sand. Bagnold describes a sandstorm thus: "A hot desiccating south wind had been blowing for some time. Now, towards midday, big grains rose into the air, attacking our eyes and faces with little smarting stabs, whistling past our ears, swirling into every corner of the cars, into our pockets, down our necks, everywhere. We were stuck on a terrace high up on a dune side, hurrying to scoop the grains away from around the wheels a little faster than they were flowing in. The wheel-grooves of our coming, running over the surface behind each car up to the bases of the now stationary back wheels, began to move sideways down-wind, leaving the cars standing isolated from the tracks they had made, as if they had been miraculously dropped from the sky. The whole surface was flowing past us; it surged round our feet, excavating hollows into which they sank unexpectedly as we stood.

"The bulk of the grains flowed as a dense fog, rising no higher than five feet from the ground. Over it we could see each other quite clearly, head and shoulders only, as in a swimming-bath. Up above, the great fine-grained crests of the dunes were on the move. Cornices dissolved as we looked, swaying along the curving surfaces in heavy dark folds, as if the mane of some

huge animal was being ruffled and reset in a new direction by the gale."[1]

Water occurs in the rocks at varying depths below the surface. Where by faulting or erosion a depression has been formed in the desert floor, springs occur, palms take root, and there are agricultural settlements. These are the oases. There are an immense number of such depressions. Some are very large and deep, forming islands of green amid the prevailing yellow and brown. Some again are saline, like the great Qattara Depression, and incultivable. Others are small and visited only at intervals by the wandering Arab. Siwa is one of the larger oases. "Looking down on Siwa from the heights of the northern cliffs ten miles away, one sees a long strip of greenery varied by deep blue lakes, laid out in the distance along the wide floor of the depression—forests of date palms, gardens and small fields, a truly joyous sight upon which generations of hungry nomad tribes must have looked with envy.

"But on closer approach it is seen to be not quite such a paradise as it first appeared. It never rains down there. As with all the Libyan oases, the life-giving water coming from below, the people battle perpetually with salt which slowly impregnates all the soil unless washed out by fresh flowing water. Fortunately the fresh water often bubbles out under considerable pressure so that the mouths of the springs can be raised, allowing of a flow of water downhill through irrigation channels. Near the source it waters and drains fruit gardens and crops. Farther on, now brackish, it supports only coarse grass which cattle eat, and the ground is salt-encrusted. Finally, it reaches the salt lakes around which only date palms grow. The air, hot and breathless, has a characteristic oasis smell, slightly sweet, of rank grass faintly charred, decaying through increasing saltiness."[2]

The Nile. The valley of the river Nile is not unlike a long and sinuous oasis. Its waters come partly from the equatorial lakes of the East African Plateau, partly from the mountains of

[1] Bagnold, R. A., "Libyan Sands," p. 159, London, 1935.

[2] *Ibid.*, pp. 81–82.

Abyssinia. The former source is steady, varying little in its flow through the year. The latter yields an abundance of water during the time of the summer monsoon rains in the highlands but relatively little throughout the rest of the year. Thus the summer flood of the Blue Nile is superimposed upon the even flow of the White Nile. The two branches of the river unite at Khartoum, in the Anglo-Egyptian Sudan. Their courses are across an almost level plateau. Below Khartoum, however, the Nile crosses a series of outcrops of hard crystalline rock; it drops relatively steeply over these barriers and then flows quietly over the intervening areas of sandstone. This is the origin of the cataracts, which occur at intervals from Khartoum to Aswan in Egypt. From above Aswan the Nile becomes deeply sunk in the sandstone plateau of Egypt. The plain on each side of the river, narrow at Wadi Halfa on the border of Egypt, widens northward. The waters that enter Egypt have in large measure lost the coarse material usually carried by a river in flood in the several sections where the flow is gentle between the cataracts. The Nile brings not only its life-giving waters to Egypt but also a fine alluvium, which for thousands of years it has been spreading over its flood plain.

It is impossible to date the origin of agriculture and the introduction of the practice of irrigation into the lower Nile Valley. Almost certainly in the third millennium B.C. the waters of the Nile, when it flooded, were impounded in enclosed cultivation patches, or basins. The fine silt settled, the water seeped or evaporated away, and seeds were planted in the mud. Basin irrigation has continued to be practiced until the present day, though it has been largely replaced by perennial irrigation, which consists in taking water from the river at all seasons of the year to water the crops. In recent years, with the introduction of cotton growing, perennial irrigation has acquired a great importance. Primitive machines, the wheel worked by ox or mule, the shaduf, and other devices, are still used to lift water from the river to the fields, but increasing dependence is placed upon the supply of water stored behind barrages built across the

river. Such dams were first built across certain of the distributaries of the Nile in its delta, followed by the Asyût, Aswan, Nag' Hammadi, and other barrages.

For many thousands of years the Nile has been discharging its waters into the almost tideless Mediterranean Sea. Little river water now reaches the coast, owing to the demands made upon it by agriculture, but vast quantities of silt have in former ages been laid down on the sea floor, building forward the delta of the Nile. The current here runs along the coast from west to east, smoothing and rounding the delta and enclosing coastal lagoons with long spits of sand.

EGYPT

The kingdom of Egypt is made up of a large desert area to the west of the Nile Valley, the valley of the Nile itself, and the more mountainous desert between the Nile and the Red Sea and the Sinai peninsula. The Libyan Desert is uninhabitable except along its Mediterranean coast and in its numerous oases. The hilly region to the east is in part barren, in part covered with scrub. Between these two regions, the population is gathered into the valley of the Nile. Here it is estimated that there are only 6 million acreas of cultivable land on which live a population of about 17 million, almost wholly dependent upon agriculture, a density of considerably over 2,000 to the square mile.[1] Agricultural holdings are very small; about two-thirds are each of less than 1 acre. Some land is cropped three times in each year. Much bears a winter crop, commonly winter wheat, barley, or pulses, and a summer crop, such as cotton, rice, or millet. Berseem, a clover, is widely grown as a fodder or as a green manure to be plowed into the ground. Yields are often high despite this intensive cropping. The alluvial soil is naturally fertile, and much use is made, at least by the wealthier landowners, of artificial fertilizers.

The population density is greater than in

[1] Warriner, Doreen, "Land and Poverty in the Middle East," p. 26, Royal Institute of International Affairs, London, 1948. The total population of Egypt was in 1949 estimated at 20,045,000.

almost every other agricultural region of the world. "Although Egypt has the most productive agriculture in the world, its real income per head is probably the world's lowest, certainly the lowest of any country with advanced agricultural methods and large capital invest-

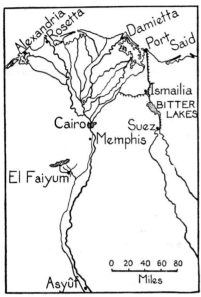

FIG. 223. The lower Nile Valley.

ment."[1] It has been estimated that the disappearance of 5 million from the rural population would make no appreciable difference to the total agricultural output. This is the extent of Egyptian overpopulation, and the total population has for many years been rising sharply. Rural settlement is generally in villages, the houses pressed closely together in order to conserve space. Only in areas recently opened up to agriculture is settlement dispersed. Rural housing is primitive in the extreme. Commonly a framework of sticks was merely covered with mud and roofed, and within this lived the family, its plowing animals, its goats and chickens.

As in other agricultural countries where there is a serious problem of overpopulation, the cities are large and congested, giving shelter if not employment to those forced off the land. Cairo is the largest, with a population of over 2,100,-500. It lies on the right bank of the Nile, near

[1] *Ibid.*, p. 38.

the head of the delta, where a low ridge comes down to the river and gives rising ground on which the earliest settlement was made. Cairo is the capital of Egypt. In spite of its great size, it cannot be said to have any dominant or even important industries. Like most oriental cities, it is filled with craftsmen and beggars, who are, in part at least, parasitical on society. A few miles to the southwest are the Pyramids and Sphinx, the most imposing remains of an earlier civilization in this region.

Alexandria (925,000) lies to the west of the Nile delta and thus is free from its silt. It has a large and sheltered harbor where Great Britain for many years possessed the treaty right to station warships. It handles much of the trade of Egypt. To the east are the smaller and less significant ports of Rosetta (Rashîd) and Damietta (Dumiât 53,500), each situated at the

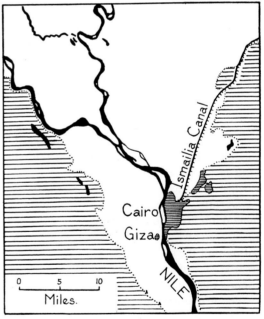

FIG. 224. The situation of Cairo. Shaded area lies above 100 feet.

mouth of one of the distributaries of the Nile and liable to silting. Opening off the Nile Valley is the depression occupied by the Fayûm oasis. This lies below the level of the Mediterranean Sea, and water from the Nile is channeled down into it for irrigation purposes.

On the eastern margin of the Nile delta is the Suez Canal, cut under the direction of Ferdinand de Lesseps in the 1860's and opened to commerce in 1869. It had had several predecessors which had followed different routes from the head of the Gulf of Suez to either the Nile or the Mediterranean Sea. The Suez Canal makes use of one of the most easterly lagoons of the Nile delta and of Lake Timsah and Bitter Lake in its course to the Gulf of Suez. It is throughout a sea-level canal, and no locks are needed, only protection from the silt of the Nile. Port Said and Suez are small ports at, respectively, its northern and southern ends, engaged in fueling and servicing the ships that use the canal rather than in the trade of Egypt itself. The canal shortens by over 4,000 miles the voyage from northwestern Europe to India and the Far East. It also makes the Mediterranean Sea a highway of commerce and restores to that sea a strategic importance which it lost when shipping made the long voyage round the south of Africa.

The exports of Egypt are almost wholly the products of her own agriculture. Of these, cotton forms about three-quarters by value and is the basis of such prosperity as Egypt enjoys. It is grown in the valley and delta as an irrigated summer crop. It depends on perennial irrigation, and its large-scale cultivation was possible only after the erection of barrages on the Nile. Most of the cotton is of the *Sakellarides* variety, a superior strain, resembling American Sea Island cotton and commanding a high price. In general it is grown by the peasants, or *fellahin*, as a cash crop on some part of each minute holding but most of the cotton exported comes from the great estates of the wealthy landowners. Egypt imports mainly manufactured goods, including textiles, machinery, and fertilizers.

LIBYA

Libya consists of two provinces: Cirenaica in the east and Tripolitania in the west. Both were occupied by the Italians during their short war with Turkey in 1911. It was not, however, until after the First World War that the economic development of the region was begun. The Arab tribesmen of the interior resisted the Italian conquest, and it was only after a campaign in 1927 that the resistance of the Senussi tribesmen of the interior was crushed. Italy regarded Libya as a strategic asset, strengthening her grip on the Mediterranean Sea and serving also as an outlet for her surplus population, though too small to ameliorate greatly the situation at home.

Northern Libya is a limestone plateau. In the Barka tableland of Cirenaica it rises to over 2,000 feet, sufficient even in this dry climate to induce a fair rainfall. Animals could be reared and crops grown, and the Italians at a very considerable expense developed a large colony after 1928. In Tripolitania, however, the coastline penetrates deeply into the desert area. The Gulf of Sidra has a low, dry, and harborless coast, and farther to the west, near the town of Tripoli itself, the climate is not really suited to crop husbandry. Such a land could be used to produce the drought-resisting olive, as the French have used southern Tunisia, but such a form of agricultural development requires little labor, and many years must elapse before there is a return on the outlay. Italy was poor, and its population problem urgent.

Most of the population of Libya lives on or near the coast, and most of it in one or other of the two urban concentrations: Tripoli in the west and the region of Bengasi and Derna in the east.

After 1945 Cyrenaica and Tripolitania were occupied by British Forces and their administration entrusted to British officials, while the Fezzan, which comprises most of the interior of Libya and adjoins French Algeria, was occupied by the French. The future of Libya was discussed at great length both by the Allied Powers and in the United Nations. The territory could not be returned to Italy; its Arab population was too ignorant and politically too immature for independence. In 1949 the General Assembly of the United Nations recommended that Libya become independent by, at the latest, the beginning of 1952. At the end of 1951, Libya gained independence, not because of her own merits, but rather because the Allies could agree on no other course.

BIBLIOGRAPHY

Bonne, A., "The Economic Development of the Middle East," London, 1945.

Egypt, *Focus*, American Geographical Society, Vol. II, No. 4, 1951.

Fisher, W. B., "The Middle East: A Physical, Social and Regional Geography," New York, 1950.

Fitzgerald, W., "Africa," London, 1934.

"Géographie universelle," Vol. XI, Afrique septentrionale et occidentale, Paris, 1937.

Hallberg, C. W., "The Suez Canal," New York, 1931.

Hornby, A. J., Northern Tripolitania: A Dry Mediterranean Coastal Region, *E.G.*, XXI, 1945, 231–251.

Issawi, C., "Egypt: An Economic and Social Analysis," Royal Institute of International Affairs, London, 1947.

James, L., The Population Problem in Egypt, *E.G.*, XXIII, 1947, 98–104.

Keen, B. A., "The Agricultural Development of the Middle East," London, 1946.

Lozach, J., "Le Delta du Nil," Royal Geographical Society of Egypt, Cairo, 1935.

Mather, D. C. M., A Journey through the Qattara Depression, *G.J.*, CIII, 1944, 152–160.

"The Middle East: A Political and Economic Survey," Royal Institute of International Affairs, London, 1951.

Report of the British Goodwill Trade Mission to Egypt, London, 1946.

Sandford, K. S., The Geology of Italian North Africa (A Review), *G.J.*, XCIV, 1939, 50–53.

Schonfield, Hugh J., "The Suez Canal," New York, 1939.

Tannous, Afif I., Egypt—Ancient and Agrarian, *Foreign Agriculture*, 1949, 202–207.

Warriner, D., "Land and Poverty in the Middle East," Royal Institute of International Affairs, London, 1948.

CHAPTER 29: *Syria and Israel*

The vast empire of the Turkish sultans in Africa and the Middle East had begun to break up before the end of the nineteenth century. The French took northwestern Africa, Great Britain occupied Egypt, and Italy conquered Libya. The peoples of the Middle East are

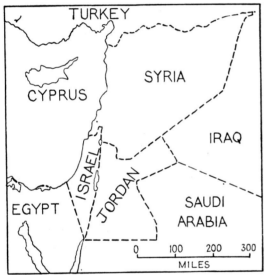

FIG. 225. Political boundaries in the Middle East. Jordan also occupies the hilly country north and south of Jerusalem.

varied in race and language but distinct in every way from the Turks. Aided by the British, they revolted against the Turks during the First World War, and after its conclusion the Middle Eastern states came into being. The problem of establishing these states was, however, complicated by the complexity of the racial groups which inhabited the area, the strategic importance of the Middle Eastern routeways and resources, and the claims of the Jewish people to a national home in Palestine. During the

confusion of the First World War conflicting promises had been made to Arabs and Jews and French. The solution adopted was the establishment of four separate states—Syria, Palestine, Tran-jordan, and Iraq—for three of which a "mandate" was given to one of the great powers. France received the mandate to occupy and administer Syria; Great Britain, that of Palestine (Israel) for the specific purpose of establishing a Jewish national home. Great Britain also received the mandate for Transjordan, which was surrendered in 1945 when Transjordan became the independent state of Jordan.

These Middle Eastern states, with Arabia, Iraq, and Egypt, but with the exception of Israel, form the Arab League. This loose organization gives some unity of purpose to the otherwise confused policies of the Arab states. In particular it focuses their hostility on the non-Arab state of Israel. In this chapter we are concerned only with those Middle Eastern states which border or are close to the Mediterranean Sea.

Syria, Lebanon, Israel, and Jordan together make up only a small area of 124,400 square miles, but little larger than Nevada or New Mexico. Along the coast of Syria, Lebanon, and Israel, all the way from the Turkish border to the Egyptian, runs a coastal plain, narrow in the north, almost squeezed out where the Lebanon Mountains come close to the coast, but widening in the south into the broad plain of Israel. Inland from the plain is a range of coastal mountains. The Amanus Mountains (Alma Dağ) are continuous with the mountains of Turkey. Interrupted by the narrow valley of the Orontes, they are continued southward in the Ansariya Mountains. These are also termi-

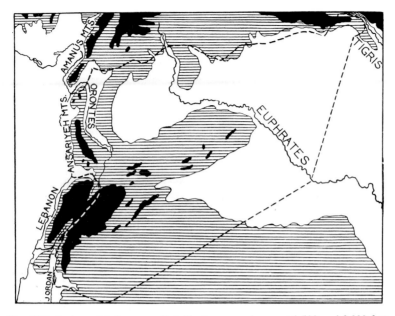

FIG. 226. Syria and Lebanon: relief. Contours are shown at 1,500 and 3,000 feet.

nated by a narrow transverse valley, but their direction is continued southward by the range which culminates in the Lebanon Mountains. The Lebanons decline in height southward as they pass into Israel. In northern Israel is the widest of the transverse gaps, the plain of Esdraelon or Jezreel. The hills of Israel are much lower and merge southward into the rugged tableland of Sinai.

East of this coastal range is a valley which is similarly continuous all the way from the Turkish border in the north to the Red Sea in the south. In the south it consists of the narrow Rift Valley, let down between parallel groups of faults. The Rift Valley in the area of the Dead Sea is considerably below sea level. Its direction is continued in the Red Sea and extends through East Africa to a point considerably to the south of the equator. Within the Middle East, the southern part of the Rift Valley forms the basin of the river Jordan. The Dead Sea, which receives its drainage, has no outlet to the ocean. Its waters evaporate and are exceedingly saline. The northern part of this valley is drained by rivers which cross the coast range by the gaps already mentioned to reach the Mediterranean Sea.

East of this central valley is another range of hills, more regular than the coastal range though nowhere so high as the Lebanon Mountains. It reaches its greatest heights in the Anti-Lebanon and Hermon Ranges, lying to the east of the Lebanon Mountains themselves. South of this, the range becomes a steep scarp overlooking the Jordan Valley and sinking gently eastward to the valley of the Euphrates in eastern Syria and Iraq. Eastward from these latter mountains stretches the rolling desert plain of Syria and Jordan.

The climate of the whole of this region is Mediterranean. Summers are very hot and dry. Winters are mild, except on higher ground, and the rainfall comes almost entirely in the winter half year. The amount of rainfall is greatest on the coastal range but diminishes southward toward the Egyptian border. A rainfall of 50 inches or more is recorded in many places in Syria, but this diminishes to less than half in the hills of Palestine.

The republic of Syria occupies over half of this small territory and spans all the physical units that have just been enumerated, from the Mediterranean Sea in the west to the Euphrates and Tigris Valleys in the east. Lebanon lies on the coast, embraces the Lebanon Mountains, and stretches inland to the Anti-Lebanon Mountains. Israel, or Palestine, occupies most of the territory between the Jordan trench and the sea, and Jordan, formely called Transjordan, occupies the semidesert area to the east. The size and population of these four states are as follows:

	Area, square miles	Population, 1949
Syria...............	66,030	3,135,000
Lebanon............	3,470	1,238,000
Israel..............	8,080	1,390,000 (1951)
Jordan.............	34,740	1,250,000 (1951)

SYRIA

After the First World War France claimed the mandate for Syria, more for sentimental than for practical reasons. The French were faced, however, by the opposition and ultimately the hostility of several of the Syrian groups. They adopted the policy of dividing their subjects in order to rule them the more effectively. Lebanon, in which the Christian population was larger than in other provinces, was constituted a separate republic. The territories of Latakia, on the coast to the north of Lebanon, and Jebel Druse, situated on the desert border of Jordan, also acquired a degree of autonomy within the Syrian state. The French administration of Syria and Lebanon was far from quiet. The Syrians were turbulent; the French heavy-handed and vindictive. The occupying forces announced their intention of ultimately leaving the country but showed no eagerness to go. Eventually, after the British had occupied the country in 1941, the Syrians and Lebanese declared their independence and have since constituted two separate republics. It cannot be said that the record of the independent states of Syria and Lebanon has been more peaceful than that of the French mandate. The countries lack both leaders and policy, they are split into a number of racial groups, and their administration is corrupt and inefficient.

Syria and Lebanon are made up of part of each of the physical regions that have already been described. In Lebanon the coastal plain is narrow and in places virtually disappears where the mountains drop steeply to the water, and the building of the railway and the coast road has been difficult. The region, however, is important because of its fertility, dense settlement, and the number and size of its ports.

The climate is Mediterranean. Summers are very hot, and winters warm. The rainfall, concentrated in the months from November to March, diminishes from the north, where it is over 40 inches, to the Israeli border, where it is little more than 20 inches. Little of the natural vegetation cover remains. The region is dotted with large, compact villages, each surrounded by its intensively cultivated fields. In addition to the subsistence crops of wheat, barley, peas, and beans, the region produces citrus fruits, olives, and small quantities of cotton, sugar, and tobacco.

Along much of this stretch of about 250 miles of coast, ports developed in early classical times. The region has never completely lost the importance which it then acquired as a center of commerce. The gaps through the Lebanon and other ranges have canalized trade from the regions of Euphrates and the Persian Gulf. The silks and spices of the East no longer reach the Mediterranean by this route, but the port of Tripoli still exports much of the petroleum from the wells of Iraq. Beirut, Tripoli, and Latakia handle between them practically all the seaborne trade of Syria, and of these three Beirut (201,500),[1] in Lebanon, is by far the most important. It is built on a rocky promontory, which gives some natural protection to the bay on its northern side, and opposite one of the few crossings of the Lebanon range. The harbors of ancient Tyre (Tyr), Sidon (Saida), and Jebeil (Byblus) are too small for modern requirements. The southern part of this coast actually forms part of the republic of Lebanon, and both Tripoli and Beirut lie in Lebanon.

[1] The population is given of cities of over 50,000 inhabitants. Figures given for Israel are not reliable. All cities of this size are named in the text.

Tripoli (65,000) lies a few miles to the south of the mouth of the Nahr el Kebir, whose valley separates the Lebanon from the Ansariya Mountains and provides the easiest route from the Syrian coast to the interior. Latakia is now, with the cession of Iskenderon to Turkey, the only significant port on the coast of Syria, but its harbor is small and has no railway connection with its hinterland. Alexandretta (Iskenderon), with the southern part of the Amanus Mountains, was incorporated into Turkey in 1939 by agreement with France. Turks were the most numerous element in its population, and the port provided an outlet for the commerce of eastern Turkey.

The coastal range is dry and stony and over large areas is completely barren. The undulating surface in which it culminates is dissected by deep and rugged gorges. The whole region is difficult of access, and this has added greatly to the importance of the routes which pass around its margins. The Ansariya Mountains rise to over 5,000 feet, and the Lebanons just reach 10,000 feet. These altitudes greatly modify the Mediterranean climate. The summers are cool, and winters, according to the height and exposure, cold and snowy. Precipitation is over 50 inches a year in many places. Little is left of the once famous forests of Lebanon. Its cedars, of which a few survive, have been cut and exported since Biblical times, when the trade was in the hands of Phoenician merchants. Since then charcoal burning has played havoc with the woodlands. Patches of coniferous woodland remain on the higher ground, an alpine flora covers the summits, and Mediterranean scrub much of the lower slopes. The valley sides are in part terraced for cultivation. Cereals, vegetable crops, and fruits, especially the grape vine, olive, and fig, are grown on the lower slopes but give way upward to more temperate crops. Settlements are confined to large villages, often impressively situated on steep crags and cliffs, as much to conserve the fertile lower ground for agriculture as to secure protection from invaders and bandits.

The depression east of the coastal mountains is drained by the meandering rivers Orontes and Litani. It is a potentially fertile region but is marshy and malarial. Rainfall diminishes rapidly to the east of the Lebanon and Ansariya. The summers become very hot, and the winters warm. The natural vegetation is steppe or semi-desert scrub. Much of the land is good only for winter grazing. In summer the grass is burned up and the flocks move to the Lebanon and Anti-Lebanon.

The trough has for many centuries been an important highway, especially that part of it which stretches southward from Homs (100,-000) and opens to the Mediterranean by way of the Litani Valley. Along this routeway came the Crusaders, and the ruins of their great castles still testify to their former occupation of the region. The castle of Krac des Chevaliers, or Kalaat el Hosn, most impressive of them all, stands high on one of the southern spurs of the Ansariya Mountains, guarding the passageway to the coast by the Nahr el Kebir Valley. The central valley is now followed by the railway from Aleppo (Alep) to both Beirut and Damascus (Damas, Esh Shâm). Both Hama (71,500) and Homs are ancient cities on this route.

The more easterly range is less a barrier to communications than is the coastal range, but the few easy routes across it have nevertheless assumed a great importance. In the north, Aleppo communicates with the Orontes Valley and the coast. West of Homs is a depression, to the existence of which Homs owed much of its early prosperity, and, lastly, between the Anti-Lebanon and Hermon is the gap west of Damascus.

Eastward of the mountains stretches a dry and rolling upland. To the north, spurs of the Kurdistan Hills reach southward across the Syrian border, and farther south low ridges of limestone stretch eastward from the Anti-Lebanon. Rivers flow from the mountains into this steppe. Their waters are used for irrigation, and where irrigation water is sufficient, a prosperous agriculture has been developed. Rainfall diminishes and over most of this region is less than 10 inches. The climate is hot; the vegetation is at best steppe, which deteriorates eastward and southeastward to scrub-covered desert. Over most of the area there is no permanent drainage. The *wadis* are occasionally occupied by streams and hold at other times sufficient moisture for a few bushes and trees to grow. Settlement is in large measure limited to the oasis towns which lie along the foot of the western mountain ranges, to the Euphrates Valley, and to the volcanic plateau of the Djebel Druze.

Largest of the oasis towns are Aleppo (320,-000) and Damascus (286,500), the former a trading center since ancient times on the caravan route from Iraq to the Mediterranean. Damascus lies on the Barada, a river which flows eastward from the Anti-Lebanon and breaks up into a number of channels, the "rivers of Damascus," which water this fertile and productive oasis. Damascus, like Aleppo, lies on an ancient caravan route. It is no longer a center of international commerce but is the focus of one of the most productive of all agricultural areas in the Middle East.

The Euphrates Valley is lined with villages and towns. Its waters are used for irrigation, and crops are taken from the narrow flood plain along its banks. On each side, however, stretches the uninhabited waste. Northeast Syria stretches across the steppe to the western bank of the Tigris.

The Djebel Druze is a basaltic plateau. The region is high enough to have a milder climate and heavier rainfall than the surrounding desert. It is well settled and cultivated.

Social Problems of Syria. Syria, which lies close to Europe, Asia, and Africa and near the places of origin of Judaism, Christianity, and Islam, has a population as mixed racially and culturally as is to be found anywhere. Apart from the Syrian majority, there are communities of Kurds, Armenians, and Assyrians in the north, of Jews and Turks in the towns of the west. The earlier variety of language, however, is tending to give way to Arabic, which is becoming the language of Syria. Religious differences, on the other hand, constitute the chief divisions between the people of Syria. The two major groups, each with two or more subdivisions, are the Moslem and the Christian. The Jews constitute a third and smaller group.

Most Moslems are *Sunnis*, or members of the orthodox group. These form a majority in Syria and a large minority in Lebanon. In addition to the *Sunnis* are several smaller groups which are regarded in varying degrees as heterodox. The *Druses* of the Djebel Druze are one of these groups. The Christian groups of Syria are even more numerous and complex than the Moslem, though Christians are a minority in the country as a whole. They may be divided into the *Uniates*, who are in communion with the Church of Rome but are independent in organization, and the *Orthodox*, who are independent in doctrine, obedience, and organization. Most numerous of the Uniate groups are the *Maronites*, who form a majority of the people of Lebanon. If we include the Nestorians, there are no less than 10 significant Christian communities in addition to a few small Protestant groups.

The great majority of the people of Syria are agriculturalists. Industry is in general limited to the domestic manufacture of cloth, carpets, pottery, and iron goods. A very few mechanically operated factories have been established, but their influence on the traditional modes of production has been slight. Agriculture is primitive and dependent upon irrigation. The import of grain foods varies inversely with the volume of rainfall during the previous year. The Syrian peasant works with crude wooden tools. His plow merely scratches the surface; he reaps with a sickle, threshes with a flail, and winnows the grain from the chaff. In the absence of fertilizers, he has resort to fallowing. Wheat is the commonest crop, but millet, maize, and rice are also grown according to the availability of water. Mediterranean fruits and such industrial crops as cotton, tobacco, and hemp are grown as cash crops, particularly in moist coastal belt.

Most of the rural population are peasant proprietors. Their holdings are frequently divided and scattered through the village fields, and many are held on a sharecropping basis. Poverty is extreme. Villages are usually large and compact. The style of the houses varies with local customs and local materials, but they are usually low, flat-roofed, and built of mud or stone. In some villages where little building

In the hills of Galilee. This is an area of poor agriculture and generally Arab settlement. (*Israel Office of Information, New York.*)

material is available, the peoples live in windowless, beehive-shaped dwellings of mud. In sharp contrast to the squalid villages of the settled cultivators are the tents of the Bedouin. These people are divided into a number of small but often conflicting groups. They range from seminomadic peoples of the steppe, who live in tents but cultivate the land and move but rarely, to the sheep and camel nomads who follow a regular, seasonal path of irrigation between winter and summer pastures. In general, the winter homes of these people are in the desert of the south and east; the summer, on the steppe margin to the west and north. Their number is difficult to estimate. It has been said that recently they numbered some 70,000 tents, each comprising a group from of 5 to 7 persons, perhaps a total of 360,000 persons. The days of raiding of the settled communities by the Bedouin are in large measure over.

LEBANON

The republic of Lebanon was established in 1944 and had hitherto been a unit within the French mandate of Syria. Territorially it is no more than an enclave on the Syrian coast. It is distinguished, however, by the greater proportion of Christians composing its population. It has shown a greater prosperity and stability than Syria, and its possession of Beirut and Tripoli, with their oil refineries, lying at the terminus of the pipe line from Iraq, is a source of considerable profit.

ISRAEL

In its main features Israel continues southward three of the physical features that have been considered in the paragraphs on Syria. There is no physical barrier separating the two countries. Israel consists of a coastal plain, wider and more productive than that of Syria; a central belt of hills; and a deep trough along the eastern border, separating Israel from Jordan.

The coast of Israel is low, straight, and almost harborless. For most of its length it is fringed with sand dunes, and only to the north of the promontory of Mount Carmel is a small sheltered bay, on which has grown up the town of Haifa. The plain varies in width from only a mile or two in the north to some 20 miles in the south. It is composed throughout of recent alluvial deposits. The soils are sandy and light, though in some places they are poorly drained

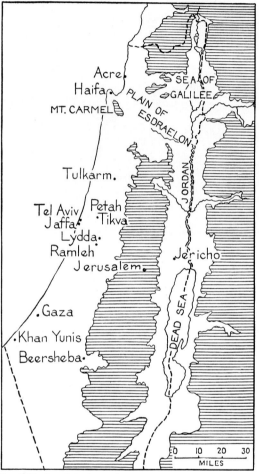

FIG. 227. Israel (Palestine): relief. Land above 1,500 feet is shaded.

and form marsh during the wet season. Rainfall is less than on the Syrian coast and is even more strongly concentrated in the winter months. Its volume diminishes from over 20 inches a year on the Syrian border to less than 10 on the Egyptian. Temperatures are high throughout the year, and the summers are very hot. Irrigation is practiced over much of the plain, and agriculture is heavily dependent upon irrigation

in all areas except the extreme north. The region was formerly covered with a Mediterranean scrub, which degenerated southward toward the Egyptian border into steppe and desert, but has, however, been settled and cultivated since very early times.

The towns of the coastal plain are sharply divisible into those of ancient origin and Biblical fame and those founded in recent years by Jewish immigrants. The former include the ancient ports of Acre (Akko) and Jaffa and inland towns such as Gaza, Lydda, and Er Ramle (102,000). The latter include the Jewish port of Tel Aviv and the newly founded towns of Khan Yunis, now occupied by Egypt, Petah Tikva, and Tulkarm (65,500). The town of Haifa may perhaps be included in the latter group, as its origin belongs only to the nineteenth century and the period of its greatest growth to the twentieth.

Haifa (160,000) has replaced the ancient port of Acre, which lies on a small promontory which admits of easy defense but not great urban expansion. Haifa was established about 8 miles away at the southern end of the Bay of Acre, a site more suitable for the growth of a great port. Haifa lies at the western end of the Esdraelon Plain, by way of which a railway gives access to the Jordan Valley and to southern Syria. It is now the chief port of Israel.

Tel Aviv, the modern town, lies close to the ancient port of Jaffa. The coast is straight, and the harbors of both Jaffa and Tel Aviv are in large measure man-made and are much less important than Haifa. Tel Aviv has grown in about 40 years from a few huts on the sand dunes to a large modern city, with a population, including that of adjoining Jaffa, of 350,000. The inland towns are all very much smaller and concerned largely with collecting the produce of their surrounding agricultural regions. Gaza, lying within a few miles of the coast on the "Way of the Sea" which has been used by caravans from the earliest historical times, is largest. It is now occupied by Egypt.

The plain of Esdraelon, or Megiddo, branches from the coastal plain to the north of Mount Carmel. It is a belt of lowland formed by the downward faulting of an earth block and bounded by steep hills. The soils are alluvial, like those of the coastal plain. The basalt of the Djebel Druze reaches thus far, and material worn from its surface adds to the fertility of the plain. It is hotter than the coastal plain, its rainfall is less, and irrigation is more often necessary.

The hills of Israel are divided by the plain of Esdraelon into the hills of Galilee and those of Samaria and Judea. All are built of young limestone, soft, easily eroded, and readily gullied by heavy rains. The vegetation of the region has suffered severely at the hands of man. The once extensive forest cover has been destroyed, and the hills are at best covered with scrub, at worst with steppe or garrigue. The population in the hills is sparse, and towns are few and small. In the Galilean hills, which are better watered than those to the south, are many Arab villages, small, compact, with flat-roofed, stone-built houses, but Nazareth and Safed are the only towns.

South of the plain of Esdraelon are the hills of Samaria, drier and less green than those of Galilee. They pass southward into the hills of Judea, an area even drier and browner. The Judean Plateau is very largely a "stony moorland, upon which rough scrub and thorns, reinforced by a few dwarf oaks, contend with multitudes of boulders, and the limestone, as if impatient of their pretence of soil, breaks out in bare scalps and prominences. There are some patches of cultivation, but though the grain springs bravely from them, they seem more beds of shingle than of soil. The only other signs of life, besides the wild bee and a few birds, are flocks of sheep and goats, or a few cattle, cropping far apart in melancholy proof of the scantiness of the herbage. Where the plateau rolls, the shadeless slopes are for the most part divided between brown scrub and grey rock; the hollows are stony fields traversed by dry torrent-beds of dirty boulders and gashed clay. Where the plateau breaks, low ridge and shallow glen are formed, and the ridge is often crowned by a village, of which the grey stone walls and mud roofs look from the distance like a mere outcrop of the rock; yet round them, or below in

the glen, there will be olive-groves, figs, and perhaps a few terraces of vines."[1]

In this hilly wilderness lie the towns of Nablus, Bethlehem, and Hebron (77,000), most of them small and agricultural. Here, too, on a dry hilltop in Judea, lies Jerusalem (155,500). The site was adopted by the Biblical King David as the Jewish capital. It was well suited for defense and became the inner sanctuary of Jewish religion and culture. It then became a focus of Christianity and subsequently one of the Moslem holy places. The importance of

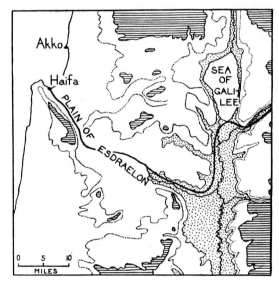

FIG. 228. Plain of Esdraelon and the situation of Haifa. Contours are shown at 750 and 1,500 feet. The dotted area lies below sea level.

Jerusalem to each of these faiths has in part occasioned the many attacks upon the city. The ancient city, enclosed by its medieval walls, contains the shrines and historic buildings, the Church of the Holy Sepulchre, the Dome of the Rock, and the Wailing Wall. It is small and congested, and a more spacious modern city to the northwest and west is coming to replace it as a business, administrative, and industrial area. Jerusalem is at present divided between the states of Israel and Jordan.

The Rift Valley of the river Jordan limits the Palestinian hills on the east. Its sides are straight

[1] Smith, Sir George Adam, "Historical Geography of the Holy Land," pp. 305–306, New York, 1897.

A Jewish settlement in the plain of Esdraelon (Jezreel). Compare this photograph with the one on p. 379, and note the careful planting. (*Israel Office of Information, New York.*)

and steep, and much of its floor is actually below sea level. This region lies in the rain shadow of the Palestinian Hills. Its rainfall is less than 20 inches a year in the north, and toward the south this diminishes to an unreliable rainfall of only 1 or 2 inches. Temperatures are high, and summers almost unbearably hot. A belt of vegetation and, in parts, of cultivation lies along the banks of the river, but away from the Jordan the eroded sides of the mountains are covered at most with a thin cover of garrigue. Much is completely bare.

In the north, where physical conditions are better, is a small agricultural population and one small town, Tiberias, lying on the western shore of the small Sea of Galilee, into and out of which flows the Jordan. Jericho, widely known as it is, has disappeared, and only a village of mud-built huts lies near the site of the fortress city built in the pre-Jewish period to protect the crossing of the Jordan. Near Jericho the Jordan enters the deep and very saline Dead Sea, in which there is no fish life at all. The salt of the sea, however, now gives rise to a chemical factory on its shores.

South of the Dead Sea a deep, dry valley continues southward to Aqaba, where it passes into the northeasterly arm of the Red Sea.

Economic Development. When the Jewish people settled in the promised land of Palestine toward the end of the second millennium B.C., they occupied the hill country of Judea. The Canaanites and Philistines inhabited the low-land regions to the north and west. The Jews were dispersed from their settlement area, partly at the hands of the Assyrian kings, partly at those of the Romans, after A.D. 70. During the long period of the Dispersion the Jewish people never lost their identity and cherished the hope that they might one day reoccupy the land of their ancestors. In 1917, the British government made a declaration that it would further the ends of the Zionist movement and assist the Jewish people to reestablish a "national home" in Palestine. The land of Palestine, which had for many centuries been under Turkish rule,

Jerusalem. The good quality of the modern building can be clearly seen. Notice the bare hills that surround the city. (*Israel Office of Information, New York.*)

was in 1923 entrusted as a mandate to Great Britain for the purpose of fulfilling the intentions of the Balfour Declaration of 6 years earlier. Jewish immigration was rapid, and Jewish population in Palestine rose from 58,000 in 1919 to 401,600 in 1928. But Palestine is a small country and has slight mineral resources. Furthermore, at the time when the mandate was established, there were in the country some 568,000 Arabs, who cultivated in a backward and inefficient manner a land which they had come to regard as their own. The area of Jewish settlement during the 'twenties and 'thirties of the present century was not that which their ancestors had been obliged to abandon during the Dispersion but the surrounding, more fertile and productive lowlands.

The Jews have used the land more effectively than the Arabs had done. In some respects the Arabs profited from the developments made by the Jews. Nevertheless the hostility of the Arabs to the large-scale immigration of the Jews was steadfast and intense, while the Jews for their part immigrated in large numbers without any careful regard for the geographical potentialities of the country or the dangers of overpopulation.

The termination of the Second World War saw a renewed immigration of Jews under conditions which made it difficult to deny them this asylum. Earlier attempts to partition Palestine into a Jewish and an Arab state had failed to meet with agreement. Those made in 1946 were no more successful. In 1948 the British mandate terminated and the state of Israel came into existence. Israel embraces mostly the areas of predominantly Jewish settlement. The political fate of Jerusalem is undecided, and the Judean hill country, an area largely Arab, was occupied by the forces of Jordan and has since been annexed to the state of Jordan. Almost three-quarters of a million Arabs have sought refuge in Jordan, while their former lands are being divided between the immigrant Jewish settlers.

The Palestinian Arabs practiced a subsistence agriculture. The Jews have developed a more intensive agriculture, making what use they can of irrigation. They depend heavily on tree crops, particularly citrus fruits and olives, for which the dry climate is best suited. The Jews have also settled in the cities, and urban occupations have of necessity absorbed a large number of the immigrants. It may be doubted whether

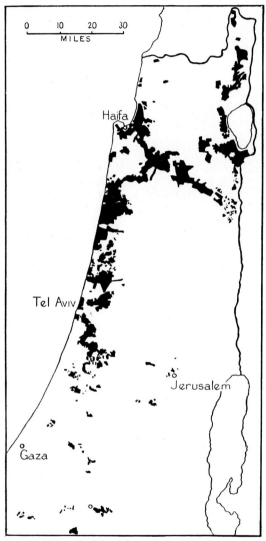

FIG. 229. Areas of Jewish settlement in Israel. This settlement is located chiefly in the lowland areas.

the agriculture of the plain can be greatly extended, and it seems unlikely that any intensive farming can be carried on in the hills. The Jews are thus turning more and more to the development of industries.

Manufacturing industries developed hitherto

are on a small scale and restricted to the lighter types of consumers' goods and textiles, footwear, leather goods, and household articles. Ancient silk and carpet industries are maintained. Soap is made from olive oil. Petroleum piped from Iraq is refined at Haifa, but the supply is always liable to interruption by the Arabs and at present is cut off. The chemical works have been established on the shores of the Dead Sea which has mineral resources but lies now in territory controlled by Jordan.

The Jewish experiment has achieved a success that some believed unattainable, but in doing so it has aroused the hostility of the surrounding "Arab" states. These argue, with some show of reason, that the Arab settlers in Israel have suffered from the Jewish occupation of the better land, and they object to the rise of this non-Arab nation in their midst. Numerically, they are very much stronger than the Jews, though not always so well or so efficiently organized. They show their hostility in many ways. They can blockade Israel on the landward side and thus interrupt, among other things, the flow of oil from Iraq to the Haifa refineries. They have supported Jordan in her seizure of the hill country to the north and south of Jerusalem, and they have promoted frontier incidents along the Syrian and Egyptian borders. On the other hand, the Jews have the powerful support, both financial and moral, of interests in Europe and America. Their position in the struggle which now divides the world has not been stated clearly. Neither Israel nor her neighbors are collaborating closely with the nations of western Europe. After the treatment they have received for many generations at the hands of Europeans, one cannot expect the Jews to show any great sympathy with the traditions and institutions of western Europe.

JORDAN

Jordan is the name of the small emirate known until recently as "Transjordan." It is considerably larger than Israel but is much less populous. It consists, like Israel, of the southward extension of certain of the physical regions of Syria. These are the mountain belt which

Haifa, view over the city toward the Mediterranean Sea. Much of the city is made up of good modern buildings. (*Israel Office of Information, New York.*)

extends southward from the Anti-Lebanon and the desert plateau to the west.

The western mountains rise steeply from the Jordan trench. Their rainfall is much higher than in the Jordan Valley but less than in the Judean hills. The vegetation is a thin scrub, and agriculture cannot be practiced without irrigation. The higher land is at best but poor pasture over which the Bedouin graze their flocks. Crops are taken from many of the valleys, but the region as a whole is a rugged, sparsely populated wilderness.

To the east, as far as the Arabian and Iraqi frontier, stretches an undulating plateau which continues the desert plateau of Syria. In the north it is covered with lava flows of recent origin, which produce a desolate landscape. Elsewhere the land is covered with thin *maquis* or grass. Toward the east the surface becomes more and more barren and vegetation yields place to sand and gravel or to bare rock.

The total population of Jordan is not known with any precision. There were probably about 450,000 in the former territory of Trans-Jordan and 400,000 in the recently occupied Palestinian territory west of the river Jordan. To these must be added about 400,000 Arab refugees from Israel. Almost all are Arabs, of whom a majority are nomadic or seminomadic. The settled population lives in villages, which resemble the closely built Arab villages of Israel, scattered along the western margin of the country. They practice a very primitive agriculture and grow cereals, of which wheat and barley are the most important. Only in the northwest of Jordan, however, is the rainfall adequate for an extensive agricultural development. The greatest possible use is made, both here and in the drier region to the southeast, of the small quantity of water available for irrigation. The foreign trade of Jordan is very small indeed. Exports consist largely of cereals, sent to Israel and Syria; imports, of textiles and foodstuffs. Industry is limited to the domestic manufacture of articles for home use. There are virtually no towns. Amman, the capital, is nothing more than a village, which derives both its name and its existence from the biblical Ammonites. The country has a single railway, the "Pilgrim Line" from Syria southward into Arabia, whose existence is due wholly to the requirements of the Moslem pilgrims to Mecca. At the time of writing (1951) Jordan is harboring the Arab refugees, estimated to number 400,-000, from Israel. The country is incapable of assimilating them, and they present a very serious international problem.

CYPRUS

The island of Cyprus lies some 50 miles off the Turkish coast. Its area is only about 3,600

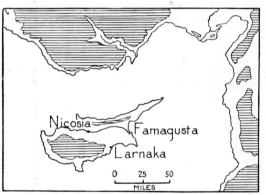

FIG. 230. Cyprus. The shaded area lies at above 1,500 feet.

square miles, of which a third is mountainous and considered to be uncultivable. It consists of a mountain range lying parallel with the straight northern coast, a plain some 10 to 20 miles in width lying to the south of this and containing most of the inhabitants, and the hilly mass of the Troodos Mountains which occupy the southern part of the island.

In climate Cyprus resembles the neighboring Turkish coast. The hilly areas have a rainfall of 40 inches or even more. Forests are extensive, though not so large as they once were. Most of the population of about 476,000 is engaged in agriculture. Holdings are small and severely fragmented. Many are too small to provide a full-time occupation, and their owners work also in the factories or mines. Wheat and barley are the most important food crops, but as in most Mediterranean areas, tree and fruit cultivation is important. Everywhere heavy dependence is placed on irrigation, and very little of the rainfall is allowed to escape to the sea. The industries of Cyprus are small and of only local importance. They are concerned chiefly with the preparation for the market of the locally grown crops of cotton and fruit. Silk is spun and woven, bricks and tiles are baked, and lace made. Though backward and poor, Cyprus enjoys living standards well above those of the other countries considered in this chapter.

Nicosia, in the midst of the central plain, is the capital and largest town, though its population is only 35,000. Famagusta, joined to Nicosia by the only railway in the island, together with Larnaca, handles most of the island's trade.

Cyprus was occupied by the Crusaders during the Middle Ages, and castles and churches are evidence of their occupance. It then passed into the hands of Venice before being taken by the Turks. In 1878, it came under British control. Its population is largely Greek in speech and Orthodox in religion.

BIBLIOGRAPHY

GENERAL

Antonius, George, "The Arab Awakening," New York, 1946.

Bonné, A., "Economic Development of the Middle East," London, 1945.

Boveri, Margret, "Minaret and Pipe-Line," Oxford, 1939.

Fisher, W. B., "The Middle East," New York, 1951.

Gibb, H. A. R., "The Arabs," Oxford, 1940.

Hitti, P. K., "History of the Arabs," London, 1940.

Hourani, A. H., "Minorities in the Arab World," New York, 1947.

Keen, B. A., "The Agricultural Development of the Middle East," London, 1946.

Kirk, George E., "A Short History of the Middle East," London, 1948.

Lewis, Bernard, "The Arabs in History," London, 1950.

"The Middle East, A Political and Economic Survey," Royal Institute of International Affairs, London, 1950.

"The Near East, Problems and Prospects," Harris Foundation Lectures, 1942, University of Chicago, 1942.

Newbigin, M. I., "Mediterranean Lands," London, 1924.

Stamp, L. D., "Asia," New York, 1950.

Warriner, Doreen, "Land and Poverty in the Middle East," Royal Institute of International Affairs, London, 1948.

ISRAEL

Bonné, A., Natural Resources of Palestine, G.J., XCII, 1908, 259–266.

Casto, E. Ray, Economic Geography of Palestine, E.G., XIII, 1907, 235–259.

Palestine Partition Commission Report, Cmd. 5854, London, 1938.

Report of the Anglo-American Committee of Enquiry Regarding the Problems of European Jewry and Palestine, Cmd. 6808, London, 1946.

Report of the British Goodwill Trade Mission to Iraq, Syria, the Lebanon and Cyprus, Board of Trade, London, 1946.

Willatts, E. E., Some Geographical Factors in the Palestine Problem, G.J., CVIII, 1947, 146–179.

SYRIA

Crowfoot, J. W., Syria and Lebanon: The Prospect, G.J., XCIX, 1942, 130–141.

Garrett, J., A Geographical Commentary on Ezekiel, G., XXV, 1939, 240–249.

———, The Site of Damascus, G., XXI, 1936, 283–296.

Hourani, A. H., "Syria and Lebanon," New York, 1946.

Report of the British Goodwill Trade Mission to Iraq, Syria, the Lebanon and Cyprus, Board of Trade, London, 1946.

JORDAN

Casto, E. Ray, and Oscar W. Dotson, Economic Geography of Trans-Jordan, E.G., XIV, 1938, 121–131.

CHAPTER 30: *Turkey*

The Turkish republic is all that remains of an empire which once embraced the shores of the Black Sea, reached almost to Vienna in the northwest and to the Persian Gulf in the southeast, and included the Middle East and the coastal zone of North Africa. The revolt of the peoples of the Danube Basin and of the Balkan peninsula deprived the Turks of most of their European possessions. Their North African and Middle Eastern territories were occupied by France, Great Britain, Italy, and Spain. After the First World War Turkey was a country peopled almost wholly by Turks, without minority problems or, in fact, any serious frontier difficulties. Turkey is divided into a small territory in Europe and a much larger territory in Asia. With the contraction of the Turkish empire during the early years of the present century, its focus has shifted from Constantinople (Istanbul) in European Turkey to Ankara in Asiatic.

While the Asiatic character of Turkey has thus been emphasized, the country has turned spiritually more and more to the West. Under the leadership of Mustapha Kemal, the "Ataturk," or Father of the Turks, from 1919 to his

The Bosporus. The view is from the Asiatic shore looking northward toward the Black Sea. There is no appreciable difference in land forms, vegetation, and settlement between European and Asiatic Turkey at this point. (*Turkish Information Office, New York.*)

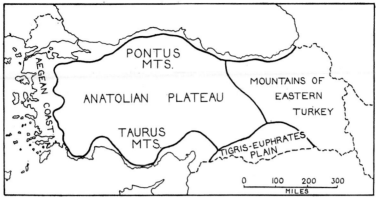

FIG. 231. Physical regions of Turkey.

death in 1938, Turkey turned its back on its Moslem and oriental past. Islam ceased to be the official faith, and practices closely associated with it were discontinued. Women no more went veiled, and men ceased to wear the fez. Attempts were made to reduce the illiteracy of the people, to improve their methods of agriculture, and to introduce Western industry. These were attended with a considerable measure of success. The productivity of Turkey has increased steadily during the past 25 years, and as its national income increased, so the products of agriculture have accounted for a diminishing proportion of the total.

European Turkey and the Straits. European Turkey is small in area and irregular in shape. From east to west it is at most 150 miles. It comprises two ranges of hills and the intervening valley of the Ergene, a tributary of the Mariça (Meric, Maritsa). The rainfall is low, generally less than 20 inches, except on the hills. The Istranca Mountains are forested, but elsewhere the land is covered by low-growing scrub or grass. The Ergene Basin is almost treeless. The peasants, who live in large villages, grow crops of corn on the more favorable land and graze flocks of sheep and goats over the steppe. The largest town other than Constantinople is Adrianople (Edirne, 185,000),[1] a large, closely built town lying on the eastern bank of the Tundza near its junction with the Mariça. It lay on the route from Constantinople up the

[1] The population of all cities of over 50,000 inhabitants is given. All cities of this size are named in the text.

Mariça Valley into the Balkans and was for long the commercial center of eastern Thrace and the Mariça Valley. The present boundary, which here follows the Mariça Valley, has reduced the city's economic significance but added to its military importance.

The Straits are in two parts, separated by the Sea of Marmara. They follow the course of a drowned river which formerly carried the discharge of the Black Sea into the Mediterranean. Both are narrow and easily controlled from the shores. Along their margins are the castles by which the "Narrows" were controlled during the Middle Ages and also the less visible defenses of the twentieth century. The more southwesterly or outer strait is the Dardanelles, a waterway 40 miles long and from 1 to 5 miles in width. On its northwestern side is the narrow, hilly Gallipoli peninsula. The inner strait, the Bosporus, is 15 miles long and from $\frac{1}{3}$ to $1\frac{1}{2}$ miles across. Near its southern extremity a creek enters from the western side, the Golden Horn, between which and the Sea of Marmara is the town of Constantinople (Istanbul, Byzantium).

The existence of the Straits is now one of the most important factors in the politics of the eastern Mediterranean. The Straits provide an outlet from the ports of southern Russia to the outer sea, and for a great deal more than a century Russia has aimed to control this waterway. Great Britain fought the Crimean War of 1854 to 1856 largely to check the Russian threat to the Mediterranean. After the defeat of

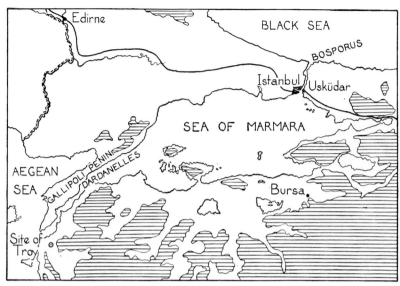

Fig. 232. Sea of Marmara and the "Straits."

Turkey during the First World War, the Straits were demilitarized. The ships of all nations were free to pass through as they wished. In 1935, by the Treaty of Montreux, Turkey was permitted once more to fortify the Straits.

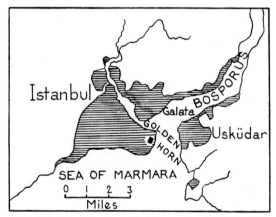

Fig. 233. The situation of Constantinople (Istanbul). The built-up area is shaded. The black square represents the site of the Mosque of Saint Sophia.

Constantinople (860,500) was established by the Emperor Constantine the Great early in the fourth century on the site of the ancient Greek city of Byzantium. It was strongly defended by the low cliffs, and across the neck of the peninsula was built the strongest line of walls known in Europe at the time. The town survived the attacks of barbarian invaders and became the capital of the eastern, or Byzantine, empire. In the fourteenth and fifteenth century this empire was conquered by the Turkish invaders from the East, and in 1453 the city of Byzantium, deemed impregnable, was taken by Sultan Mohammed II and remained until 1919 the capital of the Turkish empire. Its site is naturally strong and commands movement through the Bosporus. The town is a maze of narrow, twisting streets. A number of the early Christian churches, with the addition of minarets, now serve as mosques. Constantinople largely has lost its governmental functions but remains a market and business city, an important port in the foreign trade of Turkey, and a city of growing industrial importance.

Asiatic Turkey. This is a plateau, ranging in height from 1,500 to 5,000 feet above sea level. On north and south it is bounded by mountain ranges, the Pontic and Taurus. To the east these converge in the tangled mountainous region of eastern Turkey. Toward the west the plateau becomes more irregular as it is trenched by the deep valleys of the short rivers which flow to the Mediterranean.

The central plateau is the most distinctive region of Turkey. It is a high rolling plateau, built mainly of hard rocks but embracing many

The plateau of central Anatolia. Much of the area is rolling steppeland. Though a great deal of agriculture is carried on by primitive means, the use of modern methods and machines is spreading. (*Turkish Information Office, New York.*)

softer and more recent beds. The region has been subjected to earth movements, which have produced a great number of fault-bounded depressions, and to vulcanicity. Volcanic deposits are numerous and widespread. In places the plugs of ancient volcanoes remain as steep, isolated hills. Lava flows and volcanic ash mantle large areas, the former producing a bare and undulating landscape, the latter soft and easily eroded into a kind of "badland."

The plateau is in part drained to the Black Sea. The Sakarya and Kizil Irmak both pursue intricate courses over the plateau and cross the northern ranges in deep gorges to the sea. Much of the plateau, however, has no direct outlet to the sea. Its short seasonal rivers discharge into lakes from which the water evaporates, or they disappear amid the sands of the steppe. The rainfall of the Anatolian Plateau is small. Few places have more than 15 inches a year, and the variation from year to year is great. The rainfall occurs mainly in the autumn and winter months, and summers are almost rainless. The temperature range, both daily and yearly, is considerable. Over much of the region the January mean is below freezing point, and toward the east extreme temperatures may be below zero. In summer temperatures are high, though moderated somewhat by the altitude of the plateau.

The vegetation of the plateau is grassland. On rising ground this gives place to scrub and to a thin coniferous woodland. Along the streams may be willows and poplars, and as the rainfall diminishes, the grassland gives way to a thin and discontinuous cover of drought-resisting plants. The steppe of Anatolia is more suited to pastoral than to crop farming, though wheat, barley, and oats are grown. A large area is irrigated, but the supply of water is inadequate for any great extension of crop farming. Large flocks of sheep and goats are reared, both for their wool and hair and for their milk and meat. The sheep are commonly of the fat-tailed variety. The Angora goat is kept for the mohair which it yields.

Population is sparse, and village settlements few and large. In the better agricultural areas are small towns, such as Eskişehir (80,000),

Konya (58,500), and Kayseri (58,000), market and industrial centers where carpets and fabrics are woven from the wool and mohair produced locally. Ankara (Angora, 227,000) is the largest town of the plateau and in 1922 became the capital of the Turkish republic. The site has long been occupied, and the modern town is overlooked by the remains of a medieval fortress. It has little to recommend it as a capital, but it is, like Madrid, centrally placed. It is uncompromisingly Turkish, and its choice emphasizes the new and nationalistic direction given to Turkish development after the losses of the First World War.

The Anatolian Plateau is bounded on the north by the broken range of the Pontic Mountains, which increase in height eastward and close to the Russian frontier attain heights of over 10,000 feet. The mountains are a barrier between the plateau and the northern coast. In places they drop steeply to the sea, almost completely preventing movement along the coast. Lowland is restricted to a number of small tracts at the heads of the bays and at the mouths of the rivers. Only two railroads cross the mountains to reach, respectively, the ports of Zonguldak and Samsun.

The Anatolian Plateau slopes downward gently toward the west. Along its western edge it is broken by the deep flow toward the Aegean Sea. The region thus consists of a series of hill ranges lying roughly from west to east, separated by broad, flat valleys. The coast, drowned by a rise of sea level, is irregular, with many deep inlets and promontories.

This region has mild winters, like those of southern Greece, and hot summers. Rainfall is much greater than on the plateau, varying from 20 inches in the lowlands to over 40 inches in the hills. It occurs almost wholly between the months of October and March. Summers are dry and hot. Vegetation is richer than on the plateau. Much is forested with Mediterranean evergreens, but drier areas and those where the forest has been destroyed are generally covered with scrub. The flat alluvial land is cultivated. Wheat and barley are grown, with maize and such industrial crops as cotton and tobacco.

Fruit crops are also of great importance. Here are raised the figs and grapes which are dried and preserved for export, and the olive and other Mediterranean fruits are grown.

The population is denser than in other parts of Turkey. There are, however, probably fewer towns than in classical times, and the sites of some ancient cities are not now known with certainty, so great was the destruction wrought here during the Middle Ages and early modern times. Smyrna (Izmir, 198,500) is the largest of these towns. It lies at the head of a deep gulf. Close by is rich agricultural lowland, and to the east a valley leads up to the plateau. Smyrna serves as the port for much of western Anatolia. It was long a center of Greek settlement and after the First World War suffered severely both from the fire which destroyed much of the town and from the expulsion of the commercial-minded Greek population.

These Greeks had lived along the Aegean coast since ancient times. They made the "Turkish" carpets and prepared the "Turkish" tobacco. But the new Turkey of the 1920's was unwilling to tolerate the continued existence of the Greek minority, which was "exchanged" for the very much smaller Turkish minority in Greece. Economically Turkey lost a great deal with the expulsion of the industrious Greek community of about 800,000 but may have gained equally by achieving a greater degree of national unity. Bursa (86,000) is second in size to Smyrna.

Very few of the islands which lie close to the Anatolian coast actually form part of Turkey. Certain very small inshore islands are Turkish, but all the larger islands with the exception of Imroz are Greek. This derives largely from the fact that they have been settled, many of them since ancient times, by the Greeks, who were active in commerce and regarded the sea as a normal medium of trade.

The Anatolian Plateau is bounded on the south, as on the north, by a range of mountains which serve very effectively to cut it off from the sea. The mountains reach heights of over 10,000 feet. They comprise several overlapping ranges, the whole being arranged in a great double bend

Antalya. This is a small port on the southern coast of Turkey. A good deal of coastwise trade is still carried on in small sailing craft, such as are seen at anchor in the bay. (*Turkish Information Office, New York.*)

which begins at the coast, bends inland to enclose the plain of Antalya, reapproaches the coast near Cape Anamur, and then trends northeastward to enclose the Anatolian Plateau on its eastern side. The Taurus Mountains experience a considerable rainfall on west-facing slopes, but the region as a whole is markedly drier than the Pontic Mountains, and the rainfall is more clearly concentrated in the winter months. Temperatures are a little warmer than in the more northerly mountains. The ranges are very largely forested. Mediterranean evergreens and temperate-zone deciduous trees grow well. Northward the forest cover becomes thinner and drier as the Taurus Mountains pass into the Anatolian steppe. The rivers which drain the mountains to the Mediterranean flow in deep, narrow gorges which are in practice impracticable for traffic of all kinds. Only one railway succeeds in following one of these valleys, that from the Adana Plain to the plateau.

In general the mountains keep close to the coast, leaving only small and discontinuous areas of plain, but in two places the mountains recede, forming extensive areas of lowland. The more westerly of these is the Antalya Plain, in which lies the small town of Antalya. The larger of the two is the Cilician or Adana Plain, enclosed between the Taurus Mountains and the Amanus Mountains of northern Syria. Both this and the Antalya Plain are low, alluvial, and very fertile. Rainfall is generally adequate, though irrigation is practiced in places. Subtropical as well as temperate crops grow well, especially if irrigation water is available. Population, however, is not large, and quite good land is either unused or developed less fully than is possible. This situation is due, more than to any other factor, to the exposure of the coast to piratical raiders and to the depopulation that has resulted from centuries of war and political disturbance. The city of Adana, however, has a population of 101,000.

Adjoining the Adana Plain is the smaller province of Hatay, which was ceded to Turkey

in 1939 from French-occupied Syria. Hatay is
fertile and potentially productive, but its chief
importance lies in the port of Alexandretta
(Iskenderon), which handles much of the trade
of Turkey. It is now the only good port of the
south coast which has a railway communication

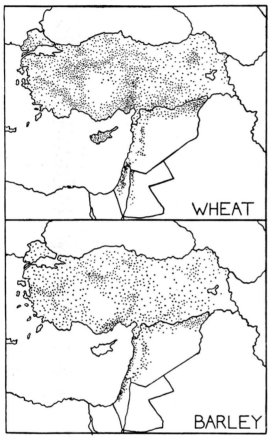

Fig. 234. Distribution of wheat and barley cultivation
in Turkey.

with the interior of Turkey. The famous Cilician
Gates provided a difficult but practicable route
into Turkey and are followed by the railroad.

Eastern Turkey. This is a sparsely populated
region of high mountain, of enclosed basin, and
of steppe and desert. The mountains of Armenia
in the northeast have a climate of extremes.
High in these mountains is the city of Erzerum
(51,000). South of the mountains are the dry
plains of the Tigris and Euphrates Valleys. This
is a region of very hot summers and cool winters.
The rainfall is small, and the plains are covered

with coarse grass, fresh and green during the
winter but parched and burned during the
summer. This passes upward into the mountain
areas of scrub and forest.

Population is sparse, much of it still seminomadic, and agriculture is unimportant. A
number of towns, important if not large, lie
close to the borders of the mountains, serving
in part as market centers at the junction of hill
and plain, in part as caravan stations on the
ancient routeway which followed the Euphrates
Valley up to Mosul, in Iraq, or Diyarbekir and
westward to the Mediterranean. The largest of
these is Gaziantep (63,000). This route is now
followed by the railway, the last section to be
built of the Baghdad Railway which was
planned by the Germans in the nineteenth
century.

Agriculture and Industry. In the years
following the First World War Turkey under-
went a social and economic revolution scarcely
less profound than that which was taking place
in Russia. The Sultan was expelled, the close
dependence of state and society upon the strict
letter of Moslem law was broken, and traditions
and practices which had hindered economic
progress were abandoned. The external trap-
pings of an oriental and Moslem society, the
fez and the veiling of women, disappeared.
Western dress made its appearance and with it
a Western attitude to agriculture and industry.

Less progress has been made in agricultural
than in industrial development. The Turks
have, however, set up agricultural-research and
plant- and animal-breeding stations. In places,
particularly in some of the rich lowland plains
of the south and west, modern, mechanized
farming practices have been introduced, and
everywhere attempts have been made to break
down wasteful, traditional methods and to
introduce to a primitive and conservative
peasantry the advantages of crop rotation and
artificial fertilizers. Agriculture employs some
two-thirds of the population of about 19,623,000.
Despite the progress that has been made locally,
most continue to use their traditional methods.
The cultivation of cereal crops has been described as "entirely primitive: the peasant

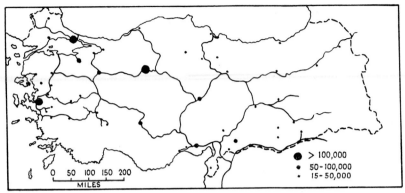

Fig. 235. Cities and railroads of Turkey.

prepares his land with the aid of his prehistoric needle plough and half-starved oxen, and sows a very mixed and degenerate seed, almost invariably too late if only because his animals are weak from lack of fodder. In the end he produces, at the cost of infinite labour, probably less than half the crop he should be producing if he set about it in good time, given good seed and lusty animals to draw the plough at his disposal, such as it is."[1]

Turkish industrial development has been carefully planned. Under the rule of the sultans manufacturing industries were almost limited to textiles, carpets, pottery, and woodwork, carried on generally on a domestic basis. The government of Kemal set out to establish factories on modern lines. Mills producing cotton and woolen cloth, silks, carpets, and rugs have been established in many of the towns of Anatolia. Turkey is now virtually self-sufficing in textiles and has a small export of silks and carpets.

The development of heavy industries has been restricted by the comparative lack of raw materials. Turkish coal resources are practically confined to a field lying close to the Black Sea coast between Eregli and Zonguldak. Its output is about 4 million tons a year. Iron-ore reserves are small and located in the remote eastern mountains. Coking ovens have been established at Zonguldak, and blast furnaces and steelworks erected at Karabuk, some 40 miles inland from

[1] "Overseas Economic Surveys: Turkey," London, 1947.

the Black Sea coast. This site, so far removed from the source of ore, was chosen when it was anticipated that all the ore used would be imported. The Karabuk ironworks are small, only about 200,000 tons a year, but supply a large proportion of the total crude-steel goods required in Turkey. Engineering and steel-finishing industries are not seriously developed, and the chemical industry remains very small. Large developments in the fields of power generation and industrial development are projected.

The state of roads and railways is in keeping with the backward economic development of the country. The Pontic and Taurus Mountains place very serious barriers between Anatolia, where most of the present industrial development is taking place, and the coasts. The railway network is inadequate, and many towns of considerable size have no railway communications at all. There is a much better network of roads, but many of these are unsurfaced and unsuitable for fast traffic.

The foreign trade of Turkey is comparatively small. Exports consist almost wholly of minerals and vegetable produce. Imports are, conversely, made up almost wholly of manufactured goods, machinery, chemicals, and fuels. It is unlikely that Turkey's industrial development will be sufficient in the near future to alter radically this pattern of raw-material export and import of manufactured goods.

We must not, however, underrate the significance of Turkey's revolution. An oriental state, governed by an autocratic and inefficient sultan, unindustrialized, with a backward agriculture, has transformed itself into a unified state, well if not quite democratically governed, with an improving agriculture and a developing industry. The new Turkey has developed without enemies, unless Soviet Russia be counted one. She has borne no animosity to the Greeks or to France and Great Britain, which did much to carve up her former empire. She forms politically, as well as geographically, a bridge between Europe and Asia. She was a member, before the Second World War, of the Balkan Entente together with Greece, Yugoslavia, and Romania, and she customarily acted in close harmony with her eastern neighbors, Iran, Iraq, and Syria. But she cannot avoid the consequences of her situation between the Black Sea and the Mediterranean. Her position forces her to become either the vassal or the opponent of Russia. Backed by the naval strength of Great Britain and supported by military help from the United States, she is determined not to become the former. The United States, in the now famous "Truman Doctrine," declared its intention of supporting both Turkey and Greece and of helping them to preserve their independence against aggression. Turkey has further received Marshall Aid. She is a member of the North Atlantic Treaty Organization and plays a vigorous part in the discussions between the Western Powers. Turkey is likely to need in the years to come all the tenacity of purpose that she has shown in recent times.

BIBLIOGRAPHY

East, W. Gordon, and O. H. K. Spate (ed.), "The Changing Map of Asia," New York, 1950.

Erinç, Sirri, Climatic Types and Variation of Moisture Regions in Turkey, *G.R.*, XL, 1950, 224–235.

—— and Tuncdilek Necdet, The Agricultural Regions of Turkey, *G.R.*, XLII, 1952, 179–203.

Fisher, W. B., "The Middle East," New York, 1950.

"General Memorandum on the 1950–51 and 1951–52 Programs," Organization for European Economic Cooperation, Paris, 1950.

"Géographie universelle," Vol. VIII, Asie occidentale, Paris, 1929.

Merriam, Gordon P., The Regional Geography of Anatolia, *E.G.*, II, 1926, 86–107.

Newbigin, M. I., "Southern Europe," New York, 1949.

"Overseas Economic Surveys: Turkey," London, 1948.

"Review of Economic Conditions in the Middle East," supplement to World Economic Report, 1949–50, United Nations, New York, 1951.

Shotwell, James T., "Turkey at the Straits," New York, 1944.

Stamp, L. D., "Asia," New York, 1950.

Stratil-Sauer, G., Cereal Production in Turkey, *E.G.*, IX, 1950, 325–336.

Stoz, Carl L., Coastal Lands of the Sea of Marmara, *J.G.*, XXXII, 1933, 305–315.

——, Life in Communities along the Bosporus, *J.G.*, XXXI, 1932, 181–192.

Thornburg, Max Weston, Graham Spry, and George Soule, "Turkey: An Economic Appraisal," New York, 1949.

Toynbee, Arnold J., and Kenneth P. Kirkwood, "Turkey," New York, 1927.

Ullyott, Philip, and O. Ilgaz, The Hydrography of the Bosphorus: An Introduction, *G.R.*, XXXVI, 1936, 44–66.

Ward, Barbara, "Turkey," Oxford, 1942.

Webster, Donald E., "The Turkey of Ataturk," Philadelphia, 1939.

CHAPTER 31: *The U.S.S.R.*

It was formerly a convention of geographers that Europe ended at the Ural Mountains, that European Russia belonged to the West, and that Siberia was as Asiatic as China and Japan. For many centuries this distinction between the Russian lands lying to the west and east of the Ural Mountains was reflected in their economic development. Such towns and industries as Tsarist Russia possessed lay for the greater part in Europe. The Asiatic lands were sparsely populated, backward, and undeveloped. Since the initiation of the First Five-Year Plan in 1928 the Russians have carried forward the process of welding the two conventional divisions of Russia into a single planned and integrated whole. This book is concerned with Europe and the Mediterranean. Its consideration cannot, however, stop at the low ridge of rounded hills that formed its traditional frontier, though discussion of lands lying farther to the east can be only very brief.

Russia is a vast country. Its area of 8,708,000 square miles is almost as great as that of the whole of North America. It stretches more than 5,300 miles from its most easterly point, East Cape opposite the shore of Alaska, to the western shore of the Black Sea and 2,900 miles from its most northerly, Cape Chelyuskin far within the Arctic Circle, to the southernmost border of Turkestan. Much of it is uninhabited forest, steppe, and desert. Russia is one of the least densely populated of countries, yet its

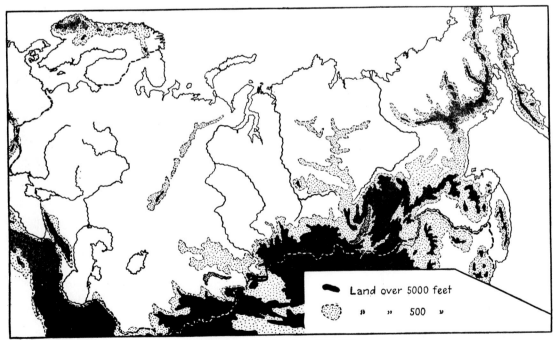

FIG. 236. Relief of the U.S.S.R.

397

resources are among the greatest. It is only recently, however, that these resources have come to be developed and used.

The Political and Economic Revolutions. The Soviet Union of today is heir to the Russia of the Tsars. The nucleus from which the earlier Russia developed was the region of low, forested hills amongst which the Volga, Oka, Dnieper (Dnepr), and Dvina take their rise. To the north lay the coniferous forests, a region of poor soil and harsh climate. To the south the forest thinned, and parkland in turn gave place to the rolling, grassy steppe. The city of Moscow (Moskva) grew up protected from the fierce nomadic Tatars of the grasslands by its curtain of woodland. It lay near the meeting place of different environments, the coniferous and deciduous woodland and the steppe, and could draw upon the resources of each.

The Russian state expanded in each direction from Muscovy, its early basis. Northward its traders and trappers pressed toward the Arctic Ocean, there to meet on the shores of the White Sea the merchants of England and the Netherlands. Toward the west the branches of the Baltic Sea invited the Russians to share more directly in the trade of the West, and Novgorod became an emporium for the merchants of the West. At the beginning of the eighteenth century the Russian Tsars conquered the territory around the head of the Gulf of Finland and there founded the town of Saint Petersburg (Petrograd, Leningrad). This "window" opening on to the West was gradually enlarged, and the absorption into Russia of the Baltic provinces and of much of Poland threw it wide open. At about the same time the Russian Tsars extended their sway into the steppes, gradually conquering the Asiatic Tartars and the Cossack frontiersmen. During the eighteenth century Azov was taken, then Odessa and the Crimea (Krym). In the nineteenth century Russian influence and then control began to penetrate the Caucasus Mountains and the Balkan peninsula and to threaten the independence of Turkey.

Eastward from Muscovy stretched forest and steppe and mountain as far as the Pacific. The inhabitants of this huge region were few and backward, as impotent to halt the Russian advance as were the North American Indians that of the white settlers. Fur trappers and miners entered and then crossed the Ural Mountains. In the late sixteenth century Russians reached Siberia, and although permanent settlements were few and small, the whole region became silently and without opposition part of the empire of the Tsars. About 1640 the Pacific Ocean was reached.

In 1917 a revolution broke which had long been threatening. The Tsarist government was overthrown, and the Tsar and his family were murdered. The landowners and the aristocracy were driven into exile. The land, the factories, and all means of production were nationalized, and the conduct of all economic and business matters passed into the hands of the workers. A period of chaos followed, made worse by the "intervention" of so-called "white armies," assisted by British, American, Japanese, and other forces. The experiment in pure communism failed and was replaced by a money economy and a strict governmental control over all activities. Order was gradually restored, and the Russians prepared to utilize the vast resources with which their country was endowed for the increase of the country's wealth and well-being.

The agriculture and industry of Russia today are in large measure the product of the years since 1928. Under the Tsars Russia was poor and backward. Agriculture was primitive and, over much of the country, self-sufficing; manufacturing industries had been established only in a few centers in European Russia, and these were generally backward in their techniques and inefficient in their methods. From the earliest days of the Bolshevik Revolution Lenin had held before the Russian people the objective of industrialization as a means of attaining higher living standards as well as greater military strength. It was not, however, until 1928 that serious moves were made in this direction. The first of the five-year plans prescribed the achievements to be accomplished within the ensuing years.

The first plan was succeeded by a second in 1934, and this in turn by a third in 1939. A Fourth Five-Year Plan was completed at the end of 1950. Each of these plans was a program of creative work. Each was made up of assignments: factories to be built, railroads to be laid down, mines to be sunk and developed, grassland to be brought under cultivation. Each plan could be carried through only by immense labor and self-sacrifice on the part of the Russian people. Goods of foreign origin had to be purchased: dynamos and turbines, steel mills and machine tools, which the Russians could not yet produce for themselves. At the same time the Russians had to purchase knowledge and skill. Technicians from the West were brought in and were paid for their services in teaching the Russian people. Vast supplies of labor were needed for the construction work going on in Russia. The imports, both material and immaterial, had to be paid for. This necessitated further exertions on the part of the Russian people to produce goods for export.

This planned development of the resources of a vast country has been highly praised and recommended for the imitation of other peoples. It has profoundly changed the face of Russia and, on balance, done something to raise the standards of living. But its achievement was not an easy process. It consisted in the accumulation of capital goods—railways, dams, hydroelectric stations, and factories—and this could be done only by consuming less and working more. Only an autocratic and ruthless authority could have carried through such an achievement. A five-year plan on Russian lines would be inconceivable in the western countries. Even in Russia it met with opposition. Fundamental to the plans was an improvement in the output of Russian agriculture and the provision of more foodstuffs for the towns. The resistance of the wealthier peasants, the kulaks, to the plans of the government led to their elimination, and small holdings were merged into collective farms, large and, by Russian standards, highly mechanized and efficient. The success of the agricultural revolution prepared the way for an intensification of the industrial.

The area of land under cultivation was greatly extended, and the methods revolutionized. State farms and collective farms were established. The former, comparatively few in number, are state-operated research and demonstration farms. The collectives are, in effect, a kind of cooperative farm. They are the village organized as a single unit, all the individual holdings absorbed into one mechanized farm. The mechanization of agriculture necessitated a supply of machinery. Practically none had hitherto been made in Russia, and vast factories were established for the purpose at Karkhov, Stalingrad, Sverdlovsk, and elsewhere.

A vast labor supply is one of the most valuable of Russia's resources, but it was far from adequate to the demands of these huge development programs. Russian policy has been to mechanize agriculture and thus to liberate labor for the factories. The "collectives" were part of this plan. At the present time the same conditions of labor shortage exist, and the collective farms are themselves being merged one with another. The collectives of the future will be larger than at present and even more efficient and machinelike in their organization. In Byelorussia, for example, the total of about 10,000 collective farms has been reduced to some 3,250; in the Ukraine, a total of 26,000 has fallen to 14,500. The workers on each of these vast farms will live in towns—"agro-towns"—each made up of "two thousand beautiful houses along asphalted streets and avenues with lawns. Two thousand two-, three-, and four-story houses with electricity, radio, water supplies and bathrooms. A central square with a statue of Stalin. Next to each house a fruit garden."[1] Such are the farms of the future.

The industrial achievement of the Russian plans is even more astounding. Production was increased by more than 350 per cent within the period 1928 to 1938. The plan was, of course, interrupted by the German invasion of the summer of 1941 and the destruction of the next 4 years. The Ukraine, one of the most productive agricultural regions and seat of more than half the Russian steel capacity, was devastated.

[1] Quoted in *The Economist* (London), Jan. 27, 1951, p. 202.

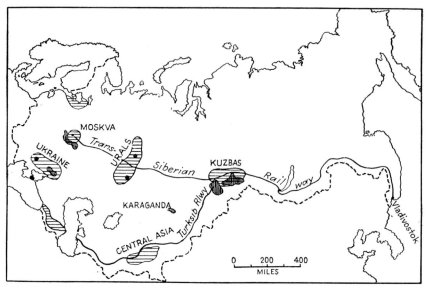

FIG. 237. Industrial regions of the U.S.S.R. The coal fields are heavily shaded.

This damage has been repaired, and Russian production is in most respects greater now than in 1941. Total production has increased by 74 per cent between 1940 and 1950. During the first three five-year plans coal production was increased more than fourfold, pig iron and steel in similar proportions, crude oil threefold, and electric power eightfold.

Under Tsarist rule the chief centers of Russian industry had been in the west, accessible to western capital, skill, and materials. Russian factory production remains today overwhelmingly in the west, in the regions of Leningrad and Moscow and in the Ukraine. These still produce a large part of the steel, textiles, chemicals, and products of engineering. But new industrial centers have been established farther to the east. The Ural Mountains, that traditional frontier with Asia, has become the scene of an important iron-mining and -smelting and steelmaking industry. Over 1,000 miles to the east, in the midst of what had hitherto been the almost untrodden wilderness of Siberia, coal was discovered and heavy industries have been established. In the ancient cities of Turkestan, in the steppes of Kazakhstan, in the Caucasus, around Lake Baikal, and in the far east of Siberia close to the shore of the Pacific, new industries have been established.

The choice of site has been determined in part by the existence of coal and iron or nonferrous ores, but equally important probably has been the desire on the part of the Soviet government to locate the new industries deep in the heart of Asia, far from the prying eyes of foreigners and as secure as it is possible to be from the attack of hostile aircraft.

The Resources of the Soviet Union. Russia is well endowed for the development she has undertaken, and perhaps her foremost resources are her almost unlimited space and her vast and rapidly increasing population. In most countries of western Europe space is limited. The mode of agriculture is most often that which can get the most out of a limited area of land irrespective of the labor involved. In Russia, an agricultural practice has been developed—the mechanized collective farm—which gets the most return in proportion to the labor expended irrespective of the amount of land used. In Russia, agricultural progress consists in introducing methods and practices that will liberate more men to work in the factories.

Russian soils are varied in quality, as might be expected in a country so large. The tundra soils of the extreme north have no agricultural value, and the great belt of forest is covered with podsol, regularly cultivable, where the climate permits, only with the use of large additions of fertilizer. The zone of mixed and deciduous forest (see Figs. 15 and 16) has a better soil; the autumn leaf fall adds humus. But the most valuable is the black earth, or chernozem, which stretches from the Black Sea to Central Asia and then occurs in isolated patches across Siberia to the Pacific Ocean. The black earth, like the good prairie soils of North America, is deep and rich in humus. It will produce large crops year after year without fertilizer. Perhaps 10 per cent of the total area of the Soviet Union may be described as first-class farming land, and at least as much again could be reckoned good farm land.

About half the Soviet Union is forested. Not all is made up of stands of exploitable timber. In Siberia are large areas of damp woodland in which the timber is of very small commercial value. Much of the forest lies too remote from railroad and waterway to be exploited in the near future. Nevertheless the timber reserves are immense, larger than those of any other country, not excluding Canada. Most of the timber is softwood; the only considerable stands of hardwood are in the western part of European Russia and in the Far East.

Russia's mineral wealth is no less considerable. Russia contains a little over 20 per cent of the estimated reserves of coal in the world. The United States is credited with about 50 per cent. The most extensive of the coal fields is the Kuznets Basin (Kuzbas), in central Siberia, which has over two-thirds of the total. The next most important are in the Ukraine and in Kazakhstan. The little developed Tunguska coal-bearing region on the borders of eastern Siberia also has large resources. The rest are small by Russian standards.

The output of coal in 1940, before the German invasion, was about 155 million tons a year. By 1950, this had risen to 264 million tons. Before, about two-thirds of the total had come from the coal fields of the Ukraine and the Moscow region; by 1950, Siberia had come to produce more than half the greatly increased total. The expansion of the coal-mining industry is taking place almost wholly in Asia.

Deposits of iron ore are widely distributed in the U.S.S.R. There are large reserves in the Krivoi Rog and Kerch areas of the Ukraine and in the Ural Mountains, especially the vast deposits at Magnitogorsk and Nizhni Tagil. There are many small deposits in the west, and reserves have been located in Siberia and Central Asia. The volume of production of iron ore today is rather uncertain. More is known about the amount and distribution of pig iron and steel. In 1950, the production of pig iron was 19,200,000 tons; in 1940, it was 15,000,000. Steel production had expanded similarly, from 18,300,000 to 27,600,000 tons. In general the total for steel *includes* that for pig iron, which was mostly used in steelmaking. The excess of steel production over pig iron represents very roughly the utilization of iron scrap.

Steel production, like coal mining, has tended to move east. Before the war almost half the total steel output was produced in the Ukraine. By 1950, the Ukraine output had increased very little. The bulk of the increase had been in the newly opened works of the Urals and Siberia, where over two-thirds of the production now takes place.

The Soviet Union is, after the United States and Venezuela, the world's greatest producer of petroleum. The smallest increase has been in the field of oil production; a total of 31,000,000 tons in 1940 had risen to only 37,600,000 tons by 1950. This is in part accounted for by the very considerable decline in productivity of the most important of the older centers of production. The Caucasus region, which before the last war had accounted for about 90 per cent of the output, is becoming exhausted, and the new developments between the Volga River and the Urals, in Turkmenistan and Uzbekistan (both in Central Asia), and in the Far East have done little more than compensate for the decline in the Caucasus. By 1950 Russia had not achieved the targets she had set herself to attain by 1942. It is not surprising that she is interested in the oil-rich areas of the Middle East. An abundant supply of petroleum and diesel oil is of greater importance to Russia than to most European countries. Russian agriculture depends very heavily on oil-driven tractors. The output of tractors has increased faster in the last 10 years than that of oil to drive them. It is said that the introduction of electrically driven tractors and farm machinery is planned for the near future.

The production of electric power has increased rapidly. The abundance of coal and the large number of big rivers that can be harnessed give Russia an advantage in this field. The generation of current increased from 48 billion kilowatt-hours in 1940 to 86.7 billion in 1950. It appears that the Soviet authorities are developing intensively their sources of electric power.

It is somewhat reassuring to compare the production of the Soviet Union and of her East European satellites with that of the United States, Canada, and the west European countries.

produced foodstuffs, and other types of consumer goods has increased, but relatively more slowly. Russia is still, in 1953, very far from being a land of plenty, and the Russian level of consumption is far below that of western Europe.

Population. The population of the Soviet Union is today one of its greatest assets. At present the total is almost certainly more than 200 million. These are varied in race and origin. They include such small remnants of ancient and primitive peoples as the Chukchi and Yukaghir of Siberia; they include also the Mongols of Soviet Asia and the Far East and the Tatar groups which migrated westward along the grassland belt and settled in the steppe area and its borderland. The Caucasus Mountains and Trans-Caucasia are also inhabited by

COMPARATIVE PRODUCTION STATISTICS

	Population, 1949	Pig iron*	Steel*	Coal*	Oil*	Electric Power, billion kilowatt-hours
U.S.S.R.	200,000 000 †	19.2	27.6	264	37.6	86.7
Russian satellites.	87,640,000	3.4	5.6	144.4	4.75	
Total.	287,640,000	22.6	33.2	408.4	42.35	
United States.	149,215,000	58.2	86.3	491.3	263.9	329.9
Canada and North Atlantic Treaty countries.	136,054,000	23	33	346	3.6	
Total.	285,269,000	81.2	119.3	837.3	267.5	

* In millions of long tons. There are approximately 6.3 barrels per ton of oil. Figures for 1949.

† The estimate given in Frank Lorimer, "The Population of the Soviet Union," League of Nations, Geneva, 1946, is 203,080,000 in 1950.

Great as has been the Russian development, her industrial potential remains very far behind that of the free nations. Its further growth is likely to encounter increasing difficulties such as that outlined in connection with the supply of petroleum.

The development within each branch of the Soviet economy is controlled from Moscow. Production is in no way a response to the demand of the consumer. The Soviet planners have ordained that the emphasis shall be placed on capital, not on consumers' goods. Faced with a choice similar to that of Goering between "guns and butter," they have chosen "machine tools, tractors, and lorries (trucks) before clothing." The output of textiles, footwear, factory-

a number of distinctive peoples, mainly of Turkic origin. Most of western Russia, however, is inhabited by Slavonic peoples, among which two groups are of greatest importance. These are the Great Russians, who speak what the rest of the world understands as the Russian language, and the Ukrainian peoples, closely related in language to the Great Russians.

Under the Tsarist rule no distinction was made in the administration of the many separate peoples which formed the Russian Empire. It is claimed that, under Soviet rule, each distinct cultural area is separated from its neighbors, its culture protected and preserved, and the government adjusted to the needs of the people. In this way, the Soviet Union is made up of 16 Soviet Socialist Republics, which, it is claimed, are self-governing in most matters touching their local administration. In addition there are 22 autonomous republics and 9 autonomous provinces. These are usually comparatively small in area and are contained within the larger Soviet republics. They are less completely self-governing but have a measure of independence sufficient to preserve their cultural identity. European Russia is made up of the three S.S.R.'s of the Russian, Ukrainian, and White Russian (Byelorussian) Soviet Republics. In addition there are three S.S.R.'s in Trans-Caucasia, namely, Georgia, Armenia, and Azerbaidzhan. The middle Volga Valley and steppe area, settled in earlier centuries by considerable numbers of Tartar peoples, now have no less than 6 autonomous republics, inhabited by the Chuvash, Udmurt, Bashkir, Tartar, Mari, and Mordvinian peoples. The seventh once contained the German colony of the Volga, but this group, which was settled near Saratov in the eighteenth century, appears to have been moved into Siberia. In addition Karelia, in part annexed from Finland; the three Baltic states of Estonia, Latvia, and Lithuania, occupied in 1940; and Bessarabia, formerly Romanian, with the addition of a small adjoining area, are also Soviet Socialist Republics. Several small territories in the Caucasus Mountains or in Trans-Caucasia are organized as autonomous Soviet Socialist Republics or as autonomous provinces, the latter having a smaller degree of local importance.

The Turkic region of Central Asia is organized into the Kazakh, Turkmen, Uzbek, Tadjik, and Kirghiz Soviet Republics. Much of the Soviet Arctic, inhabited only by small and backward tribes, is administered as a number of autonomous republics and autonomous provinces.

The population of the Soviet Union has increased sharply in recent years. The birth rate appears to be one of the highest in the world, and it has been predicted that the total by 1970 will be 251 million.[1] It is likely that not more than 15 per cent of this total would be made up of the more primitive tribes. In 1939, about a third of the total population was classed as urban, as against only 18 per cent of a smaller total in 1926. The urbanization of contemporary Russia is no less characteristic than is its industrialization. The great size of the new towns is a feature of this development. Moscow had over 4 million and Leningrad over 3 million inhabitants. In addition, no less than 11 cities had each over 500,000 and 81 over 100,000. It is highly probable that these figures have been greatly exceeded, so rapid has been the expansion of towns in recent years.[1]

The immense achievement of modern Russia must not be allowed to disguise the weakness from which the country suffers and the cost at which this industrialization has been achieved. Much depends upon the functioning of a vast transport organization. So great a volume of work was carried through, as has been indicated, only by allowing little leisure and freedom to the working people. The Russian leaders may be planning a "brave new world," but it is essentially one of their own design. It is not to be supposed that the overworked Russian views the achievements of his government with the rapture manifested by those foreigners who, from a safe distance, evince such devotion to Russian ideals.

The Natural Regions of Russia. The U.S.S.R. is, except along the southern borders of Asiatic Russia, a region of gentle relief. The great rivers of European Russia rise in hills which do not exceed 1,200 feet above the level of the distant ocean. The Ural Mountains, conspicuous on the relief map, in general do not exceed 3,000 feet. This great plain is built for the most part of rocks of great geological age. On the borders of Finland in the north and in central Siberia are rocks among the oldest in the crust of the earth. They are much folded, but worn down to an undulating plain. Elsewhere these ancient rocks are covered with later deposits of limestone, chalk, and sandstone

[1] Notestein, Frank W., "The Future Population of Europe and the Soviet Union," p. 312, League of Nations, Geneva, 1944.

[1] The size of Russian cities mentioned in the text is not in general given. The most recent figures are of 1939 and these are probably of little value now.

which have been little influenced by earth movements and lie almost as flat as the level plains to which they have given rise. During the Ice Age the glaciers extended far over European Russia and deposited boulder clay and moraine.

The Ural Mountains are a north-south ridge of folded mountains, similar in age, origin, and

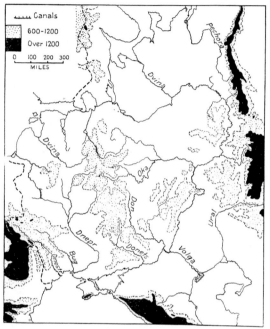

Fig. 238. Relief of European Russia.

maturity to the highlands of central Europe. The hills of the southern part of the Crimean peninsula, together with the rugged and glaciated Caucasus, are part of the Alpine fold ranges. The sharpest irregularities in the plain of European Russia have been produced by the deposition of glacial drift. The Valdai Hills, the highest in Russia west of the Ural Mountains, are composed essentially of moraine.

The major divisions of Russia are based, not on the terrain, as in Germany and most other countries, but upon factors of climate and soil, which are reflected in the vegetation. The transition from tundra to forest, from forest to steppe is the most profound in Russian geography, and its influence has been very considerable on the course of the history of Russia.

Much of that part of Russia, both European and Asiatic, which lies within the Arctic Circle

is mantled with tundra. The climate of this region is severe. Winters are long and cold. The inadequate statistics suggest that January averages fall to below −30° in the region of the Taimyr peninsula. Summers are short and cool. Rarely does July show an average temperature of 50°, and in few places is the average above freezing point during more than 6 months out of the 12. The extreme west of the Russian tundra has a climate resembling that of Norwegian and Swedish Lapland. Winters are cold, but the North Atlantic Drift carries a body of relatively warm water into the Arctic Ocean. The Arctic port of Murmansk is ice-free in winter, and for some distance farther to the east a passage can be maintained with icebreakers through the pack. East of Novaya Zemlya, however, the

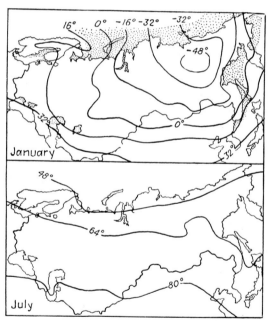

Fig. 239. Temperatures in the U.S.S.R. in January and July. Stippled area indicates portion of sea frozen in winter.

difficulties of navigation become very much greater and the length of the open season shorter.

In much of the tundra the subsoil remains frozen throughout the year. The pale summer sun thaws out the surface. Water from melting snow and ice spreads over it. Drainage is impeded, and the land reduced to an impassable morass. These conditions are intensified by the behavior of the Russian rivers. The Ob and Enisei (Yenisei) take their rise far to the south in the Asiatic steppes or even in the mountains which border Mongolia and Sinkiang. Though the rivers are frozen in winter, the ice breaks early in the south, and as spring spreads slowly northward, so do the floods of the north-flowing rivers. In the tundra their waters spread out over the still partly frozen soils, impeding movement and trade.

The vegetation of the tundra—lichen, moss, creeping plants, and stunted, plantlike trees—has already been described. The region is of slight economic value. Its inhabitants are few and mainly related to the Lapps or the Eskimo. Their life is nomadic; their dependence on the wandering herds of reindeer absolute.

Off the flat and barren coast of northern Russia are groups of equally barren and inhospitable islands. Novaya Zemlya interposes a barrier in the coastal shipping route, forcing vessels to use the rocky Kara Strait. Off Cape Chelyuskin, the most northerly point of the Old World, are islands which lie within 10° of the pole. It is not difficult to envisage circumstances in which they might become of considerable, though not necessarily economic, value to Russia. Yet this Arctic coast is not wholly destitute of permanent settlement. On the shores of its bays and estuaries are small groups of log huts standing beside the rough jetties and landing stages, where the timber, floated down the Arctic rivers, is loaded on to the steamers which ply along the arctic seaways.

In the Asiatic areas of the Taiga temperatures unparalleled elsewhere in the world have been recorded, and over a large area the January average sinks to −50°. The rainfall is low and over most of the Asiatic Taiga is less than 20 inches a year. In spite of this the summer is longer than in the Tundra and the Taiga is covered with coniferous forest. The soils are generally podsol. Coniferous trees provide little humus, and under the conditions of slight evaporation and slow runoff, the soil moisture becomes acid and breaks down and removes the more valuable soil constituents. Much of the surface is covered with boulder clay and moraine, and hollows are often peat-filled. In places the glacial deposits have been re-sorted by waters that discharged from the melting ice sheets, and there are extensive areas of fluvioglacial deposits, some fertile and productive, others sterile wastes of sand and gravel.

Attempts have been made in recent years to extend agriculture into the forest zone of northern Russia, but the soil and climate are unfavorable, and such progress as has been made has been at a very high cost. The chief resource of the Taiga is its timber. Spruce and fir predominate, with some larch and birch. The value of the timber varies. Not all is of merchantable quality, and a great deal is too remote from road, river, and rail to be marketed.

The timber industry in Asiatic Russia depends upon the river highways. These are slow flowing and deep, and the logs are floated down them to the sea. The northern Dvina, which takes its rise within the Taiga, enters the White Sea at the port of Archangel (Arkhangelsk) and is of great significance in the timber traffic. Importance attaches also, however, to the Ob and Enisei. Igarka, on the Enisei, handles the timber which is sent by the northern sea route to the ports of western Europe.

In European Russia the coniferous forest stretches into the basin of the Volga, into Finland and the Baltic States. Leningrad lies within the coniferous forest, and Moscow just beyond its edge. South of the continuous belt of coniferous trees are scattered stands of pine, fir, and larch almost to the borders of the steppe.

The White Sea carries the waters of the Arctic Ocean far into the forest belt, and the ports of Archangel, Onega and Kandalaksha are open for a large part of the year. Between the White Sea and the Gulf of Finland is a depression along the margin of the ancient shield of Scandinavia in which lakes have formed, including Lake Ladoga and Lake Onega. These, with a number of smaller lakes and their tributary streams, have provided a route along which the Russians have cut the

White Sea Canal, facilitating the movement of merchandise between the Soviet Arctic and Leningrad and encouraging the development of industries dependent on timber and pulp.

On the southern margin of the Taiga the climate becomes less severe, the winters shorter, the soil more productive and more easily cultivated. The clearings in the forest are larger, the

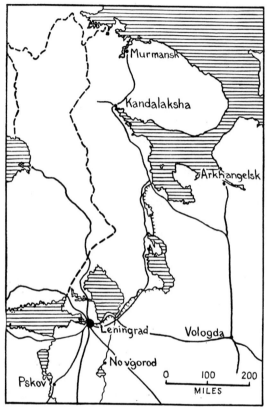

Fig. 240. The Leningrad industrial region.

population greater, and towns more numerous. In the upper valley of the Volga are industrial towns, still dependent on the timber of the northern forests, though metallurgical and other industries become increasingly important toward the south.

Beyond the Urals the Taiga has been even less developed. The Trans-Siberian Railway was built along its open southern edge. A few towns have grown up on the great rivers within the forest edge, but population is slight, and the great Siberian forest almost untouched.

The deciduous forest of the U.S.S.R. is small in area compared with the other regions of the Soviet Union. It is that part of the forest belt where the winters are mild enough and summers long enough for the oak and elm to grow. The autumn leaf fall provides more humus than is to be found in the northern forest. The soil is richer, less acid, more productive, and easier to work. The deciduous forest forms a wedge reaching eastward from Poland, separating the steppe from the northern forest. East of the Volga it is continued as a narrow belt, interrupted by the Ural Mountains, into Siberia. On its northern edge is mixed woodland; on its southern, parkland or wooded steppe.

Much of the deciduous forest belt lies within the Byelorussian Soviet Socialist Republic. It embraces territory formerly Polish. It contains the flat, ill-drained region of the Pripyat (Pripet) marshes and the moraines which continue eastward from the great Baltic terminal moraine. From the morainic deposits which comprise the low Valdai Hills the western Dvina flows to the Baltic Sea, the Volkhov to Lake Ladoga, the Dnieper southward to the Black Sea, and the Volga with its tributaries southeast to the Caspian.

Most of the deciduous forest belt, at least the European part of it, has been glaciated and is now covered with boulder clay and belted by the sinuous lines of moraine. It is a hummocky country, with sharp changes in soil and drainage in short distances, in some places dry and fertile, in others poorly drained and uncultivated. The Pripyat or Pinsk marshes in Byelorussia are the largest of such areas. Vast areas of marsh, a maze of sluggish rivers, and a poor peasantry living in self-sufficiency and isolation on what are virtually islands only a foot or two above the level of the waters characterize this region. Pinsk, small and unpretentious, is the capital and only town of the marshes.

To the south of the marshes the land rises to the open, rolling platform of Podolia. Between the Dvina, Lovat, Dnieper, Don, and Volga the land swells into low, rounded hills. The headwaters of each river system approach those of the others. The portages from one to the other are short and not difficult, and from the earliest stages of Russian history traders from the Baltic reached the Black Sea by these routes. Here grew up the earliest towns of Russia: Smolensk, Chernigov, and Kiev "the Golden." Moscow did not attain to any great importance until these cities of the steppe margin had been overrun by Tartar invaders. Kiev was destroyed, its trade routes severed, and its merchants driven northward into the deep forest. Here, in shelter and protection, the state of Muscovy developed.

The deciduous forest region has now no great extent of woodland to show. During the centuries of rural settlement inroads were made on the woodland; land was broken up and cultivated. The region is now dotted with villages and small towns. A mixed farming predominates, with wheat, rye, barley, oats, potatoes, and dairy farming. Flax and sugar beet are produced for the factories.

The forest formerly passed through open woodland into the steppe. The latter is a region of low rainfall, less than 15 inches and, in large areas, less than 10. Winters are cold, but summers are hot, and the frost-free period is longer than in all other parts of Russia except the Crimea. The rainfall is not generally enough for tree growth, and sparse woodland occurs only along watercourses. The steppe is a rolling grassy plain. The shallow valleys are sunk so far below its surface that their waters cannot be used for irrigation. The winter snows melt early. Spring flowers and grass grow quickly, and the steppe puts on a beauty which many Russian writers have tried to fix in words. With the heat of summer the grass turns brown and sere before its time. The ground is parched and hard, the air is heavy with dust, and even the sun shines paler through the haze. A heavy convectional storm cleanses the air and moistens the soil, but quickly in the great heat the land again dries out.

The steppe lies very largely outside the glaciated area, and it is the absence of boulder clay that accounts, in part at least, for the relative absence of tree growth. The lighter soil of the nonglaciated region less readily supports a forest cover. The soil of the steppe is characteristically chernozem.

The primeval, grassy steppe is now cut up by tractors and dotted with factories. It is difficult, amid the collective farms, to visualize the Tartar hordes or the Cossack frontiersmen who once rode over its great spaces. The steppe reaches from the foot of the Carpathians eastward to Siberia, and yet farther to the east are isolated areas of steppe, which stretch into Mongolia and Manchuria. The European steppe is crossed by the great Russian rivers: the Dniester, Bug, Dnieper, Donets, and Don flowing into the Black Sea; the Volga and Ural to the Caspian. These rivers are broad, deep, and slow flowing. Navigation is hindered by ice in winter and in places by a low water level in summer. Nevertheless, the rivers of the steppe and their northward continuation into the forest zone are greatly used for navigation and carry a large part of the heavy merchandise transported in this part of the U.S.S.R.

It is a feature of the rivers of the steppe that their right-hand, or western, banks often rise steeply above the level of the river while the eastern are low, flat, and sometimes marshy. Early towns, like Kiev, Saratov, and Stalingrad (Tsaritsin), were set high up on the western bank, with the cliff, the river, and the marsh to protect them from their enemies of the Asiatic steppe. Such a position, however, gave them little protection against the Germans, coming from the west, in 1941.

The steppe is now the most important and productive agricultural region of the U.S.S.R. Wheat, largely wintersown, is the chief crop in the south. Farther inland, where the climate is more extreme, spring-sown wheat is more important. Barley is also grown, and on the northern margin of the steppe sugar beet and rye are important. Animal husbandry is important in all the steppe region; cattle are reared in the moister areas; sheep and goats in the drier.

The Crimean peninsula is moister and milder than the steppe. It is almost wholly surrounded by the sea, only the narrow Perekop isthmus joining it with the mainland. In the north it is a level expanse of grassland. On the south is a range of dry and rugged limestone mountains. The coast which they shelter has mild winters and hot dry summers. It resembles the Mediterranean in its wealth of flowering shrubs, fruits, and dark evergreens, and on its shore are health resorts. Its largest town, Sevastopol, lies on the southwest coast and has a good harbor. Kerch, in the east of the peninsula, has become a center of metallurgical industries with the opening up of its iron ores.

Toward the southeast the grass of the steppe becomes thinner and passes gradually into the desert of Soviet Central Asia. Unlike the deserts

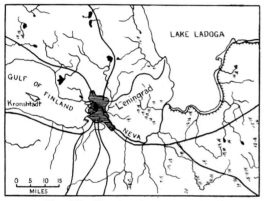

Fig. 241. The situation of Leningrad.

of North Africa and the Middle East, that of Russia has winters of great severity. The Caspian Sea, which lies almost wholly within the region of semidesert, has no outlet to the ocean and lies some 84 feet below the level of the Black Sea. Its salinity is high, and its water of no agricultural value. From the Caspian Sea the desert and dry steppe stretch eastward to the mountains which separate the U.S.S.R. from China.

Lake Aral, which, like the Caspian Sea, has no outlet, lies in the midst of this region. The whole area has a rainfall of under 10 inches, and much has less than 5. The land is level or rolling. Areas of shifting sand dunes have formed in parts. The only permanent settlements are around the few oases and along the rivers that flow into this region from the mountains to the south and southeast. The volume of rainfall increases in these directions, and more water is available for irrigation from the mountain streams. Here have grown up the cities of Soviet Central Asia (see page 416).

The Leningrad Region. The city of Leningrad, originally called Saint Petersburg, was founded by the Tsar Peter the Great early in the eighteenth century. It was the gateway through which this westernizing Tsar hoped to bring into Russia the more advanced culture and technology of the West. It became the capital of the Tsars and remained so until the center of government was transferred in recent years to Moscow. Leningrad was established in the marshy valley of the river Neva, about 3 miles above its entry into the Gulf of Finland. Despite the difficulties of the site, its liability to flood, and the many small waterways which branch from the Neva, it was a well-planned and well-built city, a fit capital of the Russian Empire.

As the chief outlet of Russia toward the west, it quickly grew in size and importance. Trade was drawn to it, and industries established. It is now a city of some 3,200,000 inhabitants, with varied industries, including metallurgical and textile. During the Middle Ages the towns of Novgorod and Pskov had been the meeting places of Russians and traders from the west. Functionally Leningrad has replaced them, though they remain industrial centers.

The Leningrad region has few industrial raw materials. There is little solid fuel, and it depends heavily on hydroelectric power generated from the Svir, Syas and Volkhov Rivers. The region is today one of the chief Russian shipbuilding centers. Nearby Kronstadt is the primary naval base. Mechanical- and electrical-engineering industries are carried on, and textiles, chemicals, and paper are made.

Leningrad is joined by canal and canalized river with Lakes Ladoga and Onega, northeast of the city, and by the White Sea Canal with the White Sea and Arctic Ocean. A smaller canal joins Lake Onega with the Volga and thus with Moscow. Navigation is important in the communications of Leningrad but is impeded by ice during the winter months.

The Leningrad region lies entirely within the belt of coniferous forest. It is of small agricultural value; its soils damp and acid. Food has to be imported from more productive parts of the Soviet Union.

The Moscow Region. Moscow (Moskva) is the oldest capital of the Russian state, which was formerly called Muscovy after it. It lies in the triangle formed by the upper course of the Volga and of its tributary the Oka and is on the Moskva River, a tributary of the latter. It was founded in the Middle Ages by people who had been driven northward from the steppe by the invading hordes of Tartars and forced to take refuge within the margin of the forest. Moscow lies where the deciduous forest thins away. To the north is the coniferous forest; to the west the mixed woodland; to the south, the trees give way gradually as the steppe is approached.

The nucleus of the early town was the fortress, or Kremlin, lying high above the steep river bank. The town which grew around it was walled; it spread beyond its fortifications, was again walled, and spread yet farther in modern times beyond its confines. It remained the capital of Russia except for a period of about 200 years before 1917, when Leningrad was the capital. Its political importance led to the building of a radiating pattern of railways, and these in their turn made possible the easy carriage of goods and the development of industries. Under the Bolsheviks Moscow again became the capital, and during the next 20 years its development as an economic and administrative center was rapid. In 1926 its population was 2,029,000; by 1939 this had risen to 4,137,000. Its varied industrial development began here in the nineteenth century, when its present network of railways was in large measure constructed. Moscow is itself the center of this region. A hundred miles to the south is the Tula coal field. Its coal is not of high quality, and much of it, together with the more abundant peat and lignite, is used in the generation of electric power. Ivanovo produces a large part of the Russian output of factory-made textiles. Kaluga and Ryazan make agricultural machinery; Kalinin (Tver) and Kolomna railroad equipment; and Yaroslavl, Shcherbakov, Rzhev, Vladimir, and Serpukhov have textile, chemical, and engineering industries. Gorki, formerly known as Nizhni Novgorod, lies 240 miles east of Moscow on the Volga. It was the scene of a famous fair at which the products of the East were exchanged for those of the West. The fair has been discontinued, but Gorki is now one of the largest and most varied of the great industrial cities of Russia. It has engineering, textile, and chemical industries; it makes aircraft and automobiles and has important oil refineries. The Volga is here a broad, navigable stream at all times of the year when it is not ice-covered. The region is a great steel-user rather than steel-maker. There was an ancient smelting industry

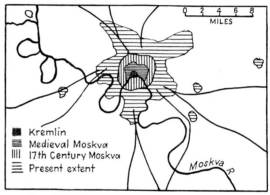

FIG. 242. The situation of Moscow (Moskva).

here, but the local resources in coal and ore are quite inadequate for a modern industry. Steel is brought in from the Ukraine. Not only has the region a developed railway network, it also uses the transport facilities offered by the Volga and its tributary the Oka. Moscow has recently been linked with the Volga by a canal. An old canal between the upper Volga and the Volkhov, which flows into Lake Ladoga, is being rebuilt and enlarged and will increase waterborne communications between Moscow and Leningrad.

The Western Republics. During the eighteenth century the small window which Tsar Peter had opened toward the west was thrown wide open. Finland, the Baltic provinces, and a large part of Poland were absorbed into Russia. Russian they remained until 1918. The victories of the German armies in Russia gave many of the border peoples the opportunity to revolt. Finland, Estonia, Latvia, and Lithuania came onto the political map. Poland was created and, after a successful military campaign, occupied a large area that had hitherto been Russian. At the same time Romania succeeded in incorporating the Russian province of Bessarabia. Though forced to recognize these territorial changes in the series of peace treaties that terminated the

FIG. 243. The western republics of Soviet Russia.

hostilities, Russia never really recognized them as final.

Under the federal structure of the Russian government, republics of small area were established along the western border of Russia: the Karelian republic in the north, the White Russian (Byelorussia) in the center, and the Moldavian in the south. These each formed

nuclei to which could be attached any territory that might be acquired from Russia's western neighbors. Western Poland was occupied in September, 1939; parts of Finland in March, 1940; Bessarabia in the following June; and the Baltic States of Estonia, Latvia, and Lithuania in August. Further small gains were made from Finland and Germany in 1945. The Karelo-Finnish Soviet Socialist Republic has incorporated the territory ceded by Finland. Estonia, Latvia, and Lithuania are separate S.S.R.'s. The annexed Polish territory is divided between the White Russian and Ukrainian republics, and Bessarabia is now included in the Moldavian republic.

The Karelo-Finnish S.S.R. is the least populous. It is a forested, lake-studded region with harsh climate and poor soil. Agriculture is of negligible importance, but there are deposits of minerals, including molybdenum. The sparse population is more closely related to the Finns than to the Russians. Folklore and mythology connect the Finns very closely with this region, from which the Finnish people claim to have come.

The Baltic republics of Estonia, Latvia, and Lithuania are part of a glaciated plain. The land is low and hummocky. The relief derives from the loops of terminal moraine and the rounded protuberances of boulder clay, known as "drumlins." The soils vary from heavy clay to light and permeable outwash sands and gravels. Many lakes occupy hollows in irregular morainic cover, and other depressions have been filled to form marsh. The climate is not unlike that of southern Sweden. Summers are warm, and winters cold. The ancient vegetation was mixed woodland, with the hardwood deciduous species gradually giving place to the softwood coniferous. Grass and fodder crops grow well. Grain crops, particularly rye and oats, are grown, but the climate is marginal for wheat cultivation.

Estonia is the most northerly, the smallest, and, in the accepted opinion, the most progressive before 1940 of the three Baltic States. The Estonian people are akin in origin to the Finns, and their language resembles Finnish.

The majority of the population is engaged in agriculture. A large part of the land is under meadow and pasture, and the country is climatically suited to dairy farming, which is conducted on much the same lines as in Denmark. Before the war dairy produce was one of its most important exports. The damp, cool climate also favors the cultivation of flax.

Tallinn, formerly called Reval, is the capital and largest city of Estonia. It lies on the southern shore of the Gulf of Finland, and though not completely ice-free in winter, its large harbor is generally accessible to large vessels. It has industries based upon the timber and dairy products of Estonia. Tartu (Dorpat) is a smaller city and site of one of the most distinguished universities in eastern Europe.

Estonia has little mineral wealth except the oil shales which are mined in northern Estonia and from which oil is extracted.

Latvia is largely the valley of the lower Dvina (Daugava), down which timber used to be floated from the forests of Russia. Riga, a city of German origin and bearing many evidences of the German culture that once was dominant here, is the port for the Dvina Valley. It served as one of the outlets for Tsarist Russia and, once again under Russian rule, is being developed as one of Russia's major outlets to the west. Riga is a city of some 386,000 people, lying on the Dvina estuary. It has textile, machinery, and timber industries and formerly exported the dairy produce, flax, and timber from its hinterland. Riga was heavily damaged during the German invasion of Russia in 1941 but has largely been restored.

Latvia resembles Estonia in its predominantly agricultural economy. Lithuania is even more agricultural than its northern neighbor. Before 1940 it was more backward, its degree of agricultural specialization was less, and its trade smaller. Much of its agriculture was on a subsistence basis. The relative backwardness of Lithuania is remarkable, as it was the only one of these states ever to have had an independent existence before 1918. The medieval kingdom of Lithuania had stretched far into the Ukraine and had even contained Kiev. In the sixteenth century it was merged with the kingdom of Poland. For almost the whole period of its recent independence, Lithuania ran a feud with Poland, which arose from the Polish seizure of Vilna (Vilnyus). The Russians have returned the city to the Lithuanians as a concession to the national pride of the latter. It is now a city of over 200,000. Kaunas (Kovno) is the second city of Lithuania, and its capital while Vilna was in Polish possession. The port of Memel (Klaipeda) was also the occasion of dispute between Lithuania and her neighbor, this time Germany, as the population was predominantly German.

In 1945, Russia annexed the northern part of East Prussia, including Kaliningrad, which had formerly been the German port and city of Königsberg. It had been before the war a city of about 370,000 inhabitants. It con ained a famous university at which the German philosopher Kant had been a professor; it was a foremost center of German culture in eastern Europe. Now most of its German population has been driven out, and the city is being made a Russian bastion. It has not been absorbed into the Lithuanian S.S.R., which it adjoins, but is controlled direct from Moscow.

White Russia, or Byelorussia, has been expanded to include part of Poland, and in fact, the whole S.S.R. was formerly Polish territory. The language spoken by its inhabitants differs little from Russian. Physically White Russia is made up of undulating boulder-clay and morainic country in the north but sinks toward the south to the valley of the Pripyat (Pripet). This, like many of the valleys of Poland and Germany, was probably cut by the streams which escaped from the melting ice during the Ice Age. The depression that was cut at this time has since accumulated silt, and lakes and marshes have formed. These are the Pripyat marshes, a wilderness of forest, marsh, and stream through which it is impossible for the stranger to pick his way. Villages lie on small islands; their inhabitants travel in shallow boats. It is a region scarcely touched by the technical developments of the twentieth century. The Poles had begun work on the reclamation

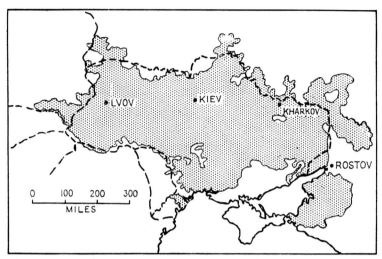

FIG. 244. The Ukrainian S.S.R. and the distribution of Ukrainian-speaking peoples.

of the area, but little progress was made before the Russians occupied the region in September, 1939. It has, in a sense, been a "natural frontier." Certainly armies have always tried to avoid the region, keeping either to the hills to the north or to the open corridor, south of the marshes, where lies the city of Lwów.

Other cities of White Russia are very much larger. Minsk, its capital, has nearly quarter of a million inhabitants, and Vitebsk and Gomel are not a great deal smaller. These cities, together with Smolensk and Chernigov, which lie just outside the eastern border of White Russia, grew up on the ancient routeway which followed the rivers and joined the Baltic with the Black Sea. They lie also on the routes developed in more recent times between Germany and the Moscow area. Many industries have been developed, including woodworking, engineering, and textile and chemical manufacture. There are, however, no fuel reserves except the local peat and timber, and rivers are too sluggish for hydroelectric power to be important. Coal is obtained from the Ukraine.

The last of these small republics located on the western border is the Moldavian S.S.R., consisting of little more than the rolling plain between the rivers Prut, on the Romanian border, and the Dniester. It has a rather dry climate with extremes of temperature. It is naturally a region of wooded steppe but is now well cultivated. Its loess soils are fertile and yield heavy crops of wheat and other cereals and sugar beet. Kishinev is the capital of the republic, a city of over 110,000 and a market and industrial center.

The Ukraine. When during the early Middle Ages trade developed between the Baltic and the Black Sea, many of the commercial centers were established on the great Russian rivers, the Dniester and Dnieper, where these crossed the steppe. This urban growth was cut short by the invasion of the Tartar peoples from Asia. For nearly a thousand years the steppe was a frontier zone, in which settled life was dangerous and difficult, where travelers moved only in convoy and outlaws found a life of freedom and danger. The word Ukraine means "frontier." The Cossacks, who inhabited parts of the region, were a group of frontiersmen, outcasts from the settled life of the forest zone. The Russia of the Tsars advanced slowly into the steppe. Peter the Great actually conquered but had to relinquish the port of Azov at the mouth of the Don. But during the eighteenth century the Russians gradually wore down the opposition of Cossacks and Tartars, established ports on the Black Sea coast, and absorbed the Ukraine into Russia.

The people of the Ukraine speak a Slavonic language akin to Russian. It is, however, a distinct language and serves as a bond of union among the Ukrainian people. The Ukrainians are the most distinctive of the peoples who live along the western fringe of European Russia. They have shown little sympathy with the Russian people and, in fact, in the early days of the Communist Revolution actually established a short-lived, independent republic. But it succumbed to the attacks of Russians and Poles, and the greater part of its territory was absorbed as an S.S.R. into the Soviet Union. During the following years anti-Russian propaganda, emanating chiefly from Germany, fell on fruitful soil in the Ukraine, and even today this is said to be the region of Russia where resistance to Soviet rule is least improbable. After the Second World War the territory of the Ukraine was extended by the addition of Sub-carpathian Russia (Carpatho-Ukraine), the small and mountainous territory already mentioned (page 253) as the Ruthene area of Czechoslovakia.

Economically the Ukraine is one of the most developed parts of the Soviet Union. It is, for the greater part, low and rolling. Its summers are hot, and winters cold, and rainfall is generally under 25 inches a year. The vegetation of the Ukraine was formerly grassland, with light woodland along its northern and western margins. To east and southeast the steppe becomes drier and poorer and eventually passes into the scrub desert of the Caspian Basin.

Much of the steppe has been under cultivation since the early nineteenth century. Its wheat was exported through Odessa long before the grain of the American prairies entered the market of western Europe. Odessa grain prices in the mid-nineteenth controlled wheat prices in most of the world's markets. This long period of cultivation has not been without its ill effects on the soil. Despite the very high value of the black earth, the fertility has been greatly diminished. Some areas are severely "gullied," and in many areas erosion has become a serious problem. It is said that remedial measures, including contour plowing, have been adopted. A large proportion of the steppe is under cultivation. Wheat, winter-sown in the south, spring-sown farther inland from the Black Sea, is still the most important crop, though it seems probable that the area under permanent grass and fodder crops has been increased in recent years. Animal husbandry appears to be more important than a generation ago. This may be a consequence of the rising standard of living in Russia, but it might more likely be a concession to the growing difficulties of soil impoverishment and erosion.

The central and western parts of the Ukraine are predominantly agricultural. Factory industries are chiefly those most closely associated with the surrounding agricultural country: the manufacture of agricultural machinery and of fertilizers, flour milling, and the preparation of other agricultural products. One of the largest cities is Lwów, before 1939 a Polish city and now a city of over 300,000, with engineering and other industries connected with the practice of agriculture. Kiev, on the high western bank of the Dnieper, is now one of the largest cities in the Soviet Union. It had a population before the war of about 850,000. The city was seriously damaged but is now largely, if not wholly, rebuilt. Kiev is one of the oldest and historically most interesting cities in Russia. Its origin in the early Middle Ages has been mentioned (page 407). For centuries it was exposed to the attack of Tartar and Mongol tribesmen from the Asiatic steppe and was on more than one occasion captured by them. It later became the capital of the Ukraine and is today a route center and industrial city, with a wide range of metallurgical, mechanical, and consumer-goods industries.

Odessa is the chief port of the western Ukraine. It was not founded until late in the eighteenth century but then grew to be a great grain port. It does not, like most other Russian ports, lie at the mouth of a river. The coast is here flat, and the harbor is liable to silting and is far from good. It is, however, icebound for only a short period in winter.

The eastern Ukraine is more industrial than agricultural. A low ridge lies from west to east about 130 miles inland from the Black Sea coast. It is made up in part of older and harder

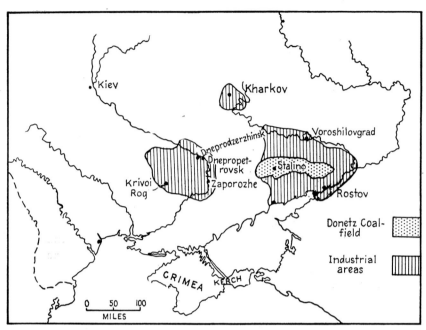

Fig. 245. The Ukraine industrial region.

rocks than those which compose the rest of the Ukraine. These are richly mineralized and contain the iron ore of Krivoi Rog and the manganese deposits of Nikopol. To the east is the important coal field of the Donets Basin (Donbas). The Donets Basin produced until recently the greater part of all coal mined in Russia. It remains today the most important single coal field.

Heavy industry was established in this region in the later years of the nineteenth century. An Englishman named Hughes erected the first modern blast furnace at a town which was named Yuzovka after him. This is now the industrial city of Stalino, with about half a million inhabitants. The only other large cities on the coal field are Makeevka and Voroshilovgrad (Lugansk). There are many small cities in which metallurgical and chemical industries are carried on. The chief centers of the iron-smelting and steelmaking industry are nearer the source of the ore. There is a large new iron and steel plant at Krivoi Rog, and there are works at Dnepropetrovsk, Dneprodzerzhinsk, and Zaporozhe, all on the Dnieper. The low-grade iron ores of the Crimean

(Kerch) peninsula are smelted on the coast of the Sea of Azov with coal from the Donets Basin.

In addition to the very important iron and steel industries of the Ukraine industrial area, there are important chemical and nonferrous metal industries. Nikopol is one of the world's greatest sources of manganese. Marginal to the area of heavy industries are many large and important steel-using cities, in which mechanical and electrical engineering and shipbuilding are of great importance. Foremost among these are Rostov, which lies outside the political limits of the Ukraine and is a great industrial city of over half a million people on the lower Don, and Kharkov, in the northern Ukraine, which rivals Kiev in size.

This industrial region depends mainly on coal for power, but the Dnieper has been harnessed at Dneprostroi, where the river cuts across the ridge of older and harder rock a few miles above the city of Zaporozhe. Zaporozhe means "beyond the rapids." The dam was destroyed during the German invasion but has since been rebuilt. The German invasion wrought immense damage in the whole of the Ukraine, but the statistics of Russian production indicate that at least the factories and mines have been repaired.

The Volga. Along the Volga, as it crosses the steppe and enters the semidesert of the Caspian Basin, are industrial towns, once centers on the trade route which followed the river. These are individually of large size and are engaged in metallurgical industries, especially those which have a direct bearing upon agriculture, such as the manufacture of tractors and machinery. Gorki (Nizhni Novgorod), at the junction of the Volga and Oka, has grown to a city of over 700,000 inhabitants. Kazan, 250 miles downstream from Gorki, lies near the junction of the Volga and Kama, up whose valley ran—and still runs—the route eastward across the Ural Mountains. Kuibishev (Samara) was also a terminus of routes to Central Asia. Stalingrad lies at the bend of the Volga within 50 miles of the Don. Between Kuibishev and Stalingrad is Saratov. All these towns owe their present industrial preeminence, as they once did their trade, to the Volga itself. Astrakhan, on the Volga delta, is a port of considerable significance in Russia, where as much as possible of the internal movement of goods is by water and where the Volga is the best of navigable highways.

Ural Mountains. The Ural Mountains, the traditional boundary of Europe, have nothing of the frontier about them. They consist of a series of roughly parallel ridges, their lower slopes forested, the higher ground passing through woods of dwarf trees to a stony waste. They are far from steep. At many points they are crossed by railways and roads. The Ural Mountains form a divide between the Volga and Pechora drainage on the west and the Ob and Irtysh on the east but are a divide in no other respect. They are of similar age and structure to the mountains of Bohemia and central Germany and are also highly mineralized. Iron-ore reserves are extensive and of a fairly high grade. Copper, lead, and zinc also occur in veins, together with manganese, nickel, wolfram, asbestos, chromium, bauxite, and other metals of lesser significance. The occurrences of coal are limited to the younger rocks which appear on each side of the Ural Mountains.

They are small but of considerable local importance. Natural-oil deposits, on the other hand, are extensive, particularly in the western slopes of the southern Urals.

In Tsarist days the Ural Mountains were not the scene of manufacturing industries beyond the smelting of iron in primitive furnaces. Their development is an achievement of the five-year plans. Coal is mainly obtained from the Karaganda coal field, a newly developed coal field, some 1,100 miles to the east in the Siberian

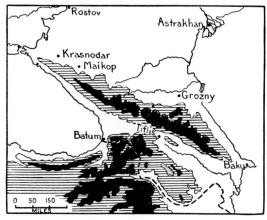

FIG. 246. The Caucasus.

Plain. The chief industrial centers of the Ural region, most of them newly founded as part of the planned development, are Sverdlovsk and Magnitogorsk, both important centers of steel and engineering industries. Nizhni Tagil, Orsk and Zlatoust are mining and metallurgical centers.

The Caucasus Region. A dry steppe reaches southward between the Sea of Azov and the Caspian. In the north it is drained by the tributaries of the Don; in the south, by the Terek and Kuban, which rise amid the peaks of the Caucasus and are fed by its melting snows. The rainfall diminishes eastward. In the west winter-sown wheat is grown, together with other grain crops, but agriculture ceases to be important as the Caspian Sea is approached. The chief resource of this region is petroleum, which is obtained in very large quantities from the northern foothills of the Caucasus Mountains. The most important producing centers

are Grozny and Maikop, where there are re-
fineries joined by pipe line not only with Black
Sea ports but also with other parts of the Soviet
Union.

The Caucasus Mountains consist of several
closely placed ranges trending northwest-south-
east. Their crest ranges from 9,000 to considerably over 12,000 feet, and there are no easy
routes across the mountains. At their extremities
they drop steeply to the sea, and although there
are practicable routes along the coast, there is
no coastal plain. The range in its physical
aspects resembles the Pyrenees but is considerably longer and higher. The highest mountain, Mount Elbrus, rises to 18,468 feet, and
Kazbek reaches 16,546. The range has a core
of crystalline rocks, in which are developed the
higher peaks, with intensely folded sedimentary
rocks on each side. The mountains are well
forested, although large areas lie above the tree
line. The topography is rugged in the extreme,
and movement within the mountains difficult.
There are many upland valleys which are in
practice cut off from the outside world. The
Caucasus industrial region is not dominated by
any particular industry. In its most northerly
town, Rostov, it borders on the Ukraine.
Krasnodar, with agricultural and engineering
industries, is the chief town of the Kuban.
Many towns of small or medium size are engaged in flour milling, in the crushing of oil
seeds, and in the preparation of other agricultural products of the region.

South of the Caucasus Mountains a region of
hills and sheltered plains stretches southward to
the mountains of Armenia. A range known as
the Little Caucasus lies parallel to the Caucasus,
with which it is joined by the hills about Tiflis
(Tbilisi). Valleys broaden eastward and westward to the Caspian and Black Seas between
the two ranges. The Caucasus Mountains protect this region in some measure from the in-
temperate winters of the steppe. The Black Sea
coast is mild, frosts are rare, and Mediterranean
fruits and flowers flourish. In the short distance
of some 200 miles one passes from the icy winters
of the steppe, experienced on the shores of the
Sea of Azov, to the warmth of the coast of
Georgia.

The climate of the more easterly valley is more
extreme. Winters are cold, though much shorter
than in the steppe. Summers are hot and moist
enough for corn and cotton to ripen. The vine
is grown, and in parts the hill slopes support tea
plantations.

Petroleum is obtained in the Kura Valley, and
the town of Baku, joined by pipe line with Batum
on the Black Sea coast, is an important producer.
Production here has been declining in recent
years. Metalliferous mining is carried on, and
the rivers of the Caucasus are being made to
provide hydroelectric power. South of the
Caucasus Mountains industries have generally
deeper roots. The drying and preparation of
tobacco, the spinning and weaving of silk and
wool are traditional occupations. But the
minerals and the small coal reserves have permitted a newer and more varied range of manufactures to be superimposed upon the older.

The trough which separates the Caucasus
from the Little Caucasus comprises in the west
the Soviet Socialist Republic of Georgia, in the
east that of Azerbaidzhan. In the hills to the
south is the Armenian Soviet Republic. The
whole Transcaucasian region is one of great
racial mixture. Its peoples are more closely akin
to those of Turkey and of Iran than to the
Russians, and the dominant religion of the
region is Islam.

Soviet Central Asia. This region lies far from
the borders of Europe and is mentioned here
only in order to complete the geographical
pattern of the Soviet Union. The steppe and the
desert merge into the vast mountain ranges
which radiate from the Pamir. The Elburz
Mountains and Hindu Kush shut in the Caspian
Sea and Turkestan on the south. Rivers flow
northward into the desert and lose themselves
amid its sandy wastes. Oases border the foothills, where cotton, grain, fruit, and livestock are
produced. Industrial development has here
been less spectacular than in Siberia or the
Urals, but many towns have grown up recently:
Alma Ata, Semipalatinsk, and Karaganda. The
Central Asian region includes also the ancient

oasis and caravan towns of Turkestan, Ash-khabad, Merv, Bukhara, Samarkand, Tashkent, and Fergana. These, like the cities of Trans-caucasia, have long-established silk, cotton, and leather industries, and it is for these, with the addition of engineering industries, that the region is now important.

The Tien Shan and the Altai Ranges stretch northeastward. Gaps through them lead into Mongolia and China. Oases blossom in the semi-desert which lies along their margin. The nomadic Kirghiz and Kazakh graze their flocks and herds, and the Soviets look for coal and iron and try to establish industrial centers as far as possible from the gaze of the outside world.

Siberia. Brief mention is made here only of the industrial regions of Siberia. The mineral bases of modern industry are undoubtedly large and varied. The Kuznets Basin between the Ob and Enisei Valleys has coal deposits which are certainly very large. These are now the basis for an intensive metallurgical industry which derives part of its iron ore from the Ural Mountains, over 1,000 miles to the west. The chief industrial centers are Novosibirsk, Barnaul, Tomsk, and Stalinsk.

Eight hundred miles southwest of the Kuzbas is the newly developed Karaganda coal field and industrial area. Farther to the east, Kras-noyarsk, Irkutsk, and other towns are the seats of growing metallurgical industries, based on the large resources of fuel and minerals in Siberia. In the Far East also, industries have been estab-lished, some of them for their military signifi-cance. If the Soviet Army were involved in war in the Far East, it would find the thread of the Trans-Siberian Railroad a slender link with the west of the Soviet Union.

Transport. The development of so vast a country with its local specializations clearly necessitates an improved network of communi-cations. The Soviet Union had two advantages: her rivers are long, broad, and deep, particu-larly suited to navigation, and the greater part of the country is flat, thus making railway building comparatively easy.

The Asiatic rivers flow northward to a sea that is icebound for much of the year. Their courses are at right angles to the direction of movement, and they are chiefly used for floating timber to the Arctic ports. The European rivers, however, radiate from the district of the Valdai Hills. The larger are easily navigated, and their upper courses are linked by canals. These are now rather old and in general too small for modern requirements, but the government proposes to enlarge existing canals as well as to cut fresh, thus establishing a network of water-ways of the highest value.

Even under Tsarist rule a network of railways had been spread over European Russia and the Trans-Siberian Railway constructed across Asia to Vladivostok on the Pacific Coast. A number of extensions were made from this line, but most of Siberia and Central Asia was not reached by any form of railway development. Since the implementation of the five-year plans the European network has been intensified, the Trans-Siberian line double-tracked, and the line from the Caspian Sea at Krasnovodsk to Turkestan extended to join the Trans-Siberian Railway at Novosibirsk. The new industrial centers of Asia have been linked with the Soviet railway system.

Ice is of scarcely less consequence in the sea-borne than in the river transport of Russia. In most of the Baltic and Black Sea ports the forma-tion of ice presents difficulties which can, how-ever, be partially overcome with the regular use of icebreakers. The ports of Riga and Leningrad, for example, are thus kept open throughout the year. The northern sea route has presented greater difficulties. The use of the Asiatic rivers and the route along the Siberian coast appeared to be necessary if the timber of the Siberian forests was to be used. The duration of the winter freeze is very much longer than in the Baltic. It is possible, with the help of ice-breakers at the beginning and end of the "open" season, for timber ships to reach Igarka, on the Enisei, and to return in a single season. A few attempts to sail from Vladivostok to Murmansk in a single season have been successful. Losses have been considerable, though even this route may become practicable if strong enough ice-breakers are used.

BIBLIOGRAPHY

Allen, W. E. D., The Caucasian Borderland, *G.J.*, XCIX, 1942, 225–237.

Balzak, S. S., V. F. Vasyutin, and Ya G. Feigin, "Economic Geography of the U.S.S.R.," American edition edited by Chauncy D. Harris, New York, 1949.

Baykov, A., "The Development of the Soviet Economic System," Cambridge, 1946.

Berg, L. S., "Natural Regions of the U.S.S.R.," translated by O. A. Titelbaum and edited by John A. Morrison and C. C. Nikiforoff, New York, 1950.

Cressey, George B., "The Basis of Soviet Strength," New York, 1945.

Dobb, Maurice, "Soviet Economic Development since 1917," London, 1948.

———, "U.S.S.R. Her Life and People," London, 1943.

Edwards, K. C., Soviet Northern Seaways, *G.*, XXVIII, 1943, 78–85.

"Géographie universelle," Vol. V., Etats de Baltique, Paris, 1932.

Goodall, George, "Soviet Russia in Maps: Its Origin and Development," London, 1942.

Gray, G. D. B., "Soviet Land," London, 1947.

Gregory, James S., and D. W. Shave, "The U.S.S.R.," London, 1944.

Harris, Chauncy D., The Cities of the Soviet Union, *G.R.*, XXXV, 1945, 107–121.

———, Ethnic Groups in Cities of the Soviet Union, *G.R.*, XXXV, 1945, 466–473.

Hubbard, L. E., "The Economics of Soviet Agriculture," London, 1939.

———, "Soviet Trade and Distribution," London, 1938.

Jorré, Georges, "The Soviet Union: the Land and Its People," translated by E. D. Laborde, New York, 1950.

Lorimer, F., "The Population of the Soviet Union," League of Nations, Geneva, 1946.

Maynard, Sir John, "The Russian Peasant and Other Studies," London, 1942.

Seifriz, William, Vegetation Zones in the Caucasus, *G.R.*, XXVI, 1936, 59–66.

Shabad, Theodore, "Geography of the U.S.S.R.," New York, 1951.

Shackleton, M. R., "Europe: A Regional Geography," London, 1950. (This contains an admirable, up-to-date account of European Russia.)

Smolka, H. P., The Economic Development of the Soviet Arctic, *G.J.*, LXXXIX, 1936, 327–343.

Stevens, A., On Russian Climates and Agriculture, *G.*, XXVIII, 1943, 6–11.

Sumner, B. H., "Survey of Russian History," London, 1944.

Turin, S. P., "The U.S.S.R. An Economic and Social Survey," London, 1944.

Thiel, E., The Power Industry in the Soviet Union, *E.G.*, XXVII, 1951, 107–122.

Volin, Lazare, "A Survey of Soviet Russian Agriculture," U.S. Department of Agriculture, Washington, D.C., 1951.

Bibliographies on the soviet Union

Conover, Helen F., "Soviet Russia: A Selected List of Recent References," Library of Congress, Division of Bibliography, Washington, D.C., 1943.

"Russia: a Select Reading List," Bristol Public Libraries, England, 1942.

Schultz, Aved., Europäisches Russland, 1929–36, *Geographisches Jahrbuch*, LII, 1937, 75–248.

"Soviet Geography, a Bibliography," 2 vols., Library of Congress, Washington, 1951.

Wright, J. K., and Elizabeth T. Platt, "Aids to Geographical Research," American Geographical Society, pp. 225–227, 1947. Lists other bibliographies, mostly in Russian.

CHAPTER 32: *Conclusion: East and West*

The medieval German chronicler Otto of Freising spoke of the "seamless web" of the Christian Europe of the Middle Ages. There was a unity in medieval Europe, exaggerated no doubt by those who look back nostalgically to the rule of a single universal church, which has not been known in modern times. Differences in medieval Europe were differences of degree, not of kind. Medieval society was not divided into nations, but into social groups. Medieval noblemen from Germany, France, the Low Countries, and Britain could join in a common undertaking, such as a crusade, without any feeling of taking part in an international venture. Merchants from all parts of Europe could meet on the same terms. Language and dialect might be a barrier but not nationality; for all were subjects of the medieval empire. All in the last resort owed allegiance to the Holy Roman Emperor, the Christian Emperor of the West.

Kings were not sovereign rulers; all were subjects of the Empire. "From the days of Constantine till far down into the Middle Ages it was, conjointly with the Papacy, the recognized center and head of Christendom, exercising over the minds of men an influence such as its material strength could never have commanded."[1]

At the end of the Middle Ages the nation-state arose, and the national king, emancipating himself from the allegiance to the Emperor, became a national sovereign in our sense. The new national government enjoyed absolute power and demanded the complete and undivided loyalty of its subjects. It governed their lives in material affairs and claimed the right to dictate their religious beliefs. *Le nouveau Messie, c'est le roi:* "the king is the new Messiah."

The Christian world of the Middle Ages was surrounded, besieged, by pagan and barbarian. From northern Norway and Sweden, through Lithuania, Poland, Hungary, and the Balkans ran the frontier of medieval Europe. On the south the Mediterranean Sea continued the boundary. Outside these limits were pagan Lapps, Tartars, and Turks and the more civilized Arabs, from whose wells of scientific knowledge the Christian could occasionally draw. A "cold war" was waged between Christian and pagan, with frequent appeals from within the "curtain" for a crusade which would expand the limits of Christendom. The idea of the crusade, vigorous all through the Middle Ages, was at no time more advertised than when the Age of Faith was drawing to a close.

The nation-states in modern times have taken on the role of expanding the frontiers of Europe and, when all is said, have performed this task more efficiently and more effectively than ever the Pope and Emperor had done. The new advances were made, not in the name of faith, but in that of the new nationalism: to gain more territory, acquire greater resources, recruit larger armies, obtain places of strategic importance in relation to other states. The frontiers of Europe were expanded. The Turks were driven from the greater part of the Balkan peninsula. The east Baltic lands were brought within the European sphere. The Moors were driven from southern Spain, and European forces in the nineteenth century conquered most of the North African coast. Above all, the Russian state was absorbed into the community

---

[1] James, Viscount Bryce, "The Holy Roman Empire," p. 1, London, 1904.

of European nations and acquired ambitions and policies like those of its neighbors to the west.

The west European nations, closely crowded in the western peninsulas of Europe, expanded overseas, building up empires in Africa, Asia, and the New World. Russia enlarged her own domestic territory, extending her rule across Asia to the Pacific. Siberia stood to the nuclear area of the Russian state in somewhat the same position as Canada or Australia to Great Britain: a vast tributary territory of great resources, with a poor and undeveloped indigenous people. There was, however, this important difference: Russia's empire was a territorial extension of the home country and in its administration was never distinguished from the metropolitan area of Russia. The British, French, and other empires are overseas. A similar degree of integration is difficult if not impossible, though Algeria is now part of France but liable to be cut off in wartime. Russia, as it were, carries her own "hump"; she has her own resources within one vast but compact territory. She has opportunities for organizing space which are denied to the western states.

If the Soviet Union is regarded as a single political unit, then it is three-quarters Asiatic in location and to a small degree Asiatic in population and culture. The Communist Revolution has deepened yet further the contrast between Russia and the west. Two aspects of this revolution should be distinguished. The essentially economic aspect was at first the more obvious: the nationalization of the land and of the means of production, the elimination of the "middle class," or *bourgeoisie*, the rise of a group of administrators or bureaucrats, the subjugation of the will of the individual to that of his class. The second and more dangerous is the development in Russia of a more intense nationalism than most west European nations had experienced. Russia has taken over from the west the worst aspects of nationalism and with it a conviction that a state of hostility, latent or open, "cold" or "hot," necessarily exists between states. States, like organisms, are competing for limited resources, and whatever may be to the advantage of one state is neces-

sarily to the disadvantage of others. This dangerous doctrine owed much to the German philosopher Hegel and has sometimes lifted its ugly head in the west. The Hitler policy in Germany and the doctrine of *Lebensraum*, or "living space," owed much to it. But in Russia it is a consistent basis of policy and is, furthermore, reinforced by the Marxist arguments regarding the course of history. Political theory requires the Russian state to wage a ceaseless war against all others. Dialectical Marxism looks forward to the overthrow of the capitalist society in the "bourgeois" countries of the West and to the triumph of communism, of which Russia is the first and greatest exponent.

In the West a political tradition has grown up, evolving from the theory and practice of the Greeks and Romans of classical times and given a new shape and new values by the Christian philosophers of the Middle Ages. In short it regarded the individual as an end. The salvation of his soul was the purpose of social organization, and social obligations were directed to the maintenance of institutions, the church and empire, dedicated to these ends. Despite occasional excesses and a trend sometimes toward an absolutist, or Hegelian, concept of the subordination of the individual to an impersonal and all-powerful state, this ancient and medieval insistence on the rights of the individual, stripped now of all Christian connotation, still survives in the West. It expresses itself in habeas corpus; in English common law, substantially the same as American; in parliamentary institutions; in a respect for individual rights and liberty that can occasionally jeopardize the existence of the state in which these individuals are organized. These are the principles, however inadequate may sometimes be the practice, which inspire the life of the states of western Europe.

The contrast between East and West is clear, but the boundary between East and West is by no means well defined. The difference is one of human values. Western values are held, but perhaps not strongly held, in the East. The Eastern code is held in some quarters in the West. Intermediate lands and peoples cling now to one side now to the other. Through the Communist control of their governments, Poland, East Germany, Czechoslovakia, Hungary, Romania, and Bulgaria adhere to the East. But some, particularly Czechoslovakia and Poland, might be detached and added to the "free" nations of the West. Spain is part of the West, but no one supposes that the best Western political traditions are exemplified in modern Spain.

Western Europe is today, as she was during the Middle Ages, a land besieged by peoples with different faiths. Then these faiths were non-Christian; now, in this secular age, they are illiberal and undemocratic. As in the Middle Ages, there is today, slowly ripening under the forces of adversity, a sense of unity in the West. Geographical patterns may sometimes repeat themselves. Western Europe is not unlike the medieval empire. Perhaps, like the medieval empire, it will protect itself and carry outward, in a great crusading surge, its liberal and democratic faith into the totalitarian lands which enclose it.

Index